Periodic table of the elements

Key

Atomic number
79
Au — Symbol of element
197.0 — Atomic weight
Gold — Name of element

Handwritten annotations: +1, +2, +3, +4, −3, −2, −1, "Transitions"

1 H 1.008 Hydrogen																		2 He 4.003 Helium
3 Li 6.941 Lithium	4 Be 9.012 Beryllium											5 B 10.81 Boron	6 C 12.01 Carbon	7 N 14.01 Nitrogen	8 O 16.00 Oxygen	9 F 19.00 Fluorine	10 Ne 20.18 Neon	
11 Na 22.99 Sodium	12 Mg 24.31 Magnesium											13 Al 26.98 Aluminium	14 Si 28.09 Silicon	15 P 30.97 Phosphorus	16 S 32.07 Sulfur	17 Cl 35.45 Chlorine	18 Ar 39.95 Argon	
19 K 39.10 Potassium	20 Ca 40.08 Calcium	21 Sc 44.96 Scandium	22 Ti 47.87 Titanium	23 V 50.94 Vanadium	24 Cr 52.00 Chromium	25 Mn 54.94 Manganese	26 Fe 55.85 Iron	27 Co 58.93 Cobalt	28 Ni 58.69 Nickel	29 Cu 63.55 Copper	30 Zn 65.41 Zinc	31 Ga 69.72 Gallium	32 Ge 72.64 Germanium	33 As 74.92 Arsenic	34 Se 78.96 Selenium	35 Br 79.90 Bromine	36 Kr 83.80 Krypton	
37 Rb 85.47 Rubidium	38 Sr 87.62 Strontium	39 Y 88.91 Yttrium	40 Zr 91.22 Zirconium	41 Nb 92.91 Niobium	42 Mo 95.94 Molybdenum	43 Tc [97.91] Technetium	44 Ru 101.1 Ruthenium	45 Rh 102.9 Rhodium	46 Pd 106.4 Palladium	47 Ag 107.9 Silver	48 Cd 112.4 Cadmium	49 In 114.8 Indium	50 Sn 118.7 Tin	51 Sb 121.8 Antimony	52 Te 127.6 Tellurium	53 I 126.9 Iodine	54 Xe 131.3 Xenon	
55 Cs 132.9 Caesium	56 Ba 137.3 Barium	57–71 Lanthanoids	72 Hf 178.5 Hafnium	73 Ta 180.9 Tantalum	74 W 183.8 Tungsten	75 Re 186.2 Rhenium	76 Os 190.2 Osmium	77 Ir 192.2 Iridium	78 Pt 195.1 Platinum	79 Au 197.0 Gold	80 Hg 200.6 Mercury	81 Tl 204.4 Thallium	82 Pb 207.2 Lead	83 Bi 209.0 Bismuth	84 Po [209.0] Polonium	85 At [210.0] Astatine	86 Rn [222.0] Radon	
87 Fr [223] Francium	88 Ra [226] Radium	89–103 Actinoids	104 Rf [261] Rutherfordium	105 Db [262] Dubnium	106 Sg [266] Seaborgium	107 Bh [264] Bohrium	108 Hs [277] Hassium	109 Mt [268] Meitnerium	110 Ds [271] Darmstadtium	111 Rg [272] Roentgenium	112 Cn [277] Copernicium	113	114 Fl [289] Flerovium	115	116 Lv [293] Livermorium	117	118	

* Lanthanoids

57 La 138.9 Lanthanum	58 Ce 140.1 Cerium	59 Pr 140.9 Praseodymium	60 Nd 144.2 Neodymium	61 Pm [145] Promethium	62 Sm 150.4 Samarium	63 Eu 152.0 Europium	64 Gd 157.3 Gadolinium	65 Tb 158.9 Terbium	66 Dy 162.5 Dysprosium	67 Ho 164.9 Holmium	68 Er 167.3 Erbium	69 Tm 168.9 Thulium	70 Yb 173.0 Ytterbium	71 Lu 175.0 Lutetium

** Actinoids

89 Ac [227] Actinium	90 Th 232.0 Thorium	91 Pa 231.0 Protactinium	92 U 238.0 Uranium	93 Np [237] Neptunium	94 Pu [244] Plutonium	95 Am [243] Americium	96 Cm [247] Curium	97 Bk [247] Berkelium	98 Cf [251] Californium	99 Es [252] Einsteinium	100 Fm [257] Fermium	101 Md [258] Mendelevium	102 No [259] Nobelium	103 Lr [262] Lawrencium

Where the atomic weight is not known, the relative atomic mass of the most common radioactive isotope is shown in brackets.

The atomic weights of Np and Tc are given for the isotopes ^{237}Np and ^{99}Tc.

CHEMISTRY 1

PRELIMINARY COURSE

JACARANDA HSC SCIENCE

CHEMISTRY 1

PRELIMINARY COURSE
JACARANDA HSC SCIENCE

GEOFFREY THICKETT

BICENTENNIAL
1807
WILEY
2007
BICENTENNIAL

jacaranda plus

First published 2007 by
John Wiley & Sons Australia, Ltd
42 McDougall Street, Milton, Qld 4064

Typeset in 10.5/12.5 pt ITC New Baskerville

National Library of Australia
Cataloguing-in-Publication data

Thickett, Geoffrey.
    Chemistry 1: preliminary course.

    Includes index.
    For secondary students.
    ISBN   978 0 7314 0410 0.

    1. Chemistry — Textbooks. 2. Chemistry — Problems,
    exercises etc. 3. Chemistry — Examinations, questions
    etc. I. Title.

    540

Cover images: © Digital Vision and © Photodisc
Wiley Bicentennial Logo: Richard J. Pacifico

Illustrated by Craig Johnson, Stephen Francis,
Terry St Ledger and the Wiley Art Studio

Typeset in India by Laserwords
Layout by Wiley Composition Services

Printed in Singapore by
Craft Print International Ltd

10 9 8 7 6

All activities have been written with the safety of both
teacher and student in mind. Some, however, involve
physical activity or the use of equipment or tools. All due
care should be taken when performing such activities.
Neither the publisher nor the author can accept
responsibility for any injury that may be sustained when
completing activities described in this textbook.

CONTENTS

CORE MODULE I

THE CHEMICAL EARTH

CORE MODULE
2

METALS

CORE MODULE 3

WATER

CORE MODULE 4

ENERGY

PREFACE

Chemistry 1: Preliminary Course is part of the Jacaranda HSC Science series. Along with *Chemistry 2: HSC Course*, this new text has been written specifically for the Chemistry Stage 6 syllabus in New South Wales.

This text has been designed to cover all syllabus points — including all 'third column' practical investigations and data analysis activities. These can be found at the end of each chapter. Syllabus content points are fully covered at an appropriate depth, with clear and accurate explanations. Question sets are included at the end of each main section.

We have also incorporated the following features to assist students in achieving the syllabus outcomes.

- *Remember* statements summarise the essential prerequisite knowledge for each section.
- *Key content* statements summarise the syllabus content covered in each section.
- *Key terms* are defined near the relevant content and in a full end-of-book glossary.
- *Questions* at the end of each section cater for the full range of student abilities.
- *Sample problems* with solutions are included throughout.
- *Syllabus focus* boxes explain the Board of Studies 'verbs' and other revised or new features of the syllabus.
- *Summary* sections are listed at the end of each chapter.
- A *Preliminary Course examination paper* in the style of the HSC exam is provided at the end of the book.

The accompanying online resources add an extra dimension, with:
- animated *learning objects* to model reactions and enhance students' understanding of concepts
- *fully-worked solutions* for all text and online questions
- additional *Checkpoint revision* questions and *Module revision* questions
- weblinks to *useful websites* relevant to each chapter.

INTRODUCTION

In his autobiography *Uncle Tungsten*, Oliver Sacks, an American neurosurgeon and science author, wrote about his boyhood fascination for chemistry:

> "*I often dream of chemistry at night ... the old enthusiasm surfaces so often in odd associations and impulses: a sudden desire for a ball of cadmium, or to feel the coldness of diamond against my face ... flowers too, bring elements to mind: the colour of lilacs in spring for me is that of divalent vanadium. Radishes for me evoke the smell of selenium.*"

As a young person, Oliver Sacks had a real passion for chemistry. Although he developed a career in neurosurgery, he still retained an abiding interest in chemistry.

The discoveries of chemists have had a remarkable effect on our society. We live longer and healthier lives because of the medications discovered by chemists. We live in a complex world of products made from synthetic polymers and plastics that were discovered by chemists. We take for granted the wonders of modern communication systems that rely on novel solid-state semi-conductors that were invented by chemists. The patient and insightful work of chemists has revolutionised our world. Few chemists achieve great fame but their contributions to society cannot be denied.

In another part of his autobiography, Oliver Sacks talks of the brief life of Henry Moseley, a British chemist who was killed in action in 1915 at the age of 27. He worked on the X-ray spectra of elements with Ernest Rutherford and, in the two years before his death, he discovered the concept of the atomic number (Z), which we use today to order the elements of the periodic table. Sacks writes:

> "*The brilliance and swiftness of Moseley's work, which was all done in a few months of 1913–14, produced mixed reactions among chemists. Who was this young whippersnapper, some older chemists felt, who presumed to complete the periodic table, to foreclose the possibility of discovering any new elements other than the ones that had been designated? What did he know about Chemistry — or the long, arduous processes of distillation, filtration, crystallisation that might be necessary to concentrate a new element or analyse a new compound? But Urbain, one of the greatest analytical chemists of all ... saw that far from disturbing the autonomy of chemistry, Moseley had in fact confirmed the periodic table and re-established its centrality.*"

Many chemists perform their greatest work when they are young, when their minds are open and not clouded with dogma. As you begin your two-year study of chemistry, think of a future in which you too may make discoveries that will contribute significantly to society. As a first step, I recommend Oliver Sacks' book to all of you. It is a great read and it will help you to understand the mind of a chemist. May some of you who read his words also develop a lifelong love of chemistry.

Geoffrey Thickett

SYLLABUS GRID

Core module 1: The chemical Earth (chapters 1–5, pages 2–105)

1. Living and non-living components of the Earth contain mixtures.

Students learn to:	pages	Students:	pages
• construct word and balanced formulae equations of chemical reactions as they are encountered	throughout	• gather and present information from first-hand or secondary sources to write equations to represent all chemical reactions encountered in the Preliminary course	throughout
• identify the difference between elements, compounds and mixtures in terms of particle theory	3–6	• identify data sources, plan, choose equipment and perform a first-hand investigation to separate the components of a naturally occurring or appropriate mixture such as sand, salt and water	35–6
• identify that the biosphere, lithosphere, hydrosphere and atmosphere contain examples of mixtures of elements and compounds	6–10		
• identify and describe procedures that can be used to separate naturally occurring mixtures of: – solids of different sizes – solids and liquids – dissolved solids in liquids – liquids – gases	12–18	• gather first-hand information by carrying out a gravimetric analysis of a mixture to estimate its percentage composition • identify data sources, and gather, process and analyse information from secondary sources to identify the industrial separation processes used on a mixture obtained from the biosphere, lithosphere, hydrosphere or atmosphere and use available evidence to: – identify the properties of the mixture used in its separation – identify the products of separation and their uses – discuss issues associated with wastes from the processes used.	33, 34 25–9, 37–8
• assess separation techniques for their suitability in separating examples of Earth's materials, identifying the differences in properties that enable these separations	12–18, 25–9		
• describe situations in which gravimetric analysis supplies useful data for chemists and other scientists	21–3		
• apply systematic naming of inorganic compounds as they are introduced in the laboratory	42, 63–4, 69		
• identify IUPAC names for carbon compounds as they are encountered.	throughout		

2. Although most elements are found in combinations on Earth, some elements are found uncombined.

Students learn to:	pages	Students:	pages
• explain the relationship between the reactivity of an element and the likelihood of it existing as an uncombined element	46–7	• plan and perform an investigation to examine some physical properties, including malleability, hardness and electrical conductivity, and some uses of a range of common elements to present information about the classification of elements as metals, non-metals or semi-metals	49
• classify elements as metals, non-metals and semi-metals according to their physical properties	40–1, 43–4		
• account for the uses of metals and non-metals in terms of their physical properties.	47	• analyse information from secondary sources to distinguish the physical properties of metals and non-metals	40, 43–4, 51
		• process information from secondary sources and use a periodic table to present information about the classification of elements as: – metals, non-metals and semi-metals – solids, liquids and gases at 25 °C and normal atmospheric pressure.	50–1

3. Elements in Earth materials are present mostly as compounds because of interactions at the atomic level.

Students learn to:	pages	Students:	pages
• identify that matter is made of particles that are continuously moving and interacting	53	• analyse information by constructing or using models showing the structure of metals, ionic compounds and covalent compounds	72–3
• describe qualitatively the energy levels of electrons in atoms	54–6	• construct ionic equations showing metal and non-metal atoms forming ions.	58
• describe atoms in terms of mass number and atomic number	54		
• describe the formation of ions in terms of atoms gaining or losing electrons	57–9		
• apply the periodic table to predict the ions formed by atoms of metals and non-metals	59–60		

• apply Lewis electron dot structures to:
  – the formation of ions
  – electron sharing in some simple molecules
	58–9, 66–7		

• describe the formation of ionic compounds in terms of the attraction of ions of opposite charge	61–2		
• describe molecules as particles that can move independently of each other	65		
• distinguish between molecules containing one atom (the noble gases) and molecules with more than one atom	65–6		
• describe the formation of covalent molecules in terms of sharing of electrons	65–6		

• construct formulae for compounds formed from:
  – ions
  – atoms sharing electrons.
	62–4, 67–9		

4. Energy is required to extract elements from their naturally occurring sources.

Students learn to:	pages	Students:	pages
• identify the differences between physical and chemical change in terms of rearrangement of particles	75–7	• plan and safely perform a first-hand investigation to show the decomposition of a carbonate by heat, using appropriate tests to identify carbon dioxide and the oxide as the products of the reaction	85–6, 89–90

• summarise the differences between boiling and electrolysis of water as an example of the difference between physical and chemical change	77	• gather information using first-hand or secondary sources to:
		  – observe the effect of light on silver salts and identify an application of this reaction
		  – observe the electrolysis of water, analyse the information provided as evidence that water is a compound and identify an application of this reaction
			87–9

• identify light, heat and electricity as common forms of energy that may be released or absorbed during decomposition or synthesis of substances and identify examples of these changes occurring in everyday life	79–81		
• explain that the amount of energy needed to separate atoms in a compound is an indication of the strength of the attraction, or bond, between them.	81–2	• analyse and present information to model the boiling of water and the electrolysis of water tracing the movements of and changes in arrangements of molecules.	84–5, 88–9

5. The properties of elements and compounds are determined by their bonding and structure.

Students learn to:	pages	Students:	pages
• identify differences between physical and chemical properties of elements, compounds and mixtures	92	• perform a first-hand investigation to compare the properties of some common elements in their elemental state with the properties of the compound(s) of these elements (e.g. magnesium and oxygen)	102–3
• describe the physical properties used to classify compounds as ionic, covalent molecular or covalent network	93		
• distinguish between metallic, ionic and covalent bonds	94	• choose resources and process information from secondary sources to construct and discuss the limitations of models of ionic lattices, covalent molecules and covalent and metallic lattices	103–4
• describe metals as three-dimensional lattices of ions in a sea of electrons	94–5		
• describe ionic compounds in terms of repeating three-dimensional lattices of ions	96–7	• perform an investigation to examine the physical properties of a range of common substances in order to classify them as metallic, ionic, covalent molecular or covalent network substances and relate their characteristics to their uses.	104–5
• explain why the formula for an ionic compound is an empirical formula	96		
• identify common elements that exist as molecules or as covalent lattices	97–8		
• explain the relationship between the properties of conductivity and hardness and the structure of ionic, covalent molecular and covalent network structures.	93, 95, 99		

Core module 2: Metals (chapters 6–10, pages 108–97)

1. Metals have been extracted and used for many thousands of years.

Students learn to:	pages	Students:	pages
• outline and examine some uses of different metals through history, including contemporary uses, as uncombined metals or as alloys	109–13	• gather, process, analyse and present information from secondary sources on the range of alloys produced and the reasons for the production and use of these alloys	117–22, 126
• describe the use of common alloys including steel, brass and solder and explain how these relate to their properties	117–22	• analyse information to relate the chronology of the Bronze Age, the Iron Age and the modern era and possible future developments.	111–13, 124–5
• explain why energy input is necessary to extract a metal from its ore	114		
• identify why there are more metals available for people to use now than there were 200 years ago.	114–15		

2. Metals differ in their reactivity with other chemicals and this influences their uses.

Students learn to:	pages	Students:	pages
• describe observable changes when metals react with dilute acid, water and oxygen	128–30	• perform a first-hand investigation incorporating information from secondary sources to determine the metal activity series	138–9
• describe and justify the criteria used to place metals into an order of activity based on their ease of reaction with oxygen, water and dilute acids	130	• construct word and balanced formulae equations for the reaction of metals with water, oxygen and dilute acid	128–30
• identify the reaction of metals with acids as requiring a transfer of electrons	130–1	• construct half-equations to represent the electron transfer reactions occurring when metals react with dilute hydrochloric and dilute sulfuric acids.	131
• outline examples of a selection of metals for different purposes based on their reactivity, with a particular emphasis on current developments in the use of metals	132–3		
• outline the relationship between the relative activities of metals and their positions on the periodic table	135–6		
• identify the importance of first ionisation energy in determining the relative reactivity of metals.	133–5		

3. As metals and other elements were discovered, scientists recognised that patterns in their physical and chemical properties could be used to organise the elements into a periodic table.

Students learn to:	*pages*	*Students:*	*pages*
• identify an appropriate model that has been developed to describe atomic structure	141	• process information from secondary sources to develop a periodic table by recognising patterns and trends in the properties of elements, and use available evidence to predict the characteristics of unknown elements both in groups and across periods	158–9
• outline the history of the development of the periodic table including its origins, the original data used to construct it and the predictions made after its construction	142–7	• use computer-based technologies to produce a table and a graph of changes in one physical property across a period and down a group.	160

• explain the relationship between the position of elements in the periodic table, and:
  – electrical conductivity
  – ionisation energy
  – atomic radius
  – melting point
  – boiling point
  – combining power (valency)
  – electronegativity
  – reactivity.
	148–54		

4. For efficient resource use, industrial chemical reactions must use measured amounts of each reactant.

Students learn to:	*pages*	*Students:*	*pages*
• define the mole as the number of atoms in exactly 12 g of carbon-12 (Avogadro's number)	168–9	• process information from secondary sources to interpret balanced chemical equations in terms of mole ratios	170–1
• compare mass changes in samples of metals when they combine with oxygen	162–5	• perform a first-hand investigation to measure and identify the mass ratios of metal to non-metal(s) in a common compound and calculate its empirical formula	179
• describe the contribution of Gay-Lussac to the understanding of gaseous reactions and apply this to an understanding of the mole concept	165–6	• solve problems and analyse information from secondary sources to perform calculations involving Avogadro's number and the equation for calculating the number of moles of a substance: $$n = \frac{m}{M}$$	169–71
• recount Avogadro's law and describe its importance in developing the mole concept	166–8		
• distinguish between empirical formulae and molecular formulae.	174–7	• process information from secondary sources to investigate the relationship between the volumes of gases involved in reactions involving a metal and relate this to an understanding of the mole.	180

5. The relative abundance and ease of extraction of metals influence their value and breadth of use in the community.

Students learn to:	pages	Students:	pages
• define the terms 'mineral' and 'ore' with reference to economical and non-economical deposits of natural resources	182	• discuss the importance of predicting yield in the identification, mining and extraction of commercial ore deposits	184, 195–6
• describe the relationship between the commercial prices of common metals, their actual abundances and relative costs of production	183–6	• justify the increased recycling of metals in our society and across the world	192–3
• explain why ores are non-renewable resources	182	• analyse information to compare the cost and energy expenditure involved in the extraction of aluminium from its ore and the recycling of aluminium.	196–7
• describe the separation processes, chemical reactions and energy considerations involved in the extraction of copper from one of its ores	186–92		
• recount the steps taken to recycle aluminium.	193		

Core module 3: Water (chapters 11–14, pages 200–77)

1. Water is distributed on Earth as a solid, liquid and gas.

Students learn to:	pages	Students:	pages
• define the terms 'solute', 'solvent' and 'solution'	201	• perform an investigation involving calculations of the density of water as a liquid and a solid using:	208–9, 213–14
• identify the importance of water as a solvent	202	$$density = \frac{mass}{volume}$$	
• compare the state, percentage and distribution of water in the biosphere, lithosphere, hydrosphere and atmosphere	202–3	• analyse information by using models to account for the differing densities of ice and liquid water	214, 225
• outline the significance of the different states of water on Earth in terms of water as:	203–6	• plan and perform an investigation to identify and describe the effect of antifreeze or salt on the boiling point of water.	207–8, 212–13
– a constituent of cells and its role as both a solvent and a raw material in metabolism			
– a habitat in which temperature extremes are less than nearby terrestrial habitats			
– an agent of weathering of rocks both as liquid and solid			
– a natural resource for humans and other organisms.			

2. The wide distribution and importance of water on Earth is a consequence of its molecular structure and hydrogen bonding.

Students learn to:	pages	Students:	pages
• construct Lewis electron dot structures of water, ammonia and hydrogen sulfide to identify the distribution of electrons	214–15	• process information from secondary sources to graph and compare the boiling and melting points of water with other similar sized molecules	231–2
• compare the molecular structures of water, ammonia and hydrogen sulfide, the differences in their molecular shapes and in their melting and boiling points	214, 220–1	• identify data and process information from secondary sources to model the structure of the water molecule and effects of forces between water molecules	232
• describe hydrogen bonding between molecules	212–13, 217–18	• choose equipment and perform first-hand investigations to demonstrate the following properties of water:	233–5
• identify the water molecule as a polar molecule	212	– surface tension	
• describe the attractive forces between polar molecules as dipole–dipole forces	212	– viscosity.	
• explain the following properties of water in terms of its intermolecular forces:	218–21		
– surface tension			
– viscosity			
– boiling and melting points.			

3. Water is an important solvent.

Students learn to:	pages	Students:	pages
• explain changes, if any, to particles and account for those changes when the following types of chemical interact with water: – a soluble ionic compound such as sodium chloride – a soluble molecular compound such as sucrose – a soluble or partially soluble molecular element or compound such as iodine, oxygen or hydrogen chloride – a covalent network structure substance such as silicon dioxide – a substance with large molecules such as cellulose or polyethylene	224–7	• perform a first-hand investigation to test the solubilities in water of a range of substances that include ionic, soluble molecular, insoluble molecular, covalent networks and large molecules • process information from secondary sources to visualise the dissolution in water of various types of substance and solve problems by using models to show the changes that occur in particle arrangement as dissolution occurs.	236 236
• analyse the relationship between the solubility of substances in water and the polar nature of the water molecule.	223–4, 227		

4. The concentration of salts in water depends on their solubility, and precipitation can occur when the ions of an insoluble salt are in solution together.

Students learn to:	pages	Students:	pages
• use solubility data to identify some combinations of solutions that produce precipitates	242–4	• construct ionic equations to represent the dissolution and precipitation of ionic compounds in water	244–5
• describe a model that traces the movement of ions when solution and precipitation occur	243, 248	• present information in balanced chemical equations and identify the appropriate phase descriptors, (s), (l), (g), and (aq), for all chemical species	244–5
• identify the dynamic nature of ion movement in a saturated dissolution	247	• perform a first-hand investigation, using microtechniques, to compare the solubility of appropriate salts in solution through precipitation reactions	260
• describe the molarity of a solution as the number of moles of solute per litre of solution using: $$c = \frac{n}{V}$$	251–4	• carry out simple calculations to describe the concentration of given solutions, given masses of solute and volumes of solution	255
• explain why different measurements of concentration are important.	256–7	• perform a first-hand investigation to make solutions to specified volume-to-volume and mass-to-volume specifications and dilute them to specified concentrations (cV = constant) • calculate mass and concentration relationships in precipitation reactions as they are encountered.	253, 261 246

5. Water has a higher heat capacity than many other liquids.

Students learn to:	pages	Students:	pages
• explain what is meant by the specific heat capacity of a substance	263–4	• choose resources and perform a first-hand investigation to measure the change in temperature when substances dissolve in water and calculate the molar heat of solution	276–7
• compare the specific heat capacity of water with a range of other solvents	264	• process and present information from secondary sources to assess the limitations of calorimetry experiments and design modifications to equipment used.	274
• explain and use the equation: $$\Delta H = mC\Delta T$$	266–8		
• explain how water's ability to absorb heat is used to measure energy changes in chemical reactions	265–6		
• describe dissolutions that release heat as exothermic and give examples	268–70		
• describe dissolutions that absorb heat as endothermic and give examples	268–70		
• explain why water's ability to absorb heat is important to aquatic organisms and to life on Earth generally	271–2		
• explain what is meant by thermal pollution and discuss the implications for life if a body of water is affected by thermal pollution.	273		

Core module 4: Energy (chapters 15–17, page 280–344)

1. Living organisms make compounds which are important sources of energy.

Students learn to:	pages	Students:	pages
• outline the role of photosynthesis in transforming light energy to chemical energy and recall the raw materials for this process	281	• process and present information from secondary sources on the range of compounds found in either coal, petroleum or natural gas, and on the location of deposits of the selected fossil fuel in Australia.	283–9, 291–2
• outline the role of the production of high energy carbohydrates from carbon dioxide as the important step in the stabilisation of the sun's energy in a form that can be used by animals as well as plants	282–3		
• identify the photosynthetic origins of the chemical energy in coal, petroleum and natural gas.	283–9		

2. There is a wide variety of carbon compounds.

Students learn to:	pages	Students:	pages
• identify the position of carbon in the periodic table and describe its electron configuration	294	• perform a first-hand investigation, analyse information and use available evidence to model the differences in atomic arrangement of diamond, graphite and fullerenes	309
• describe the structure of the diamond and graphite allotropes and account for their physical properties in terms of bonding	294–5	• process and present information from secondary sources on the uses of diamond and graphite and relate their uses to their physical properties	309
• identify that carbon can form single, double or triple covalent bonds with other carbon atoms	296–8	• identify data, and choose resources from secondary sources such as molecular model kits, digital technologies or computer simulations to model the formation of single, double and triple bonds in simple carbon compounds	309
• explain the relationship between carbon's combining power and ability to form a variety of bonds and the existence of a large number of carbon compounds	296–8		

3. A variety of carbon compounds are extracted from organic sources.

Students learn to:	pages	Students:	pages
• describe the use of fractional distillation to separate the components of petroleum and identify the uses of each fraction obtained	299–301	• perform a first-hand investigation and gather first-hand information using the process of fractional distillation to separate the components of a mixture such as ethanol and water	310–12
• identify and use the IUPAC nomenclature for describing straight-chain alkanes and alkenes from C1 to C8	301–4	• plan, identify and gather data from secondary sources to model the structure of alkanes and alkenes C1 to C8	312
• compare and contrast the properties of alkanes and alkenes C1 to C8 and use the term 'homologous series' to describe a series with the same functional group	301–4	• process and present information from secondary sources and use available evidence to identify safety issues associated with the storage of alkanes.	312
• explain the relationship between the melting point, boiling point and volatility of the above hydrocarbons, and their non-polar nature and intermolecular forces (dispersion forces)	305–6		
• assess safety issues associated with the storage of alkanes C1 to C8 in view of their weak intermolecular forces (dispersion forces).	305–6		

4. Combustion provides another opportunity to examine the conditions under which chemical reactions occur.

Students learn to:	pages	Students:	pages
• describe the indicators of chemical reactions	314	• solve problems and perform a first-hand investigation to measure the change in mass when a mixture such as wood is burnt in an open container	337–8
• identify combustion as an exothermic chemical reaction	314–15		
• outline the changes in molecules during chemical reactions in terms of breaking and making bonds	314–16	• identify the changes of state involved in combustion of a burning candle	321–3, 338–9
• explain that energy is required to break bonds and energy is released when bonds are formed	316	• perform first-hand investigations to observe and describe examples of endothermic and exothermic chemical reactions.	336–7
• describe the energy needed to begin a chemical reaction as activation energy	316–17		
• describe the energy profile diagram for both endothermic and exothermic reactions	317–18		
• explain the relationship between ignition temperature and activation energy	318–19		
• identify the sources of pollution that accompany the combustion of organic compounds and explain how these can be avoided	320		
• describe chemical reactions by using full balanced chemical equations to summarise examples of complete and incomplete combustion.	320–1		

5. The rate of energy release is affected by factors such as type of reactant.

Students learn to:	pages	Students:	pages
• describe combustion in terms of slow, spontaneous and explosive reactions and explain the conditions under which these occur	331–3	• solve problems, identify data, perform first-hand investigations and gather first-hand data where appropriate, to observe the impact on reaction rates of:	339–41
• explain the importance of collisions between reacting particles as a criterion for determining reaction rates	328–9	– changing temperature	
• explain the relationship between temperature and the kinetic energy of particles	327	– changing concentration	
		– size of solid particles	
• describe the role of catalysts in chemical reactions, using a named industrial catalyst as an example	330–1	– adding catalysts	
• explain the role of catalysts in changing the activation energy and hence the rate of chemical reaction.	329–30	• process information from secondary sources to investigate the conditions under which explosions occur and relate these to the importance of collisions between reacting particles	332–3, 343–4
		• analyse information and use the available evidence to relate the conditions under which explosions occur to the need for safety in work environments where fine particles mix with air	343–4
		• analyse information from secondary sources to develop models to simulate the role of catalysts in changing the rate of chemical reactions.	342

Chemistry Stage 6 Syllabus © 2002 Copyright Board of Studies NSW for and on behalf of the Crown in right of the State of New South Wales.

About eBookPLUS

jacaranda *plus*

Next generation teaching and learning

This book features eBookPLUS: an electronic version of the entire textbook and supporting multimedia resources. It is available for you online at the JacarandaPLUS website (www.jacplus.com.au).

Join **thousands** of other students & teachers in discovering the **next generation** in **teaching** and **learning solutions**...

Using the JacarandaPLUS website

To access your eBookPLUS resources, simply log on to www.jacplus.com.au using your existing JacarandaPLUS login and enter the registration code. If you are new to JacarandaPLUS, follow the three easy steps below.

Step 1. Create a user account

The first time you use the JacarandaPLUS system, you will need to create a user account. Go to the JacarandaPLUS home page (www.jacplus.com.au), click on the button to create a new account and follow the instructions on screen. You can then use your nominated email address and password to log in to the JacarandaPLUS system.

Step 2. Enter your registration code

Once you have logged in, enter your unique registration code for this book, which is printed on the inside front cover of your textbook. The title of your textbook will appear in your bookshelf. Click on the link to open your eBookPLUS.

Step 3. View or download eBookPLUS resources

Your eBookPLUS and supporting resources are provided in a chapter-by-chapter format. Simply select the desired chapter from the drop-down list. Your eBookPLUS contains the entire textbook's content in easy-to-use HTML. The student resources panel contains supporting multimedia resources for each chapter.

Once you have created your account, you can use the same email address and password in the future to register any JacarandaPLUS titles you own.

Using eBookPLUS references

eBookPLUS logos are used throughout the printed books to inform you that a multimedia resource is available for the content you are studying.

Searchlight IDs (e.g. **INT-0001**) give you instant access to multimedia resources. Once you are logged in, simply enter the searchlight ID for that resource and it will open immediately.

Minimum requirements

JacarandaPLUS requires you to use a supported internet browser and version, otherwise you will not be able to access your resources or view all features and upgrades. Please view the complete list of JacPLUS minimum system requirements at http://jacplus.desk.com/customer/portal/articles/463717.

Troubleshooting

- Go to the JacarandaPLUS help page at www.jacplus.com.au/jsp/help.jsp.
- Contact John Wiley & Sons Australia, Ltd. Email: support@jacplus.com.au Phone: 1800 JAC PLUS (1800 522 7587)

ACKNOWLEDGEMENTS

The author would like to thank Lynette and Stuart for their support throughout the long process of bringing this book to its readers. He hopes that the readers will find this work a useful text to help them prepare for the Preliminary and HSC courses in Chemistry. He would also like to thank the editorial team at John Wiley & Sons for their commitment to this project.

The publisher would like to thank the following copyright holders, organisations and individuals for their assistance and for permission to reproduce copyright material in this book.

Images:
• Austral International/Adrian Seafort **110** • ANTPhoto.com.au: /Bruce Thomson **200**; /N.H.P.A. **192**; Grant Dixon **209** (bottom) • Australian Picture Library: /CORBIS/Archivo Iconografico **111** (bottom); /Corbis/Bettmann **141**; /Corbis/Gary Braasch **206**; /David Lees **28**; /Heritage Image Partnership Limited **162** (bottom); /J. Carnemolla **314**; /John Garrett **12**; /Joseph Sohm **273** • Coo-ee Picture Library **332** • © Corbis Images **223** (top), **294**, **322** • © Creatas **120** • David Grabham **111** (top) • © Digital Stock/Corbis Corporation **61** (right), **201** (bottom) • © Digital Vision **7, 74, 115, 262** • Fairfax Photo Library: /Brendan Esposito **284** (bottom left); /Glenn Campbell **181**; /Robert Pearce **205**; /Robert Rough **280** • © Richard Megna/Fundamental Photographs, NYC **150** (bottom left) • Geoffrey Thickett **77, 87, 228, 251, 263, 327, 338** • Getty Images: /National Geographic/Randy Olson **113**; /Stone/Bruce Forster **182** (bottom); /Stone/Greg Pease **114**; /Stone/Joe McBride **117**; /Stone/Lonnie Duka **47**; /Stone/Paul Chesley **188** (top left); /The Bridgeman Art Library **108**; /The Image Bank/Alexandra Michaels **53** (glass); /The Image Bank/David Gould **100**; /The Image Bank/Romilly Lockyer **80**; /The Image Bank/Will & Deni McIntyre **284** (right); /Time Life Pictures **300** • © Image 100 **207** • John Wiley & Sons Australia **189**; /photo by Werner Langer **21** • © Medio Images **2** • Newspix **289** (right); /AFP **185** (left); /Megan Lewis **185** (right) • © PhotoAlto **42** (right) • © PhotoDisc, Inc. **39** (periodic table), **53** (balloons), **107, 119** (right), **132, 279, 286** • photolibrary.com **42** (left); /A.G.E. Fotostock **223** (bottom); /Erin Garvey **136** /Heinz Mollenhauer **119** (left); /John Yates **289** (left); /Ken Eward **296**; /Photo Researchers, Inc. **109** (bottom), **121**; /Photo Researchers, Inc./Charles D. Winters **39** (flask), **40** (right), **46, 66, 75, 149** (top left); /Photo Researchers, Inc. /DOE/Science Source **94**; /Photo Researchers, Inc./Hermann Eisenbeiss **215**; /Photo Researchers, Inc./Kaj R. Svensson **285**; /Photo Researchers, Inc./Lee Snyder **76**; /Photo Researchers, Inc./Ray Ellis **284** (top); /Richard Woldendorp **293**; /Robin Smith **25**; /SPL **127, 133, 144** (bottom), **146** (left), **167** (top right); /SPL/Adam Hart-Davis **199**; /SPL/Andrew Lambert Photography **4** (left, centre), **129, 130, 168** (bottom); /SPL /Arnold Fisher **53** (crystal), **109** (top left); /SPL/Cristina Pedrazzini **280**; /SPL/Damien Lovegrove **193**; /SPL/David Parker **92** (right); /SPL/David Taylor **128** (top), **242**; /SPL /Dirk Wiersma **1, 3, 109** (top right); /SPL/Dr Kari Lounatmaa **282**; /SPL/Geoff Tompkinson **4** (right); /SPL/Jerry Mason **313**; /SPL/Klaus Guldbrandsen **40** (left); /SPL/Martin Land **23** (left); /SPL/Martin Land **58, 96**; /SPL/Martyn F. Chillmaid **23** (right), **52, 61** (left, centre), **128** (bottom), **241, 245**; /SPL /Mauro Fermariello **161**; /SPL/Michael Barnett **187**; /SPL /Michael Donne **320**; /SPL/Peter Chadwick **204** (left); /SPL /Roberto de Gugliemo **92** (left); /SPL/Shelia Terry **140** (left); /SPL/Sinclair Stammers **91**; photolibrary.com Royalty Free **306** • Photo courtesy of Woodside Energy Ltd **288** • Photograph courtesy of Xstrata Copper **13**

Text:
• HSC Chemistry Exam Paper © Board of Studies NSW for and on behalf of the Crown in right of the State of New South Wales, 2005 **inside front cover**, **inside back cover**

Every effort has been made to trace the ownership of copyright material. Information that will enable the publisher to rectify any error or omission in subsequent reprints and editions will be welcome. In such cases, please contact the Permissions Section of John Wiley & Sons Australia, Ltd.

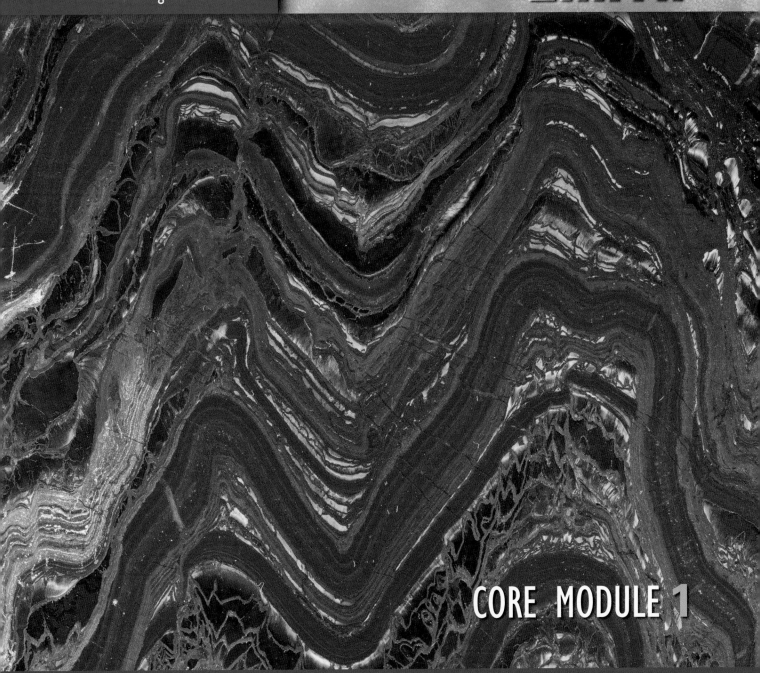

THE CHEMICAL EARTH

CORE MODULE 1

Chapter 1

MIXTURES IN THE EARTH

Introduction

The Earth and all its living and non-living components consist of complex mixtures. The rocks of the Earth are composed of mixtures of many different minerals. The oceans, rivers and lakes contain water in which many substances are dissolved or suspended. The atmosphere is a mixture of many gases including oxygen, nitrogen and carbon dioxide. Living things, from the lowest life forms to the most complex forms, contain mixtures of simple and complex compounds.

In this chapter

Figure 1.1

The Earth can be divided into various zones or spheres. The rocks of the cliff face and the sandy beach are part of the lithosphere. The ocean and the water in the sand are part of the hydrosphere. The air and clouds are part of the atmosphere. The living things in the ocean water, in and on the sand of the beach and flying in the air are all part of the biosphere.

1.1 CLASSIFICATION OF MATTER

Elements, compounds and mixtures

Chemistry is an ancient science. Inquiring minds over the centuries have wondered about the interesting variety of materials that make up our Earth. Humans have used the materials of the Earth to build their homes, monuments and roads. They have used materials such as gold as money and to make ornaments. They have used salt for seasoning and preserving food, and as a form of money. They have used coal and oil as fuels for warmth and as a source of energy to power machines.

Chemistry is the study of matter. Chemists classify matter in many ways. One way is to classify matter as solids, liquids or gases at room temperature. Another more useful scheme is to classify matter as pure or impure. In everyday life, we use the term 'pure' to describe things that are not contaminated with other substances. Pure water does not contain parasites, salt or mud. Chemists have developed more exact definitions of the terms 'pure' and 'impure'.

- *Pure substances* have a fixed composition and fixed properties. They cannot be decomposed by simple physical separation techniques.

- *Impure substances* are mixtures. They have variable composition and variable properties. They can be separated into their components by various physical separation techniques.
  Pure substances can be further classified into elements and compounds.

- *Elements* are the simplest pure substances consisting of only one type of atom. They cannot be broken down (or decomposed).

- *Compounds* are also pure substances. They are composed of two or more elements that are chemically bonded together. They are composed of a fixed number of atoms of each component element. They can be decomposed into their component elements or into simpler compounds.

Table 1.1 lists some examples of pure and impure substances. The chemical symbols for elements and the chemical formulae for compounds are also included.

Table 1.1 Classification of matter

Elements	Compounds	Mixtures
oxygen, O	water, H_2O	air
silver, Ag	silver oxide, Ag_2O	brass
magnesium, Mg	magnesium sulfide, MgS	steel
silicon, Si	silicon dioxide, SiO_2	sand

The Earth's crust contains elements, compounds and mixtures. The two most abundant elements are oxygen and silicon. Silicon is present in many compounds and in mixtures of compounds but is rarely found as the free element. Pure, crystalline silicon (figure 1.3) has a greasy feel, like graphite. Sand is a mixture of silicon dioxide and many other substances. Quartz crystals are composed of interlocking silicon dioxide tetrahedra in a relatively pure form. Such large crystals often take thousands or millions of years to grow to such a size deep in the Earth's crust.

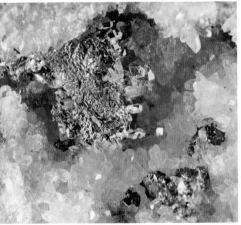

Figure 1.2
Gold is a pure substance, while the rock around it contains mixtures of various compounds.

CHAPTER 1 MIXTURES IN THE EARTH   **3**

physical properties: the properties characteristic of a chemical substance (such as melting point, boiling point, colour, density and conductivity)

Pure substances have fixed **physical properties**. Thus, the melting and boiling points of different elements and compounds are unique to that substance. The boiling point of pure water is 100 °C at 100 kPa pressure (standard pressure). This is not true for mixtures. For example, the boiling point of salt water depends on the amount of salt dissolved in the water. The greater the salt concentration, the greater the boiling point.

Table 1.2 shows some examples of the fixed physical properties of some common elements and compounds. The properties of the compounds are quite different from their component elements. This shows that compounds are not just mixtures of elements.

Table 1.2 Physical properties of some common elements and compounds

Substance	copper	oxygen	copper (I) oxide, Cu_2O	copper (II) oxide, CuO
Colour	salmon pink	colourless	red	black
State (at 25 °C/100 kPa)	solid	gas	solid	solid
Density (g/cm³ at 25 °C/100 kPa)	9.0	1.3×10^{-3}	6.0	6.4
Melting point (°C)	1085	−219	1235	1326

Particle models

Chemists use models to understand the differences between elements, compounds and mixtures. The components of matter can be visualised in terms of different types of particle. Atoms are the basic building blocks of matter. Sometimes, atoms of the same element or different elements group together to form more complex particles called molecules. The number of atoms in a molecule is shown using a subscript next to the symbol for the element. For example, N_2 represents a nitrogen molecule that has two atoms of nitrogen.

Elements are composed of atoms or molecules. Examples include:
- helium (single atoms or monatomic molecules, He)
- oxygen (diatomic molecules, O_2)
- phosphorus (tetra-atomic molecules, P_4).

Compounds are composed of fixed numbers of atoms of different elements. Examples include:
- ammonia, NH_3
- zinc oxide, ZnO
- carbon dioxide, CO_2.

homogeneous mixture: a mixture in which all the particles are uniformly distributed

heterogeneous mixture: a mixture in which the particles are not uniformly distributed

Mixtures have various particle types and compositions. The particles of each component in **homogeneous mixtures** are distributed uniformly; they are not uniformly distributed in **heterogeneous mixtures**. Sugar solutions in water are homogeneous mixtures as the sugar particles are uniformly mixed with the water particles. Muddy water is a heterogeneous mixture as the heavier mud particles settle under gravity to form a sediment.

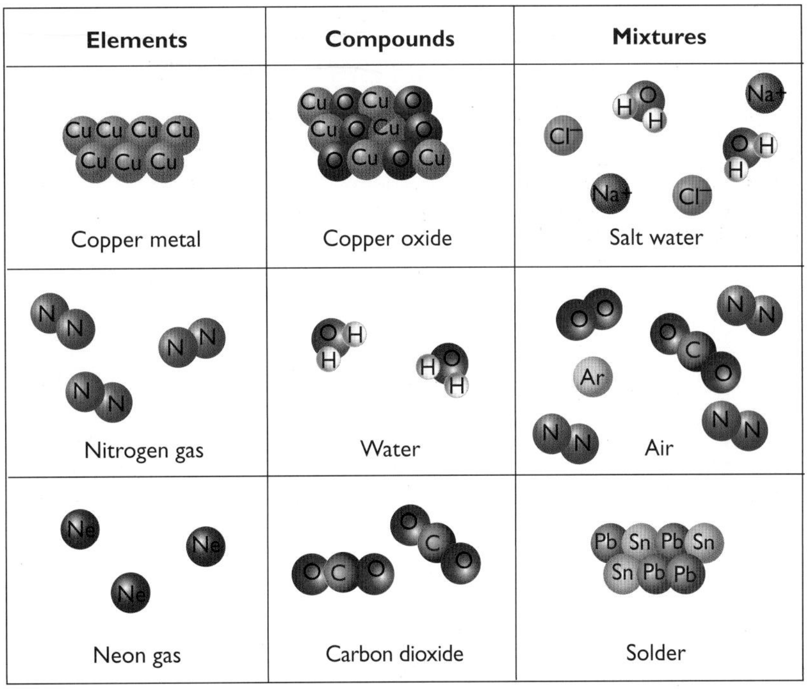
Elements
Compounds
Mixtures
Copper metal
Copper oxide
Salt water
Nitrogen gas
Water
Air
Neon gas
Carbon dioxide
Solder

Figure 1.4
Particle diagrams showing the differences between elements, compounds and mixtures

SYLLABUS FOCUS

1. USING INSTRUCTION TERMS CORRECTLY

When answering questions, it is important to know what the instruction terms (verbs) require you to do. Here are some examples.

'Classify'
This instruction term requires you to group things into categories. Thus, pure substances can be grouped into elements and compounds.

Example:
Classify barium as an element or compound.

Answer:
Element

'Define'
This instruction term requires you to state the meaning of a term or identify the essential features of a concept.

Example:
Define the term 'molecule'.

Answer:
A molecule is the smallest part of a substance that can exist independently but still retain the characteristic properties of that substance.

'Explain'
This instruction term requires you to provide reasons for why or how a process occurs, or to make the relationship between things evident.

Example:
Explain why barium is classified as an element.

Answer:
Barium is classified as an element because it is a simple, pure substance that cannot be broken down into anything simpler.

1.1 QUESTIONS

1. Classify the following as mixtures or pure substances.
   (a) Air
   (b) Sea water
   (c) Carbon dioxide
   (d) Granite
   (e) Calcium

2. Classify the following pure substances as elements or compounds.
   (a) Glucose
   (b) Silver
   (c) Ammonia
   (d) Lead
   (e) Copper (II) oxide

3. Classify the particle models in figure 1.5 as elements, compounds or mixtures.

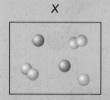 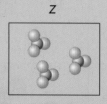

X   Y   Z

Figure 1.5 Particle model diagrams

4. Define the terms:
   (a) homogeneous mixture
   (b) heterogeneous mixture.

5. Explain why the properties of copper (II) oxide (see table 1.2) are quite different from the properties of copper and oxygen.

6. Classify each of the particle models in figure 1.6 as homogeneous mixtures or heterogeneous mixtures.

P   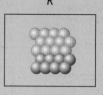 Q   R   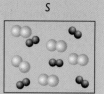 S

Figure 1.6 Particle model diagrams of different mixtures

7. The following information about solutions of sulfuric acid was collected from a chemical data book.

Table 1.3

Concentration of sulfuric acid solution (%w/w)	5	10	15	20	25
Density of acid solution at 20 °C (g/cm³)	1.032	1.066	1.102	1.139	1.178

   (a) Classify sulfuric acid solutions as homogeneous or heterogeneous mixtures.
   (b) Explain how the tabulated data is typical of a mixture rather than a pure substance.

1.2 MIXTURES AND THE SPHERES OF THE EARTH

The spheres of the Earth

The Earth is believed to be about five billion years old. It formed from a swirling gas and dust cloud that orbited the primitive Sun. Gravitational compression and heating, as well as heat from radioactive decay, caused many minerals to melt and form new chemical compounds. Geologists have determined that the Earth eventually formed into a layered structure with dense metals, such as iron, at its centre, and lighter minerals, containing elements such as silicon, oxygen and aluminium, forming a solid crust at the surface. As the Earth cooled, water vapour condensed and formed the oceans and seas. The atmosphere has changed over the eons of time. Some light gases, such as hydrogen, have escaped into space, and the amount of oxygen has changed considerably in response to the evolution of life forms.

Remember

Before beginning this section, you should be able to:
- identify some common mixtures
- identify the importance of water as a solvent
- describe aqueous mixtures in terms of solute, solvent and solution.

Figure 1.8 shows the layered structure or spheres of the Earth, starting with the lithosphere, which consists of the rigid, outer crust and the upper mantle. The inner mantle and core are not shown. The hydrosphere consists of the surface oceans, rivers, lakes and glacial water; it also extends into the atmosphere and lithosphere. In the atmosphere, water can exist as water vapour as well as liquid microdroplets in clouds. The biosphere is also an extensive region where living things are found. Scientists have discovered simple life forms deep within the hot crust as well as near volcanic vents on the ocean floor. Microscopic life forms have also been found in the highest levels of the atmosphere.

Figure 1.7
The biosphere is a part of the atmosphere, hydrosphere and lithosphere.

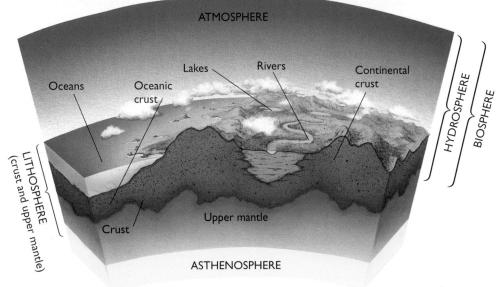

Figure 1.8
The spheres of the Earth

Mixtures in each sphere

Within each sphere of the Earth there is a complex mixture of chemical substances.

Lithosphere

mineral: a naturally occurring, crystalline solid that has a fixed chemical composition or a composition that varies between strict limits. Some minerals are pure elements, such as gold and sulfur, but most minerals are chemical compounds.

The lithosphere contains many different types of **mineral** that are combined in different proportions to form sedimentary, igneous and metamorphic rocks. Silicates, oxides, carbonates and sulfides are some of the common minerals found in the lithosphere. The sand that forms the beaches along our coasts consists mainly of silicon dioxide. Humans mine mineral resources to manufacture metals and alloys. Many of these minerals are oxide and sulfide compounds of metals, such as aluminium, iron, lead and silver. Extraction of metals from these minerals requires the removal of the unwanted minerals that make up the rock.

The common rock-making minerals and their chemical compositions are listed in table 1.4.

Table 1.4 Common rock-making minerals

Mineral	Composition
quartz	SiO_2
orthoclase feldspar	$KAlSi_3O_8$
muscovite mica	$KAl_3Si_3O_{10}(OH)_2$
olivine	$(Mg, Fe)_2SiO_4$
calcite	$CaCO_3$

Tables 1.5 (a) and (b) show the abundance of some of the elements that make up the Earth's crust, and the abundance of elements in the whole Earth. The high percentage of oxygen and silicon in the crust reveals the abundance and importance of silicate minerals in the crust. Iron is the most abundant element in the whole Earth due to the massive amount of iron in the Earth's core.

Table 1.5 (a) Abundance of elements in the Earth's crust

Element	Abundance in the crust (%w/w*)
oxygen	46.6
silicon	27.7
aluminium	8.2
iron	5.0
calcium	3.6
sodium	2.8
potassium	2.6
magnesium	2.1
all others	1.4

*%w/w = percentage by weight

(b) Abundance of elements in the whole Earth

Element	Abundance in the whole Earth (%w/w*)
iron	35
oxygen	30
silicon	15
magnesium	13
nickel	2.4
sulfur	1.9
calcium	1.1
aluminium	1.1
others	<1

*%w/w = percentage by weight

Hydrosphere

Water is the most abundant compound in the hydrosphere. Consequently, oxygen and hydrogen are the most abundant elements in this sphere. Most of the Earth's water (97.2%) is present in the oceans and 2.2% is present as polar ice and glaciers. The lithosphere contains 0.6% of the Earth's water and only 0.001% is found in the atmosphere.

Sea water contains many dissolved minerals, which make up about 3.5%w/w. Evaporation of sea water yields salts, such as sodium chloride, together with smaller amounts of magnesium chloride, calcium chloride and sodium sulfate.

Table 1.6 shows the abundance of various elements in sea water.

Table 1.6 Abundance of elements in sea water

Element	Abundance (%w/w)
oxygen	86.0
hydrogen	10.8
chlorine	1.9
sodium	1.1
magnesium	0.1

Atmosphere

Nitrogen and oxygen are the major gases of the atmosphere. Carbon dioxide accounts for only 0.037%. Table 1.7 shows the composition of gases in the troposphere, which is the lowest layer of the atmosphere.

Table 1.7 Abundance of dried gases in the troposphere

Gas	Composition (%v/v)*	Composition (%w/w)
nitrogen	78.09	75.3
oxygen	20.94	23.1
argon	0.93	1.3
carbon dioxide	0.037	0.049
neon	0.0018	0.0013
helium	0.0005	0.0007
methane	0.00015	0.00008

*%v/v = percentage by volume

Biosphere

The biosphere is the region of the Earth where living things are found. The ecosystems in which these life forms are found occupy the hydrosphere, lithosphere and the atmosphere.

Most living things are composed of cells. Cells contain large amounts of water so oxygen and hydrogen are abundant in the biosphere. Carbon compounds are the basis of life. Cells contain complex carbon compounds such as carbohydrates, fats, proteins and nucleic acids.

Table 1.8 shows the most abundant elements in living cells. Nitrogen and sulfur are important elements in proteins, while calcium and phosphorus are important structural elements in bones and membranous tissue.

Table 1.8 Most abundant elements in living cells

Element	Abundance (%w/w)
oxygen	60.0
carbon	21.0
hydrogen	11.0
nitrogen	3.5
calcium	2.5
phosphorus	1.2
chlorine	0.2
sulfur	0.15

SYLLABUS FOCUS

2. USING INSTRUCTION TERMS CORRECTLY

When answering questions, it is important to know what the instruction terms (verbs) require you to do. Here are some examples.

'Identify'

This instruction term requires you to recognise and name a substance process, event or person.

Example:
Identify the element that is the basis of all life forms.

Answer:
Carbon

'Account'

This instruction term requires you to state reasons for an observation or statement.

Example:
Account for the fact that nitrogen is the fourth most abundant element (by weight) in living things.

Answer:
Nitrogen compounds include proteins and nucleic acids. These are vital components of living cells. Thus, nitrogen is abundant but not as abundant as oxygen and hydrogen, which are also present in water, carbohydrates and fats.

'Predict'

This instruction term requires you to suggest a result or outcome based on available evidence.

Example:
One litre of sea water is slowly evaporated, and the mass of water and the mass of crystals formed are determined by weighing. Predict which material will have the greater mass.

Answer:
Water (see evidence in table 1.6)

'Justify'

This instruction term requires you to support an argument or conclusion.

Example:
Magnesium strips are known to burn brightly when oxygen is present. Two magnesium strips were ignited and placed in separate jars X and Y containing either air or pure oxygen. Magnesium burnt more brightly in jar X than in jar Y. Predict which jar contained air. Justify your response.

Answer:
Jar Y contained air. Air contains only 20.94% oxygen so the chemical reaction will be less vigorous than in pure oxygen.

1.2 QUESTIONS

1. Identify the element that is in greatest abundance, in terms of weight, in the:
   (a) lithosphere
   (b) hydrosphere
   (c) atmosphere.

2. Arrange the following elements in decreasing order of abundance in sea water: chlorine, hydrogen, sodium, oxygen.

3. Account for the high percentage by weight of oxygen in living cells.

4. (a) Calculate the total percentage by weight of the five most abundant elements in sea water.
   (b) Draw a pie graph of the data in table 1.6.

5. (a) Identify the three most abundant elements in the atmosphere.
   (b) Calculate the total percentage by volume of the three most abundant elements in the atmosphere, using the information in table 1.7. Then determine the percentage by volume of all other gases.
   (c) Draw a divided bar graph of the atmospheric abundance data (by volume) to show the relative abundance of the three main gases and all other gases.

6. Account for the high abundance of silicon in the lithosphere.

7. Predict which salt would form the greatest mass of crystals if 100 mL of sea water is evaporated to dryness. Justify your answer.

8. Use the information in table 1.9 to identify the type of compound in each of these spheres in which the following elements are present.
   (a) lithosphere
       (i) lead, (ii) aluminium and (iii) calcium
   (b) hydrosphere
       (i) oxygen and (ii) sodium
   (c) atmosphere
       (i) carbon and (ii) oxygen
   (d) biosphere
       (i) nitrogen and (ii) phosphorus

9. Use the information in table 1.9 to identify the location in the spheres of the Earth in which the following compounds could be found.
   (a) magnesium carbonate
   (b) glucose
   (c) potassium chloride
   (d) silicon dioxide

Table 1.9

Location	Common elements	Major form
biosphere (living components)	hydrogen, oxygen	water
	phosphorus, calcium	calcium phosphate (bones)
	carbon, hydrogen, oxygen	carbohydrates, fats
	carbon, hydrogen, oxygen, nitrogen, sulfur	proteins
	carbon, hydrogen, oxygen, nitrogen, phosphorus	nucleic acids (DNA and RNA)
lithosphere	platinum, gold	free elements
	magnesium, calcium	carbonate minerals
	silicon, aluminium, iron, phosphorus	oxide minerals
	oxygen, silicon	silicate minerals
	copper, silver, lead	sulfide minerals
atmosphere	nitrogen, oxygen, argon	free element
	oxygen	water
	carbon	carbon dioxide
hydrosphere	hydrogen, oxygen	water
	sodium, potassium, chlorine, bromine, iodine	dissolved sea salts

1.3 *PHYSICAL SEPARATION TECHNIQUES*

physical separation techniques: separation processes that do not chemically alter the components of the mixture. These processes include filtration, evaporation, crystallisation, distillation, froth flotation, magnetic separation and centrifugation.

gangue: the unwanted (non-valuable) material present in an ore body

Useful materials in the spheres of the Earth usually need to be separated from unwanted material. For example:
- salt is obtained from sea water by evaporating the water
- metallic minerals are removed from unwanted rocky material by crushing, sieving and froth flotation
- oxygen is extracted from the air by fractional distillation of liquid air.

In this section, we will examine some useful **physical separation techniques** that have been developed over several hundred years to separate mixtures.

Separating solids

Solid particles of different particle size or weight can be separated using techniques such as sieving, sedimentation, magnetic separation or froth flotation.

Sieving

In metal mining industries, the mined ore is first crushed and ground to produce finely powdered grains. The grinding separates the valuable minerals from each other and from the **gangue**. The crushed ore is then screened using large wire-mesh sieves. The size of the mesh is adjusted to ensure the ore is finely ground.

Sedimentation

Heavy mineral grains in alluvial deposits can be removed from unwanted grains of rock (gangue) by sedimentation and panning. Gold grains can be separated by swirling the alluvial material with water and allowing the lighter material to be decanted and washed out of the pan, leaving the heavy gold grains behind.

In other mining operations, the finely ground ore from the sieving process is mixed with water. A slurry is formed. This slurry is transported through pipes to the gravity separators or jigs. Gravity causes the heavier particles to sediment faster. The lighter, finely ground material that contains a greater proportion of the valuable minerals is directed to the flotation tanks.

Figure 1.9
Salt can be extracted from salt water commercially by evaporation.

Froth flotation

This separation technique was first developed in Broken Hill (1901–02) at the silver, lead and zinc mines. The ground minerals are mixed with water, detergents and other oily chemicals ('collectors'). Air is blown through the mixture to create a froth to which the mineral grains adhere. The floating froth layer is scraped from the surface and removed for further treatment. This material is referred to as the *concentrate*, as it has a much higher percentage of metallic minerals than the original ore. The gangue does not float, so sediments to the bottom of the vessel.

Figure 1.10a
Froth flotation separating the mineral ore from the gangue

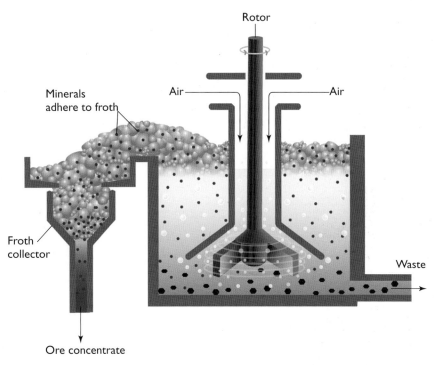

Figure 1.10b
The froth flotation technique creates a floating froth layer containing mineral grains, which is removed for further treatment.

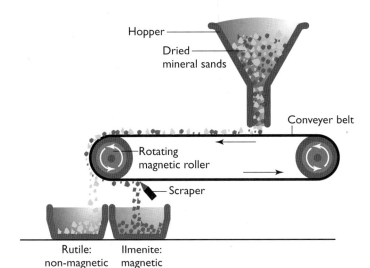

Figure 1.11
Magnetic separation of solids

Magnetic separation

Some iron mineral grains (such as magnetite, Fe_3O_4) can be separated from the grains of crushed rock by magnetic separation. This technique can also be used to separate the magnetic ilmenite minerals from non-magnetic rutile minerals in sand mining operations. The mixture can pass along a conveyor belt beneath a turning magnetic roller. The magnets hold the ilmenite longer on the belt while the rutile falls off the end of the belt.

Separating solids and liquids

Filtration and centrifugation are two common methods of separating solids from liquids.

Filtration

Insoluble solids can be separated from *soluble* solids by filtration. Sand grains can be separated from a mixture of sand grains and copper sulfate crystals by adding the mixture to sufficient water. The mixture is then stirred until all the copper sulfate dissolves. In a laboratory, the mixture is poured through a filter paper. The copper sulfate solution passes through the pores in the paper into a collection beaker below. This clear solution is called the *filtrate*. The insoluble sand grains (the *residue*) are retained in the filter. To collect these grains of sand, the residue on the filter paper is washed with clean water and then dried in a low temperature oven. The dry sand grains can then be retrieved from the paper. For successful filtration, the grain size of the insoluble component must be larger than the pore size of the filter. Various grades of filter paper are manufactured to deal with insoluble residues of various grain sizes.

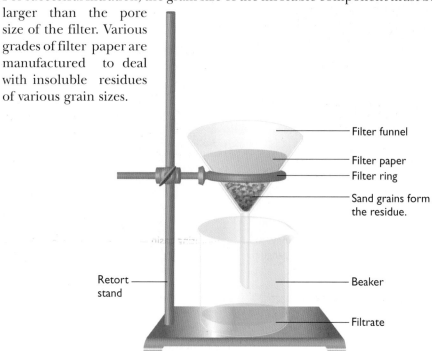

Filter funnel

Filter paper
Filter ring

Sand grains form the residue.

Retort stand

Beaker

Filtrate

Figure 1.12
Filtration in the laboratory

Solutions cannot be separated into solute and solvent by filtering, as the dissolved particles are too small and pass through the pores of the filter.

Filtration is commonly used as one of the steps in the purification of our water supplies. Water is filtered through beds of sand and gravel before passing on to later stages of purification.

Centrifugation

Centrifuges can be used to accelerate the process of sedimentation of a suspension. The suspension is spun at high speed so sediments collect at the base of the centrifuge tubes in layers according to their particle size and weight.

Centrifuges are used in many different industries. Cream can be separated from milk, and blood cells can be separated from plasma by this technique.

Gaseous and particle emissions can be treated by centrifugation to minimise air pollution. *Particulates*, such as soot and dust, in polluted air can be quite small (1–10 micrometres). These particles collect on the walls of the centrifugal separators.

Separating dissolved solids and liquids

Evaporation and crystallisation are used to separate dissolved solids from liquids.

Evaporation

Commercially, salt crystals can be recovered from salt water by evaporation in large salt pans. The process of evaporation separates a mixture by vaporising the low boiling component to leave the high boiling component as a residue. Water's **boiling point** of $100\,°C$ is much lower than that of sodium chloride ($1465\,°C$). Thus, the salt does not vaporise even if salt water is evaporated using the heat from a Bunsen burner. Evaporation is also used to dry the residues produced by filtration.

Crystallisation

Crystallisation is commonly used to purify impure salts. The impure salt is dissolved in water at a high temperature to create a concentrated solution. The mixture is then cooled and the salt crystallises, leaving the impurity in solution. This crystallised salt contains much less of the impurity than before. The salt can then be filtered and dried.

Crystallisation is employed in the sugar industry to extract sugar crystals from sugarcane syrup.

boiling point: the temperature at which the pressure exerted by the vapour above a liquid is equal to the external atmospheric pressure. Normal boiling points are measured at a standard pressure of 100 kPa.

1.1 PRACTICAL ACTIVITIES

Separation of a simple mixture

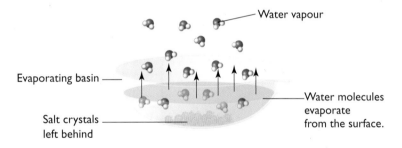

Figure 1.13
Crystals forming in a saturated solution during evaporation

Water vapour

Evaporating basin

Water molecules evaporate from the surface.

Salt crystals left behind

SAMPLE PROBLEM 1.1

Use table 1.10 to explain why and how 100 g of potassium nitrate, KNO_3, crystals containing $5\%\text{w/w}$ of potassium bromide, KBr, impurity can be purified by crystallisation.

Table 1.10

Temperature (°C)	Solubility (g/100 g water)	
	Potassium nitrate, KNO_3	**Potassium bromide, KBr**
10	20	60
60	104	85

SOLUTION

Both salts are quite soluble in water at $60\,°C$ but only KBr is appreciably soluble at $10\,°C$. The impure KNO_3 crystals can be purified by preparing a solution of the impure salt at $60\,°C$ and allowing it to cool to $10\,°C$.

The 100 g sample contains 95 g of KNO_3 and 5 g of KBr. The sample will completely dissolve in 100 g of water at $60\,°C$. The solution is now allowed to cool in an ice bath to $10\,°C$. At this temperature, only 20 g of the original 95 g of KNO_3 will remain dissolved. The other 75 g crystallises out. All of the 5 g of KBr remains dissolved at $10\,°C$. The purified KNO_3 crystals can be extracted by filtration.

Separating liquids

Immiscible liquids can be separated using a separating funnel. **Miscible** liquids can be separated by distillation.

miscible: describes liquids that mix to form one phase. For example, water and ethanol mix to form alcoholic solutions in all proportions.

Separating funnel

Some liquids do not dissolve in each other. Kerosene and water, for example, do not mix. They form separate layers with the less dense kerosene floating on top of the water. Separation is achieved by placing the mixture in a separating funnel and opening the tap to let out the lower layer into a clean vessel below. Figure 1.14 shows how a solution of iodine in tetrachloromethane can be separated from salt water. The salt water does not mix with the organic solvent and forms a separate layer on top. The lower (more dense) layer can be run off into a beaker, and then the salt water can be poured into a separate beaker.

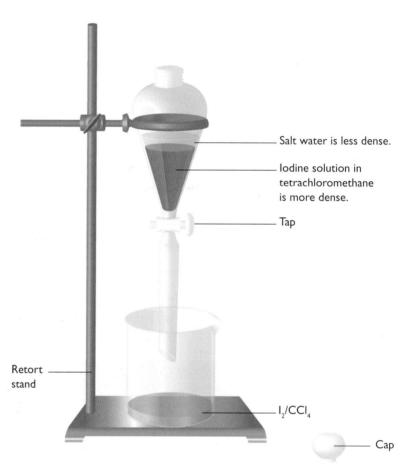

Salt water is less dense.

Iodine solution in tetrachloromethane is more dense.

Tap

Retort stand

I_2/CCl_4

Cap

Figure 1.14
Using a separating funnel to separate a solution of iodine in tetrachloromethane from salt water

Distillation

Distillation is a technique in which a solution of liquids may be separated on the basis of their different boiling points. When a liquid mixture is boiled in a distillation apparatus, the lowest boiling point component vaporises first and its vapour condenses back to the liquid state in the cooler parts of the apparatus. The condensed liquid is called the distillate and it is richer in the more **volatile** (lower boiling point) component.

volatile: describes substances that readily vaporise and exert a high vapour pressure.

Distillation can also be used to separate the solvent in a solution formed on mixing a solid and a liquid. Thus, fresh water can be obtained by distilling salt water.

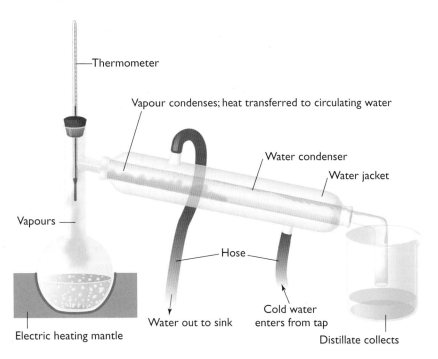

Figure 1.15
Distillation apparatus

Simple distillation is practical only if the liquids in the solution have quite different boiling points. Whenever the components have similar boiling points, the separation process is never complete and the distillate is only marginally richer in the more volatile component. Thus, pure alcohol is never produced by simple distillation as some water is always present in the distillate. However, when wine is distilled, the distillate is richer in alcohol as the alcohol is more volatile than the other components of the mixture.

Fractional distillation is used to improve the separation of components that have similar boiling points. This will be discussed in later examples about the oil industry and about separating the components of air.

Separating gases

Pure gases are produced commercially and distributed in compressed form to hospitals and industries. Oxygen, for example, is needed by patients with respiratory diseases. It is also used in the welding industry for oxyacetylene torches. Argon, neon and helium can be used in coloured advertising signs. Liquefied gases are also produced for a wide range of applications. For example, liquid nitrogen is used to snap-freeze food.

Mixtures of gases can be separated using both physical and chemical techniques.

Zeolite sieves

Oxygen gas can be separated from the air using a process called *pressure swing adsorption* (PSA). This process uses the selective adsorption of nitrogen, moisture and carbon dioxide by a molecular sieve called *zeolite*. The zeolite crystals are aluminium silicate and contain many channels and internal surfaces that selectively adsorb certain gases and allow others to pass through. The emerging oxygen is 90–95% pure.

Cryogenic air separation

High purity oxygen, nitrogen and argon are obtained using **cryogenic** air separation technology. Before the separation begins, the air must be filtered to remove dust and small particles. It is then compressed at about 6 bar and cooled. Condensed water is removed at this stage. Any remaining water and carbon dioxide are removed using the zeolite molecular sieve technology described above. The gas mixture is then cooled to cryogenic temperatures (–200 °C) until it liquefies. Distillation columns are then used to separate the components of the liquid air according to their different boiling points. A plant that produces nitrogen gas uses only one distillation column as nitrogen has the lowest boiling point (–196 °C) of all the components in liquefied air. As the liquid air is warmed slightly, the nitrogen gas vaporises and is collected. Plants that produce oxygen gas, which has a boiling point of –183 °C, require an argon column to separate the oxygen from argon, as argon's boiling point is –186 °C, very close to oxygen's. In practice, any oxygen present in argon is removed by reaction to form water, which is then removed by a molecular sieve dryer.

Figure 1.16 shows the fractional distillation technology used to separate the gaseous components of air. It is important to note that the cold nitrogen that distills off first is also used to cool the heat exchangers surrounding the air compressors.

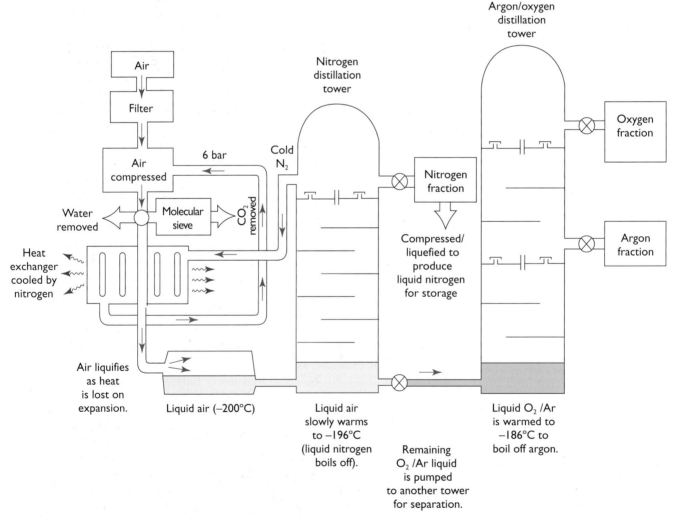

Figure 1.16 Fractional distillation of air

3. PERFORMING AND REPORTING ON FIRST-HAND INVESTIGATIONS

The practical investigations that you perform in the laboratory use the scientific method. In some cases, you will follow a written procedure validated by other chemists. In other cases, you will design the procedure using second-hand data research.

Here are some important points to consider in performing and reporting on first-hand investigations.

Safety issues: It is important to perform a safety check before conducting an experiment. Material safety data sheets (MSDS) are available for all chemicals used in the school laboratory. These may be available as a print copy or on a computer file. Make sure you understand the dangers of all chemicals you use.

Some general safety rules include:
- Always wear safety glasses.
- Tie back long hair so that it does not interfere with the experiment. Do not wear bulky clothing that can catch on apparatus.
- Take care not to spill chemicals on your skin, clothing or bench. Take immediate action if this happens.
- Use a fume hood when poisonous gases are generated.
- Do not touch hot apparatus. Allow it to cool before moving it.
- Take care when carrying materials around the laboratory.

Keeping records: Observations and data should always be recorded in a logbook and not on scraps of paper. Date each page for future reference. Record numerical data in tables using appropriate headings.

Accuracy and precision: Accurate measurements and observations are important in science experiments. There will always be some uncertainty in any measurement. Measurement errors depend on the equipment used and the skill of the investigator.

Experimental accuracy (how far the result is from the accepted value) and precision (reproducibility) can be improved by:
- avoiding parallax error when using measuring devices
- reading the bottom of the meniscus when measuring volumes of liquids
- repeating experiments and, if necessary, excluding outlying values, which are significantly deviant from the mean

- collecting results from other groups to increase the number of samples. This makes the average more likely to be closer to the true value.
- practising techniques so you become more adept at using the equipment.

Selecting the appropriate equipment can also improve accuracy. Here are some examples.
- Use electronic probes and data loggers connected to a graphics calculator or computer to collect more precise data.
- Use a millimetre ruler to measure length. The readings will be accurate to 0.5 mm.
- Use a measuring cylinder rather than a beaker to measure volumes of liquids more accurately. In a 10 mL measuring cylinder with 0.2 mL divisions, the readings will be accurate to 0.1 mL.
- Burettes and pipettes measure volumes of liquids to an accuracy of 0.05 mL — more accurate than measuring cylinders.
- Weigh using an electronic balance rather than a beam balance. Some electronic balances weigh to an accuracy of 0.01 g or 0.001 g.
- Use a digital stopwatch rather than an analogue watch to record time. Most watches are accurate to 0.01 s. Your reaction time will be greater than this, so repeated measurements help to minimise error.

Validity: The experimental design and method must ensure that you measure what you aim to measure.

To ensure the experimental method is valid, you need to collect second-hand data to determine how others (including experts in the field) have tackled similar problems. Discuss these issues with other members of your work team.

For example, if you aim to separate a water-soluble solid from an insoluble one, you need to know how to ensure that all the soluble material has been removed. This may require repeated washing of the solid with warm water. You need to know how many such washings are needed.

Your experiment will be valid only if it satisfies the requirements of the investigation and produces a result that answers the aim of the investigation.

Reliability: The results of your experiment will be reliable only if repeated measurements give the same values (or a very narrow range of values) within the limits of the experimental design. Minimisation of experimental errors helps to ensure experimental reliability. It is quite common to repeat experiments five or more times to improve reliability. Controlling other variables and making precise and accurate measurements are also essential for reliability.

1.3 QUESTIONS

1. Rewrite each statement by choosing the correct word.
   (a) A mixture of ethanol and water forms a suspension/solution.
   (b) The particles in a solution/suspension settle out when the mixture is left to stand on a laboratory bench.
   (c) Centrifuging a solution/suspension causes the particles to separate.
   (d) The particles of a solution/suspension are not separated when passed through a filter paper.

2. A knowledge of their relative solubilities in liquids such as water can be used to separate mixtures of solids. In each of the following cases, 2 g of each pair of solids is mixed together. Explain whether filtration techniques would be successful in separating them. The solubility of each substance in water is given in brackets.
   (a) magnesium sulfate (36.4 g/100 g water) and lead iodide (0.08 g/100 g water)
   (b) barium carbonate (0.002 g/100 g water) and silver oxide (0.002 g/100 g water)

3. Evaporation and distillation are common techniques used to separate solids or liquids from solutions. In each of the following cases, state the separation technique (evaporation or distillation) that should be used to recover each of the indicated components from the mixture.
   (a) Pure water from sea water
   (b) Salt crystals from sea water
   (c) Nickel sulfate from a green solution of nickel sulfate

4. A suspension can be filtered more rapidly by 'fluting' the filter paper. This technique is shown in figure 1.17. Explain why filtration is faster using a fluted filter rather than a normal cone.

5. When a solution of salt is heated in an evaporating basin over a hotplate or Bunsen burner, salt crystals form as their solubility limit is exceeded. As the solution becomes more concentrated, salt grains often escape ('spit') from the hot mixture. Suggest two ways of overcoming this problem. Justify your answer in each case.

6. A water condenser is used in most experiments involving distillation. Sometimes an air condenser can be used in place of a water condenser in a simple distillation. Predict under what circumstances the air condenser can be used.

7. Table 1.11 shows the solubility of copper (II) sulfate crystals in water as a function of temperature.

Table 1.11

Temperature (°C)	10	20	30	40	50	60	70
Solubility (g/100 g water)	18	20	24	28	34	42	50

   (a) Use the data provided to plot a solubility curve for copper sulfate crystals. Draw the line of best fit.
   (b) Copper (II) sulfate crystals (55 g) are dissolved in 100 g of hot water. The solution is evaporated to remove half of the water and then cooled to 25 °C. Calculate the mass of copper (II) sulfate crystals that are formed.
   (c) A 50 g sample of impure copper sulfate contains 45 g of copper (II) sulfate and 5 g of potassium nitrate. The solubility of potassium nitrate in water is:
   - 20 g/100 g water at 10 °C
   - 60 g/100 g water at 40 °C
   - 104 g/100 g water at 60 °C.
   Describe a practical method for obtaining a pure sample of blue copper (II) sulfate crystals.

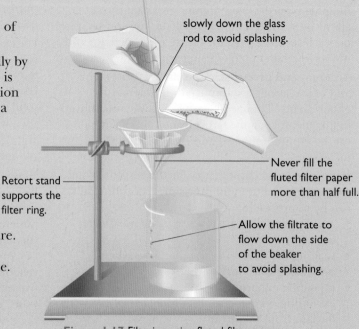

slowly down the glass rod to avoid splashing.

Retort stand supports the filter ring.

Never fill the fluted filter paper more than half full.

Allow the filtrate to flow down the side of the beaker to avoid splashing.

Figure 1.17 Filtering using fluted filter paper

1.4 *GRAVIMETRIC ANALYSIS*

Remember

Before beginning this section, you should be able to:
- identify internationally recognised symbols for common elements
- distinguish between elements and compounds
- distinguish between compounds and mixtures.

Key content

By the end of this section, you should be able to:
- describe situations in which gravimetric analysis supplies useful data for chemists and other scientists
- gather first-hand information by gravimetric analysis of a mixture to estimate its percentage composition.

Analytical chemists have developed quantitative techniques for analysing the composition of materials. Gravimetric analysis is a very important analytical method used by chemists. It involves separating the components of the material and accurately determining their mass. The percentage composition of the material can then be calculated.

Gravimetric analysis can be used to determine the:
- composition of a mixture using physical separation techniques
- percentage composition of a compound using chemical and physical separation techniques.

For example, to mine an ore body economically, there must be a minimum percentage of metal present in the ore. For lead, this minimum is 2%w/w, which is considerably higher than the average percentage of lead in crustal rocks (0.002%w/w). To determine the percentage of lead in an ore sample, the lead must be extracted quantitatively from a known weight of its ore. The lead can be extracted as the pure metal or as a pure compound. Great care must be taken to weigh all materials accurately and to ensure that solids are completely transferred from one container to another — for example, from a beaker onto filter paper.

Gravimetric analysis can be used in many other industries and laboratories. It can be used to determine the:
- percentage by weight of ingredients (sugar, fat, fibre) in food. This analysis is recorded on the packaging.
- purity and composition of alloys used for building construction
- extent of heavy metal pollution in river water and human food
- percentage composition of new compounds produced by chemical and medical research.

Examples of gravimetric analysis

The following worked examples show how chemists can use chemical and physical separation techniques to gravimetrically analyse natural materials such as minerals.

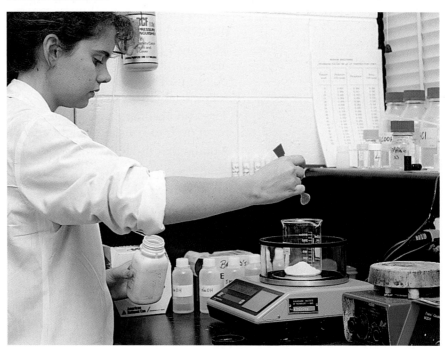

Figure 1.18
Chemists use accurate electronic balances to weigh materials for analysis.

Analysis of sphalerite

Sphalerite is a mineral containing the element zinc in the form of zinc sulfide. An analytical chemist had the task of determining the percentage by weight of zinc in a sample of the mineral, using the following method.

The chemist first weighed a sample of sphalerite and dissolved it in a minimum of sulfuric acid to release the sulfide as hydrogen sulfide (rotten egg gas). The acid was then neutralised with excess sodium hydroxide to produce an alkaline solution of zinc.

When silver-coated platinum electrodes were inserted into the solution and a DC electric current passed through it, zinc metal was deposited at the negative electrode (cathode). When all the zinc had been deposited, the cathode was removed, dried and weighed. The mass of zinc deposited could then be determined using a suitable calculation. Assume that the chemist obtained the following results.

$$\text{initial mass of sphalerite} = 0.30 \text{ g}$$
$$\text{initial mass of cathode} = 12.75 \text{ g}$$
$$\text{final mass of cathode + zinc deposit} = 12.95 \text{ g}$$

Use this data to determine the percentage by weight of zinc in the sphalerite.

SOLUTION

$$\text{mass of zinc deposited} = 12.95 - 12.75$$
$$= 0.20 \text{ g}$$
$$\% \text{ of zinc in sphalerite sample} = 0.20/0.30 \times 100$$
$$= 67\%\text{w/w}$$

eBook *plus*

Gravimetric analysis of lead in galena

Analysis of galena

In areas such as Broken Hill, lead is normally found in minerals such as galena (lead sulfide). Analysis of galena requires converting the lead to pure lead chromate and weighing the product — a pure sample of lead chromate contains 64.1% lead by weight.

The procedure requires weighing the sample of galena and then dissolving it in a minimum of nitric acid. A slight excess of a yellow potassium chromate solution is then added to precipitate the lead as yellow lead chromate.

The lead chromate precipitate is filtered and washed. It is then dried in an oven to constant weight and weighed.

Assume that the following results are obtained.

$$\text{mass of galena} = 0.500 \text{ g}$$
$$\text{mass of dry lead chromate} = 0.663 \text{ g}$$

Use this data to determine the percentage by weight of lead in the galena.

SOLUTION

Lead chromate contains 64.1% lead, so
$$\text{mass of lead} = 0.663 \times 64.1/100$$
$$= 0.425 \text{ g}$$
$$\% \text{ of lead in galena sample} = 0.425/0.500 \times 100$$
$$= 85\%\text{w/w}$$

Figure 1.19
Galena (left) is an important source of lead (right).

1.2 PRACTICAL ACTIVITIES

Gravimetric analysis of a mixture 1

1.3 PRACTICAL ACTIVITIES

Gravimetric analysis of a mixture 2

1.4 DATA ANALYSIS

Separation and analysis of a mixture

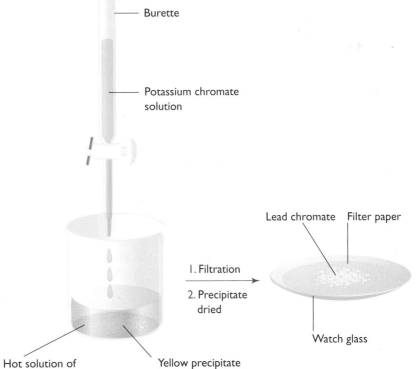

Burette

Potassium chromate solution

Lead chromate   Filter paper

1. Filtration

2. Precipitate dried

Watch glass

Hot solution of lead produced by dissolving the galena in nitric acid.

Yellow precipitate of lead chromate forms as the chromate ions react with the lead ions.

Figure 1.20
Gravimetric analysis of lead

4. USING INSTRUCTION TERMS CORRECTLY

When answering questions, it is important to know what the instruction terms (verbs) require you to do. Here are some examples:

'Distinguish'

This instruction term requires you to recognise differences between objects, processes or concepts.

Example:

Distinguish between physical and chemical separation techniques.

Answer:

Physical separation techniques are used to separate components without changing them chemically. Chemical techniques make use of one or more chemical changes to achieve separation of components.

'Outline'

This instruction term requires you to indicate briefly the main features of a concept or procedure.

Example:

Outline the steps a student would take to identify which of three liquids was the most volatile.

Answer:

Connect a pressure gauge to three identical containers, each containing exactly the same volume of the appropriate liquid. The container that shows the highest equilibrium vapour pressure on the gauge contains the most volatile liquid.

1.4 QUESTIONS

1. (a) Distinguish between the terms 'qualitative analysis' and 'quantitative analysis'.
   (b) Describe one example of each type of analysis.

2. A student was supplied with a stoppered bottle containing a mixture of kerosene and water.

   (a) The mixture had separated into two layers. Explain why this separation occurred.

   (b) Identify the liquid present in the lower layer.

   (c) Outline the steps to gravimetrically determine the percentage by weight of kerosene in the mixture.

3. A 15.0 g sample of sterling silver contained 13.95 g of silver. The remainder was copper. Calculate the percentage by weight of each metal in the sterling silver.

4. Pewter utensils are composed of 85% tin, 8% copper and 7% bismuth by weight. Calculate the mass of each metal in a pewter drinking goblet with a mass of 250 g.

5. Students were asked to analyse a mixture of sand and salt water to determine its percentage composition of each component by weight.

   (a) Each team designed a method to perform the task. One suggested that they should first determine the total mass of the sand and salt water mixture. Explain how the students performed this task.

   (b) The next step was to choose an appropriate method to separate the sand from the salt water. Identify the best physical separation technique to use.

   (c) Explain how the salt can be separated from the salt water.

   (d) One group's results are shown below. Calculate the % composition of the mixture.

total mass of sand + salt water + beaker	= 185.79 g
mass of beaker	= 143.61 g
mass of sand (dried)	= 24.88 g
mass of salt (dried)	= 1.25 g

   (e) Discuss the likely sources of error in this experiment.

1.5 INDUSTRIAL SEPARATION OF MIXTURES

Remember

Before beginning this section, you should be able to:
• identify the importance of water as a solvent
• describe aqueous mixtures in terms of solute, solvent and solution
• identify situations where the processes of filtration, sedimentation, sieving, distillation, chromatography, evaporation, condensation, crystallisation and magnetic attraction are appropriate to separate components of a mixture.

Key content

By the end of this section, you should be able to:
• identify data sources, gather, process and analyse information from secondary sources to identify the industrial separation processes used on a mixture obtained from the biosphere, lithosphere, hydrosphere or atmosphere, and use the available evidence to:
  – identify the properties of the mixture used in its separation
  – identify the products of separation and their uses
  – discuss issues associated with wastes from the processes used.

The spheres of the Earth are a rich source of raw materials. Most of these raw materials exist as mixtures. Over thousands of years, humans have discovered ways of extracting useful substances from these mixtures. In the last 200 years, large industries have developed to provide materials for a rapidly increasing population. Unfortunately, the environment has often suffered as waste materials from these processes pollute and damage the planet.

Industrial methods for separation of mixtures

An example of an industrial separation process for each sphere of the Earth will now be investigated. Tables 1.12 to 1.15 summarise the key information for an example from each sphere. Choose one of these spheres for detailed study.

Figure 1.21
Nickel smelter in Western Australia. Nickel sulfide ore is flash smelted to produce an enriched nickel matte.

Lithosphere — separation of nickel from a nickel ore

Western Australia produces much of Australia's nickel. By the end of the twentieth century, the nickel produced in Western Australia represented 14% of world production. Nickel is a silvery-white metal that is more ductile than iron. When alloyed with other metals, it improves strength, toughness and corrosion resistance.

Table 1.12 Separation of nickel from a nickel ore

Sphere	lithosphere
Mixture to be separated	pentlandite ore — a nickel sulfide ore containing iron sulfide and other rocky impurities
Product(s) of separation	nickel
Uses of product(s)	nickel alloys used in: <ul><li>stainless steel (60% of the world's nickel output is used in stainless steel)</li><li>coinage</li><li>monel metal (highly corrosion-resistant nickel alloy used in shipbuilding and food processing equipment)</li></ul>
Properties of components used to separate the mixture and refine the final product	<ul><li>Metal sulfide minerals are separated from the unwanted rock-making minerals by their ability to adhere to froth created in froth flotation tanks.</li><li>Nickel **matte** is heavier than the impurities, so sinks to the bottom of the **smelter** to be recovered.</li><li>Iron impurities form insoluble precipitates when nickel matte is dissolved in ammonia.</li><li>Dissolved copper impurities can be removed (as insoluble copper sulfide) from the nickel–ammonia solution by passing hydrogen sulfide gas through the solution. Nickel is left behind in solution.</li><li>Nickel–ammonia solutions can be reduced to nickel metal by hydrogen gas. Alternatively, electrolytic cells can be used to obtain pure nickel at inert cathodes.</li></ul>
Extraction procedure	*Concentration* <ul><li>Ore (1–4% nickel) is crushed to a fine powder and mixed with water.</li><li>Nickel sulfide mineral is separated from gangue by froth flotation.</li><li>The fine, powdered concentrate contains 10–12% nickel.</li></ul> *Smelting* <ul><li>The sulfide concentrate is flash smelted in an oxidising atmosphere at high temperature. The iron and sulfur oxidise and the heat released from the process produces a liquid nickel matte.</li><li>A 'nickel matte' (72% nickel) sinks to the bottom of the furnace and is allowed to solidify.</li></ul> *Refining* <ul><li>Copper and iron sulfides are the major contaminants to be removed. Iron is removed as an insoluble hydroxide and copper as an insoluble sulfide.</li><li>The matte is treated with oxygenated ammonia solution to **leach** out the nickel.</li><li>Reduction of the filtered solution with hydrogen or by electrolysis at inert cathodes produces 99.8% pure nickel metal.</li></ul>
Waste management issues	<ul><li>Waste is stored in dumps and tailings ponds, which must be constructed so that waste does not enter water systems or contaminate surrounding land. Most slag wastes are dense silicates.</li><li>Acid rain can be produced if sulfurous gases from the smelter enter the atmosphere. Conversion of sulfur wastes to sulfuric acid can significantly reduce this problem.</li><li>Smelters must be situated so that prevailing winds don't blow gaseous emissions over populated areas.</li></ul>

matte: a smelted mixture in which the percentage of metal is higher than in the unsmelted ore concentrate

smelting: an industrial process in which high temperatures are used to melt and reduce ore concentrates to produce a metal or a matte

leach: use a liquid to dissolve a valuable product from a solid mixture such as a matte

1.5 DATA ANALYSIS

Extraction of aluminium from the lithosphere

Hydrosphere — separation of bromine from salt lakes

Bromine is a dense, red-brown, fuming liquid that is highly toxic with a very pungent smell. It is extracted from salt lakes (such as the Dead Sea) that contain high levels of bromide salts such as magnesium bromide.

Bromine has been used to manufacture chemicals called halons (or bromofluorocarbons), which were used for fire-extinguishing systems in aeroplanes and large computer networks. Halons, along with other brominated compounds such as methyl bromide and ethylene dibromide, were shown to have caused severe depletion of the Earth's ozone layer. Although these bromine compounds are currently produced in limited amounts in some countries overseas, they are being phased out as the result of decisions made at the Montreal Protocol climate conferences.

Table 1.13 Separation of bromine from salt lakes

Sphere	hydrosphere
Mixture to be separated	magnesium bromide salt solution from salt lakes
Product(s) of separation	bromine
Uses of product(s)	• manufacture of fumigant compounds • manufacture of flameproofing agents • silver bromide emulsion used in photography
Properties of components used to separate the mixture and refine the final product	• Bromide salts are more soluble than chloride salts in water; the chloride salts can be removed by fractional crystallisation. • Bromide ions are readily oxidised to bromine by chlorine. • Bromine has a very low boiling point ($59\,^\circ\text{C}$) and is readily condensed.
Extraction procedure	*Partial evaporation and fractional crystallisation* • The less soluble non-bromide salts are allowed to crystallise from the partially evaporated salt solution and then filtered off. *Oxidation of bromide solution* • Chlorine gas is passed through the solution of bromide salts to convert bromide ions to bromine. *Condensation of bromine vapour* • Bromine vapours are collected and condensed to form liquid bromine.
Waste managment issues	• The salt waste produced from evaporation of the salt water must not be allowed to contaminate agricultural land. • Bromine and chlorine vapours are toxic; factories must be located away from populated areas so that prevailing winds do not blow towards such areas. • Bromine is transported in lead-lined steel tanks secured with reinforced, steel roll-frames. • Acidic by-products of the manufacturing process must not be allowed to contaminate ground water.

Atmosphere — separation of argon from the air

Argon is an important noble gas. It is inert and can be used to create an inert atmosphere for high-temperature, metallurgical procedures such as welding. It is extracted from air by cryogenic fractional distillation.

Table 1.14 Separation of argon from the air

Sphere	atmosphere
Mixture to be separated	air
Product(s) of separation	argon (and other atmospheric gases)
Uses of product(s)	• inert atmosphere for metallurgy • blue-green discharge lamps ('neon' signs)
Properties of components used to separate the mixture and refine the final product	• chemically inert • different boiling point from other air components (but close to oxygen)
Extraction procedure	*Compression* • Air is cooled cryogenically and compressed. *Rapid expansion* • Air cools and liquefies. *Fractional distillation* • Argon is separated from other gases (except oxygen) when the temperature rises to −186 °C. • Oxygen is removed by its reaction with hydrogen to form water. Argon does not react as it is inert. • After removing water using a molecular sieve dryer, the argon is re-cooled.
Waste managment issues	• Heat must dissipate slowly into the environment to reduce thermal pollution.

Biosphere — separation of olive oil from olives

Olive oil is an important natural product, which humans have extracted and used for thousands of years. Traditional methods involve crushing the fruit and mixing the product with water. The light oil floats to the top and can be decanted. Modern technology using hammer mills and centrifuges has improved the extraction process.

Figure 1.22
Olive oil can be extracted from the fruit by crushing, grinding and centrifuging.

Table 1.15 Separation of olive oil from olives

Sphere	biosphere
Mixture to be separated	olive oil and crushed olive flesh/seed
Product(s) of separation	olive oil
Uses of product(s)	cooking
Properties of components used to separate the mixture and refine the final product	• Olive oil is less dense than water and can be separated by centrifugation (and/or decantation). • Olive oil does not dissolve in water.
Extraction procedure	*Crushing/grinding* • The fruit is crushed in a metal hammer mill to produce a paste. *Beating* • The paste plus some water is beaten to remove more oil from cells. Salt may be added to assist osmotic breakdown of the cells and release of oil. *Centrifuging* • The mixture is placed in a horizontal centrifuge and spun at high speed. The light oil forms the upper, inner layer, and water and heavier fruit fragments forms the outer layers. • The inner, floating oil layer continuously overflows a weir and is collected through a separate portal. • Water is removed by rotating internal scrolls through a separate exit. The pulp phase is discharged using rotating internal scrolls.
Waste managment issues	• The pulp waste contains about 6% oil. Specialised plants can use solvent extraction to remove some of this oil. • In some countries, the dried pulp waste is used as a home fuel, mulch, fertiliser or animal feed.

1.5 QUESTIONS

1. Pitchblende is a common uranium ore; it contains uranium oxide, U_3O_8. The mildly radioactive ore is mined and then transferred to a mill.
   (a) Explain the purpose of the milling stage.
   (b) The finely crushed ore is mixed with water to form a slurry and then treated with sulfuric acid to leach out the uranium oxide.
      (i) Explain the meaning of the term 'leaching'.
      (ii) The leached mixture is allowed to sediment. Predict what material forms the sediment.
   (c) The leached mixture is decanted and filtered, and then undergoes solvent extraction to produce a yellow powder called yellowcake. This is about 98% U_3O_8.
      (i) Explain why the mixture is decanted before filtering.
      (ii) Classify this stage as a physical or chemical separation.
   (d) Discuss the environmental issues of producing yellowcake.

2. Centrifugation is used in the nuclear power industry. Natural uranium consists of two isotopes: U-238 and the lighter U-235. For uranium to be used as a nuclear fuel, the proportion of the lighter U-235 isotope must be increased from its normal concentration of 1% to 3–4%. This process is called enrichment. The process involves converting natural uranium into gaseous uranium hexafluoride, UF_6. The gas mixture is then centrifuged.

   (a) Predict whether the heavier uranium-238 hexafluoride molecules will be concentrated at the walls of the centrifuge or closer to the central axis.

   (b) Identify the physical and chemical separation processes used in this enrichment process.

3. Plant essences and extracts are often called essential oils. They are used in perfumes, pharmaceuticals and deodorants. One common method of extracting these essential oils from plant tissue is steam distillation. This technique allows such oils to volatilise at temperatures well below their normal boiling points. The steam used is generated in a separate vessel. The steam–oil vapour mixture that emerges from the distillation retort passes into the condenser and is allowed to cool and condense. The liquid produced consists of oil and water, which form two distinct layers in the separator.

   Figure 1.23 shows a diagram of a typical steam distillation apparatus.

   (a) Identify the pieces of equipment labelled A–D in figure 1.23.

   (b) Identify the locations (A–D) where (i) vaporisation and (ii) condensation occur.

4. Edible oils are extracted from a range of fruits, nuts and seeds. Table 1.16 provides information about the yield of oil from various seeds using simple mechanical presses or mortars to crush the seeds.

Table 1.16

Seed	Moisture content (%)	Oil content (%)	Yield of oil after extraction (%)
canola	9	40–45	25
sesame	5	25–50	45
sunflower	5	25–50	25

   (a) Identify which of the listed seeds gives the greatest yield of oil.

   (b) The oil released from the crushed and mashed seeds has to be separated from the water and fibrous solids. A simple method is to allow the mixture to stand for several days before removing the oil. Explain which property of the mixture allows the separation of the components.

   (c) The oil obtained from the method described in (b) can be further purified using a procedure known as clarification. In this method the impure oil is filtered and then heated to 100 °C.

      (i) Identify the component that is removed by filtration.

      (ii) Identify the component that is removed by heating to 100 °C.

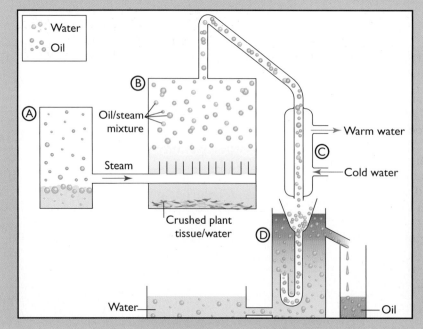

Figure 1.23
Steam distillation equipment

5. The first column of table 1.17 lists separation methods used in industry. The second column is a jumbled list of the properties used in the separation processes. Match the separation methods to the properties.

Table 1.17

Separation method	Separation property
A. sieving	1. solid has much higher boiling point than liquid
B. filtration	2. small differences between the boiling points of liquids in a mixture
C. evaporation	3. difference in particle size
D. fractional distillation	4. liquids are immiscible
E. separating funnel	5. solid is insoluble in a liquid

eBook *plus*

Weblinks

eBook *plus*

Checkpoint Revision 1

eBook *plus*

Checkpoint Revision 1 Answers

SUMMARY

• Mixtures of elements and compounds exist in the lithosphere, hydrosphere, atmosphere and biosphere.

• The abundance of elements varies in the lithosphere, hydrosphere, atmosphere and biosphere.

• Pure substances are materials with a uniform and fixed composition. Elements and compounds are examples of pure substances.

• Physical techniques can be used to separate mixtures into their component pure substances.

• The physical properties of different substances are used to separate mixtures of these substances. Different methods of physical separation are used to separate different mixtures.

• Gravimetric analysis supplies useful data for chemists about the composition of materials.

PRACTICAL ACTIVITIES

1.1 PRACTICAL ACTIVITIES

SEPARATION OF A SIMPLE MIXTURE

Aim

To recover sand and salt from a mixture of sand and salt water using physical separation techniques

Background

The following information about the components of a mixture can be used to design a procedure to separate them.

- Sand is insoluble in water and salt water.
- Salt is soluble in water.
- Sand and salt have boiling points well above the temperature of a hotplate or Bunsen burner flame.
- Sand particles are too large to pass through the pores of a filter paper.
- The salt in saltwater solutions can pass through the pores of a filter paper.
- Salt water spits and splatters salt crystals if it is allowed to boil and evaporate rapidly.
- Drying ovens (at about 70 °C) can be used to evaporate concentrated solutions slowly and safely.
- A wash bottle is useful to wash solid residues out of a beaker or to wash a residue in a filter paper.
- A glass rod is a useful guide when pouring liquids or suspensions from one vessel to another.

Safety issues

- Wear safety glasses throughout this experiment.
- Identify other safety issues relevant to this experiment by reading the method.

Materials

- clean sand
- two 150 mL beakers
- 150 mL salt water (2%w/w)
- 10 mL measuring cylinder
- evaporating basin
- glass rod
- filter funnel
- filter paper
- filter ring and stand
- electric hotplate
- drying oven
- clock glass
- wash bottle

Method

Making the mixture

1. Add about half a teaspoon of clean sand to a clean, dry 150 mL beaker.
2. Measure out 10 mL of the supplied salt water using a measuring cylinder. Add the salt water to the beaker.
3. Stir the mixture with a glass rod.

Separating the mixture

1. Review the information provided in the background to this experiment.
2. Design a method to separate the sand and salt as separate dry solids. Use the materials listed above in this experiment.
3. Record this method in your logbook and have it checked by the teacher before proceeding.
4. Use your approved method to separate the mixture to obtain separate samples of dry sand and salt.

Results and conclusion

Briefly describe the outcome of your investigation.

Analysis

Answer the following questions in your report on this experiment.

1. Describe the safety issues that you have identified.
2. Explain how you ensured that all the salt was recovered in the filtrate at the end of the filtration stage.
3. Explain how you ensured that the final sample of sand was completely dry.
4. Explain the importance of only half filling the filter cone with the mixture during filtration.

PRACTICAL ACTIVITIES

1.2 PRACTICAL ACTIVITIES

GRAVIMETRIC ANALYSIS OF A MIXTURE 1

Aim

To determine the percentage composition of a saltwater solution

Background

Simple distillation can be used to separate salt and water from a saltwater solution. The percentage composition of the mixture can be determined by weighing the salt water and the separated salt and water.

Safety issues

- Wear safety glasses throughout this experiment.
- Identify other safety issues relevant to this experiment by reading the method.

Materials

- Quick-fit distillation kit with 150 mL distillation flask
- boiling chip
- electronic balance
- 150 mL beaker
- 50 mL of salt water (about 4%w/w)
- 100 mL measuring cylinder
- Bunsen burner, tripod and gauze mat
- retort stands, bossheads and clamps

Method

1. Set up the Quick-fit apparatus carefully. Use figure 1.15 as a guide or observe the apparatus set up by the teacher.
2. Weigh the distillation flask with its boiling chip. Weigh a clean, 150 mL beaker. Record these weights in your logbook.
3. Use a measuring cylinder to pour 50 mL of the salt water into the distillation flask and reweigh. Then calculate the mass of salt water used.
4. Connect the flask to the distillation apparatus and place the beaker at the outlet of the condenser. Ensure that water is flowing through the condenser before heating the flask.
5. Distill the mixture with *gentle* heating to prevent salt water entering the condenser.
6. Near the end of the distillation, reduce the heat by moving the Bunsen burner back and forth under the gauze mat. Stop heating once all the water has evaporated and salt is left behind.
7. Allow the flask to cool before removing it from the apparatus.
8. Weigh the distilled water and the distillation flask (containing the salt and boiling chip). Then calculate the mass of salt and water recovered.
9. Clean up all equipment as well as your workbench.

Results and analysis

1. Construct a table to show all the collected and calculated data.
2. Determine by calculation whether the original mass of salt water equals the combined mass of the distilled water and salt crystals. Account for any discrepancies.
3. Use your answer to question 2 to estimate the uncertainty in your analysis.
4. Calculate the percentage by weight of salt and water in the saltwater solution.
5. Discuss how the accuracy and reliability of this experiment could be improved.
6. Identify the safety issues in this experiment.

Conclusion

Write a brief conclusion for this experiment.

1.3 PRACTICAL ACTIVITIES

GRAVIMETRIC ANALYSIS OF A MIXTURE 2

Aim

To determine the percentage by weight of hydrated barium chloride in a mixture containing sodium chloride

Background

Hydrated barium chloride has the chemical formula $BaCl_2.2H_2O$. Two molecules of water are associated with each crystalline unit. This water can be driven off by heating the compound. In mass terms, 100.00 g of hydrated barium chloride crystals produce 14.75 g of water on dehydration.

The amount of hydrated barium chloride in the sample can be calculated by weighing the sample before and after heating.

Safety issues

• Wear safety glasses throughout this experiment.
• Identify other safety issues relevant to this experiment by reading the method.

Materials

• crucible and lid
• pipeclay triangle
• Bunsen burner, tripod
• tongs
• electronic balance
• mixture of hydrated barium chloride and sodium chloride (AR grade)

Method

1. Place the crucible and lid on a pipeclay triangle supported by a tripod.
2. Heat the crucible to a dull red heat for several minutes and then allow it to cool to room temperature.
3. Move the crucible and lid onto the balance using tongs. Avoid touching the crucible. Weigh the crucible and lid. Record this mass in your logbook.
4. Add about 2 g of the salt mixture to the crucible. Replace the lid and reweigh accurately. Then calculate the mass of salt mixture used.
5. Use tongs to place the crucible back on the pipeclay triangle. The lid should be tilted slightly to allow water vapour to escape during heating. Heat the crucible to red heat for 10 minutes and allow the crucible to cool to room temperature.
6. Reweigh the crucible and its contents.
7. Clean up all equipment.

Results and analysis

1. Construct a table to show all the collected and calculated data.
2. Calculate the mass of water evolved on heating the mixture.
3. Then, by ratio, calculate the mass of hydrated barium chloride in the original mixture (see background information).
4. Determine the mass of sodium chloride in the original mixture.
5. Calculate the percentage composition by weight of the mixture of salts.
6. Explain why reheating and cooling the salt mixture several times improves the accuracy of the experiment.
7. Compare your results with those of other groups. Explain why all groups may not obtain the same results.
8. Identify the safety issues in this experiment.

Conclusion

Write a brief conclusion for this experiment.

DATA ANALYSIS

1.4 DATA ANALYSIS

SEPARATION AND ANALYSIS OF A MIXTURE

Part A: Separation

Students were supplied with a solid mixture of copper (II) oxide, iron and sodium sulfate. Their aim was to separate the mixture into its components using physical separation techniques.

Step 1: Gathering information
The students found information about these substances from various data sources (table 1.18).

Step 2: Processing the information
1. The students used their gathered information to design a method of separating the three components of the mixture. Their proposed method is shown below as a randomly arranged list of numbered steps. Write the numbers of the following steps in the correct order.

   Separation steps (jumbled)

   (i) Wash the residue in the filter cone with a little water.
   (ii) Stir the powdered mixture repeatedly with a bar magnet covered in cling wrap.
   (iii) Powder the solid mixture using a mortar and pestle and put the powdered mixture in a small beaker.
   (iv) After filtering and drying the residue, slowly evaporate the filtrate in an evaporating basin.
   (v) Add a small volume of water to the remaining solids and stir with a glass rod to dissolve the sodium sulfate.
   (vi) Collect and dry the white sodium sulfate crystals in the evaporating basin.
   (vii) Place the copper (II) oxide residue and filter paper on a clock glass and dry in a drying oven.
   (viii) Filter the mixture through a filter paper cone supported in a filter funnel.
   (ix) Remove the magnet covered in iron powder and deposit the powder in a Petri dish.

2. Discuss why the students used only physical separation methods rather than a chemical separation method involving sulfuric acid.

Part B: Analysis

The students were then asked to devise and perform an experiment to determine the percentage of copper in the original mixture using both physical and chemical separation procedures.

Following further data gathering they devised the following method.

(i) Weigh 5.0 g of the powdered mixture.
(ii) Repeat the separation method used in part A.
(iii) Collect the copper (II) oxide residue on the filter paper.
(iv) Place the paper and residue in a small beaker and dissolve the black solid with sufficient dilute sulfuric acid.

Table 1.18

Substance	copper (II) oxide	iron	sodium sulfate
Colour	brown/black	silvery grey	white
Solubility in water (g/100 g water)	0	0	19.4
Melting point (°C)	decomposes	1435	884
Density (g/cm³)	6.4	7.9	2.7
Magnetic properties	non-magnetic	magnetic	non-magnetic
Reaction with dilute sulfuric acid	dissolves to form blue solution of copper (II) sulfate	dissolves slowly, evolving hydrogen gas forming very pale green solution	dissolves without reaction

(v) Remove and wash the paper free of solution.

(vi) Electrolyse the solution using clean, weighed graphite electrodes until all the copper is deposited on the negative electrode.

(vii) Dry the copper-covered electrode and reweigh.

(viii) Calculate the mass of copper deposited on the electrode.

The students performed the experiment and their collected data is recorded below.

mass of powdered mixture = 5.0 g
mass of copper recovered = 0.47 g

1. Use this data to determine the percentage by weight of copper in the mixture.

2. Identify the steps of the method that involve (a) physical and (b) chemical separation methods.

3. Explain how the accuracy of the method could be improved.

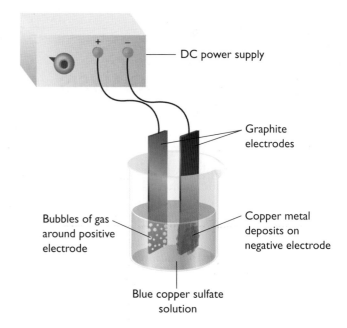

Figure 1.24 Electrolysis of the copper (II) sulfate solution

DATA ANALYSIS

1.5 DATA ANALYSIS

EXTRACTION OF ALUMINIUM FROM THE LITHOSPHERE

Aluminium is a familiar metal in modern society. It is the most abundant metal in the Earth's crust but considerable energy is needed to release the metal from its compounds. To achieve a profit, mining companies process bauxite ore concentrate only if it contains a minimum of 40% aluminium by weight. Bauxite is an orange-red, pebbly solid that contains aluminium in the form of hydrated aluminium oxide, $Al_2O_3.xH_2O$ (where $x = 1$ and 3), as well as impurities of: iron (III) oxide, Fe_2O_3; silicon dioxide, SiO_2; and clay. Due to the presence of impurities, the percentage by weight of aluminium in bauxite is typically about 18%w/w. The impurities must be removed and the ore concentrated before the aluminium is extracted. During processing, the hydrated aluminium oxide is converted to alumina, Al_2O_3. Alumina has a very high melting point (2054 °C) and must be mixed with cryolite to be melted before electrolytic extraction.

Part A: Extraction

1. The following flow chart summarises the steps for extracting aluminium from bauxite. Letters A to H correspond to various physical and chemical processes. Match these letters to the extraction steps in the jumbled list below.

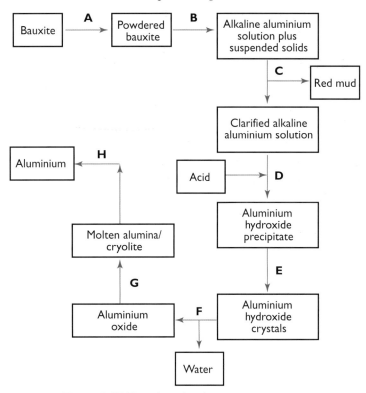

Figure 1.25 Flow chart for aluminium extraction

Extraction steps (jumbled)

(i) The hot solution is filtered to remove insoluble impurities.

(ii) Molten aluminium forms at the cathode; it is tapped off the base of the tank and run into moulds to cool and solidify.

(iii) The hot solution is cooled and acidified with acid to precipitate the aluminium as aluminium hydroxide.

DATA ANALYSIS

(iv) The bauxite ore (mined at Weipa, Queensland, and Gove, Northern Territory) is ground into a powder in a grinding mill. The bauxite minerals are partly separated from the unwanted gangue minerals.

(v) The aluminium hydroxide crystals are washed and filtered.

(vi) The alumina is dissolved in molten sodium aluminium fluoride (cryolite, Na_3AlF_6) at $1000\,°C$. The molten mixture is electrolysed using inert graphite anodes and an iron cathode. The electrolysis proceeds at 5 volts and 150 000 amps.

(vii) The ground bauxite is mixed with concentrated sodium hydroxide solution at high pressure and temperature. The aluminium oxide in the ore dissolves (leaches) to form a soluble aluminium compound.

(viii) The aluminium hydroxide is heated at $1200\,°C$ to produce alumina, Al_2O_3, and water vapour. This process is called calcination.

2. Identify the physical separation steps in the flow chart.

Part B: General questions

1. Write the chemical formula for hydrated aluminium oxide if $x = 3$.

2. Alumina contains 53% aluminium by weight, which is more than the 40% required. Explain why a minimum of 40% is needed.

3. Gases released from the electrolytic cells include carbon dioxide and hydrogen fluoride. Fluoride gases affect plants and animals near aluminium refineries. Legislation prevents the aluminium industry releasing high levels of toxic gases over vulnerable areas. This requires either cleaning exhaust gases, which adds to the cost of producing aluminium, or selecting more suitable sites for refineries. Discuss some of the problems of selecting a site for an electrolytic aluminium factory.

4. The aluminium hydroxide is heated to a temperature of $1200\,°C$. Identify the physical state of the alumina product at this temperature.

5. Explain why electrolysis is not performed on molten alumina but, rather, on a molten mixture of alumina in cryolite.

Chapter 2

ELEMENTS

Introduction

Elements are the simplest pure substances. They cannot be broken down into anything simpler by chemical means. The periodic table of the elements is an evolving document. By the end of 2006, 117 elements had been indentified. Of these, hydrogen is by far the most abundant element in the universe. On Earth, oxygen is the most abundant element due to its presence in many rock-making minerals as well as its important roles in the hydrosphere, atmosphere and biosphere. The great majority of elements occur naturally but some have been synthesised using high-powered particle accelerators.

In this chapter

Figure 2.1

Blue-black crystals of the non-metal iodine sublime to produce a purple vapour composed of diatomic iodine molecules.

2.1 CLASSIFYING ELEMENTS

The physical properties of elements

Every pure substance has its own unique set of physical properties. These physical properties include:

- *melting point* — the lowest temperature at which a solid changes to a liquid at normal atmospheric pressure (100 kPa).
- *boiling point* — the lowest temperature at which a liquid changes to a **vapour** such that the vapour exerts a pressure of 100 kPa.
- *density* — the mass of the substance per unit volume, measured at 25 °C and 100 kPa.
- *electrical conductivity* — the quantity of electric current transmitted through a unit cube of the material when there is a potential difference of 1 volt across the cube.
- *thermal conductivity* — the rate at which heat energy is transferred through a unit cube of the material when there is a 1° temperature difference across the cube.

These properties can be used to check whether an element is 100% pure or contaminated by impurities. Chemical data books provide lists of these physical properties for each natural element. Table 2.1 gives examples of these physical properties for some common elements, showing that these three elements are quite different. A chemist can check whether a sample of copper is pure by measuring its physical properties. If the melting point of the copper sample is not 1085 °C, the sample must be contaminated with impurities. Impurities tend to lower the melting points of pure substances. Similarly, if a copper sample is impure, its density will not be 8.96 g/cm³.

Table 2.1 Physical properties of some common elements.

Element	copper	iodine	silicon
Melting point (°C)	1085	114	1410
Boiling point (°C)	2572	184	3267
Density (g/cm³)	8.96	4.94	2.3
Electrical conductivity (MS/m)	58.4	1×10^{-13}	1×10^{-3}
Thermal conductivity (J/s/m/K)*	401	0.45	148

(*K = Kelvin temperature units — each Kelvin unit is the same size as a Celsius degree; 100 °C = 373 K and 0 °C = 273 K)

vapour: the gaseous form of a substance that is normally a solid or liquid at standard temperature and pressure

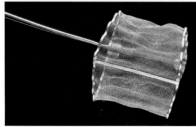

Figure 2.2
Titanium (above) is a metal with a low density while platinum (right) has a high density.

SAMPLE PROBLEM 2.1 ▶▶

The mass and volume of a sample of copper were measured:

mass of sample (m) = 123.86 g
volume of sample (V) = 14.00 cm³

Calculate the density of the sample and determine whether the sample is pure or impure.

SOLUTION ▶▶▶▶▶

$$d = m/V$$
$$= 123.86/14.00$$
$$= 8.85 \text{ g/cm}^3$$

This density is slightly lower than that of pure copper (8.96 g/cm³) so the sample is slightly impure.

SAMPLE PROBLEM 2.2 ▶▶

A student uses an electronic temperature probe and data logger to measure the temperature of a sample of lead as it was heated slowly and uniformly from 320 °C to 336 °C. The results are shown in table 2.2.

Table 2.2

Time (min)	0	1	2	3	4	5	6	7	8	9
Temperature (°C)	320	323	326	327	327	327	328	330	333	336

(a) Plot the data as a line graph.
(b) Chemical data books list the melting point of lead as 327 °C.
   (i) Identify the region of the graph that corresponds to the melting point of lead.
   (ii) Account for the shape of the graph.
   (iii) The student concludes that the sample of lead is pure. Justify this conclusion.

SOLUTION ▶▶▶▶▶

(a)

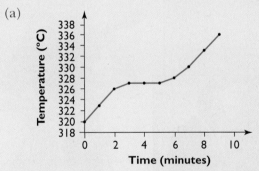

Figure 2.3

(b) (i) The 'plateau' or inflexion region corresponds with the melting point of lead.
   (ii) The temperature rises uniformly from 320 °C to 326 °C. The rate of temperature rise then slows, and the temperature stops rising while the lead is melting. The added heat does not raise the temperature of the lead but causes it to change state. Once all the lead has melted (between 5 and 6 minutes), the temperature rises once more as the added heat warms the melted lead.
   (iii) The student is correct because the lead has a constant (fixed) melting point that matches the literature data. Impure lead would not have a distinct melting point and any impurities would reduce the melting point below 327 °C. We would not expect a plateau region in the temperature–time graph if the sample were impure.

2.1 PRACTICAL ACTIVITIES

Investigating the physical properties of elements

5. USING SYMBOLS TO IDENTIFY ELEMENTS

The study of chemistry is simplified by the use of symbols. Each element is identified by a unique symbol that consists of one or two letters. The first letter is written in uppercase. If there is a second letter, it is written in lowercase. The symbols chosen for elements are not always related to their English names. The symbols for some elements are based on its Latin, Greek or German name. For example, the symbol for gold is Au (from the Latin word *aurum*). Elements are often named after mythological gods, countries, scientists, properties or astronomical objects. For example, gallium is named after *Gallia*, the ancient name for France. Table 2.3 gives the origins of some element names. Use the periodic table on the inside cover of this book to find other examples.

Table 2.3 Origins of some element names

Element	Symbol	Source of element name	Category
curium	Cm	Pierre and Marie Curie	scientist
germanium	Ge	Germany	country
helium	He	*helios*, Greek word for Sun	astronomy
iodine	I	*iodes*, Greek word for violet	property
thorium	Th	Thor (Norse god of war)	mythology

Figure 2.4
Some elements are named for their properties, such as their colour (far right), while others are named after famous scientists, such as Marie and Pierre Curie (above), or figures in mythology, such as Thor (right).

Classifying elements according to their physical properties

The known elements may be classified conveniently into groups on the basis of their physical properties. We will consider two of these groupings: physical state, and metallic or non-metallic properties.

Physical state

Elements can be classified as solids, liquids or gases at standard temperature and pressure (25 °C and 100 kPa). The vast majority of elements are solids. Two elements are liquids (bromine and mercury) and eleven are gases. Table 2.4 lists the gases of the periodic table. Note that some gaseous elements exist as **diatomic molecules**. These elements mainly occupy the upper right corner of the periodic table.

> diatomic molecule: a molecule consisting of two atoms chemically bonded together

Table 2.4 Gaseous elements

H_2	He	N_2	O_2	F_2	Ne	Cl_2	Ar	Kr	Xe	Rn

Heating and cooling can convert elements from one state to another. For example, gallium, which has a melting point of 30 °C, can be liquefied by holding it in your hand. Other elements require much more heat to melt them.

SAMPLE PROBLEM 2.3

Elements *A*, *B* and *C* have the following melting (m.p.) and boiling (b.p.) points.
  Element *A:* m.p. = −71 °C, b.p. = −62 °C
  Element *B:* m.p. = −39 °C, b.p. = +357 °C
  Element *C:* m.p. = +2610 °C, b.p. = +5560 °C
Classify these elements as solid, liquid or gas at standard temperature and pressure.

SOLUTION

Element *A* has both melting and boiling points below 25 °C so it is a gas at standard temperature and pressure. (This is the radioactive gas radon.)

Element *B* is a liquid at room temperature as its melting point is below 25 °C but its boiling point is above 25 °C. (This is the liquid metal mercury.)

Element *C* is a solid at room temperature as both its melting and boiling points are well above 25 °C. (This is the heavy metal molybdenum.)

Metals, non-metals and semi-metals

Another common way of classifying elements is to group them according to their metallic or non-metallic properties. Elements that do not fit conveniently into either group are called semi-metals.

Chemists use a range of physical properties to classify elements into one of these three groups. The most important of these properties are lustre, electrical conductivity and malleability. In general:

> lustrous: shiny
>
> malleable: able to be shaped without breaking by rolling, hammering or pressing
>
> ductile: able to be drawn into wires without breaking
>
> brittle: describes a substance that shatters into fragments when hammered

- *metals* are **lustrous**, **malleable** and **ductile**, and have a high electrical conductivity
- *semi-metals* have a low sheen, are moderately malleable and have semi-conductor properties
- *non-metals* are dull, **brittle** and non-conductors of electricity.

Table 2.5 provides a summary of the physical properties of metals, semi-metals and non-metals, and some representative examples. In the year 2007, 117 elements were known. Of these, 92 are classified as metals, 7 as semi-metals and 18 as non-metals. (*Note:* At the time of writing, element 117 had not been synthesised. Element 118 was finally confirmed in 2006 following its discovery in 2002.)

Table 2.5 Physical properties of metals, semi-metals and non-metals

Group	metals	semi-metals	non-metals
Appearance	lustrous	low sheen	dull
Electrical conductivity	high	low (semi-conductors)	nil (insulators)
Thermal conductivity	high	high	low (insulators)
Malleability and ductility	high	moderate	nil (brittle)
Density	generally high	intermediate	low
Boiling point	generally high	very high	low
Strength	high	variable	low
Examples	sodium, magnesium, iron, chromium, zinc, platinum, gold, mercury, lutetium	boron, silicon, germanium, arsenic, antimony, tellurium, astatine	hydrogen, helium, carbon, nitrogen, oxygen, fluorine, neon, phosphorus

Table 2.6 compares some of the physical properties of a typical metal, semi-metal and non-metal.

Table 2.6 Properties of a typical metal, semi-metal and non-metal

Element	silver (metal)	silicon (semi-metal)	sulfur (non-metal)
Lustre	high	moderately high	low
Electrical conductivity (MS/m)	63	1×10^{-3}	1×10^{-21}
Density (g/cm³)	10.5	2.3	2.1
Melting point (°C)	962	1410	113
Boiling point (°C)	2212	3267	445

2.2 DATA ANALYSIS
Classifying elements

2.1 QUESTIONS

1. Select the element that is classified as a semi-metal.
   A Tungsten
   B Fluorine
   C Xenon
   D Boron

2. Select the element that is classified as a metal.
   A Tellurium
   B Iridium
   C Silicon
   D Germanium

3. Use the melting (m.p.) and boiling (b.p.) points provided to classify the following elements as solids, liquids or gases at 25 °C and 100 kPa.
   (a) Xenon (m.p. = –112 °C, b.p. = –108 °C)
   (b) Iridium (m.p. = 2450 °C, b.p. = 4500 °C)
   (c) Caesium (m.p. = 28 °C, b.p. = 669 °C)
   (d) Barium (m.p. = 725 °C, b.p. = 1640 °C)

4. The density of a sample of platinum was determined by measuring the mass and volume of the sample. The results of the experiment are:

   mass of sample (m) = 155.65 g
   volume of sample (V) = 7.50 cm^3

   (a) Calculate the density of the platinum sample using this data.
   (b) Chemical data books list the density of pure platinum as 21.4 g/cm^3. Is the sample of platinum pure?
   (c) Use the periodic table to identify the symbol for platinum.
   (d) Use the periodic table to classify platinum as a metal, semi-metal or non-metal.

5. A sample of gallium was put in a test tube and heated in a beaker of warm water. A temperature probe connected to a data logger was placed in the melted gallium to monitor its temperature. The tube of melted gallium was put in a test-tube rack and allowed to cool slowly. The data in table 2.7 was collected as the gallium cooled.

(a) Identify the dependent variable in this experiment.
(b) Plot a line graph of this data.
(c) Identify the freezing point of this gallium sample. Justify your answer.
(d) Identify the melting point of this gallium sample. Justify your answer.
(e) Chemical data books list the melting point of pure gallium as 30 °C. Is the sample pure?
(f) Use the periodic table to classify gallium as a metal, semi-metal or non-metal.

6. Use the following data to classify each element as a metal, semi-metal or non-metal.
   (a) Element *A* is lustrous and silvery in appearance, and it has a high electrical conductivity.
   (b) Element *B* can be drawn into long, thin wires.
   (c) Element *C* has a low melting point and shatters into tiny crystals when hammered.
   (d) Element *D* has a very high melting point and is a semi-conductor of electricity
   (e) Element *E* is a gas at standard temperature and pressure.
   (f) Element *F* has a high thermal conductivity and is highly malleable.

7. Arsenic is a poisonous element; its symbol is As. Arsenic oxide can be used to kill pests such as termites. Natural arsenic is an element that can exist in different structural forms known as allotropes. The yellow form of arsenic exists as a tetratomic molecule and is very volatile. It is unstable at 25 °C and gradually changes to the grey form. The grey form is lustrous, very brittle and a good conductor of heat. The grey form is a poor electrical conductor while the yellow form is a non-conductor of electricity.
   (a) Identify the properties of arsenic that are similar to those of metals.
   (b) Explain why arsenic is classified as a semi-metal.

Table 2.7

Time (min)	0	1	2	3	4	5	6	7	8	9
Temperature (°C)	36	34	32	31	30	30	30	29	28	26

2.2 THE PROPERTIES AND USES OF ELEMENTS

Remember

Before beginning this section, you should be able to:
- identify internationally recognised symbols for common elements.

Key content

By the end of this section, you should be able to:
- explain the relationship between the reactivity of an element and the likelihood of it existing as an uncombined element
- account for the uses of metals and non-metals in terms of their physical properties
- plan and perform an investigation to examine some uses of a range of common elements
- analyse information from secondary sources to distinguish the physical properties of metals and non-metals.

alloy: a mixture of a metal with one or more other elements (these other elements are usually metals)

Chemical reactivity of elements

If you place a crystal of sodium in water, it reacts violently and generates considerable quantities of heat. A similar crystal of gold does not react with water at all. These observations show that different elements have different reactivities. Reactivity is a chemical property that is related to the electronic structure of the element. Some elements, such as potassium and fluorine, are highly reactive while others, such as argon, are inert.

- *Unreactive* elements can exist as free elements in nature.
- *Reactive* elements combine with other substances in the environment to form compounds.

Metals such as caesium, potassium, calcium and magnesium are very reactive elements. They readily combine with oxygen or water to form compounds. In contrast, gold is very unreactive and is sometimes called a *noble metal*. Gold reacts with other chemicals only under extreme conditions. This explains why gold can be found as a free metal in the lithosphere. Such free metals are called *native metals*. Native iron is found as meteoric iron, but it is usually alloyed with nickel. Platinum, palladium, osmium, rhodium, ruthenium and iridium are often found together as metallic **alloys**.

Figure 2.5
Sodium is very reactive and must be stored in the absence of water and air.

Of the non-metals, fluorine and oxygen are the most reactive and helium and neon are the least reactive. Helium and neon are examples of *noble gases*. All the noble gases exist as free elements in nature.

Although oxygen is reactive and forms many compounds, it also exists as a free element in the atmosphere due to the very low reactivity of nitrogen and argon gases. Other reactive elements can exist as free elements in nature if they are in environments that protect them from reaction. Thus, sulfur can be found in the lithosphere in vast subterranean ore bodies because of its insolubility in water and its low reactivity with oxygen at low temperatures. Table 2.8 lists the elements that can exist free in nature.

Table 2.8 Elements can exist free in nature or as alloys.

Exist separately as metals or as alloys with one another									
Au	Ag	Hg	Pt	Pd	Os	Ir	Rh	Ru	Fe
Exist separately as non-metals									
He	Ne	Ar	Kr	Xe	Rn	N_2	O_2	S	C

Metals can be ranked according to their chemical reactivity with other materials such as oxygen, water and acids. This list is referred to as the activity series. Table 2.9 lists the common metals in decreasing order of reactivity.

Table 2.9 Activity series of some common metals

Most active										Least active
K	Na	Ca	Mg	Al	Zn	Fe	Pb	Cu	Hg	Ag	Au

Uses of elements

The uses of elements are directly related to their physical and chemical properties. For example, aluminium is a malleable metal that can be readily formed into saucepans, window frames and thin foils for cooking. Its high thermal conductivity allows rapid heat transfer to the food in saucepans or through foil. Its high tensile strength and reduced tendency to corrode makes it an excellent building material.

Table 2.10 lists some common elements and the properties that make them useful in our society.

Figure 2.6
Aluminium is a malleable metal. It can be pressed and rolled into sheets.

2.3 **DATA** ANALYSIS

Properties and uses of elements

Table 2.10 Uses and properties of some elements

Element	Use	Property related to use
copper	electrical wiring	ductility; high electrical conductivity
iron	structural building materials	high tensile strength
zinc	galvanising of iron	high reactivity allows it to preferentially corrode and protect the iron
gold	ornaments, jewellery	lustre; highly unreactive
argon	atmosphere for welding and metallurgy	inert
helium	meteorological balloons	low density
silicon	computer chips, transistors	semi-conductor

2.2 QUESTIONS

1. Identify the metal that is used as a filament in incandescent light bulbs.
   A Iron
   B Magnesium
   C Tungsten
   D Gold

2. Identify the list that correctly places the metals in increasing order of chemical reactivity.
   A Iron, calcium, lead, gold
   B Silver, copper, iron, magnesium
   C Copper, zinc, potassium, magnesium
   D Potassium, zinc, iron, silver

3. Tungsten is a very useful metal. It can be obtained from the mineral *wolframite*, so is sometimes called wolfram, which provides its symbol W. Wolframite is often found in combination with tin ores and, in the early days, this made the tungsten difficult to isolate. Tungsten requires considerable heat to melt; its melting point is 3410 °C and boiling point is 5930 °C. The metal was first used as the filament in electric light bulbs in 1913. Tungsten is classified as a heavy metal, along with gold and platinum. Its density is 19.3 g/cm³; it has high tensile strength; its carbide is exceptionally hard.

   Identify the properties of tungsten that make it suitable for use as (a) filaments in electric light bulbs and (b) as a component of tool steel.

4. Titanium is used as a structural metal in aircraft and spacecraft. Identify from the following list of properties those that make this metal useful for aircraft and spacecraft.
   • melting point = 1660 °C; boiling point = 3287 °C
   • density = 4.50 g/cm³ (compared with 7.86 g/cm³ for iron and 2.70 g/cm³ for aluminium)
   • electrical conductivity = 2.3 MS/m (compared with 63 MS/m for silver)
   • thermal conductivity = 22 J/s/m/K (compared with 237 J/s/m/K for aluminium)
   • high tensile strength

5. Match the use of the indicated element in the first column of table 2.11 to a property in the second column.

Table 2.11

Element and use	Property
A. copper — cooking pots	1. high electrical conductivity
B. lead — roof sheeting	2. low corrosion
C. carbon (graphite) — electrodes	3. high thermal conductivity
D. gold — jewellery	4. soft and malleable
E. chromium — stainless steel sinks	5. inert and lustrous

SUMMARY

• Elements are composed of small particles called atoms. Atoms can form larger aggregates called molecules.

• Elements cannot be physically separated or decomposed.

• Elements can be classified as metals, semi-metals or non-metals according to their physical properties. These properties determine their use.

• Metals are shiny and conduct electricity.

• Non-metals are dull and are electrical insulators.

• Semi-metals have some properties that are similar to metals and others that are similar to non-metals.

• Unreactive elements can exist as free elements in nature.

• Reactive elements must be stored away from air or moisture.

• Reactive elements combine with other substances in the environment to form compounds.

2.1 PRACTICAL ACTIVITIES

INVESTIGATING THE PHYSICAL PROPERTIES OF ELEMENTS

Aim

To collect first-hand data on the physical properties of some elements to classify them into groups

Safety issues

- Wear safety glasses throughout this experiment.
- Do not touch iodine crystals or breathe the vapours; examine them in a sealed tube.
- Identify other safety issues relevant to this experiment by reading the method.

Materials

- samples (granules, wires, sheets) of zinc, magnesium, iron, copper, lead, tin, aluminium, sulfur (melted and allowed to cool into lumps), red phosphorus, iodine, graphite (carbon) rods
- 1 cm cubes of various metals such as aluminium, zinc, iron, copper, lead and tin
- DC power supply
- light bulb on stand
- electrical leads/clips
- ammeter
- Petri dishes
- electronic balance
- 10 mL measuring cylinder
- ball hammer

Method

1. Appearance

    For each element provided, describe its colour and state whether it is lustrous or dull.
2. Electrical conductivity

    (a) Set up a simple electrical circuit as shown in figure 2.7 using a 12 V DC power supply and electrical meters or lamps.

    (b) Connect each element sample into the circuit and measure the relative brightness of the lamp (use a rating scale) or measure the current on the ammeter/milliammeter). Record your observations in your logbook.

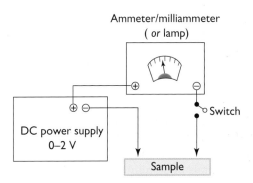

Figure 2.7
Circuit for testing electrical conductivity

3. Density

    (*Note:* Weigh samples in a dish or on filter paper.)

    (a) Some metal samples are available as 1 cm cubes, so their volume is 1 cm^3. Measure their mass on an electronic balance and calculate their density.

    (b) For solid samples that are irregular in shape, measure their mass on an electronic balance and their volume by displacement of water in a small measuring cylinder. Dry the sample after use.

4. Malleability and hardness

    (a) Use a ball hammer to determine whether the solid samples deform or shatter when struck. (*Note:* Iodine should be tested only in a fume hood, using only one crystal.)

    (b) Identify which samples are ductile by finding out whether they are available as wires.

    (c) Identify which samples are malleable by finding out whether they are available as sheets.

Results and analysis

1. Tabulate your collected data.
2. Examine the data and classify the element samples as metals or non-metals. Construct a table to show your classification.
3. Justify the classifications you made in 2.
4. Rank the metals in order of decreasing density.

Conclusion

Write a brief conclusion for this experiment.

DATA ANALYSIS

2.2 DATA ANALYSIS

CLASSIFYING ELEMENTS

Aim

To use second-hand data to classify elements as:

(a) solids, liquids or gases

(b) metals, non-metals or semi-metals

Materials

- 2 copies of the periodic table
- coloured pencils or highlighters

Part A: Solids, liquids and gases

Most elements are solids so we will process data for only selected elements to determine whether they are solids, liquids or gases. Table 2.12 provides the melting and boiling points of selected elements.

Table 2.12

Element symbol	Melting point (°C)	Boiling point (°C)	State (solid, liquid or gas)
He	–272	–269	
Li	180	1342	
O	–219	–183	
F	–220	–188	
Ne	–249	–246	
S	113	445	
Cl	–101	–34	
Ar	–189	–186	
Se	217	685	
Br	–7	59	
Kr	–157	–152	
I	114	184	
Xe	–112	–108	
Rn	–71	–62	

1. Copy table 2.12 into your workbook.

2. Use the data in table 2.12 and the following rules to determine whether the selected elements are solids, liquids or gases, and complete the last column of the table.
   - An element is a solid if its melting point is greater than 25 °C.
   - An element is a liquid if its melting point is less than 25 °C and its boiling point is greater than 25 °C.
   - An element is a gas if its boiling point is less than 25 °C.

3. Hydrogen and nitrogen are gases; mercury is a liquid. All other elements, apart from those listed in the table, are solids.

4. Label a copy of the periodic table, 'Solids, liquids and gases'.
   (a) Select a colour (such as green) to represent solids. Colour all the elements of the periodic table that are solids with this colour.
   (b) Choose a second colour (such as blue) for liquids. Colour all the elements that are liquids with this colour.
   (c) Choose a third colour (such as violet) for gases. Colour all the elements that are gases with this colour.

Part B: Metals, non-metals and semi-metals

Most elements are metals and so we will process data for only selected elements.

1. Use the following clues to classify and list these elements as metals, non-metals or semi-metals.
   - All the gaseous elements listed in table 2.13 are non-metals.
   - Six of the seven semi-metals have the following atomic weights: 10.81, 28.09, 72.59, 74.92, 121.75, 127.6.
   - Element 85 is a semi-metal.
   - Bromine is a fuming, red-brown liquid.
   - Carbon is brittle in its graphite form and a non-conductor in its diamond form.

2. Copy and complete table 2.13 in your workbook. The elements listed in the table are metals if their electrical conductivity is greater than 0.1 MS/m; otherwise they are non-metals.

DATA ANALYSIS

Table 2.13

Element symbol	Electrical conductivity (MS/m)	Metal or non-metal
P	10^{-15}	
S	10^{-21}	
Ga	3.9	
Se	10^{-4}	
I	10^{-13}	
Hg	1.0	

3. Apart from the elements mentioned in 1 and 2 above, all other elements are metals.

4. Label a copy of the periodic table, 'Metals, non-metals and semi-metals'.

   (a) Select a colour (such as red) to represent metals. Colour all the elements of the periodic table that are metals with this colour.

   (b) Choose a second colour (such as orange) for semi-metals. Colour all the elements that are semi-metals with this colour.

   (c) Choose a third colour (such as yellow) for non-metals. Colour all the elements that are non-metals with this colour.

General questions

1. Identify the location of gaseous elements in the periodic table.

2. Identify the location of non-metallic elements in the periodic table.

3. Describe the location of semi-metals in the periodic table in relation to the metals and non-metals.

2.3 DATA ANALYSIS

PROPERTIES AND USES OF ELEMENTS

Table 2.14 lists some common elements and their uses. Examine each of these and complete the table by selecting all of the following properties that are related to each use.

(a) ductility

(b) malleability

(c) low reactivity

(d) low adherence to other materials such as glass

(e) high lustre and reflectivity

(f) low melting point

(g) high electrical conductivity

(h) high density

(i) uniform expansion rate on heating

Table 2.14

Element	Use	Properties related to use (a)–(i)
silver	mirrors	
mercury	thermometers	
tin	plating of steel	
lead	soldering (lead alloy)	
lead	sinkers (for fishing)	
aluminium	high voltage cables and wires	
nickel	coinage	
chromium	plating of steel and copper	

Chapter 3

COMPOUNDS

Introduction

Compounds are formed when different elements react chemically. This chemical interaction involves the outermost electrons of the atoms of each element. To understand the differences between chemical compounds, we must have a sound understanding of the structure of the atom and the way electrons behave.

In this chapter

Figure 3.1

Compounds of transition metals, such as copper and chromium, are highly coloured.

3.1 THE STRUCTURE OF THE ATOM

The particle nature of matter

In your junior science course, you learnt that matter is made up of small particles that are in constant motion. The particles in solids are packed closely together and, even though their positions are fixed in the crystal, the individual particles can vibrate. The particles in liquids can move about (or flow) because they are not locked into fixed positions. The particles in gases are widely separated and move very much faster than those in liquids. The rapid motion of gas particles allows them to spread out rapidly so that they eventually occupy the entire space of their container.

Solids and liquids are often classified as condensed matter. The closeness of the particles makes solids and liquids almost incompressible. Gases, however, are easy to compress as there is considerable free space between their particles.

Chemists have discovered that there are many different types of particles that make up matter. These include:
- *atoms* — the smallest particles of an element that can take part in a chemical reaction
- *molecules* — the smallest part of a pure substance that can exist separately. Molecules are usually composed of two or more atoms chemically bonded together, although the noble gases (including helium and argon) are regarded as monatomic (single-atom) molecules.
- *ions* — charged atoms or charged molecules. Ions can be positively or negatively charged.

These different types of particle will be investigated in later sections.

Figure 3.2
The three physical states of matter. Solids have a definite shape and volume; liquids have a definite volume but an indefinite shape; and gases have an indefinite shape and volume.

Figure 3.3
Three different types of particle: atoms, molecules and ions

Sub-structure of atoms

Atoms are composed of three fundamental particles called *protons*, *neutrons* and *electrons*. The simple Bohr model (1913) describes atoms in the following terms:
- The atom consists of a small central *nucleus* containing the protons and neutrons. The nucleus represents about 99.95% by weight of the atom. Its diameter, however, is very small (about 0.001 picometres) compared with atomic diameters (about 100 pm).

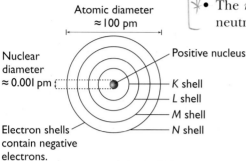

atomic mass unit (amu):
1 amu = 1.661 × 10⁻²⁷ kg

Atomic diameter
≈100 pm

Nuclear
diameter
≈0.001 pm

Positive nucleus

K shell
L shell
M shell
N shell

Electron shells
contain negative
electrons.

Figure 3.4
Sub-structure of the atom

- Protons are positively charged particles and neutrons have no charge. These particles have similar masses: mass of proton (m_p) = 1.007 **atomic mass units (amu)**; mass of neutron (m_n) = 1.008 amu.
- The *atomic number* (Z) of an element is the number of protons in the nucleus.
- The *mass number* (A) of an element is the total number of protons and neutrons in the nucleus.
- The electrons occupy stable *energy levels* around the nucleus. The electrons occupy the greatest volume of the atom.
- Electrons are negatively charged particles.
- Electrons have a very small mass $(m_e$ = 0.00055 amu) compared with protons and neutrons. They move so rapidly that they are sometimes referred to as an 'electron cloud'.
- The number of protons in neutral atoms equals the number of electrons.

Nuclear symbols

Each element has its own unique atomic number (Z). This is the number used to organise the elements in the periodic table.

Any element E can be represented by the following symbol:

$$_Z^A E$$

where A is the atomic mass and Z is the atomic number. The number of neutrons in any element can be determined by subtracting Z from A.

SAMPLE PROBLEM 3.1

For each of the elements listed below:
  (i) represent each element using its nuclear symbol
  (ii) calculate the number of neutrons present in the nucleus.
(a) Carbon-12 $(Z = 6, A = 12)$
(b) Oxygen-16 $(Z = 8, A = 16)$
(c) Sodium-23 $(Z = 11, A = 23)$

SOLUTION

(a) (i) $_6^{12}C$ (ii) neutrons = $A - Z = 12 - 6 = 6$

(b) (i) $_8^{16}O$ (ii) neutrons = $16 - 8 = 8$

(c) (i) $_{11}^{23}Na$ (ii) neutrons = $23 - 11 = 12$

Isotopes

isotopes: atoms of an element that have different mass numbers (A) due to the presence of different numbers of neutrons

Many elements have isotopic forms. These **isotopes** have slightly different masses due to differences in the number of neutrons present in the nucleus. For example, natural carbon consists of three isotopic forms: $_6^{12}C$, $_6^{13}C$, $_6^{14}C$. Carbon-12 is the most abundant (98.9%) of these forms. Carbon-13 has one more neutron in its nucleus than carbon-12; carbon-14 has two more neutrons in its nucleus than carbon-12.

Electron energy levels

The Bohr model of the atom describes electrons existing in stable energy levels at different radial distances from the nucleus. These energy levels are often referred to as *electron shells*.

Table 3.1 shows the number of electrons associated with each electron energy level. Each shell is designated with a shell number (n = 1, 2, 3 etc.) and a shell symbol (K, L, M etc.). The lowest energy shell is the K shell. It is the closest shell to the nucleus.

Table 3.1 Energy levels

Energy level (n)	Energy level symbol	Maximum population of electrons
1	K	2
2	L	8
3	M	18
4	N	32
5	O	50

- The maximum number of electrons in each shell is determined by the formula: $2n^2$ (where n = 1, 2, 3 etc.).

- Electrons fill the lowest energy levels first. Thus, an atom with six electrons (carbon) has two electrons in the K shell and the remaining four electrons in the L shell.

- The pattern of electrons in each shell is called the *electron configuration*. The electron configurations of some representative elements are shown in table 3.2 and figure 3.6. Using table 3.2, we can write the electron configuration for sodium as 2, 8, 1, and for argon as 2, 8, 8.

- Although the M shell can contain up to 18 electrons, it is not filled until the element copper (2, 8, 18, 1). Thus, elements with atomic numbers between 19 and 28 have incomplete M shells and one or two electrons in the N shell. Table 3.2 shows the example for potassium (Z = 19), calcium (Z = 20) and scandium (Z = 21).

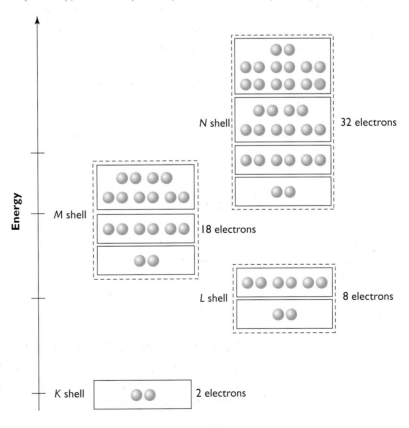

Figure 3.5
Energy levels in the atom

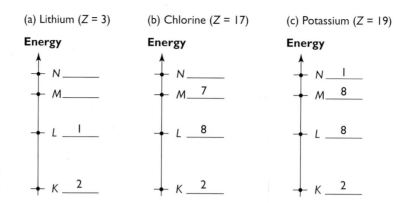

(a) Lithium (Z = 3)   (b) Chlorine (Z = 17)   (c) Potassium (Z = 19)

Figure 3.6
Electron configuration diagrams

Table 3.2 Electron configurations for a representative set of elements

Z	Element	K shell	L shell	M shell	N shell
1	hydrogen	1			
2	helium	2			
3	lithium	2	1		
9	fluorine	2	7		
10	neon	2	8		
11	sodium	2	8	1	
17	chlorine	2	8	7	
18	argon	2	8	8	
19	potassium	2	8	8	1
20	calcium	2	8	8	2
21	scandium	2	8	9	2

Noble gas configurations (stable octets)

The noble gases are the key to understanding the pattern of electron configurations. These configurations are listed in table 3.3.

Table 3.3

Z	Element	Electron configuration
2	He	2
10	Ne	2, 8
18	Ar	2, 8, 8
36	Kr	2, 8, 18, 8
54	Xe	2, 8, 18, 18, 8
86	Rn	2, 8, 18, 32, 18, 8

Apart from helium, which has a filled K shell, the remaining noble gases have eight electrons (an octet) in their outer shell.

- It is apparent that an octet of electrons in the outer shell confers stability to an atom. Noble gases are the most unreactive elements.
- The outer shell of the atom is called the *valence shell*. Electrons in this shell are called **valence electrons**.

In the next section, we will examine how other elements can achieve a stable octet in their valence shells.

valence electrons: electrons that occupy the outer (valence) shell of an atom

3.1 QUESTIONS

1. Select the statement that correctly identifies the nature of particles in a gas.
   A The particles are fixed in a lattice and can only vibrate.
   B The particles in a gas are far apart and in rapid motion.
   C Gases are incompressible because their particles have only small free spaces between them.
   D Gases are always composed of diatomic molecules.

2. Select the correct statement concerning the sub-structure of the atom.
   A Electrons have greater mass than protons or neutrons.
   B The diameter of a typical atom is about 100 000 times greater than the nuclear diameter.
   C The mass number of an element is the number of protons in the nucleus.
   D The nucleus is neutral as it contains equal numbers of positive and negative particles.

3. Copy and complete table 3.4 in your workbook. You will need to refer to the periodic table in some cases.

Table 3.4

Element	Symbol	Z	A	Number of neutrons
sulfur	(a)	16	32	(b)
(c)	I	53	127	(d)
strontium	(e)	38	(f)	50
(g)	Hg	(h)	200	120
(i)	Rn	86	(j)	140

4. Write the electron configurations of the following elements.
   (a) $^{11}_{5}B$
   (b) $^{14}_{7}N$
   (c) $^{24}_{12}Mg$
   (d) $^{32}_{16}S$
   (e) $^{39}_{19}K$

5. Element X is represented by the nuclear symbol $^{28}_{14}X$.
   (a) Identify this element.
   (b) Write the electron configuration for this element.
   (c) Identify the number of valence electrons in the atoms of this element.
   (d) Another isotope of this element has one more neutron. Write the nuclear symbol for this isotope using the correct symbol for this element.

6. An element Q has the electron configuration 2, 8, 14, 2.
   (a) What is the atomic number of this element?
   (b) Use the periodic table to identify this element.
   (c) Classify this element as a metal, non-metal or semi-metal.
   (d) An isotope of this element has 30 neutrons in its nucleus.
      (i) Calculate the mass number of this isotope.
      (ii) Write this isotope using its nuclear symbol and correct chemical symbol.

3.2 IONS AND IONIC BONDING

Ion formation and electron energy levels

In section 3.1, we saw that the most stable electron configurations are the noble gas configurations. Other elements can achieve stable electron configurations by losing or gaining electrons. In so doing, they form ions. Stable ions have noble gas configurations.

Ions

Neutral atoms contain equal numbers of positive protons and negative electrons. Atoms can become charged; they are then called ions. Ions can be positively charged or negatively charged.

Remember
Before beginning this section, you should be able to:
• identify that a new compound is formed by rearranging atoms rather than creating matter
• classify compounds into groups based on common chemical characteristics
• construct word equations from observations and written descriptions of a range of chemical reactions.

- *Cations* are positively charged ions formed by atoms losing one or more electrons.

  Example: Sodium loses one electron. Its ionic half-equation is

  $$Na \rightarrow Na^+ + e^-.$$

- *Anions* are negatively charged ions formed by atoms gaining one or more electrons.

  Example: Chlorine gains one electron. Its ionic half-equation is

  $$Cl + e^- \rightarrow Cl^-.$$

Metals tend to form positive ions. Non-metals tend to form negative ions.

Ions and the valence shell

Metals lose their valence shell electrons to achieve noble gas electron configurations. Having lost these valence shell electrons a stable shell is now exposed.

Example: In each of the following cases, the ion formed has the same electron configuration as a neon atom.

$$\begin{array}{lll} Na & \rightarrow & Na^+ \;\; + \; e^- \\ 2,8,1 & & 2,8 \end{array}$$

$$\begin{array}{lll} Mg & \rightarrow & Mg^{2+} + \; 2e^- \\ 2,8,2 & & 2,8 \end{array}$$

$$\begin{array}{lll} Al & \rightarrow & Al^{3+} \; + \; 3e^- \\ 2,8,3 & & 2,8 \end{array}$$

Non-metals gain electrons into their valence shell to achieve a noble gas configuration.

Example: In each of the following cases, the ion formed has the same electron configuration as an argon atom.

$$\begin{array}{lll} Cl & + \; e^- \; \rightarrow & Cl^- \\ 2,8,7 & & 2,8,8 \end{array}$$

$$\begin{array}{lll} S & + \; 2e^- \rightarrow & S^{2-} \\ 2,8,6 & & 2,8,8 \end{array}$$

$$\begin{array}{lll} P & + \; 3e^- \rightarrow & P^{3-} \\ 2,8,5 & & 2,8,8 \end{array}$$

The gain and loss of electrons can be visualised using diagrams known as *Lewis electron dot structures.* These diagrams show the arrangement of valence shell electrons only; the inner shells are not shown. Figure 3.8 shows some examples of Lewis electron dot structures for elements gaining and losing electrons.

Figure 3.7
The mineral fluorite contains the ionic compound calcium fluoride, CaF_2, as its main component. Its beautiful crystals are often cubic in shape and appear in a variety of colours.

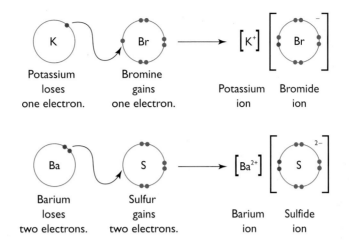

Figure 3.8
Lewis electron dot structures (showing the outer shells only)

SAMPLE PROBLEM 3.2

SOLUTION

When a potassium atom ($Z = 19$) loses two electons, it forms an ion. Use electron configurations to discuss the stability of the ion formed.

Neutral potassium atoms have 19 positive protons and 19 negative electrons. If two electrons are lost, the potassium ion has 19 protons but only 17 electrons, so the ion has a +2 charge. The 17 electrons occupy the energy levels to produce the configuration 2, 8, 7. This is not a stable noble gas configuration so the K^{2+} ion formed is not stable.

Ions and the periodic table

The horizontal rows of the periodic table are called *periods*. The vertical columns of the periodic table are called *groups*. Elements within each group have the same number of valence shell electrons.

Example: The members of group II have the following electron configurations.

> Be 2, 2
> Mg 2, 8, 2
> Ca 2, 8, 8, 2
> Sr 2, 8, 18, 8, 2
> Ba 2, 8, 18, 18, 8, 2
> Ra 2, 8, 18, 32, 18, 8, 2

All elements in group II are metals. They can achieve a noble gas configuration by losing the two electrons in their valence shell. Thus, all the stable cations of group II have a charge of +2. Therefore, stable cations of group II include Be^{2+}, Mg^{2+}, Ca^{2+}, Sr^{2+}, Ba^{2+} and Ra^{2+}.

There are both stable anions (N^{3-} and P^{3-}) and cations (Sb^{3+} and Bi^{3+}) in group V. This occurs because the elements at the bottom of group V are increasingly metallic and form cations rather than anions.

Table 3.5 shows some of the stable cations and anions of the main block of the periodic table. The main block excludes the transition metals, lanthanides and actinides of group II. Some elements do not form stable simple ions so these are left blank in table 3.5. The noble gases do not form ions as their atoms are stable.

SAMPLE PROBLEM 3.3

The first four members of group VII of the periodic table are fluorine, chlorine, bromine and iodine.

(a) Use the periodic table to obtain their atomic numbers and write the electron configuration of each of these four elements.

(b) Write the symbols for the most stable ions of this group. Justify your answer.

SOLUTION

(a) The atomic numbers are 9, 17, 35 and 53. The electron configurations are:

  F 2, 7
  Cl 2, 8, 7
  Br 2, 8, 18, 7
  I 2, 8, 18, 18, 7.

(b) All elements of group VII have seven valence electrons. This is one short of a stable octet. Thus, each atom needs to gain one electron to form a stable ion with a noble gas configuration. The stable anions are:

  F⁻ 2, 8
  Cl⁻ 2, 8, 8
  Br⁻ 2, 8, 18, 8
  I⁻ 2, 8, 18, 18, 8.

Table 3.5 Some of the common stable ions of the periodic table*

I	II	III	IV	V	VI	VII
H^+ H^-						
Li^+	Be^{2+}			N^{3-}	O^{2-}	F^-
Na^+	Mg^{2+}	Al^{3+}		P^{3-}	S^{2-}	Cl^-
K^+	Ca^{2+}	Ga^{3+}	Ge^{2+}		Se^{2-}	Br^-
Rb^+	Sr^{2+}	In^{3+}	Sn^{2+} Sn^{4+}	Sb^{3+}	Te^{2-}	I^-
Cs^+	Ba^{2+}	Tl^+ Tl^{3+}	Pb^{2+} Pb^{4+}	Bi^{3+}		

*Elements that do not form stable simple ions are left blank.

Some generalisations can be made from table 3.5.

- Hydrogen can lose an electron to form H^+ or gain an electron to fill the *K* shell and form H^-.

- Metals from groups I, II and III form cations with a charge equal to their group number.

- Non-metals from groups V, VI and VII form anions with a charge equal to their group number minus eight. For example, oxygen forms an ion with a charge of $6 - 8 = -2$.

- Some non-metals and semi-metals do not tend to form simple ions.

- Some heavy metals, such as lead, can form ions with more than one charge.

Ionic bonds and ionic compounds

Cation and anion formation are usually linked. To form a cation, electrons must be removed from a metal atom. This is achieved by non-metal atoms accepting the electrons to form anions.

The cation and anion formed attract one another and form a compound. The *electrostatic attraction* between a cation and an anion is called an *ionic bond*. The compound formed is called an *ionic compound*.

Examples:

1. Sodium chloride

Sodium atoms have one valence electron in their M shells. Chlorine atoms have seven valence electrons in their M shells. When a sodium atom reacts with a chlorine atom, an electron is transferred from the sodium atom to the chlorine atom so that the ions formed have stable noble gas configurations. Therefore,

$$\text{Na} + \text{Cl} \rightarrow \text{Na}^+ + \text{Cl}^- \rightarrow \text{Na}^+\text{Cl}^-$$
$$2, 8, 1 \quad 2, 8, 7 \quad 2, 8 \quad 2, 8, 8 \quad \text{sodium chloride}$$

An ionic bond forms between the sodium ions and chloride ions. The solid that forms is an ionic salt called sodium chloride. Its chemical formula is NaCl. (It is not necessary to show the charges on the ions; this is understood.) Figure 3.9a shows a Lewis electron dot structure of this reaction.

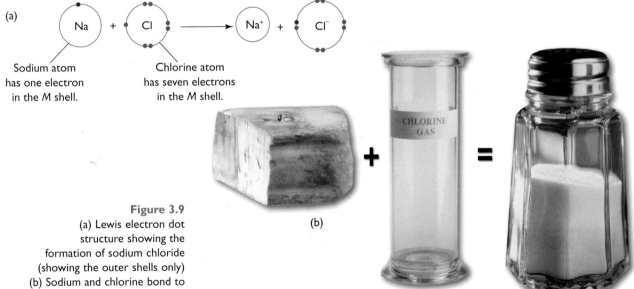

(a)

Sodium atom has one electron in the M shell.

Chlorine atom has seven electrons in the M shell.

(b)

Figure 3.9
(a) Lewis electron dot structure showing the formation of sodium chloride (showing the outer shells only)
(b) Sodium and chlorine bond to make sodium chloride.

2. Magnesium oxide

Magnesium atoms have two valence electrons in their M shells. Oxygen atoms have six valence electrons in their L shells. When a magnesium atom reacts with an oxygen atom, two electrons are transferred from the magnesium atom to the oxygen atom so that the ions formed have noble gas configurations. Therefore,

$$\text{Mg} + \text{O} \rightarrow \text{Mg}^{2+} + \text{O}^{2-} \rightarrow \text{Mg}^{2+}\text{O}^{2-}$$
$$2, 8, 2 \quad 2, 6 \quad 2, 8 \quad 2, 8 \quad \text{magnesium oxide}$$

The chemical formula for the ionic compound formed is MgO. Figure 3.10 shows a Lewis electron dot structure of this reaction.

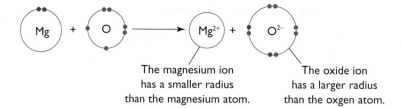

Figure 3.10
Lewis electron dot structure
showing the formation of
magnesium oxide (showing
the outer shells only)

The magnesium ion
has a smaller radius
than the magnesium atom.

The oxide ion
has a larger radius
than the oxgen atom.

SAMPLE PROBLEM 3.4

The chemical formula of potassium sulfide is K_2S. It is formed when potassium atoms react with sulfur atoms.

(a) Use the periodic table to identify the atomic numbers of potassium and sulfur.

(b) Write the electron configurations of these elements.

(c) Use symbols to write a balanced chemical equation to show how many atoms of potassium react with one atom of sulfur. Justify your answer by writing the electron configurations of the ions formed.

(d) Draw a Lewis electron dot structure for this chemical reaction and for the ionic compound formed

SOLUTION

(a) The atomic number of potassium is 19 and sulfur is 16.

(b) The electron configuration of K is 2,8,8,1.
The electron configuration of S is 2,8,6.

(c) Two potassium atoms are required to react with one sulfur atom to form stable ions.

$$K + K + S \rightarrow K^+ + K^+ + S^{2-} \rightarrow K_2S$$

2,8,8,1   2,8,8,1   2,8,6   2,8,8   2,8,8   2,8,8   potassium sulfide

(d)

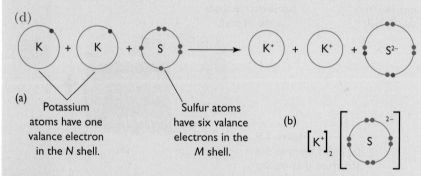

(a)
Potassium
atoms have one
valance electron
in the N shell.

Sulfur atoms
have six valance
electrons in the
M shell.

(b)

$$\left[K^+\right]_2 \left[\quad S \quad\right]^{2-}$$

Figure 3.11 Lewis electron dot structures showing (a) the reaction between potassium and sulfur and (b) potassium sulfide

Valency, formulae and nomenclature

The ability of an element to combine with other elements to form compounds can be expressed by the term **valency**.

In the case of ionic compounds, the valency of each element is the number of electrons lost or gained by the reacting metal and non-metal. Consequently, the valency of the element is equal to the charge on each ion. Valency is, therefore, related to the electron configuration and the number of electrons in the valence shell. Because hydrogen has one electron in its valence shell, its valency is 1. Other elements have valencies equal to one, or whole number multiples of one. Table 3.6 lists the valencies of some common metals and non-metals.

valency: the combining power of an element written in terms of the number of hydrogen atoms (which have a valency of +1) that it will combine with

Table 3.6 Valencies of common metal ions and non-metal ions

+1	+2	+3	−1	−2	−3
copper (I), Cu^+ hydrogen, H^+ lithium, Li^+ potassium, K^+ silver, Ag^+ sodium, Na^+	barium, Ba^{2+} calcium, Ca^{2+} iron (II), Fe^{2+} lead (II), Pb^{2+} magnesium, Mg^{2+} tin (II), Sn^{2+}	aluminium, Al^{3+} iron (III), Fe^{3+}	bromide, Br^- chloride, Cl^- fluoride, F^- hydride, H^- iodide, I^-	oxide, O^{2-} sulfide, S^{2-}	nitride, N^{3-} phosphide, P^{3-}

Chemical formulae

Table 3.6 showing valencies can be used to construct the chemical formulae of ionic compounds. The following rule should be used:

- The sum of positive and negative valencies of ionic compounds is zero.

Examples:
1. Calcium fluoride

$$\text{Valency of } Ca^{2+} = +2$$
$$\text{Valency of } F^- = -1$$

To have a zero sum of valencies in calcium fluoride, there must be two fluoride ions for each calcium ion. So,

$$(+2) + (-1) + (-1) = 0$$

Thus, the chemical formula is CaF_2.

2. Silver sulfide

$$\text{Valency of } Ag^+ = +1$$
$$\text{Valency of } S^{2-} = -2$$

To have a zero sum of valencies in silver sulfide, there must be two silver ions for each sulfide ion. So,

$$(+1) + (+1) + (-2) = 0$$

Thus, the chemical formula is Ag_2S.

SAMPLE PROBLEM 3.5 〉〉

SOLUTION 〉〉〉〉

An ionic salt formed between aluminium and a non-metal X has the formula Al_2X_3. Calculate the valency of element X.

Aluminium has a valency of +3. Let x be the valency of X. The sum of the valencies is zero, so

$$2(+3) + 3(x) = 0$$
$$x = -2$$

So, the valency of X is −2.

Nomenclature of ionic compounds

The following naming rules apply to ionic compounds.

- The cation is named first.
- The anion is named second.
- Where a metal can have several different valencies, a Roman numeral is used to indicate the valency in the name of the compound.
- The *-ide* suffix for the non-metal is used in simple **binary compounds**.

binary compounds: **compounds made up of only two elements**

Examples:
1. BaH_2 Cation: barium ion; anion: hydride ion; name: barium hydride
2. FeO Cation: iron (II) ion; anion: oxide ion; name: iron (II) oxide
3. Cu_2S Cation: copper (I) ion; anion: sulfide ion; name: copper (I) sulfide
4. CuS Cation: copper (II) ion; anion: sulfide ion;
         name: copper (II) sulfide

Polyatomic ions (radicals)

Many ionic compounds are composed of polyatomic ions rather than simple ions. Polyatomic ions are charged molecules. Their names often have the suffix *-ate* or *-ite*. Table 3.7 lists some common polyatomic ions and their valencies.

Table 3.7 Valencies of common polyatomic ions

+1	−1	−2	−3
ammonium, NH_4^+	acetate, CH_3COO^- hydrogen carbonate, HCO_3^- hydroxide, OH^- nitrate, NO_3^- nitrite, NO_2^-	carbonate, CO_3^{2-} chromate, CrO_4^{2-} dichromate, $Cr_2O_7^{2-}$ sulfate, SO_4^{2-} sulfite, SO_3^{2-}	phosphate, PO_4^{3-}

Chemical formulae for compounds containing polyatomic ions are constructed using the same valency rules.

Examples:
1. Sodium chromate

   Valency of sodium = +1

   Valency of chromate = −2

   To have a zero sum of valencies in sodium chromate, there must be two sodium ions for each chromate ion. So,

   $$(+1) + (+1) + (-2) = 0$$

   Thus, the chemical formula is Na_2CrO_4.
2. Ammonium phosphate

   Valency of ammonium = +1

   Valency of phosphate = −3

   To have a zero sum of valencies in ammonium phosphate, there must be three ammonium ions for each phosphate ion. So,

   $$(+1) + (+1) + (+1) + (-3) = 0$$

   Thus, the chemical formula is $(NH_4)_3PO_4$. (Note the use of brackets in this case.)

SAMPLE PROBLEM 3.6

An ionic compound forms between barium ions and permanganate ions. Its chemical formula is $Ba(MnO_4)_2$. Calculate the charge on the permanganate ion and write the symbol for this ion.

SOLUTION

The valency of barium ions = +2. Let the valency of the permanganate ion equal x.

As the valencies sum to zero,

$$(+2) + 2x = 0$$

$$x = -1$$

Thus, the valency of the permanganate ion is −1 and the charge is −1. The symbol is MnO_4^-

3.2 QUESTIONS

1. Element M has the electron configuration 2, 8, 8, 2. Element N has the electron configuration 2, 8, 7.
   (a) Classify M as a metal or non-metal.
   (b) Classify N as a metal or non-metal.
   (c) Determine the chemical formula for the ionic compound formed between M and N.

2. Use tables 3.6 and 3.7 to determine the chemical formulae for the following ionic compounds.
   (a) Silver sulfide
   (b) Barium iodide
   (c) Aluminium phosphide
   (d) Magnesium nitride
   (e) Ammonium nitrate
   (f) Calcium sulfite
   (g) Sodium dichromate
   (h) Iron (III) hydrogen carbonate

3. Name the following ionic compounds.
   (a) $SrCl_2$
   (b) AgI
   (c) Fe_2S_3
   (d) PbO_2
   (e) $CaCr_2O_7$
   (f) $BaBr_2$
   (g) KCH_3COO

4. Draw Lewis electron dot structures for:
   (a) potassium chloride
   (b) barium oxide
   (c) aluminium oxide.

5. Calculate the valency of the nominated element in each of the following ionic compounds.
   (a) X in X_2S
   (b) Y in Na_3Y
   (c) Z in $Z_2(SO_4)_3$

6. Discuss, in terms of electron configurations, the stability of an ion that is formed when:
   (a) an aluminium atom ($Z = 13$) loses two electrons
   (b) a phosphorus atom ($Z = 15$) gains three electrons.

7. Write ion half-equations for each of the following processes.
   (a) A gallium atom loses three electrons.
   (b) An iodine atom gains one electron.
   (c) A lead atom loses two electrons.

8. (a) Write electron configurations for the first three elements of group I of the periodic table.
   (b) Explain how group I elements can achieve noble gas electron configurations.

3.3 MOLECULES AND COVALENT BONDING

Types of molecules

Molecules have previously been defined as the smallest part of a pure substance that can exist separately. Another way of saying this is that molecules are particles that can move independently of one another.

Some molecules are elements and some are compounds. Here are some examples of molecules:

- *monatomic molecules*
  - helium atoms, He
  - argon atoms, Ar

- *diatomic molecules*
  - oxygen, O_2
  - nitrogen, N_2
  - hydrogen iodide, HI
  - carbon monoxide, CO

Remember
Before beginning this section, you should be able to:
• identify that a new compound is formed by rearranging atoms rather than creating matter
• classify compounds into groups based on common chemical characteristics
• construct word equations from observations and written descriptions of a range of chemical reactions.

Figure 3.12
White phosphorus is a very reactive non-metal. Each molecule contains four phosphorus atoms.

- *triatomic molecules*
  - ozone, O_3
  - water, H_2O
  - sulfur dioxide, SO_2
  - carbon dioxide, CO_2
- *tetra-atomic molecules*
  - white phosphorus, P_4
  - ammonia, NH_3

When you examine the list of molecules above, you will observe that they are composed of non-metals. Non-metal atoms can bond to other non-metal atoms and achieve stable electronic arrangements. This is discussed in the next section.

Sharing electrons and covalent bonding

Non-metal atoms can achieve electron shell stability by sharing electron pairs with other non-metals. Stable octets are achieved by this process.
- The sharing of electron pairs between neighbouring atoms is called a *covalent bond*.

There are three types of covalent bond:
- *single bond* — One electron pair is shared.
- *double bond* — Two electron pairs are shared.
- *triple bond* — Three electron pairs are shared.

Water   Methane   Oxygen   Carbon dixode

Figure 3.13
Particle models of various molecules

Examples:

1. Hydrogen molecules, H_2
Each hydrogen atom has one electron in its valence shell. Rather than one atom donating its electron to the other, the two atoms share the available valence electrons to form a covalent bond. This covalent bond holds the two atoms together strongly to form a stable diatomic molecule.

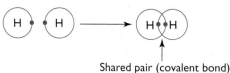

Shared pair (covalent bond)

Figure 3.14
Lewis electron dot structure of covalent bond formation in hydrogen molecules

2. Hydrogen chloride molecules, HCl
Chlorine atoms have seven valence electrons. A stable octet could be achieved by donation of an electron from a hydrogen atom to the chlorine atom. This does not happen in the gaseous state. Rather each atom donates an electron to form a shared pair. The hydrogen now has a stable *K* shell and chlorine has a stable octet in the *M* shell.

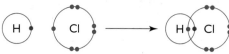

Figure 3.15
Lewis electron dot structure of covalent bond formation in hydrogen chloride molecules (showing the outer shells only)

3. Carbon dioxide molecules, CO_2

Carbon atoms have four valence electrons and oxygen atoms have six valence electrons. Both oxygen atoms achieve stable octets by sharing two electron pairs. A double covalent bond links each oxygen atom to the central carbon atom.

Figure 3.16
Lewis electron dot structure of covalent bond formation in carbon dioxide molecules (showing the outer shells only)

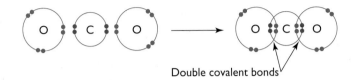

Double covalent bonds

Structural formulae

Another way of showing the bonding arrangements in molecules is to draw structural formulae. In structural formulae, the electron pair notation is replaced by bond-line representation as follows:

single bond: —

double bond: =

triple bond: ≡

Figure 3.17 shows examples of structural formulae of some common molecules.

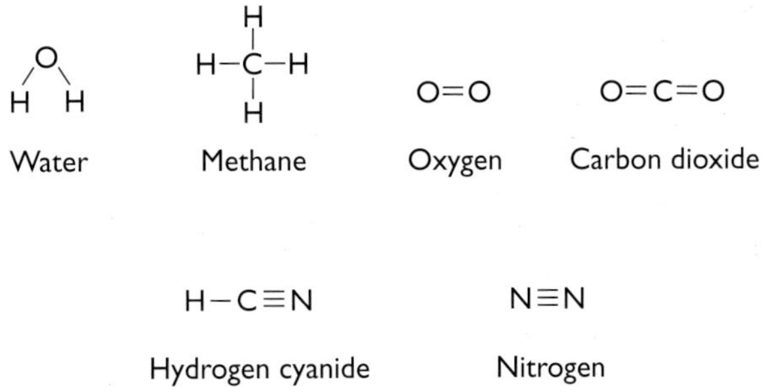

Water   Methane   Oxygen   Carbon dioxide

Figure 3.17
Structural formulae of some molecules

H—C≡N   N≡N

Hydrogen cyanide   Nitrogen

Molecular compounds

Molecular compounds are often referred to as covalent molecular compounds. This reinforces the idea that the bonding between atoms is due to the sharing of electron pairs.

Covalency and formulae

The concept of valency in molecular compounds is defined in terms of shared electron pairs. The covalency (or valency) of an element in a molecular compound equals the number of electron pairs that are shared to achieve a stable valence shell. Table 3.8 lists the valencies of some common elements in molecular compounds.

Table 3.8 can be used to construct chemical formulae for molecular compounds. The following rules should be used:

- For simple binary molecular compounds, the sum of the valencies of one element should match the sum of the valencies of the other element.
- For molecular compounds composed of three elements, the sum of the valencies of the first two elements should equal the total valency of the third element.
- In molecular formulae, the first element should have the lowest periodic group number or be in a lower period (higher period number) if both

elements are from the same group. (*Note:* There are some exceptions to this rule involving oxygen in molecular compounds with Cl, Br or I.)

Table 3.8 Valencies of non-metallic elements in molecular compounds

Non-metal	Common covalency*
hydrogen, (H)	1
fluorine, F	1
chlorine, Cl	1 (3, 5, 7)
bromine, Br	1 (3, 5, 7)
iodine, I	1 (3, 5, 7)
oxygen, O	2
nitrogen, N	3, 5 (1, 2, 4)
phosphorus, P	3, 5
sulfur, S	2, 4, 6
carbon, C	4

*The values in brackets are less common valencies.

Examples:
1. Nitrogen trichloride
N has a valency of 3 and chlorine has a valency of 1. Thus, three atoms of chlorine are required so that the total valency of chlorine matches the valency of nitrogen.

$$3 = 3 \times 1$$

The chemical formula is NCl_3. Note that nitrogen, which is in group V, is written before chlorine, in group VII.
2. Bromine pentafluoride

SAMPLE PROBLEM 3.7

Calculate the valency of the nominated element in each of the following molecular compounds.
(a) N in N_2O
(b) I in HIO_4

SOLUTION

(a) Oxygen has a valency of 2. Let the valency of each nitrogen atom equal x.

Thus, $2x = 2$

$x = 1$

So, the valency of nitrogen in N_2O is 1.
(b) Oxygen has a valency of 2 and hydrogen has a valency of 1. Let the valency of iodine equal x.

Thus, $1 + x = 4 \times 2$

$x = 7$

So, the valency of iodine in HIO_4 is 7.

Br has a valency of 5 and fluorine has a valency of 1. Thus, five atoms of fluorine are required so that the valency of bromine matches the total valency of fluorine.

$$5 = 5 \times 1$$

The chemical formula is BrF_5. Note that bromine is a lower member of group VII than fluorine and so is written first.

Nomenclature of molecular compounds

Table 3.9 lists the Greek prefixes commonly used to indicate the number of each type of atom in the molecular compound.

Table 3.9 Greek prefixes

1	2	3	4	5	6	7	8	9	10
mono	di	tri	tetra	pent	hex	hept	oct	non	dec

The following naming rules apply to molecular compounds.

- The non-metal with the lower group number is named first. (*Note:* There are some exceptions to this rule, such as dichlorine heptoxide, Cl_2O_7.)
- Use the Greek prefixes to specify the number of atoms of each element. (The prefix 'mono' is omitted in some cases.)
- For simple binary compounds, the suffix *-ide* is used in place of the last few letters of the second element.

Examples:
1. N_2O is dinitrogen oxide.
2. N_2O_4 is dinitrogen tetroxide.
3. CO is carbon monoxide.
4. SO_3 is sulfur trioxide.

Some molecular compounds, however, are known by their common name rather than their systematic names. Water is the best example of this. Table 3.10 shows some other examples of the use of common names.

3.1 DATA ANALYSIS
Analysing crystal structures

Table 3.10 Using common names

Molecular formula	Name
H_2O	water
NH_3	ammonia
CH_4	methane
NO	nitric oxide
N_2O	nitrous oxide

SAMPLE PROBLEM 3.8

SOLUTION

Name the following molecular compounds.
(a) NO_2
(b) PCl_5

(a) The two atoms of oxygen are called 'dioxide'. So, the name is nitrogen dioxide.
(b) The five atoms of chlorine are called 'pentachloride' (not 'pentchloride'). So, the name is phosphorus pentachloride.

 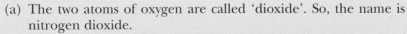

6. USING INSTRUCTION TERMS CORRECTLY

When answering questions, it is important to know what the instruction terms (verbs) require you to do. Here is an example.

'Describe'

This instruction term requires you to provide characteristics and features of substances, processes or concepts.

Example:

Describe the process of covalent bond formation between two non-metals such as hydrogen and fluorine.

Answer:

The hydrogen atom has one valence electron and the fluorine atom has seven valence electrons.

Each atom donates one electron to form a shared pair between them. This shared electron pair is called a covalent bond.

lattice: the geometric arrangement of particles in a crystal

3.3 QUESTIONS

1. Use table 3.8 to determine the chemical formulae for the following molecular compounds.
   (a) Hydrogen fluoride
   (b) Sulfur dichloride
   (c) Carbon tetrabromide
   (d) Phosphorus triiodide
   (e) Iodine chloride

2. Name the following molecular compounds.
   (a) BrCl
   (b) PBr_3
   (c) NI_3
   (d) H_2S
   (e) H_3P

3. Calculate the valency of the nominated element in each of the following molecular compounds.
   (a) S in SO_3
   (b) I in HIO_3
   (c) P in PCl_5
   (d) N in HNO_2
   (e) N in HNO_3

4. Classify the following molecules according to the number of atoms per molecule.
   ozone, ammonia, hydrogen fluoride, argon, sulfur dioxide, nitrous oxide, methane, carbon monoxide, neon, hydrogen phosphide
   Present your classification in symbolic terms in tabular format.

5. Draw Lewis electron dot structures for each of the following molecules.
   (a) Water
   (b) Ammonia
   (c) Oxygen gas
   (d) Ethyne, C_2H_2

   Extension

6. Figure 3.18 shows the unit cell of the crystal **lattice** of a fluoride of calcium.

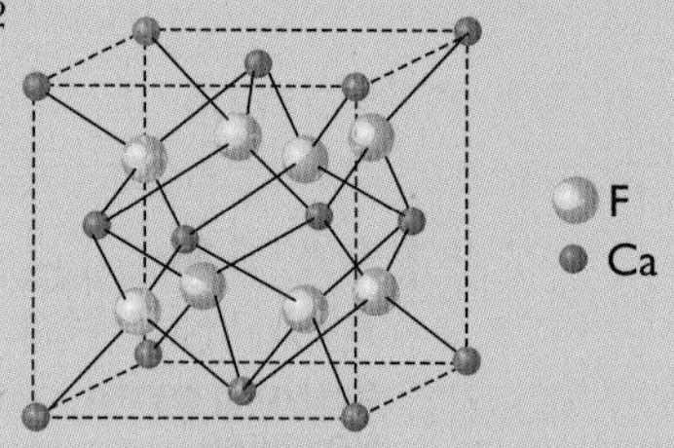

Figure 3.18 Unit cell of a fluoride of calcium

   (a) Classify calcium fluoride as ionic or molecular.
   (b) Use figure 3.18 and the following instructions to deduce the chemical formula for this fluoride of calcium.
   • Atoms/ions within the bulk of the unit cell belong to that cell alone. Count the number of these atoms/ions.
   • Atoms/ions at the corners are shared by eight other unit cells. Count the number of these atoms/ions and divide by eight.
   • Atoms/ions in the centre of each face are shared by two cells. Count the number of these atoms/ions and divide by two.
   • Determine the simplest ratio of calcium to fluorine.

eBook *plus*

Weblinks

eBook *plus*

Checkpoint
Revision 2

eBook *plus*

Checkpoint
Revision 2 Answers

SUMMARY

- Each element is composed of one or more of its own unique type of atom.

- Atoms are composed of smaller particles called electrons, protons and neutrons.

- Electrons are arranged in shells or energy levels around the nucleus.

- The nucleus contains protons and neutrons.

- Compounds have fixed chemical compositions.

- Ions are formed when atoms gain or lose electrons. Cations are positive ions and anions are negative ions.

- Lewis electron dot structures can be used to visualise ion formation and electron sharing in molecules.

- Ionic compounds are formed when cations and anions combine in fixed ratios. The attraction between oppositely charged ions is called an ionic bond.

- Molecular substances form when non-metal atoms bond to other non-metal atoms by sharing electron pairs in a covalent bond.

- Some elements exist as molecules in nature.

- Valency rules help us construct formulae for compounds. Valency can be related to the electron configuration of an atom.

- A system of nomenclature is used to name each unique compound.

3.1 DATA ANALYSIS

ANALYSING CRYSTAL STRUCTURES

Chemists use different types of models to help visualise the structure of materials. We have already seen how Lewis electron dot structures can help us understand the arrangement of valence electrons around each atom.

In the following examples, the models represent the arrangement of atoms, ions or molecules in the solid crystalline state. These structures are also called crystal lattices. You will look at lattices in greater depth in chapter 5 so you may elect to complete this data analysis after studying that chapter.

Metallic crystals

Figure 3.19 shows models for the crystal lattice structures of iron and zinc.

1. Explain how each lattice shows that these substances are elements.
2. Describe the lattice structure of each metal and identify any major differences.

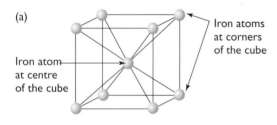

(a)

Iron atom at centre of the cube

Iron atoms at corners of the cube

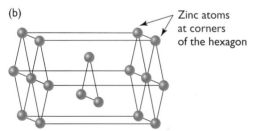

(b)

Zinc atoms at corners of the hexagon

Figure 3.19 Lattice structures of (a) iron and (b) zinc

Ionic crystals

Figure 3.20 shows two different models of the crystal lattice of sodium chloride. One is a ball-and-stick model and the other is a space-filling model.

1. Explain what the 'sticks' in figure 3.20a represent?
2. Identify the number of sodium ions that are immediate neighbours to each chloride ion in the bulk of the lattice.

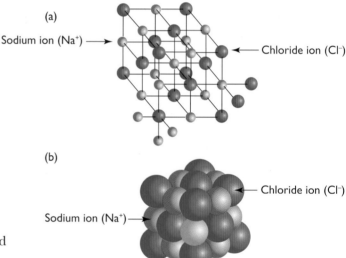

(a)

Sodium ion (Na⁺) →

← Chloride ion (Cl⁻)

(b)

Chloride ion (Cl⁻)

Sodium ion (Na⁺) →

Figure 3.20 Sodium chloride lattice as a (a) ball-and-stick model and (b) space-filling model

3. Identify the number of chloride ions that are immediate neighbours to each sodium ion in the bulk of the lattice.
4. State one advantage of the space-filling model over the ball-and-stick model.

Extension

Covalent molecular crystals

Covalent molecular crystals are investigated more thoroughly in chapter 5. These lattices are composed of molecules held together by weak intermolecular forces. Figure 3.21 shows the *unit cell* of the xenon difluoride lattice. A unit cell is the simplest repeating unit of a crystal lattice. The whole crystal is built up of such unit cells packed together in three dimensions.

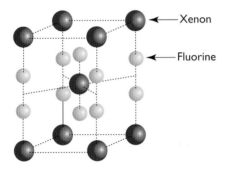

Figure 3.21 Xenon difluoride unit cell

1. Write the chemical formula for xenon difluoride.
2. Explain why xenon difluoride is an unusual compound.
3. Use the information below to explain how the unit cell can be used to determine the chemical formula of this compound.
   - Atoms within the bulk of the unit cell belong to that cell alone.
   - Atoms at the corners are shared by eight unit cells.
   - Atoms on the edges are shared by four unit cells.

Chapter 4

CHEMICAL EXTRACTION

Introduction

Chemists use different forms of energy to extract elements from their compounds. In some cases, the chemical bonds that bind the elements are not very strong so only a small amount of energy is needed to separate the elements. In other cases, where the bonding is strong, considerable amounts of energy are required.

In this chapter

Figure 4.1

Iron is extracted from iron ore in a furnace. Molten iron can be cast or converted to steel. Considerable energy is required for these chemical processes.

4.1 PHYSICAL AND CHEMICAL CHANGE

sublimation: the process of a solid turning directly into a vapour without the formation of the liquid state. For example, iodine crystals sublime to form purple iodine vapour on heating.

intermolecular forces: weak attractive forces between all types of matter. These forces are weaker than chemical bonds.

Physical changes

Chemists define a physical change as one that does not lead to the formation of new chemical substances. In comparative terms, physical changes involve small energy changes. Where physical changes involve a change of state, they can easily be reversed. Ice, for example, can be readily converted to liquid water by heating. Cooling will reverse the process and turn the water back to ice. In this case, no new substances have formed. Physical changes include:

- *filtration:* Muddy water can be easily separated into its two components by filtration (see figure 4.3). Mixing the separated components can readily reform the mixture.

- *evaporation and distillation:* Salt can be recovered readily from salt water by distillation. The evaporation and condensation processes are physical changes. Mixing the separated salt and water can readily reform the salt water.

- *cutting, hammering and rolling:* Metals can be cut into pieces or rolled to produce thin sheets. The processes of melting and solidification can rejoin the pieces.

- *change of state:* Melting and solidification, as well as evaporation and condensation discussed above, are physical changes. Melted butter quickly turns back to solid butter when placed in the refrigerator. The **sublimation** of dry ice into gaseous carbon dioxide is also a physical change.

Figure 4.4 shows particle diagrams illustrating the concept of a physical change.

In some physical changes, chemical bonds are broken or formed to achieve the change. For example, when copper is rolled, the metallic bonds are broken and reformed. The formation of salt crystals when salt water evaporates requires the formation of ionic bonds. In other cases, there are only weak physical forces between molecules. For example, when water solidifies, the water particles are held in the crystal lattice by physical forces of attraction. These **intermolecular forces** will be investigated in chapters 11–14.

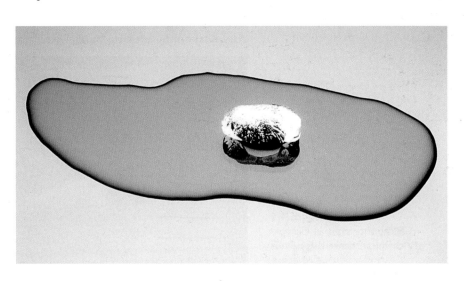

Figure 4.2
The melting of ice to form water is an example of a physical change. It involves a change of state that can easily be reversed.

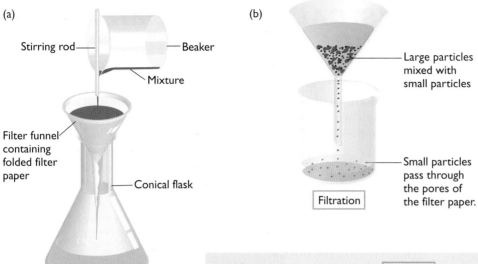

(a)

Stirring rod — Beaker

Mixture

Filter funnel
containing
folded filter
paper

Conical flask

(b)

Large particles
mixed with
small particles

Small particles
pass through
the pores of
the filter paper.

Filtration

Figure 4.3
Filtration is a physical process.
(a) The mud in muddy water is
separated from the water.
(b) The larger particles of mud do
not pass through the pores of the
filter, but the smaller particles do.

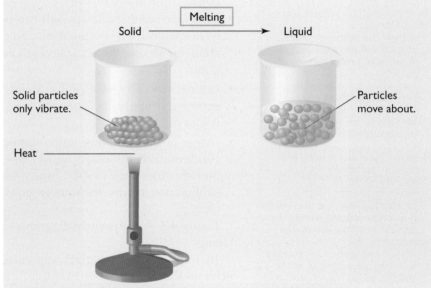

Melting

Solid → Liquid

Solid particles
only vibrate.

Particles
move about.

Heat

Figure 4.4
Particle diagram showing
physical change

Chemical changes

Chemical changes form new chemical substances. This process requires
breaking and reforming chemical bonds. Significantly more energy is
required for chemical changes than for physical changes. Also, reversal of
chemical change may be quite difficult. A burning match is an example
of a chemical change that cannot be reversed. Figure 4.5 illustrates some
chemical changes using particle diagrams.

Figure 4.5
A burning match is an example
of a chemical change that cannot
be reversed.

Reaction of lead oxide with carbon

Lead oxide   +   Carbon   →(Heat)→   Lead   +   Carbon monoxide

Reaction of hydrogen and iodine

Hydrogen   +   Iodine   →(Heat)→   Hydrogen iodide

Figure 4.6
Particle diagrams of chemical change

coke: the black solid formed following distillation of coal. Coke is composed mainly of carbon.

4.1 PRACTICAL ACTIVITIES
Investigating the electrolysis of water

4.4 DATA ANALYSIS
Boiling and electrolysing water

Figure 4.7

electrolysis: the decomposition of a chemical substance (in solution or the molten state) by the application of electrical energy

Some examples of chemical changes include:

- *extracting a metal from a mineral:* Iron metal can be extracted from iron (III) oxide in a blast furnace. The iron mineral is mixed with carbon (**coke**) and heated to high temperatures in a blast of air. The carbon undergoes a chemical change in air to form carbon monoxide, and heat energy is released. The carbon monoxide combines with the iron (III) oxide to produce molten iron and carbon dioxide. The overall chemical change is summarised by the following word and balanced chemical equations.

iron (III) oxide + carbon monoxide → iron + carbon dioxide

$$Fe_2O_3(s) + 3CO(g) → 2Fe(l) + 3CO_2(g)$$

- *dissolving a metal in an acid:* Magnesium metal is an active metal that reacts rapidly with dilute hydrochloric acid to produce hydrogen gas and a solution containing magnesium chloride. Heat is released in this reaction. The overall chemical change is summarised by the following word and balanced chemical equations.

magnesium + hydrochloric acid → magnesium chloride solution + hydrogen gas

$$Mg(s) + 2HCl(aq) → MgCl_2(aq) + H_2(g)$$

- *electrolysis of water:* Water is not a good conductor of electricity but it can be made conductive by adding a little dilute sulfuric acid. If the acidified water is then electrolysed, it breaks down to form hydrogen and oxygen gases. The electrolysis causes a chemical change. Mixing the hydrogen and oxygen gases together will not produce water unless the mixture is ignited with a spark or flame.

7. WRITING BALANCED CHEMICAL EQUATIONS

The following information summarises the steps involved in writing a balanced chemical equation.

1. *Reactants* are the chemicals that are allowed to react. Write them on the left-hand side of the arrow.

2. *Products* are the chemicals produced in the reaction. Write them on the right-hand side of the arrow.

3. Write the word equation for the reaction.

4. Use the valency rules to write the chemical formula under each reactant and product.

5. Check each side of the equation for atom conservation.

6. If the atoms are unbalanced, place coefficients in front of each formula so that they are balanced. Re-check that the atoms are now balanced.

7. Use standard abbreviations to write the physical state next to each reactant and product:
   (s) = solid; (l) = liquid; (g) = gas;
   (aq) = aqueous or dissolved in water.

Example:
Combustion of methane

1. Reactants: methane gas, oxygen gas

2. Products: carbon dioxide gas, liquid water

3. Word equation:

   methane + oxygen $\rightarrow$ carbon dioxide + water

4. Write the correct formula for each substance. (*Remember:* CH_4 is a compound containing one carbon atom and four hydrogen atoms.)

   $$CH_4 + O_2 \rightarrow CO_2 + H_2O$$

5. Check for atom conservation (number of atoms of each element).

   Reactants: C = 1; H = 4; O = 2
   Products: C = 1; H = 2; O = 3

   Therefore, atoms numbers do not balance.

6. Insert coefficients to balance the atoms; for example, the '2' in front of H_2O represents two molecules of water.

   $$CH_4 + 2O_2 \rightarrow CO_2 + 2H_2O$$

7. Re-check atom balance.

   Reactants: C = 1; H = 4; O = 4
   Products: C = 1; H = 4; O = 4

   Atom balance has been achieved. The equation is balanced.

8. Insert physical states.

   $$CH_4(g) + 2O_2(g) \rightarrow CO_2(g) + 2H_2O(l)$$

4.1 QUESTIONS

1. Classify the following processes as physical or chemical changes.
   (a) Melting lead
   (b) Pulling copper to form long wires
   (c) Caramelising sugar by heating
   (d) Combustion of candle wax
   (e) Centrifuging whole blood

2. Jessica poured 50 mL of water into a beaker and heated it with a Bunsen burner flame. She noticed bubbles of a colourless gas rising through the water as it heated. On reaching boiling point, the water formed a colourless vapour. When a cold clock glass was held above the beaker, the water vapour condensed into a clear, colourless liquid. This liquid was collected and its physical properties tested and compared with the original water sample. They were found to be identical. Jessica took a further sample of liquid water and electrolysed it at platinum electrodes. A colourless gas evolved at the positive electrode. This gas was observed to make a flame burn more brightly. At the negative electrode, a colourless gas was formed that burnt explosively in air when ignited.
   (a) State the conclusions that can be made about water from the heating evidence alone.
   (b) Jessica wondered whether her observations could be used to conclude that water was an element. Would she be justified in such a conclusion?

3. Iron is grey in colour. Sulfur is yellow. Both are chemical elements. Bert placed powdered samples of iron and sulfur in a mortar and ground them together for several minutes until the colour was uniform. A magnet was then held above the mortar and Bert observed that the iron particles clung to the magnet leaving the yellow powder at the bottom of the mortar.

(a) Classify the magnetic separation as a physical or chemical change. Explain your classification.

(b) Explain whether or not a new chemical substance was formed after the two powders were ground together.

4. Write balanced chemical equations for each of the following word equations.

(a) iron (II) oxide (s) + carbon monoxide (g) → iron (molten) + carbon dioxide (g)

(b) potassium (solid) + oxygen gas → potassium oxide (solid)

(c) silver carbonate (solid) → silver + carbon dioxide gas + oxygen gas

(d) aluminium + oxygen gas → aluminium oxide (solid)

(e) sodium (solid) + chlorine gas → sodium chloride (solid)

5. Figure 4.8 shows a particle diagram of the interaction between sulfur and oxygen gas. Explain whether the process is a chemical change or physical change.

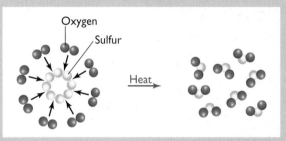

Figure 4.8 Particle diagram of an interaction between sulfur and oxygen

4.2 ENERGY AND CHEMICAL CHANGE

Decomposition and synthesis

Various forms of energy can be used to decompose chemical compounds or to synthesise compounds from elements of other compounds. In this section, we will examine some common examples of **decomposition** and **synthesis** reactions.

Decomposition reactions

Various forms of energy, including heat, light and electricity, can be used to decompose compounds. Here are some everyday examples of decomposition reactions:

- Heat energy is used in our industrialised society to decompose minerals to produce metals in smelters.

- In nature, ultraviolet light energy decomposes ozone molecules into oxygen gas and oxygen radicals. This process is important in preventing most high-energy UV rays reaching the Earth's surface.

- Lightning initiates decomposition reactions in the atmosphere by providing electrical energy to various gas molecules.

- Airbags in cars contain the chemical sodium azide, which decomposes by detonation to produce a large volume of nitrogen gas to inflate the airbag during a crash.

Here are some examples of decomposition reactions that can be performed in a laboratory.

Remember

Before beginning this section, you should be able to:
- qualitatively describe reactants and products in decomposition reactions
- identify that a new compound is formed by rearranging atoms rather than creating matter.

decomposition: the process of breaking a compound down into its component elements or simpler compounds

synthesis: the formation of a compound from its elements or a more complex compound from simpler compounds

4.2 PRACTICAL ACTIVITIES

Thermal decomposition of magnesium carbonate

4.5 DATA ANALYSIS

Investigating the purity of limestone by thermal decomposition

Figure 4.10
Decomposition of sodium azide produces nitrogen gas, which inflates a car's airbag.

Examples:

1. Thermal decomposition of gold oxide
When a sample of brown gold (III) oxide is heated over a Bunsen burner flame in a test tube, it readily decomposes to produce a sample of lustrous gold. The oxygen is evolved as oxygen gas.

$$\text{gold (III) oxide} \rightarrow \text{gold} + \text{oxygen gas}$$
$$2Au_2O_3(s) \rightarrow 4Au(s) + 3O_2(g)$$

2. Light decomposition (photolysis) of silver bromide
Silver bromide is decomposed by light in the ultraviolet part of the spectrum. The white crystals darken as black grains of silver metal form. Bromine vapour is released in the process.

$$\text{silver bromide} \rightarrow \text{silver} + \text{bromine vapour}$$
$$2AgBr(s) \rightarrow 2Ag(s) + Br_2(g)$$

3. Electrolytic decomposition of molten lead (II) bromide
Lead (II) bromide crystals melt at a relatively low temperature ($373\,°C$) to form a clear, colourless liquid. The liquid is heated to $400\,°C$ and electrolysed using inert electrodes; air is removed from the apparatus during electrolysis to prevent any other reactions. A brown vapour of bromine is evolved at the positive electrode and silvery globules of lead form at the surface of the negative electrode and sink to the bottom of the vessel.

$$\text{lead (II) bromide (liquid)} \rightarrow \text{lead (liquid)} + \text{bromine vapour}$$
$$PbBr_2(l) \rightarrow Pb(l) + Br_2(g)$$

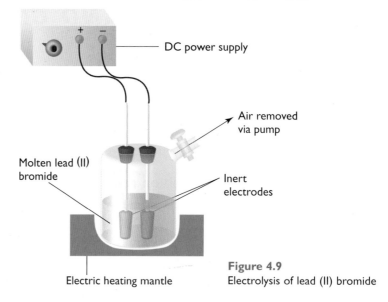

DC power supply

Air removed via pump

Molten lead (II) bromide

Inert electrodes

Electric heating mantle

Figure 4.9
Electrolysis of lead (II) bromide

Synthesis reactions

Many chemical compounds can be readily synthesised from their elements in a laboratory. Heat energy is the normal form of energy used to initiate synthesis reactions, although some are initiated by light and electrical energy.

Here are some everyday examples of synthesis reactions:

• Lightning can supply sufficient energy to nitrogen and oxygen molecules in the atmosphere to initiate synthesis of nitric oxide. A similar process occurs in a car's engine, where the spark causes nitrogen and oxygen molecules to combine.

- Rust is an oxide of iron that forms when iron structures are exposed to oxygen in the air.
- The ammonia industry synthesises ammonia directly by combining nitrogen and hydrogen gases at high temperatures and pressures over a catalyst.

Here are some more examples of synthesis reactions.

Examples:

1. Synthesis of iron (III) chloride using heat energy

Iron wool can be heated briefly in a Bunsen flame and then placed in a gas jar of chlorine gas. The jar rapidly becomes filled with brown iron (III) chloride smoke. Moisture in the jar causes the iron (III) chloride to dissolve rapidly to form deep brown droplets.

$$\text{iron + chlorine gas} \rightarrow \text{iron (III) chloride}$$
$$2Fe(s) + 3Cl_2(g) \rightarrow 2FeCl_3(s)$$

2. Synthesis of hydrogen chloride using light

Hydrogen gas combines explosively with chlorine gas when the reaction mixture is exposed to light. The light provides the necessary energy to break the chemical bonds of the chlorine molecule. (*Note:* This reaction should not be performed in the school laboratory.)

$$\text{hydrogen gas + chlorine gas} \rightarrow \text{hydrogen chloride gas}$$
$$H_2(g) + Cl_2(g) \rightarrow 2HCl(g)$$

4.3 PRACTICAL ACTIVITIES

The effect of light on silver halides

Bond energies

The amount of heat necessary to separate atoms in a compound is a measure of the strength of the attractive or bonding forces between oppositely charged ions in ionic compounds, or between atoms in covalent molecules.

Ionic bonds

To understand the different strengths of ionic bonds, we can compare the energy required to decompose some ionic oxides to produce 1 kg of the metal. Table 4.1 shows that more energy is required to extract magnesium from its oxide than zinc or silver. We can conclude that the ionic bonds between magnesium ions and oxide ions are much stronger than those between oxide ions and either silver or zinc ions.

Table 4.1 Energy required to decompose ionic compounds

Metal produced	Compound decomposed	Energy required to produce 1 kg of metal (kJ)
silver	silver oxide, Ag_2O	144
zinc	zinc oxide, ZnO	5 323
magnesium	magnesium oxide, MgO	24 774

Covalent bonds

Table 4.2 compares the average bond energies of covalently bonded atoms. It shows that multiple covalent bonds are stronger than single covalent bonds. Thus, molecules such as nitrogen and carbon dioxide are quite thermally stable. In the atmosphere, nitrogen gas is essentially inert. Humans breathe in air but do not use the nitrogen so breathe it out again. Nitrogen-fixing bacteria are some of the few organisms on Earth that can use nitrogen directly. The high energy of a lightning flash can also break the bond between nitrogen atoms.

Table 4.2 Average bond energies of some covalent bonds

Covalent bond	Bond energy ($\times 10^{-19}$J/bond)	Compound in which bond is located
O—H	7.7	water
H—H	7.2	hydrogen gas
O=O	8.3	oxygen gas
C=O	13.3	carbon dioxide
N≡N	15.7	nitrogen gas

4.2 QUESTIONS

1. When a photographic film is exposed to light it darkens. This darkening happens because
   A light decomposes the silver nitrate in the emulsion.
   B silver atoms are formed as silver ions accept electrons ejected from bromide ions.
   C bromine atoms lose electrons to form bromide ions.
   D light photons cause an electron to be transferred from a silver ion to a bromide ion.

2. White magnesium carbonate thermally decomposes to form white magnesium oxide and carbon dioxide gas. A student performs this experiment in the school laboratory. Select the statement that is true about this experiment.
   A There is a colour change as the magnesium carbonate is heated.
   B The 'pop' test can be used to identify carbon dioxide as the gaseous product of the reaction.
   C Complete decomposition has occurred if the final white solid product does not effervesce when treated with drops of hydrochloric acid.
   D Magnesium oxide will decompose to magnesium and oxygen if the material is heated for too long.

3. A common synthesis reaction that occurs in the atmosphere during lightning storms is the reaction between nitrogen and oxygen. Select the balanced equation that correctly identifies the reaction that occurs.
   A $N_2(g) + O_2(g) \rightarrow 2NO(g)$
   B $N_2(g) + O_2(g) \rightarrow NO_2(g)$
   C $N(g) + O(g) \rightarrow NO(g)$
   D $N(g) + 2O(g) \rightarrow NO_2(g)$

4. A sample of blue-green copper (II) carbonate is heated strongly. It turns black and a colourless gas is evolved. The gas is passed into a beaker of clear limewater. The limewater goes milky white in colour.
   (a) Use the result of the limewater test to identify the gas evolved.
   (b) Predict the chemical formula of the black product of the decomposition reaction by writing a balanced chemical equation for the thermal decomposition reaction.
   (c) A 10.00 g sample of the blue-green powder was heated so that it decomposed completely. The mass of the remaining black powder was 6.44 g. Calculate the percentage loss in weight during decomposition of the copper (II) carbonate.

5. Luigi heated a sample of sodium in a Bunsen flame until it melted and started to burn. He placed the burning sodium in a gas jar of chlorine. The sodium burnt with a bright yellow flame and clouds of a white, crystalline smoke were formed.

(a) State whether energy was released or absorbed in this reaction.

(b) Identify the white, crystalline substance that was synthesised in this reaction.

(c) Luigi collected the white substance and heated it in a crucible until it melted. He inserted electrodes into it and passed an electric current through the melted material. A silvery substance appeared at the negative electrode and a gas was released at the positive electrode.

  (i) State whether energy was released or absorbed in this electrolysis.

  (ii) Identify the new substances produced at each electrode.

6. (a) Zinc sulfide and magnesium sulfide are decomposed to form their elements, using 10 000 kJ of energy in each reaction. Use table 4.3 to compare the masses of zinc and magnesium that are formed, assuming that there is no energy wastage.

(b) Identify the more stable sulfide. Justify your response.

7. Energy is supplied to break the covalent O—H bonds in 10 000 gaseous water molecules. Use table 4.2 to answer the following questions.

(a) Identify the number of O—H bonds in each water molecule.

(b) Assuming no energy wastage, calculate the total amount of energy required.

(c) Identify the products of this decomposition reaction.

(d) Explain why these products readily recombine to form water.

Table 4.3

Metal produced	Compound decomposed	Energy required to produce 1 kg of metal (kJ)
zinc	zinc sulfide, ZnS	3 151
magnesium	magnesium sulfide, MgS	14 280

SUMMARY

- Compounds are pure substances with fixed chemical compositions.

- Physical changes do not lead to the formation of new substances. A chemical change leads to the formation of new substances.

- Compounds can be separated into their component elements by chemical separation techniques. Energy is required for this process.

- Heat, light and electricity are common forms of energy used to decompose compounds into their component elements or to produce simpler compounds.

- Heat (and sometimes light) is released during the synthesis of compounds from their elements.

- The strength of bonds between atoms or ions can be estimated from the energy needed to decompose a compound into its component elements.

4.1 PRACTICAL ACTIVITIES

INVESTIGATING THE ELECTROLYSIS OF WATER

Aim

To use a voltameter to electrolyse acidified water

Safety issues

- Wear safety glasses throughout this experiment.
- Ensure that water and chemicals do not come into contact with electrical wiring.
- Identify other safety issues relevant to this experiment by reading the method.

Materials

- hydrogen voltameter with platinum electrodes
- DC power pack
- leads and alligator clips
- retort stand and clamps
- test-tube rack
- 2 medium test tubes
- 2 rubber stoppers
- wooden splint
- wax taper
- matches
- 200 mL water acidified with 50 mL of 2 mol/L sulfuric acid

Method

1. Ensure that your safety glasses are on.
2. Assemble the apparatus as shown in figure 4.11. Note which electrodes are connected to the positive and negative terminals of the DC power pack.
3. With the taps open, fill the arms of the voltameter with acidified water. Close the taps. Add some more acidified water to the reservoir.
4. Connect the leads to the voltameter using alligator clips.
5. Turn on the current and adjust the voltage to 4–6 V.

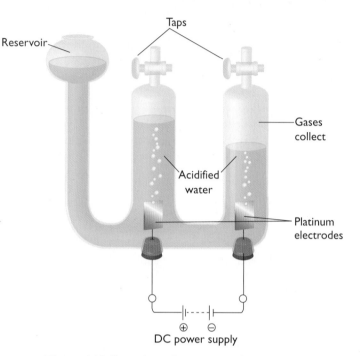

Figure 4.11 Electrolysis of water in a voltameter

6. Observe the electrolysis and record your observations in your workbook.
7. Adjust to a higher voltage and observe the rate of electrolysis.
8. Continue the electrolysis until one arm is filled with gas. Note whether this is the tube containing the positive or negative electrode. Turn off the current.
9. Collect the gases in separate labelled test tubes. Place a test tube over the end of one arm of the voltameter and slowly open the tap to expel the gas. Stopper the tube and place it in the test-tube rack. Repeat with the other arm.
10. Invert the test tube containing gas from the positive electrode and test it with a glowing wooden splint. Record your observations. A positive test indicates oxygen.
11. Invert the test tube containing gas from the positive electrode and test it with a lighted wax taper. Record your observations. A positive test indicates hydrogen.
12. Clean up and return all equipment.

PRACTICAL ACTIVITIES

Results and analysis

1. Construct a suitable table and tabulate your observations.
2. Compare the volumes of gases collected at the two electrodes.
3. Identify the gases in each tube on the basis of the tests performed.
4. Describe how the rate of electrolysis changed as the voltage increased.
5. Summarise the evidence that electrolysis is a chemical change and that water is a compound.
6. Gather and process second-hand data to identify a practical use for the electrolysis of water.

Conclusion

Write a brief conclusion for this experiment.

4.2 PRACTICAL ACTIVITIES

THERMAL DECOMPOSITION OF MAGNESIUM CARBONATE

Aim

To investigate the thermal decomposition of magnesium carbonate

Safety issues

- Wear safety glasses throughout this experiment.
- Take care not to touch the hot tube.
- Identify other safety issues relevant to this experiment by reading the method.

Materials

- 5 large test tubes
- rubber stopper with glass delivery tube (see figure 4.12)
- bosshead, clamp and stand
- Bunsen burner
- 2 Petri dishes
- spatula
- powdered magnesium carbonate
- limewater
- 1 mol/L hydrochloric acid
- phenolphthalein indicator

Method

Ensure that your safety glasses are on.

Part A

1. Place a scoop of magnesium carbonate in one test tube and half-fill another test tube with limewater. Set up the apparatus as shown in figure 4.12.
2. Heat the magnesium carbonate gently at first and then strongly using a blue Bunsen flame. Allow the gas evolved to bubble into the tube of limewater and observe any changes. After several minutes, and while still heating the magnesium carbonate, remove the tube of

PRACTICAL ACTIVITIES

limewater and place it in a test-tube rack. This stops limewater entering the hot tube, due to pressure differences when heating ceases, and causing the tube to break.

3. Continue to heat the magnesium carbonate for about another 10 minutes. Turn off the Bunsen burner and allow the tube and contents to cool.

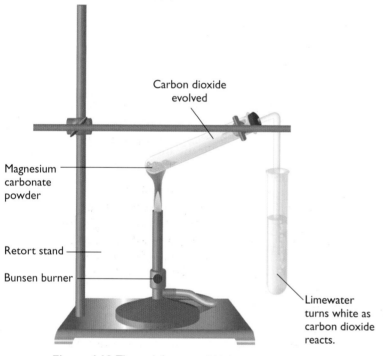

Carbon dioxide evolved

Magnesium carbonate powder

Retort stand

Bunsen burner

Limewater turns white as carbon dioxide reacts.

Figure 4.12 Thermal decomposition apparatus

Part B
1. When the heated tube from part A is cold, put a sample of the heated white powder in a Petri dish.
2. Put a small amount of unheated magnesium carbonate in another Petri dish.
3. Add drops of 1 mol/L hydrochloric acid to each dish. Record your observations and note any differences in the rate of fizzing.
4. Put a small amount of unheated magnesium carbonate in a clean test tube and a small amount of the heated solid in another. Add about 2 mL of water to each tube and mix. Add 4 drops of phenolphthalein indicator to each tube and note the differences in the colour of the indicator. Record all your observations.

Results and analysis
1. Record all your observations in a suitable format.
2. The following word equation describes the thermal decomposition reaction:

magnesium carbonate →
    magnesium oxide + carbon dioxide

(a) Describe the experimental evidence that carbon dioxide was formed on heating the magnesium carbonate.
(b) Magnesium carbonate is a weak base in water. Magnesium oxide is a stronger base than magnesium carbonate. Phenolphthalein is pale pink in weakly basic solutions and deeper pink or crimson in solutions that are more basic. Describe the experimental evidence that magnesium oxide was produced in the reaction.
(c) Use your observations from the experiment with hydrochloric acid to explain whether or not your sample of magnesium carbonate completely decomposed on heating. Justify your response.
(d) Write a symbolic equation for the decomposition reaction.
3. When hydrochloric acid reacts with magnesium carbonate, there is a rapid effervescence as carbon dioxide is evolved. The word equation is:

magnesium carbonate + hydrochloric acid →
    magnesium chloride + water + carbon dioxide

Write a balanced symbol equation for this reaction.

Conclusion
Write a brief conclusion for this experiment.

PRACTICAL ACTIVITIES

4.3 PRACTICAL ACTIVITIES

THE EFFECT OF LIGHT ON SILVER HALIDE SALTS

Aim

To investigate the effect of sunlight and UV light on silver salts and to identify an application of this reaction

Background

In this experiment, you will make silver halide salts by precipitation from silver nitrate solution. The silver halides are silver chloride, silver bromide and silver iodide.

Figure 4.13 Some silver salts decompose under UV light. These three samples of silver chloride were placed in Petri dishes. One sample (top) is being irradiated with UV light. The samples at front are the control (left) and one that has previously been exposed to UV (right). The latter has turned grey due to the formation of metallic silver.

Safety issues

- Wear safety glasses throughout this experiment.
- Do not look at the bulb in the UV lamp.
- Do not allow silver salts to contact your skin.
- Identify other safety issues relevant to this experiment by reading the method.

Materials

- 3 small Petri dishes
- 3 glass rods
- ultraviolet lamp
- 0.1 mol/L silver nitrate in dropper bottle
- 0.1 mol/L sodium chloride in dropper bottle
- 0.1 mol/L sodium bromide in dropper bottle
- 0.1 mol/L sodium iodide in dropper bottle

Method

1. Ensure that your safety glasses are on.
2. Work in groups for this investigation. One group will investigate the effect of sunlight on the silver salts; a second group will investigate the effect of ultraviolet (UV) light on these salts; a third group will place the dishes in a dark cupboard.
3. Label three Petri dishes '1', '2' and '3'. Put 20 drops of silver nitrate solution in each dish.
4. Add 20 drops of sodium chloride solution to dish 1 and mix with a stirring rod. Observe the reaction and record your observations.
5. Add 20 drops of sodium bromide solution to dish 2 and mix with a stirring rod. Observe the reaction and record your observations.
6. Add 20 drops of sodium iodide solution to dish 3 and mix with a stirring rod. Observe the reaction and record your observations.
7. One group will expose the precipitates in dishes 1, 2 and 3 to sunlight (e.g. near a window) for about 5–10 minutes. The second group will use the ultraviolet lamp to expose each dish in turn to UV light for the same amount of time. The third group will place the dishes in the dark as a control. Compare and record all results.
8. Clean up and return all equipment.

DATA ANALYSIS

Results and analysis

1. Construct a table to record your observations. Complete the table.
2. Compare the effects of sunlight and UV light on each silver salt explaining any differences.
3. Explain the importance of the control dishes.
4. Write balanced chemical equations for each precipitation reaction.
5. The effect of light on silver salts has a practical application in film (non-digital) photography. Photographic film is covered with a fine gelatine emulsion containing grains of silver bromide. The photosensitive material decomposes on exposure to light to form tiny clusters of silver atoms and bromine atoms at the surface of the crystalline grains. Exposure to more light produces more silver. The process is completed by the developer solution during film processing, resulting in a 'negative' film in which the darkest areas correspond to areas where most metallic silver was formed.

   (a) A photon of light ejects an electron from a bromide ion to form a bromine atom. Write an ion/electron half-equation for this process.
   (b) Ejected electrons are accepted by silver ions, forming silver metal. Write an ion/electron half-equation for this process.

Conclusion

Write a brief conclusion for this experiment.

4.4 DATA ANALYSIS

BOILING AND ELECTROLYSING WATER

BOILING AND ELECTROLYSING WATER

Part A: Boiling water

Figure 4.14 shows a particle diagram of water heated on an electric hotplate to 100 °C and 100 kPa.

1. Use the key in figure 4.14 to identify the particles present in the:
   (a) liquid state
   (b) vapour state.
2. Use figure 4.14 to explain why this process is a physical change rather than a chemical change.
3. Explain why the temperature of the water remains at 100 °C throughout the process.

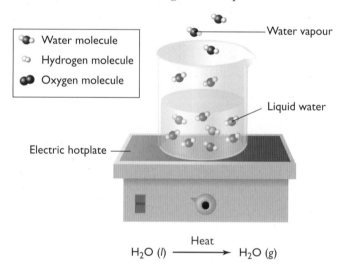

$$H_2O \; (l) \xrightarrow{\text{Heat}} H_2O \; (g)$$

Figure 4.14 Particle diagram of boiling water

DATA ANALYSIS

Part B: Electrolysing water

Figure 4.15 shows a particle diagram of the electrolysis of water at platinum electrodes in a voltameter after the electrolysis has been operating for some time. (A small amount of sodium sulfate was added to the water to make it conductive but this does not alter the results – these ions are not shown.)

1. Use the key in figure 4.15 to identify the particles present in the water.
2. Use the key in figure 4.15 to identify the gases that have formed in the arms of the voltameter.
3. Use figure 4.15 to explain why this process is a chemical change rather than a physical change.
4. Suggest a reason why platinum is used for the electrode rather than some other metal.
5. The following half-equations describe processes occurring at the surface of each electrode.

$$2H_2O(l) + 2e^- \rightarrow H_2(g) + 2OH^-(aq) \quad (1)$$
$$2H_2O(l) \rightarrow O_2(g) + 4H^+(aq) + 4e^- \quad (2)$$

Which of these equations is consistent with the events occurring in figure 4.15 at the:
(a) positive electrode?
(b) negative electrode?

4.5 DATA ANALYSIS

INVESTIGATING THE PURITY OF LIMESTONE BY THERMAL DECOMPOSITION

The apparatus shown in figure 4.16 was used to determine the loss in weight as a limestone sample (impure calcium carbonate) was heated. Limestone does not decompose significantly over a Bunsen flame and so an electric furnace was used. The reaction tube was weighed and a sample of powdered limestone added to the tube. The tube and its contents were weighed and connected to the apparatus. Powdered sodium hydroxide was added to the U-tube to absorb the acidic carbon dioxide evolved on heating. The limestone was heated very strongly until no further decomposition took place. The reaction tube and its contents were reweighed after cooling to room temperature.

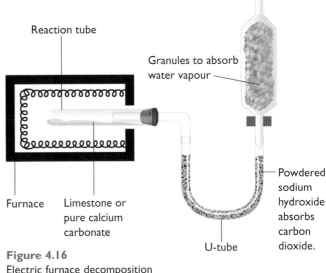

Figure 4.16
Electric furnace decomposition of limestone and calcium carbonate

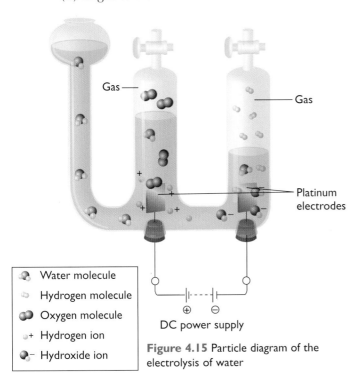

Key:
- Water molecule
- Hydrogen molecule
- Oxygen molecule
- Hydrogen ion
- Hydroxide ion

Figure 4.15 Particle diagram of the electrolysis of water

DATA ANALYSIS

The experiment was repeated with a known sample of pure calcium carbonate rather than limestone. The results are shown in table 4.4.

Table 4.4

	Limestone	Pure calcium carbonate
Initial mass of reaction tube	24.145 g	24.145 g
Initial mass of reaction tube + sample	27.275 g	27.288 g
Final mass of reaction tube + sample	25.989 g	25.906 g

1. Calculate the percentage loss in weight on the thermal decomposition of the:
   (a) limestone
   (b) pure calcium carbonate.
2. Determine the percentage of pure calcium carbonate in the limestone. (*Hint:* Use your answers from question 1.)
3. State the assumptions that you have made in answering question 2.
4. For each experiment, determine the increase in weight of the U-tube. State the assumption that you are making.
5. The reaction in the U-tube can be represented by the word equation:

carbon dioxide (gas) + sodium hydroxide (solid) →
         sodium hydrogen carbonate (solid)

   Write a chemical equation for this reaction.

Chapter 5

BONDING AND STRUCTURE

Introduction

The types of chemical bond and the structure of crystal lattices ultimately determine the properties of a chemical substance. These properties govern the practical uses of these substances in our daily lives.

In this chapter

Figure 5.1

Quartz, SiO_2, is a three-dimensional covalent network lattice. Each silicon atom is bonded to four oxygen atoms and each oxygen atom is bonded to two silicon atoms. The resulting mineral is hard and crystalline.

5.1 PROPERTIES AND CLASSIFICATION

Remember

Before beginning this section, you should be able to:
- classify compounds into groups based on common chemical characteristics
- identify a range of common compounds using their common names and chemical formulae.

Key content

By the end of this section, you should be able to:
- identify differences between physical and chemical properties of elements, compounds and mixtures
- describe the physical properties used to classify compounds as ionic, covalent molecular or covalent network
- perform a first-hand investigation to compare the properties of some common elements in their elemental state with the properties of the compound(s) of these elements (such as magnesium and oxygen).

chemical properties: the properties relating to the chemical reaction of a substance with other chemicals (such as acids, bases and oxidising agents)

Properties of elements, compounds and mixtures

Iron is a metal that is widely used in modern society. It is extracted from ore bodies located in various regions of Australia including Western Australia. The physical and **chemical properties** of the ore (a mixture) and its pure components are quite different.

Red-brown *haematite*, iron (III) oxide, is an important iron mineral. In Australia, this mineral is mined extensively and transported to blast furnaces for conversion to iron and steel.

The properties of this compound and its component elements are listed in table 5.1.

Table 5.1 Properties of iron (III) oxide and its elements

Substance	iron	oxygen	iron (III) oxide
Appearance	grey-silvery lustrous metal	colourless gas	red-brown solid
Density (g/cm³)	7.9	0.0013	5.2
Melting point (°C)	1535	–219	1565
Boiling point (°C)	2750	–183	
Solubility in water (g/100 g)	insoluble	0.004	insoluble
Reaction with hydrochloric acid	forms iron (II) chloride and hydrogen gas	no reaction	forms iron (III) chloride and water

Iron is used extensively in building construction, where it is normally alloyed with other elements to improve its strength, hardness and durability. Steelmaking in Australia is an important economic enterprise as it contributes significantly to our national wealth. The magnetic nature of iron leads to its extensive use in magnets, compasses and electromagnets.

5.1 PRACTICAL ACTIVITIES

Comparing the properties of a compound and its component elements

Figure 5.2
Iron oxide (a) and iron (b) have different crystal structures and different properties. In its pure, anhydrous form, iron (III) oxide (haematite) is ochre brown, but is sometimes black.

Classification of chemical compounds

Physical properties can be used to classify compounds into three groups or types of lattice. These groups are:

- ionic compounds
- covalent molecular compounds
- covalent network compounds.

Table 5.2 shows the characteristic physical properties of each of these crystal lattice structures, shown in figure 5.3. (*Note:* Melting points less than 500 °C are generally called 'low', those between 500–1500 °C are called 'high', and those greater than 1500 °C are called 'very high'. There are, however, exceptions to this.)

Table 5.2 Physical properties of crystal lattices.

Type of compound	ionic	covalent molecular	covalent network
Particles forming the lattice*	cations and anions	molecules	atoms
Forces holding the particles in the lattice	ionic bonds	intermolecular forces	covalent bonds
Electrical conductivity	solid: zero molten: good aqueous solution: good	solid: zero molten: zero aqueous solution: zero (unless molecule reacts to form ions)	solid: zero molten: zero aqueous solution: zero (as solids are insoluble in water)
Melting point	high	low	very high
Other crystal properties	hard; brittle	soft; brittle	very hard; brittle

*'Lattice' is the geometric arrangement of particles in a crystalline solid.

Ionic   Covalent molecular   Covalent network

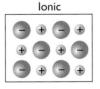 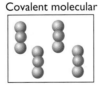

Figure 5.3
Particle diagrams of crystal lattice groups

 **SAMPLE PROBLEM 5.1**

Identify the crystal lattice group to which compound X belongs based on the following physical properties: white, crystalline solid; melting point = 41 °C; boiling point = 182 °C; soluble in water; non-conductor of electricity in the solid, molten and aqueous states.

SOLUTION

X is a covalent molecular compound. It has zero electrical conductivity in all states, so cannot be ionic. It has low melting and boiling points, which is not characteristic of covalent networks. Therefore, X is a covalent molecular compound.

5.1 QUESTIONS

1. Use the data in table 5.1 to explain why iron (III) oxide cannot be a simple mixture of iron and oxygen.

2. Iron metal dissolves slowly in dilute hydrochloric acid to form iron (II) chloride.
   (a) Identify the gas produced in this reaction.
   (b) Write a balanced chemical equation for this reaction.
   (c) Describe the differences between this reaction and the reaction of iron (III) oxide and dilute hydrochloric acid. (*Hint:* Use table 5.1.)

3. Identify the crystal lattice groups into which compounds can be classified.

4. Name the crystal lattice group to which each of the following statements applies.
   (a) The lattice is composed of discrete molecules.
   (b) The lattice has a three-dimensional network of covalent bonds.
   (c) The crystals do not conduct electricity except when melted.

5. Identify the crystal lattice groups to which compounds A and B belong based on the following physical properties.

   Substance A:
   white; crystalline; density = 2.0 g/cm³;
   melting point = 770 °C;
   boiling point = 1437 °C;
   solubility in water = 36 g/100 g water;
   aqueous solution conducts electricity.

   Substance B:
   white; crystalline; density = 2.1 g/cm³;
   melting point = 24 °C; boiling point = 173 °C;
   reacts with water to produce a solution that conducts electricity; solid does not conduct electricity; does not conduct electricity when melted.

5.2 LATTICES

Metallic lattices and properties

Metals generally have a range of properties that distinguish them from other substances. These physical properties allow us to make inferences about the structure of the metallic crystal. Table 5.3 lists these metallic properties, inferences that could explain these properties and a model to explain the properties.

Figure 5.4
Uranium is a heavy, radioactive metal.

Key content

By the end of this section, you should be able to:

- distinguish between metallic, ionic and covalent bonds
- describe metals as three-dimensional lattices of ions in a sea of electrons
- describe ionic compounds in terms of repeating three-dimensional lattices of ions
- explain why the formula for an ionic compound is an empirical formula
- identify common elements that exist as molecules or as covalent lattices
- explain the relationship between the properties of conductivity and hardness and the structure of ionic, covalent molecular and covalent network compounds
- choose resources and process information from secondary sources to construct and discuss the limitations of models of ionic lattices, covalent molecules and covalent and metallic lattices
- perform an investigation to examine the physical properties of a range of common substances in order to classify them as metallic, ionic or covalent molecular or covalent network substances and relate their characteristics to their uses.

Table 5.3 Properties of metallic lattices

Physical properties	Inferences about structure	Model to explain properties
High melting and boiling points	Strong forces exist between particles in the crystal lattice.	Large amounts of energy are needed to overcome the strong attraction between the positive metal ions and the mobile electrons.
High electrical and thermal conductivity	Freely moving charged particles are present in the lattice.	In response to an applied potential difference, the mobile electrons move in one direction to produce an electric current. The mobile electrons have greater kinetic energy when the metal is heated; they transfer energy faster.
High density	The metal atoms are tightly packed in the crystal lattice.	The metal ions can be either tightly packed or relatively heavy atoms with small radii.
High lustre	The surface structure of metals allows light to reflect readily.	Light photons are rapidly absorbed and released by the mobile electron cloud.
Highly malleable and ductile	The forces between the particles respond to a distorting force by establishing new, equally strong bonds.	When shearing forces are applied to the lattice, the layers of ions slide over each other and the mobile electrons stabilise the new lattice structure.

Model of a metallic crystal

The model of the metallic crystal, shown in figure 5.5, has the following features.

1. Positive metal ions (rather than neutral atoms) are arranged in a regular three-dimensional lattice.
2. A 'cloud' or 'sea' of **delocalised electrons** moves throughout the lattice.
3. Delocalised electrons have been lost from the valence shell of each metal atom and belong to the lattice as a whole.
4. The attraction between the positive metal ions and the delocalised electron cloud stabilises the lattice.
5. The attraction between the metal ions and electron cloud is called the **metallic bond**. Metallic bonds are strong chemical bonds.

delocalised electrons: electrons that are not bound to any one atom but are free to move throughout the lattice

metallic bond: a strong attractive force that holds metal ions in their crystal lattice; the attraction between metal ions and the sea of mobile electrons

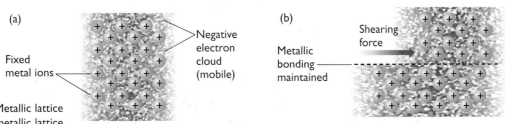

(a)

Fixed metal ions

Negative electron cloud (mobile)

(b)

Shearing force

Metallic bonding maintained

Figure 5.5 (a) Metallic lattice (b) Malleability of a metallic lattice

Ionic lattices and properties

Ionic crystals are characterised by a continuous three-dimensional arrangement of cations and anions. Attraction between oppositely charged ions is called an *ionic bond*, which are strong chemical bonds. Generally, ionic solids have high melting points because of the strong ionic bonds throughout the lattice. These ionic bonds also explain the hardness of ionic crystals. However, ionic crystals are brittle and shatter when hammered. Shearing forces cause ions of similar charge to come in close contact, leading to strong repulsion, so the crystals shatter.

Unlike metallic lattices, ionic lattices do not have free electrons or free ions to carry charge if a voltage is applied across the crystal, so ionic crystals do not conduct electricity. If a crystal is melted or dissolved in a suitable solvent such as water, the ions are no longer bound to the lattice and are free to move. Such molten salts or ionic solutions are good electrical conductors.

Figure 5.6 shows some common ionic lattices. Note that the ions are arranged in several different patterns depending on their size.

(a)

Titanium oxide

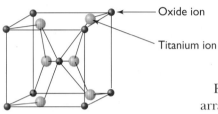

Oxide ion

Titanium ion

(b)

Calcium carbonate

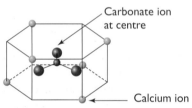

Carbonate ion at centre

Calcium ion

Figure 5.6 Ionic lattices:
(a) titanium oxide and
(b) calcium carbonate

Figure 5.7
Fool's gold is the mineral *pyrite*, FeS_2.
It is an ionic crystal.

Empirical formulae

The empirical formula of a compound represents its atomic or ionic composition expressed as a simple whole number ratio.

Examples:

1. Ethane is a covalent molecular compound with the molecular formula C_2H_6. Its molecules are composed of two atoms of carbon bonded to six atoms of hydrogen. The C : H ratio of 2 : 6 is not the simplest ratio. The simplest ratio is 1 : 3, so the empirical formula of ethane is CH_3.

2. Benzene is also a covalent molecular compound. Its molecular formula is C_6H_6. The C : H ratio of 6 : 6 is not the simplest ratio. The simplest ratio of atoms is 1 : 1, so the empirical formula of benzene is CH.

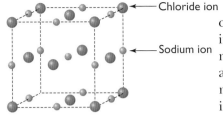

Figure 5.8
Unit cell for sodium chloride

Ionic compounds present a different problem because their lattices are continuous in three dimensions, and there are no discrete molecules as in molecular compounds. Consequently, chemists identify the simplest repeating unit of the crystal and call it the *unit cell*. In the unit cell, there are some ions that belong to that cell only, while others at edges and corners belong partly to other cells. When these fractions of ions are taken into account, the simplest ratio of ions can be determined for the unit cell. This simple ratio is the empirical formula of the ionic compound. Let us examine an example for sodium chloride; figure 5.8 shows its cubic unit cell.

The unit cell for sodium chloride shows the following:

- One sodium ion is at the centre of the cell.
- Twelve sodium ions occupy the centre of each edge. These ions are shared by a total of four unit cells.
- Eight chloride ions occupy the corners of the cell. These ions are shared by a total of eight unit cells.
- Six chloride ions occupy the centres of each face of the cell. Two adjoining unit cells share these ions.

Thus, for sodium chloride, the total number of sodium ions belonging to each unit cell: $= 1 + \left(\frac{1}{4} \times 12\right) = 1 + 3 = 4$

and the number of chloride ions: $= \left(\frac{1}{8} \times 8\right) + \left(\frac{1}{2} \times 6\right) = 1 + 3 = 4$.

The ratio of sodium ions to chloride ions is 4 : 4 or 1 : 1, so the empirical formula of sodium chloride is NaCl.

When we write the chemical formula of an ionic compound, we are writing its empirical formula. This represents the ratio of ions throughout the whole crystal lattice.

SAMPLE PROBLEM 5.2 >>

Write the empirical formulae for the following ionic compounds:

(a) barium bromide

(b) iron (III) sulfide.

SOLUTION >>>>>>

Use the valency rules to work out the chemical formula of each ionic compound. This will also be its empirical formula.

(a) valency of barium = +2;
valency of bromide = −1; empirical formula is BaBr$_2$

(b) valency of iron (III) = +3;
valency of sulfide = −2; empirical formula is Fe$_2$S$_3$

Covalent network lattices and properties

Covalent network compounds, such as silicon dioxide (shown in figure 5.9) and silicon carbide, are composed of a three-dimensional array of atoms linked by strong covalent bonds. Such a structure is very strong and rigid, which explains the hardness of such substances. Like ionic crystals, they shatter under high shearing forces.

Covalent network compounds, as well as covalent network elements such as diamond, have very high melting points. For example, silicon dioxide has a melting point of 1713 °C and silicon nitride has a melting point of 1900 °C. They do not conduct electricity in the solid state as there are no free electrons or ions to allow conduction. Covalent network compounds are also highly insoluble in common solvents.

Carbon in the form of graphite is an example of a covalent network crystal (shown in figure 5.9). It does conduct electricity due to the presence of free electrons along one axis of the lattice. Diamond (which is also a form of carbon) forms a strong covalent network lattice, so does not conduct. It is the hardest natural substance.

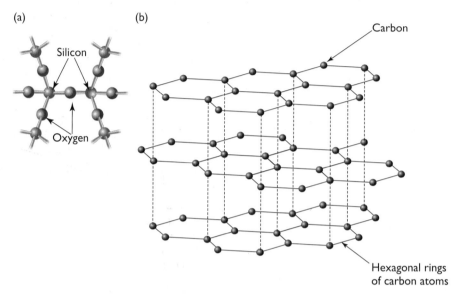

(a)

Silicon

Oxygen

(b)

Carbon

Hexagonal rings of carbon atoms

Figure 5.9
Covalent network structure of (a) silicon dioxide and (b) graphite

5.2 PRACTICAL ACTIVITIES

Modelling crystal lattices

5.3 DATA ANALYSIS

Comparing the properties of crystals

Covalent molecular lattices and properties

Covalent molecular lattices, such as ice and dry ice (solid carbon dioxide) contain discrete molecules arranged in various geometric patterns. These molecules are held in place within the lattice by intermolecular forces, which are not as strong as normal chemical bonds. Comparatively little energy is required to break these attractive forces, so such crystals have low melting points. These weak forces also make these crystals soft and readily deformable.

The absence of mobile charge carriers (such as electrons in metals, or ions in molten ionic salts) means that such crystals do not conduct electricity, even when melted or dissolved in a suitable solvent. Figure 5.10 shows the lattice structures of some covalent molecular compounds.

It is also important to remember that some common non-metals, such as sulfur, iodine and phosphorus, also form covalent molecular crystals. Such crystals have low melting points and readily shatter when subjected to shearing forces.

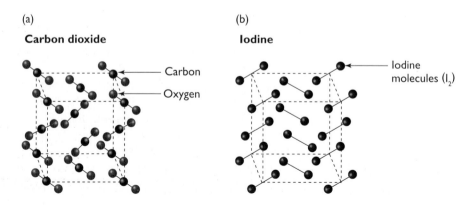

(a)

Carbon dioxide

Carbon

Oxygen

(b)

Iodine

Iodine molecules (I_2)

Figure 5.10
Structures of covalent molecular crystals: (a) carbon dioxide and (b) iodine

8. USING KEYS TO CLASSIFY CRYSTALS

Dichotomous keys can be used to classify crystals into lattice groups based on measured physical properties. Two different ways of representing a dichotomous key are shown below. The first is a written key where you make choices (A or B) at each step. The second is a diagrammatic key that allows you to make choices and move along different paths of the key as you respond to each question.

Written key

1A. The solid crystal conducts electricity. .... Metallic crystal
1B. The solid crystal does not conduct electricity. .... *Go to 2.*
2A. The melted crystal conducts electricity. .... Ionic crystal
2B. The melted crystal does not conduct electricity. ... *Go to 3.*
3A. The solid has a very high melting point
  (much higher than 500 °C). .... Covalent network crystal
3B. The solid has a very low melting point. .... Covalent molecular crystal

Diagrammatic key

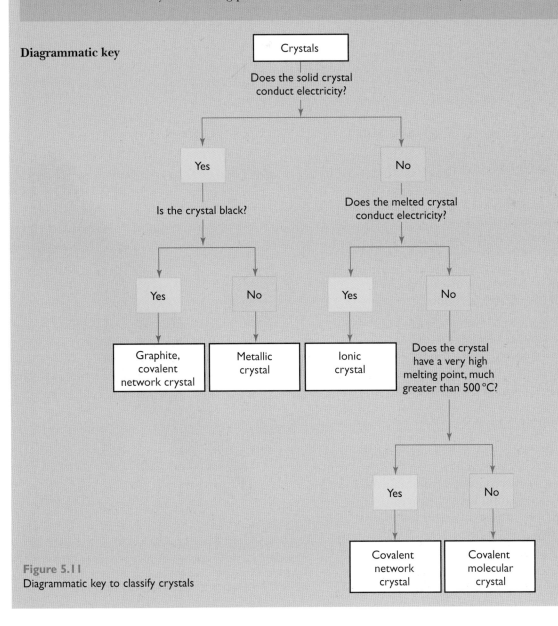

Figure 5.11
Diagrammatic key to classify crystals

5.2 QUESTIONS

1. Classify the following substances into one of the four crystalline groups: ionic, metallic, covalent network or covalent molecular.
   (a) Cobalt
   (b) Silicon nitride
   (c) Barium iodide
   (d) Nickel oxide
   (e) Phosphorus
   (f) Diamond

2. Sonja was provided with an unknown solid X. Her teacher asked her to devise some laboratory tests that would allow her to determine the type of bonding in the crystal. Describe the tests that Sonja will conduct.

3. Explain, in terms of structure and bonding, the following differences in physical properties.
   (a) Manganese has a high melting point (1244 °C) and oxygen has a low melting point (−219 °C).
   (b) Zinc conducts electricity but zinc oxide does not.
   (c) Nickel is lustrous but nickel oxide is dull.
   (d) Tungsten has a much greater density than aluminium.

4. Use the model of the structure and bonding within a metallic crystal to explain the following properties of silver.
   (a) Silver has a high melting point (962 °C).
   (b) Silver is an excellent electrical conductor.
   (c) Silver is lustrous when new but gradually becomes coated in a black deposit.
   (d) Silver is malleable and ductile.

5. Ahmed placed some iodine crystals in a beaker and gently heated the beaker. The iodine crystals sublimed to produce purple vapours.
   (a) Classify iodine into its correct lattice group.
   (b) Explain why iodine vapour forms so readily on heating the solid.
   (c) Ahmed observed that, when the iodine vapour came into contact with a cold surface, fine crystals of iodine reformed. Write an equation for this process.
   (d) Classify the process in (c) as physical or chemical.

6. Substance K consists of white, waxy crystals that melt readily at 51 °C. The substance does not conduct electricity when solid or melted.

   (a) Classify substance K into one of the four crystalline groups. Justify your answer.
   (b) Predict whether this waxy solid would be soluble in water or kerosene. Justify your answer.

7. Some white crystals were found in an unlabelled bottle. The crystals did not dissolve in water or kerosene. They did not conduct electricity in the solid state.
   (a) Explain whether or not the information above is sufficient to classify this white substance into a crystalline group.
   (b) The crystals were heated until they melted and found to be a good conductor. Classify the crystals into their correct group.

8. Graphite is a black solid. Some chemists consider it to be an unusual non-metal.
   (a) Identify the element present in graphite.
   (b) Name two physical properties of graphite that are not typical of non-metals.
   (c) Classify graphite into its correct lattice group.

Figure 5.12
Graphite is made of flat sheets of carbon atoms. Weak dispersion forces hold these flat sheets together. Graphite is used in pencils because the sheets of carbon readily rub off onto the paper. It is also used as dry lubricant.

9. USING INSTRUCTION TERMS CORRECTLY

When answering questions, it is important to know what the instruction terms (verbs) require you to do. Here is an example.

'Discuss'
This instruction term requires you to identify issues and provide points for and against.

Example:
Discuss the issues associated with modelling a metallic crystal.

Answer:
Physical models do not reveal all the essential features of a metallic crystal. It is simple to show the location of each metal ion in the lattice using either ball-and-stick or space-filling models, but the representation of the mobile electron cloud is very difficult. The use of animation is more suitable for showing the nature of the pervading electron cloud throughout the lattice. Animated models can also show why metals are lustrous and good electrical conductors.

eBook *plus*

Weblinks

eBook *plus*

Module
Revision 1

eBook *plus*

Module
Revision 1 Answers

SUMMARY

- Elements and compounds differ in their physical and chemical properties. The properties of these materials determine their use.

- Crystalline solids can be classified as metallic, ionic, covalent network or covalent molecular lattices.

- Metallic bonds are found in metals. These bonds are formed by interaction of the mobile electron cloud and the positive metal ions in the lattice.

- Ionic bonds are found in ionic compounds. They are the attractive forces between oppositely charged ions.

- Covalent bonds are formed by the sharing of electron pairs between neighbouring atoms. Covalent bonds link atoms in a molecule.

- The properties of different crystals can be related to their lattice structures and the types of chemical bonding within the lattice.

- Metallic crystals, ionic crystals and covalent network crystals have strong three-dimensional bonding throughout the lattice.

- Covalent molecular crystals have weak bonding between the molecules in the crystal lattice.

5.1 PRACTICAL ACTIVITIES

COMPARING THE PROPERTIES OF A COMPOUND AND ITS COMPONENT ELEMENTS

Aim

To compare the properties of magnesium, oxygen and magnesium oxide

Safety issues

- Wear safety glasses throughout this experiment.
- Do not look directly at magnesium as it burns; the light may damage your eyes.
- Identify other safety issues relevant to this experiment by reading the method.

Materials

- 2 gas jars and lids
- teaspoon
- manganese dioxide
- 10 mL measuring cylinder
- 3% hydrogen peroxide
- 3 strips of magnesium ribbon, about 4 cm long
- tongs
- watch glass
- test-tube holder
- 4 test tubes and stoppers
- 1 mol/L hydrochloric acid
- magnesium oxide

Method

Ensure that your safety glasses are on.

Part A: Oxygen gas and magnesium metal

1. Prepare a gas jar of oxygen by placing half a teaspoon of manganese dioxide powder in a gas jar and adding 10–20 mL of 3% hydrogen peroxide. Allow air to be expelled initially and then cover the jar with a gas jar lid. Record your observations.

2. Examine the samples of magnesium ribbon and describe their appearance.

3. Support a 4 cm strip of magnesium ribbon with a pair of tongs. Ignite the end of the magnesium and allow it to burn over a watch glass.

4. Repeat step 3 by igniting a second strip and allowing it to burn in the gas jar of oxygen prepared in step 1 above. Compare the combustion of magnesium in air and oxygen.

5. Place a 4 cm strip of magnesium in a test tube and add 5 mL of dilute hydrochloric acid. Observe and record your observations.

6. The following data has been gathered for oxygen gas and magnesium. Use this data to write a comparison of these two elements.

Oxygen
- discovered in 1773 by Karl Scheele, Sweden
- colourless
- odourless
- supports combustion (rekindles a glowing wooden splint)
- melting point = −219 °C
- boiling point = −183 °C
- solubility in water = 0.004 g/100 g water
- thermal conductivity = 0.0026 J/s/m/K (compared with 80 J/s/m/K for iron)
- electrical conductivity = 0
- structure: diatomic molecule

Magnesium
- discovered in 1808 by Humphry Davy, England
- silvery-grey solid
- malleable and ductile
- melting point = 650 °C
- boiling point = 1110 °C
- insoluble in water
- thermal conductivity = 156 J/s/m/K (compared with 429 J/s/m/K for silver)
- electrical conductivity = 22 MS/m (compared with 63 MS/m for silver)
- structure: metallic crystal

PRACTICAL ACTIVITIES

Part B: Magnesium oxide

1. Examine a sample of magnesium oxide and describe its appearance.

2. Heat a small sample of magnesium oxide in a dry test tube over a Bunsen flame. Determine whether the solid is stable when heated.

3. Place a very small amount of magnesium oxide in a small clean test tube and test its solubility in 5 mL of tap water. Stopper the tube and shake thoroughly. Record your observations.

4. Test the solubility of a very small amount of magnesium oxide in 5 mL of dilute hydrochloric acid. Record your observations.

5. The following additional data has been collected for magnesium oxide. Use this data and your observations in the above tests to write a description of this compound and compare its properties with those of its component elements.

Magnesium oxide
- melting point = 2852 °C
- boiling point = 3600 °C
- insoluble in water

Results and analysis

1. Record all your observations in an appropriate format.

2. Magnesium metal and magnesium oxide both react with hydrochloric acid to produce a solution of magnesium chloride.
   (a) Write balanced chemical equations for each of these reactions.
   (b) Identify any differences between these two chemical changes.

Conclusion

Write a brief conclusion for this experiment.

5.2 PRACTICAL ACTIVITIES

MODELLING CRYSTAL LATTICES

Aim

To construct and describe a variety of crystal lattices

Materials

- graphite ball-and-stick model
- molecular modelling kits
- table tennis balls, plasticine or similar
- foam balls
- toothpicks

Method

Divide into groups. Each group should construct a different model. All groups can observe and discuss these models.

Part A: Metallic crystal — sodium

Sodium is an active metal with a body-centred cubic lattice. Use 9 balls of the same size and colour to construct the unit cell of its crystal lattice. The unit cell represents the simplest unit of the crystal lattice. The lattice is made up of repeating unit cells. Use the ball-and-stick model in figure 5.13 as a guide to each of the three layers of the cell.

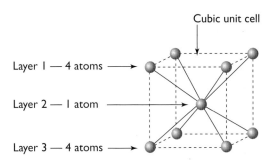

Figure 5.13
Ball-and-stick model of unit cell of sodium

DATA ANALYSIS

Part B: Ionic crystal — caesium chloride

Caesium chloride also forms a body-centred cubic crystal, but the caesium ion occupies the centre of the cell and the eight chloride ions occupy the corners. Caesium ions are about 5% smaller in radius than chloride ions. Use this description to make your model. Select one coloured ball for the caesium ion and select eight balls of a different colour for the chloride ions.

Part C: Covalent network crystal — graphite

Figure 5.9b shows a ball-and stick model of the graphite lattice. Use foam balls and toothpicks to construct a space-filling model of part of this lattice.

Part D: Covalent molecular crystal — carbon dioxide

Figure 5.14 shows a ball-and-stick model of the unit cell of solid carbon dioxide. Use the molecular model kit or plasticine and toothpicks to construct enough carbon dioxide models to build the unit cell.

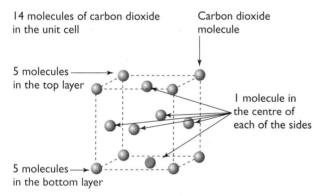

14 molecules of carbon dioxide in the unit cell

Carbon dioxide molecule

5 molecules in the top layer

1 molecule in the centre of each of the sides

5 molecules in the bottom layer

Figure 5.14
Ball-and-stick model of carbon dioxide unit cell

Results and analysis

1. Draw clear, labelled diagrams of each model constructed.
2. Discuss the advantages and limitations of the models.

Conclusion

Write a brief conclusion for this experiment.

5.3 DATA ANALYSIS

COMPARING THE PROPERTIES OF CRYSTALS

Part A

Properties of four solid substances (A, B, C and D) were investigated by experiment.

1. Process the data in table 5.4 and classify these solids into one of the four crystalline groups. Justify your conclusions.
2. Another twenty crystals were tested. The students found that most ionic crystals dissolved in water but not in kerosene, and that most covalent molecular crystals dissolved in kerosene but not water. They found that metallic and covalent network crystals did not dissolve in either solvent. The students used this new information to create a key to classify crystals. Here is the beginning of the key.

> 1A. The crystal does conduct electricity. ....
>   Metallic crystal
> 1B. The crystal does not conduct electricity. ....
>   *Go to 2.*

Complete the key.

Part B

Read the following description of the properties of substance E and then answer the questions that follow.

Substance E is composed of clear, red crystals. When the red crystals are heated, they crackle and change into a blue liquid, which cools to form a blue solid. Heating also produces vapour of substance X. The vapour is allowed to condense to form a colourless liquid that is a non-conductor of electricity. The colourless liquid of substance X is cooled until it forms a white solid. The solid of substance X does not conduct electricity. The red crystals of substance E are found to be quite soluble

DATA ANALYSIS

in water, but they do not dissolve in kerosene. Neither the red crystals nor the blue solid conducts electricity, although the red, aqueous solution of substance E is a good conductor.

1. Classify substance E into one of the four crystalline groups. Justify your conclusion.
2. Classify substance X into one of the four crystalline groups. Justify your conclusion.
3. Explain the structural relationship between the red and blue solids.

Table 5.4

Substance	A	B	C	D
Appearance	dull, black	lustrous, silvery	yellow crystals	white crystals
Melting point (°C)	3974	419	113	decomposes
Effect of heating to 1000 °C in a vacuum	no visible change	forms a silvery liquid	turns to red-brown, viscous liquid	crackles; brown gas forms
Appearance after heating	no effect	silvery solid	brown solid	yellow solid forms
Solubility in water	insoluble	insoluble	insoluble	soluble
Solubility in kerosene	insoluble	insoluble	soluble	insoluble
Electrical conductivity of solid crystal	good	good	zero	zero
Electrical conductivity of melted crystal		good	zero	
Electrical conductivity of aqueous solution				good

METALS

CORE MODULE 2

Chapter 6

METALS AND ALLOYS

Introduction

Metals have been used and exploited by humans for many thousands of years. The discovery of metals and the development of methods to extract them from their ores is closely linked to the cultural development of humans. Modern society depends on metals for the construction of buildings, transportation and the transmission of information. They are also used for jewellery, cooking and eating utensils and weapons of war. Metals can be used for these purposes because of their unique properties that set them apart from other elements.

In this chapter

Figure 6.1

This antique silver and gold has been cleaned and polished. These statuettes from around 3160 BP regained their original shiny appearance. This demonstrates that these elements are very resistant to corrosion.

6.1 *THE HISTORY OF METALS*

Metals and their contemporary uses

Metals have a wide variety of uses related to their physical and chemical properties. Let us examine four important metals used extensively in our society.

Copper

Copper has been used by humans for over 8000 years. It can be found in small amounts as the free element, and this form is called *native copper*. Most copper is present in nature as sulfide minerals. Examples of these minerals include *chalcopyrite*, $CuFeS_2$, and *chalcocite*, Cu_2S. Copper metal can be extracted from these minerals by smelting them in a furnace in the presence of charcoal. (We will examine the smelting process fully in chapter 10.)

Copper is a salmon-pink, lustrous metal that is highly malleable and ductile. It has very high electrical and thermal conductivity. It is unreactive and slow to corrode in the environment. The major uses of copper in modern society are related to these properties, summarised in table 6.1.

Table 6.1 Properties and uses of copper

Use	Property
electrical wiring	high electrical conductivity and ductility
saucepan bases	high heat conductivity and malleability
water pipes/fittings	high malleability and resistance to corrosion
ornaments	lustre and malleability

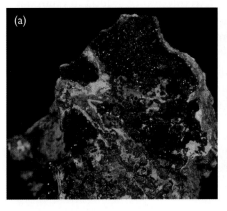

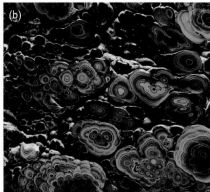

Figure 6.2
(a) Azurite and (b) malachite are basic copper carbonates.

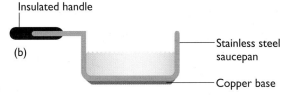

Insulated handle

Stainless steel saucepan

Copper base

Figure 6.3
(a) Native copper embedded in rock and
(b) copper on the base of a steel saucepan

Figure 6.4
Magnesium alloys are used in car wheels because of their high strength and low density.

sacrificial anode: an active metal that corrodes more readily than another, thus protecting the less active metal

Magnesium

Magnesium is a strong, lightweight, silvery metal. It does not exist as a free element in nature. Its common minerals include *magnesite*, $MgCO_3$, and *dolomite*, $MgCO_3.CaCO_3$. Magnesium metal was first prepared in 1808 when Humphry Davy decomposed fused magnesium chloride by electrolysis. Its uses are based on its chemical reactivity, low density and the brilliant white light produced on combustion. These properties are summarised in table 6.2.

Table 6.2 Properties and uses of magnesium

Use	Property
fireworks	high reactivity with oxygen — produces bright white light when burnt in air
structural alloy in aircraft and cars	low density
steelmaking (removal of sulfur from molten steel)	high reactivity with sulfur — combines with sulfur in steel to form stable magnesium sulphide
production of titanium metal	high reactivity — used to reduce titanium salts to titanium metal at high temperatures
corrosion protection of iron structures	high reactivity — acts as a **sacrificial anode** to protect steel ships from corrosion

Lead

Lead is a very soft, dense, blue-grey metal with a low melting point (327 °C). It is not found free in nature. Its common minerals include *galena*, PbS, and *cerussite*, $PbCO_3$. Lead metal was first produced about 5500 years ago by the reduction of galena in charcoal fires. Its low melting point and high density meant that the molten lead flowed and collected at the base of the campfire. Because lead is soft and malleable, the Romans worked it extensively. They even used lead to construct pipes for transporting water. The major uses of lead in modern society are related to its density, malleability, conductivity and ability to shield against radiation. Table 6.3 summarises its uses and properties.

Table 6.3 Properties and uses of lead

Use	Property
sheet lead for roofing/ flashing	malleability and resistance to corrosion due to the formation of a stable oxide on its surface
soldering metal wires (lead alloyed with tin)	low melting point of lead alloys; good electrical conductivity of lead and tin
electrodes in car batteries	good electrical conductivity; malleability and low chemical reactivity in sulfuric acid
shielding against radiation	ability to absorb ionising radiation
fishing sinkers	high density; malleability; softness; resistance to corrosion

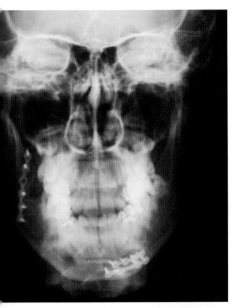

Figure 6.5
Titanium plates and pins are used to hold this broken jaw together.

Titanium

Titanium is a silvery, white metal of low density, high tensile strength and high corrosion resistance. It is not found as a free metal in nature and the first samples of metallic titanium were not produced until 1791. High purity samples of the metal became available after 1887. Titanium is present in minerals such as *rutile*, TiO_2, and *ilmenite*, $FeTiO_3$, which are found in beach sand along the Australian coast. Titanium is both lightweight and very strong. When it is alloyed, it is 30% stronger than steel and has an extraordinary resistance to metal fatigue (cracking). It is, however, difficult to work with and expensive. Table 6.4 summarises its properties and uses.

Table 6.4 Properties and uses of titanium

Use	Property
structural metal (or alloy) in aircraft, spacecraft, racing yachts and racing bicycles	high tensile strength; low density; high melting point; low thermal conductivity; high corrosion resistance (particularly in salt water)
surgical implants	high tensile strength; low density; high corrosion resistance; minimal allergic response in human tissue

Discovery and extraction of metals

metallurgy: the science of metals

The science of metals is called **metallurgy**. It is one of the oldest sciences because humans first discovered metals over 10 000 BP (years before present). By about 2700 BP, only seven metals were known: gold, copper, silver, lead, tin, iron and mercury. Some, such as gold, could be found as uncombined or **native metals** while others, such as tin, were produced by smelting their ores. Copper and iron were known as both native and smelted metals.

native metal: a metal found free (uncombined) in nature

Archaeologists believe that metallurgy began in the Middle East about 10 000 BP and that the technologies for metal extraction and production of metal alloys developed in that region and gradually spread towards Europe and Asia. The major points in this history are listed below.

Gold

Gold was arguably the first metal to be used by humans at least 10 000 BP. Gold was of great significance to the ancient Egyptians. Nubia, in southern Egypt, was a valuable source of gold. One hundred mines operated in this area and slaves were forced to dig deep shafts to extract the metal from quartz veins. After crushing the gold-bearing quartz in stone mills, the crushed ore was washed with water to remove the quartz powder. The heavy gold dust and granules left behind were melted and purified in large clay vessels. Moulds were used to create ingots of gold. Small ingots were hammered and shaped into rings and taken back to northern Egypt where they were fashioned into jewellery.

Figure 6.6
The head of the mummy of Egyptian Pharaoh Tutankhamen (who died about 3330 BP) was coated with pure gold.

The Copper Age (9000–5000 BP)

While gold was being mined in Egypt, the hills and rocky plains at various sites in the Middle East (such as northern Iraq, eastern Saudi Arabia and Jordan) were being mined for veins of native copper. The extracted copper was heated (annealed) and beaten to produce fishhooks, pins and jewellery. The copper was harder than gold and more useful for tool-making. The blue and green copper ores in these hills were used in powdered forms as decorative paints. The process of smelting was developed between 7000 and 6000 BP, and this allowed copper ores to be reduced to metallic copper. This process (see figure 6.7) involved:

- crushing and grinding the ore to a fine powder
- mixing the powdered ore with charcoal and placing it in a furnace. The charcoal fuelled the fire and acted as the **reducing agent**.
- using bellows to blast air into the furnace to raise the temperature of the burning charcoal.

In early, open smelters, the temperature was too low (about 800–900 °C) to melt the copper (melting point = 1085 °C), so grains of copper formed in the glassy **slag** produced by the quartz in the ore. The grains were recovered by crushing the solidified slag. Later, in closed smelters, the temperature was high enough to melt the copper so it could run out of the base of the smelter and be cast into moulds.

reducing agent: a substance (such as charcoal or carbon monoxide) that removes oxygen from a metal oxide during smelting to release the metal

slag: waste material from a smelter or furnace

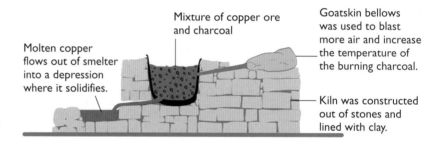

Mixture of copper ore and charcoal

Goatskin bellows was used to blast more air and increase the temperature of the burning charcoal.

Molten copper flows out of smelter into a depression where it solidifies.

Kiln was constructed out of stones and lined with clay.

Figure 6.7
The early process of smelting copper ore

Eventually, clay moulds were produced in a great variety of shapes so that copper axe heads, spear points, daggers, arrowheads and chisels could be cast. These copper tools were expensive to produce and not as strong as their stone equivalents. Despite this, copper became widely used, especially in the manufacture of eating utensils, such as cups, plates and forks.

Anthropologists classify the period between 6000 and 5000 BP as the height of the Copper Age. As the Copper Age, declined the Bronze Age developed.

6.1 DATA ANALYSIS
Timeline: The history of copper

The Bronze Age (6000–3000 BP)

About 6000 BP, while closed-furnace smelting was being developed in the Middle East, metalsmiths discovered a way of producing harder materials from copper. They produced a hard alloy of copper and arsenic called *arsenic bronze*. The ores in which copper minerals were found were often contaminated with other metals such as arsenic, lead, nickel and bismuth. Lead contaminants softened the copper but arsenic contaminants produced a harder, finer product that was more readily worked and cast. Thus, arsenic bronzes became favoured over pure copper.

Further experimentation showed that tin produced the best alloy with copper. *Tin bronzes* (containing about 10% tin) were harder and less brittle than arsenic bronzes. In the process of making tin bronze, in places such as Kestel in eastern Turkey, tin metal was produced by smelting tin ores, such as *cassiterite*, SnO_2, with charcoal. The ingots of purified tin were then combined and melted with copper in a furnace to produce molten bronze.

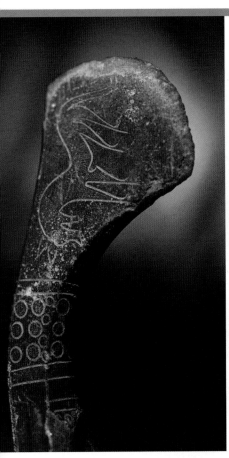

Figure 6.8
About 6000 BP, humans started to manufacture bronze and use it to make tools, jewellery and containers.

Tin bronze could be more readily shaped and sharpened than copper, so cutting tools and weapons of war could be made from it. Bronze weapons allowed nations to conquer their less developed neighbours. The rulers of these kingdoms and empires demanded bronze for their palaces and tombs. Tin ores did not occur in the Middle East and so they had to be traded from England, continental Europe and Armenia. By 4000 BP, an extensive trade network had developed with Europe. European contact with the metalsmiths of the Middle East led to the development of this technology in many European countries including Spain. By 2800 BP, vast copper deposits were being mined in central European countries, such as Austria, and this copper was turned into bronze by European bronzesmiths.

The Bronze Age reached its height in the period 4300–3000 BP. As the Bronze Age declined, it was replaced by the Iron Age.

The Iron Age (3500–2000 BP)

The Iron Age marked the emergence of a new smelting technology that allowed humans to exploit iron. Unlike copper ores, which could be smelted easily, much higher temperatures were required to smelt iron ores. Also, the iron formed was not as malleable as copper unless it was red-hot, and impurities were more difficult to remove. The Bronze Age continued for thousands of years because native copper was much more abundant than native iron. Initially, the only source of native iron was *meteoric iron*. By chipping off pieces of meteoric iron, early iron-workers could make iron weapons that were harder than bronze weapons. This type of iron was resistant to corrosion because of its high nickel content.

The Iron Age probably began in the Middle East about 3500 BP. Crushed iron ore and charcoal were mixed together and placed in a furnace where they were smelted. The temperature was raised using air from blowpipes and bellows to fan the fire. The iron obtained from these primitive smelters was in the form of a black, spongy mass. Early iron-smiths (or blacksmiths) discovered that, if the iron was exposed to too much carbon, it became hard and brittle. Chemists later discovered that this was due to the formation of crystals of *cementite*, Fe_3C.

The black, spongy mass of iron produced in these furnaces was not very useful. Blacksmiths hammered this impure iron at red heat to squeeze out the solid impurities and to burn off most of the carbon. The hot iron was beaten and folded thousands of times at the forge. This process removed most of the cementite crystals. The final product was called *wrought iron*. By 2100 BP, strips of iron were being used for various purposes including chariot wheels and barrel hoops. The Chinese developed the high-temperature blast furnace, where the temperature was high enough to produce molten iron that could be cast into moulds.

Smelted iron became a vital part of the culture of the Iron Age people. Iron nails, knives and sickle blades have been discovered in archaeological digs in Iran. The blacksmiths also discovered how to convert iron into the alloy we call steel. The iron was heated at high temperature with charcoal (carbon) and then quenched in cold water. The process incorporated small quantities of carbon into the iron to produce steel. Flexible shafts with sharp cutting edges could be made from steel, which is ideal for weapons such as swords. This technology developed to very high levels in Damascus (Syria) and in India. The strength of steel made it useful for construction of machines and a wide variety of structural purposes.

Figure 6.9
Blacksmiths modified the properties
of iron and steel.

Because of their greater tensile strength and the hardness of iron alloys, iron and steel gradually replaced copper alloys. The Iron Age ended with the start of the modern era about 2000 BP. We continue to make extensive use of steel.

The wide variety of metals

The discovery of metals is related to the technological development of societies. Seven metals were known to the ancients (see table 6.5). Some metals, such as lead and tin, owe their discovery to the development of high-temperature furnaces and smelters. Many metals are so strongly bound to other elements in their ores that considerable energy is required to break the chemical bonds and release the metal. The more reactive the metal, the more energy is required to release it from its compounds.

Some metals were not discovered until the nineteenth century because heat energy alone was not sufficient to decompose their compounds. The invention of electrolytic decomposition led to the discovery of active metals such as sodium and potassium in 1807 and magnesium in 1808. Early attempts to smelt aluminium ores were unsatisfactory as considerable heat was required and the aluminium vapourised in open furnaces. Although aluminium was eventually produced using a high-temperature (2000 °C), closed smelter, it was found to be more efficiently prepared from its oxide using electrolytic decomposition.

The discovery of active metals such as sodium and magnesium resulted in discoveries of other metals using the process of reduction. These active metals could remove oxygen or other non-metals from the compounds of other metals, leading to the release of the free metal. Titanium is produced commercially today by reacting magnesium with fused titanium chloride.

The metals beyond uranium in the periodic table owe their production to nuclear technology. Some of these are produced by neutron bombardment of other elements in nuclear reactors. Firing high-velocity, metallic ions, produced in a particle accelerator, into metallic targets forms new elements. The heavy elements produced by the fusion of the two nuclei are highly radioactive and decay rapidly.

Over the last 200 years, metals have become readily available due to ongoing improvements in mining, smelting techniques and transportation. Chemists, metallurgists and chemical and mining engineers are responsible for this increase in metal supplies. Much of this change has been driven by the needs of our technological society.

Table 6.5 lists a selection of metals that were discovered over the last 10 000 years. Most were discovered in the last 200 years as technology has improved.

Table 6.5 The discovery of metals

Period of discovery	Selection of metals discovered
before 750 BC	gold, silver, copper, iron, lead, tin, mercury
1201–1700 AD	zinc, bismuth
1701–1800 AD	cobalt, nickel, manganese, tungsten, uranium, titanium, chromium
1801–1900 AD	potassium, sodium, calcium, magnesium, aluminium, indium, gallium, radium
1901 AD–present	europium, rhenium, francium, neptunium, plutonium, curium, einsteinium

SYLLABUS FOCUS

10. THE HISTORY OF CHEMISTRY

The chemistry syllabus places an emphasis on students acquiring a background knowledge of the history of chemistry. This involves developing deep knowledge of:

- the developmental nature of our understanding about matter and its interactions
- the part that an understanding of matter and its interactions plays in shaping society
- how our understanding of matter and its interactions is influenced by society.

The study of metals requires students to link the discovery of metals to changes in society, from agricultural communities, through industrialisation, to our current technological society.

Societies that moved beyond the use of stone, by extracting metals from ores, formed settled communities where individuals were responsible for providing others with a particular service or product. The production of smelted metal allowed these societies to produce new tools and weapons that were superior to the old ones. The ability of metals to be shaped and drawn is important in

this development. Eventually, metals were used to construct large machines and ocean vessels that allowed commerce to spread across the globe. Metals, such as copper, also provided a means of communications between distant communities using inventions such as the telegraph and the telephone.

Figure 6.10 This compressed copper tubing is on its way to a recycling plant. Copper is in heavy demand today, mainly for electrical wiring and communication cables.

6.1 QUESTIONS

1. Identify each of the following metals.
   (a) A metal with the chemical symbol Cu
   (b) A jewellery metal mined in Egypt over 9000 BP
   (c) A grey metal that can be extracted from the mineral galena
   (d) A metal used in light, structural alloys that was prepared in 1808 AD by the electrolysis of its molten chloride
   (e) A metal extracted from the minerals rutile and ilmenite

2. Identify which metal in table 6.6 (below):
   (a) has the lowest density
   (b) is the best electrical conductor
   (c) is used as a base for many saucepans
   (d) is used as a component of a low-temperature alloy
   (e) is a liquid at 3000 °C
   (f) is a liquid at 400 °C
   (g) is used in spacecraft because of its low density and low thermal conductivity.

3. (a) The period around 9000–5000 BP is called the Copper Age, with the height occurring about 6000–5000 BP. Explain what archaeologists mean by the use of the term 'Copper Age' to describe human history.
   (b) People who worked with copper were called coppersmiths. Explain how the earliest coppersmiths obtained metallic copper from copper ores.

4. (a) The Bronze Age followed the Copper Age. Bronze replaced copper in regions with access to other metals that could be alloyed with copper.
      (i) Name the two common metals present in a modern bronze alloy.
      (ii) Describe how the composition of bronze changed during the period of the Bronze Age.
   (b) The early forms of bronze were not as satisfactory as later forms. Identify what caused metalsmiths to search for improved forms of bronze.
   (c) Some meteors contain iron. This meteoric iron was the first form of iron used by humans. This occurred during the Copper and Bronze Ages but iron remained a fairly uncommon metal. Explain the reason for this.

5. The early Iron Age overlapped the late Bronze Age.
   (a) Identify the time and place where it is believed that the Iron Age began.
   (b) The first iron furnaces produced a black, spongy mass of impure iron that was very brittle. Explain the cause of this problem.
   (c) Describe how an early blacksmith could convert the brittle, black iron into a more malleable and flexible form.
   (d) Good swords should be soft and flexible, but their edges should be sharp and hard. Describe how a blacksmith can convert iron to steel.

Table 6.6

Metal	Melting point (°C)	Boiling point (°C)	Density (g/cm³)	Electrical conductivity (MS/m)	Thermal conductivity (J/s/m/K)
gold	1064	2808	19.3	44	317
copper	1085	2572	8.96	58.4	401
lead	327	1740	11.3	4.8	35
iron	1535	2750	7.86	110.3	80
magnesium	650	1110	1.74	22	156
calcium	842	1484	1.55	29	200
titanium	1660	3287	4.5	2.3	22

6. Smelting has long been used to extract metals such as lead from their ores. A simple method of smelting a lead ore is illustrated in figure 6.11. A sample of red lead oxide powder is placed in a cavity in a carbon block and subjected to intense heat from a Bunsen burner flame. Air is blown onto the sample through a blowpipe. (This method of extracting lead is not used commonly now because of the toxicity of lead.)

(a) Identify the types of chemical bonds that have to be broken to release lead from its ore.

(b) The blowpipe provides additional oxygen. Explain why this is important.

(c) Explain why carbon is an essential reactant in this reaction.

(d) Colourless gases are released in the reaction. Predict the composition of these gases. Justify your answer.

(e) Lead is formed as the red oxide decomposes. Describe the appearance of the lead at this stage.

(f) Write a word equation for this reaction.

(g) Identify the safety issues in this investigation.

7. Cobalt and nickel were discovered in the eighteenth century, but calcium and magnesium were not discovered until the early nineteenth century. Identify reasons why magnesium and calcium were not discovered earlier.

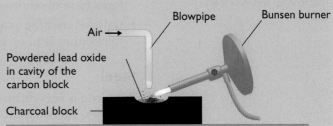

Figure 6.11 Extraction of lead on a carbon block

8. Identify why there are more metals available for people to use now than there were 200 years ago.

6.2 ALLOYS

Common alloys and their uses

Remember

Before beginning this section, you should be able to:
- recall that the properties of different metallic crystals can be related to their lattice structures and the strength of the metallic bonding within the lattice.

Key content

By the end of this section, you should be able to:
- describe the use of common alloys, including steel, brass and solder, and explain how these relate to their properties
- gather, process, analyse and present information from secondary sources on the range of alloys produced and the reasons for the production and use of these alloys.

alloy: a mixture of a metal with one or more other elements (These other elements are usually metals.)

Ancient metallurgists and modern chemists discovered that mixing metals with other elements can produce desirable properties. This process of making an **alloy** is called alloying. Most alloys are **homogeneous** solid solutions, also called *substitutional alloys*. The cupronickel alloy used in Australian coinage is an example of a homogeneous alloy in which some copper atoms are substituted by similar-sized nickel atoms. Some alloys, however, have distinct regions existing within the crystal lattice, so are described as **heterogeneous** or *interstitial alloys*. The examples in figure 6.13 show that the size of the atom of the minor component influences the structure of the alloy's lattice.

Figure 6.12
Some bicycle frames are manufactured from titanium–aluminium–vanadium alloys.

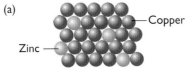

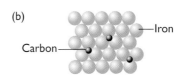

Figure 6.13
Lattice structures of alloys: (a) brass, a homogeneous alloy and (b) steel, a heterogeneous alloy

The inclusion of small quantities of other atoms in the crystal lattice of a metal changes the properties of the metal. Such disturbance of the crystal lattice and the creation of *lattice defects* explains many of these property changes. These changes include:

- colour changes. For example, brass is yellow but copper is salmon-pink.
- increased hardness. For example, tungsten steel is harder than iron.
- reduced malleability. For example, high carbon tool steel is much less malleable than iron.
- reduced electrical conductivity. For example, cupronickel alloys and brass have much lower electrical conductivity than pure copper.
- reduced melting point. For example, solder has a lower melting point than either lead or tin.

Steel

Pure iron is very difficult to prepare. Iron from the blast furnace contains about 4% carbon as well as variable amounts of silicon, sulfur, phosphorus and manganese. This form of iron is known as *pig iron*, which is too brittle for most structural materials. It can be remelted and cast to form *cast iron*, which is used for grates and balustrades.

Pig iron can be converted to a more useful iron alloy called *steel* using the basic oxygen steelmaking (BOS) process. Magnesium is added to the melted pig iron to remove most of the sulfur. Pure oxygen is then blasted onto the surface of the melted iron to oxidise the carbon, silicon and phosphorus impurities. Aluminium is added to remove excess dissolved oxygen in the steel before it is poured out of the converter to cool and solidify. The impurities from this process remain in a waste known as slag.

The percentage of carbon or other metals in the steel is used to classify it into further categories. Steel can be classified as *carbon steel* (table 6.7) or *alloy steel* (table 6.8). The uses of each type of steel is related to its properties.

Table 6.7 Carbon steels

Name	% carbon*	% manganese**	Properties	Uses
mild steel	<0.2	0–0.4	soft; malleable; ductile; corrodes rapidly	sheet steel, car bodies, nails, roofing, pipes, nuts and bolts, wires
structural steel	0.3–0.6	0.6–1.65	hard; moderate ductility; corrodes rapidly	railway tracks, girders, beams, axles, crankshafts, forgings
high carbon steel	0.6–1.3	0.3–0.9	very hard; very low malleability; brittle; corrodes fairly rapidly	axe heads, small tools, scissors, springs, high-strength wires

*More carbon makes the steel harder and less malleable.

**Manganese hardens and toughens the steel and makes it less brittle.

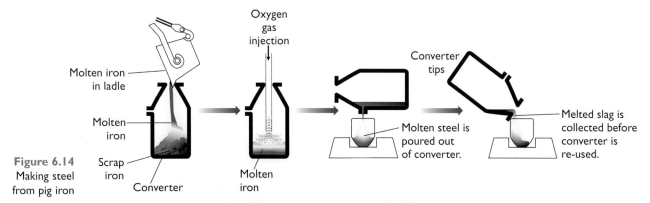

Figure 6.14
Making steel from pig iron

Molten iron in ladle
Molten iron
Scrap iron
Converter
Oxygen gas injection
Molten iron
Converter tips
Molten steel is poured out of converter.
Melted slag is collected before converter is re-used.

Table **6.8** Alloy steels

Name	% carbon	Other metals	Properties	Uses
stainless steel	0.1–1.5	12–30% Cr 0–8% Ni	high corrosion resistance; abrasion resistance; high tensile strength	kitchen sinks, surgical instruments, cutlery, valves, flanges
high nickel steel	<0.05	18% Ni 8% Co 4% Mo 0.8% Ti	tough; high corrosion resistance; high weldability	aircraft undercarriages, dies, engine parts
high speed steel	0.4–1.0	14–18% W 3–5% Cr 0.2–1.0% V	hard at high temperatures; high heat resistance; high tensile strength	high-speed cutting tools

The addition of various metals changes the property of the steel. For example:

- chromium increases resistance to corrosion, heat and abrasion
- nickel increases strength and hardness
- tungsten increases hardness and abrasion resistance, and strength and hardness at high temperatures
- molybdenum increases hardness and strength, and corrosion resistance in marine environments.

Figure 6.15
(a) Structural steel is used for railway tracks and mild steel is used for train carriage sheeting. These differences in usage are related to the physical properties of the steel. (b) Stainless steel has properties that make it suitable for surgical instruments.

Brass

The major metals in brass are copper and zinc. The proportion of copper to zinc affects the colour of the alloy. Brass is typically a golden-yellow colour and it can be used in costume jewellery. A more reddish brass for special enamelled jewellery is made from 80–85% copper and 20–15% zinc. The presence of zinc makes it much stronger and harder than copper. The higher the proportion of zinc, the greater the hardness and tensile strength. Brass can also be highly polished, which makes it useful for ornamental materials and brass musical instruments.

Figure 6.16
Marching bands pride themselves on the shine on their brass instruments.

Smaller amounts of other metals, such as lead, tin and aluminium, may be added to change the property of brass. Table 6.9 lists some common brass alloys. The method of formation of the alloy causes variations in its crystalline structure, which affect its strength and hardness. Tensile strength measures the tensional (or pulling) forces that the alloy can withstand before breaking. Hardness can be measured on a number of scales including the Mohs scale and the Brinell scale.

Table 6.9 Brass

% Cu	% Zn	Tensile strength (kg/mm^2)	Hardness (Brinell scale)	Uses
85	15	17–18	45–60	red brass; soft so used for cheap jewellery that is to be gold plated
70	30	17–20	45–65	cartridge brass; brass tubes, sheets, wires and marine fittings
60	40	25–31	50–75	Muntz metal; bolts and nuts and machine parts

Solder

The major metals in solder are lead and tin. The proportion of lead to tin affects the melting point of the alloy. The melting point of solder is usually less than either lead (327 °C) or tin (232 °C). Solder is a fusible alloy used to join wires and electrical components in circuits. It adheres strongly to other metals in the solid and liquid states. Other metals present in minor amounts in solder are antimony and bismuth. Table 6.10 lists some common types of solder. The *solidus–liquidus* range is the temperature range in which the alloy is semi-solid or plastic.

The solder used by electricians must conduct well and not have a wide plastic range before it solidifies. Plumbers, however, need a solder that remains plastic for a longer time so they can adjust the joints.

Table 6.10 Solder

%Pb	%Sn	Solidus–liquidus temperature range (°C)	Uses
36	62	178–190	(with 2% Ag) silver soldering for specialised electronic circuits
50	50	183–212	general-purpose plumber's solder
60	40	183–188	general-purpose solder for electrical connections — allows short soldering time
70	30	183–258	automotive plumber's solder for radiator and body repair — wide plastic range allows it to be worked longer
92	8	280–305	thermostat soldering

There are also special lead-free solders in which silver is a major component. Silversmiths and jewellers use these silver solders to create personal jewellery. Some examples include:
- hard silver solder (high melting point): 75% Ag; 22% Cu; 3% Zn
- easy flow silver solder (low melting point): 45% Ag; 24% Cd; 16% Zn; 15% Cu.

6.2 DATA ANALYSIS
The melting points of solders

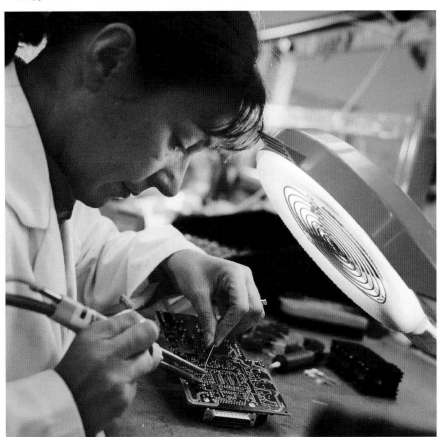

Figure 6.17
Silver solder is used in the manufacture of circuit boards.

Use the data in table 6.11 to answer the following questions.

(a) Determine the melting points of pure tin and pure lead.

(b) An alloy consisting of 48% tin is held at 225 °C. Explain whether the alloy is a solid, paste (plastic) or liquid at this temperature.

(c) Identify the alloy with the greatest plastic range.

(d) Explain which solder would be most suitable for soldering electrical wires.

Table 6.11 Lead–tin solder

%Sn	%Pb	Temperature at which solder becomes plastic (°C)	Temperature at which solder becomes liquid (°C)
0	100		327
10	90	234	302
48	52	183	218
60	40	183	188
100	0		232

SOLUTION

(a) Melting point of lead = 327 °C, melting point of tin = 232 °C

(b) It would be a liquid as it is above its melting point of 218 °C.

(c) Solder with 10% Sn : 90% Pb has a 68 °C plastic range, which is the largest in table 6.11.

(d) Solder with 60% Sn : 40% Pb has the lowest plastic range, so will set or melt fastest, which is important for electrical work.

6.2 QUESTIONS

1. Nickel is added to copper to make the cupronickel that is used for our coins. Which property of the alloy is improved by the presence of the nickel?
   A Weight
   B Strength and hardness
   C Heat conductivity
   D Melting point

2. Select the statement that is true of mild (low carbon) steel.
   A Its carbon content is between 0.3 and 0.6%.
   B It is very hard and brittle.
   C It is used for sheet metal roofing.
   D It is ductile but not malleable.

3. Select the statement that is true of brass.
   A The greater the tin content, the harder the brass.
   B Brass is a silvery alloy that contains mainly zinc and tin.

C Red brass has a high percentage of copper and is relatively soft.
   D The tensile strength of brass is less than for pure copper.

4. (a) Explain why homogeneous alloys can be referred to as 'solid solutions'.
   (b) An alloy is made from two metals *A* and *B*. Examination of the alloy under a scanning electron microscope shows that various regions of the crystal lattice contain discrete grains of *A* and *B*. Explain whether this alloy is homogeneous or heterogeneous.

5. Steelmaking is an important industry in Australia. The iron that emerges from the smelter is called pig iron.
   (a) Explain why pig iron is not used directly in the construction industry.
   (b) Pig iron is converted to steel in the BOS process. Identify the element within the pig iron that must be reduced in concentration to produce steel.

(c) Tungsten and molybdenum may be added in the process of making steel. Describe how these elements change the properties of the steel.

(d) There are many forms of stainless steel but all are resistant to corrosion. Identify the two metals that commonly provide this resistance to corrosion.

6. Modern bronze is an alloy of copper.

(a) The superiority of bronze over copper led to the development of the Bronze Age and the decline of the Copper Age. Explain how bronze is superior to copper.

(b) Tin bronze can contain up to 14% by weight of tin. Calculate the maximum weight of tin that can be added to 5000 kg of melted copper to produce bronze.

(c) Australia's one- and two-dollar coins are made of a type of aluminium bronze. The typical composition of these coins is 92% Cu : 6% Al : 2% Ni. Calculate the mass of each metal that is needed to make 5000 kg of bronze for these coins.

7. Three manufactured carbon steel items were analysed and their percentage carbon by weight determined. The results were: item X, 1.1% C; item Y, 0.1% C and item Z, 0.35% C. The items were (in random order) nails, axe head and girder. Identify each item.

eBook plus

Weblinks

eBook plus

Checkpoint
Revision 3

eBook plus

Checkpoint
Revision 3 Answers

SUMMARY

- Metals have been used by humans for a variety of purposes for about 10 000 years.

- Some metals such as gold can be found as native metals.

- Energy is required to extract a metal from its ore.

- Some copper ores can be decomposed by heating them with charcoal in a simple kiln. Copper and its alloys were produced in this way. This period in history is called the Copper Age and Bronze Age.

- Higher temperature kilns were used to extract iron from its ores. This period in history is called the Iron Age.

- The use of metals has changed over time.

- Metals can be alloyed to change their properties and uses. New alloys are being developed.

- Metals are non-renewable resources. Recycling of metals has become increasingly important.

DATA ANALYSIS

6.1 DATA ANALYSIS

TIMELINE: THE HISTORY OF COPPER

In this activity, you will develop and annotate a timeline of the history of copper.

1. Organise the following second-hand data into chronological (date) order and then develop a timeline for the history of copper. This timeline can be produced in several formats including a two-column table using a computer application or a wall chart. You may like to use the Internet to gather additional data for your copper timeline. (*Note:* These dates are based on 2006 so will change each year.)

Europe

- Europe (600 BP) — hulls of wooden ships covered in copper sheeting to protect against algal growth
- Europe (215 BP) — copper rolling mills powered by steam engines produce copper sheet
- Germany (191 BP) — copper wires used in first electromagnetic telegraph
- England (169 BP) — Michael Faraday develops first dynamo using a copper disc and wire.
- Bohemia (Czech Republic) (4400 BP) — copper mining
- Netherlands (192 BP) — first telescope made from brass
- Italy (205 BP) — Volta makes first battery using copper and zinc plates.
- Netherlands (348 BP) — Huygens develops brass pendulum and gears for a pendulum clock.
- Hungary (266 BP) — dissolved copper in spring water used as a medication

The Americas

- USA (7 BP) — IBM replaces aluminium with copper in its microcircuitry on silicon chips.
- USA (118 BP) — Statue of Liberty completed; 80 tonnes of copper used in its construction
- North America (500 BP) — Native Americans use native copper to manufacture jewellery and ceremonial objects.
- West Indies (500 BP) — copper mining and production of cast copper hatchets
- North America (256 BP) — copper mining established by Dutch settlers near New York. They learnt of copper from Native Americans who made copper pipes.
- Peru (1300 BP) — Incas use copper and bronze for tools and weapons.

Middle East

- Iraq and Sumeria (10 000 BP) — native copper melted, forged and cast
- Egypt (4500 BP) — copper tubing used for waterworks
- Iran (5800 BP) — chisels and spatulas manufactured from copper
- Egypt (5000 BP — Sumerian metalworkers show how copper can be cast into useful utensils and ornaments.
- Israel (5300 BP) — axes, saws and spearheads manufactured from copper
- Cyprus (4900 BP) — copper coins used for tolls to provide funds to build the pyramids
- Turkey (9250 BP) — copper artefacts manufactured

DATA ANALYSIS

Asia

- China (2220 BP) — copper coinage developed
- India (5000 BP) — copper mining in north-west India
- India (3200 BP) — copper used to repair image of Buddha
- Thailand (5600 BP) — bronze used for tools and jewellery
- China (3400 BP) — bronze-casting industry in northern China

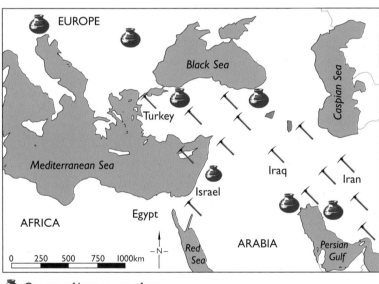

EUROPE

Black Sea

Caspian Sea

Turkey

Mediterranean Sea

Iraq

Iran

Israel

Egypt

AFRICA

ARABIA

Persian Gulf

Red Sea

0 250 500 750 1000km

—N—

🏺 Centres of bronze manufacture

⚒ Copper mines

Figure 6.18 Map of ancient copper mines and bronze industries in the Middle East

2. Briefly discuss how your timeline shows the spread of copper technology from the Middle East to Asia, Europe and the Americas.

6.2 DATA ANALYSIS

MELTING POINTS OF SOLDERS

Tables 6.12 and 6.13 list the melting points of various compositions of solder. Use these tables to answer the following questions.

1. Use table 6.12 to plot a line graph of the melting point of the lead–tin solders as a function of the percentage of lead in the solder. Draw the line of best fit through the data points.
2. Use your graph to estimate the melting point of a solder with a composition of 70% lead and 30% tin.
3. Use your graph and table 6.13 to compare the melting points of a solder with a composition of 36% Pb : 64% Sn and a solder with a composition of 36% Pb : 60% Sn : 4% Ag. How does the addition of silver affect the melting point of the alloy?

4. Consider lead–tin solders and lead–tin–silver solders with a high lead composition (such as 93% lead). Use table 6.13 and your graph to compare the melting points of these high lead solders. Does the addition of silver affect the melting point of high lead solders in the same way as low lead solders, as in question 3.
5. The melting point of a 69% Pb : 30% Sn : 1% Sb alloy is 250 °C. Use your answer to question 2 to describe how replacing 1% of the lead with antimony affects the melting point of the alloy.

Table 6.12 Melting points of lead–tin solders

Lead (%)	0	20	37	40	50	60	90	100
Melting point (°C)	232	210	183	188	215	235	302	327

Table 6.13 Melting points of lead–tin–silver solders

Lead (%)	36	36	57	62	70	93	97.5	97.5
Tin (%)	62	60	40	36	27	5	0	0.75
Silver (%)	2	4	3	2	3	2	2.5	1.75
Melting point (°C)	190	180	312	179	312	301	305	310

Chapter 7 METALS AND REACTIONS

Introduction

Metals differ in their reactivity with other chemicals such as air, water and acids. Some metals such as sodium are so reactive that they cannot exist as the free element in nature. Gold is so unreactive that native gold is commonly found in natural deposits. The reactivity of metals influences their uses. Reactivity is a chemical property that will be examined in this section.

In this chapter

Figure 7.1

Sodium must be stored away from air and water as it is a very reactive metal.

7.1 METALS AND THEIR REACTIVITY

inert: describes a substance that does not react with other substances

Reactions of metals

The reactivity of metals can be determined experimentally by observing the speed of reaction of the metals with common chemical reagents such as water, oxygen and dilute acids.

Reaction with water

Results of experiments to compare the reactions of a selection of common metals with water, hot water and steam are shown in table 7.1. It shows that either oxides or hydroxides are formed.

Table 7.1 Reactivity of metals with water

K, Na, Ca	react with cold water to form hydroxide ions and release hydrogen gas
Mg	reacts with hot water to form hydroxide ions and release hydrogen gas
Al, Zn, Fe	react with steam at red heat to form oxide ions and release hydrogen gas
Sn, Pb, Cu, Hg, Ag, Au	no reaction

Figure 7.2 Magnesium burns brightly in air or oxygen.

The reaction rate is highest for active metals. Unreactive metals such as copper and gold do not react; they are **inert**. Potassium, sodium and calcium are the most reactive metals with water. The following equations illustrate some of the reactions described in table 7.1.

- Sodium + water
  Word equation:

  sodium metal + water → sodium hydroxide solution + hydrogen gas
  Balanced chemical equation:

$$2Na(s) + 2H_2O(l) \rightarrow 2NaOH(aq) + H_2(g)$$

- Iron + steam
  Word equation:

  iron metal + steam → iron oxide solid + hydrogen gas

  Balanced chemical equation:

$$Fe(s) + H_2O(g) \rightarrow FeO(s) + H_2(g)$$

Figure 7.3
Magnesium reacts with hot water, forming bubbles of hydrogen gas on its surface.

Reaction with oxygen

Experiments can be conducted to observe the reaction of metals with air (21% oxygen). The metals are normally heated (e.g. in a Bunsen flame) to initiate the reaction. The hot metals can also be plunged into gas jars of oxygen. The results of such experiments are shown in table 7.2.

Table 7.2 Reactivity of metals when heated in air or with oxygen

K, Na, Ca	burn rapidly to form oxides or **peroxides**
Mg, Al, Zn, Fe	burn readily if powdered or as fine fibres to form oxides
Sn, Pb, Cu, Hg	become coated with oxide layers during heating
Ag, Au	no reaction

peroxide: a compound containing the peroxide radical O_2^{2-}

Potassium, sodium and calcium are highly reactive to oxygen while silver and gold are unreactive. The following equations illustrate some of the reactions in table 7.2.

- Calcium + oxygen
  Word equation:

  calcium metal + oxygen gas → calcium peroxide solid

  Balanced chemical equation:

  $$Ca(s) + O_2(g) \rightarrow CaO_2(s)$$

- Mercury + oxygen
  Word equation:

  mercury metal + oxygen gas → mercury (II) oxide solid

  Balanced chemical equation:

  $$2Hg(s) + O_2(g) \rightarrow 2HgO(s)$$

Reaction with dilute acids

The reaction of metals in dilute solutions of hydrochloric or sulfuric acid has been determined and the results are shown in table 7.3.

Table 7.3 Reactivity of metals with dilute acids

K, Na	effervesce very rapidly producing hydrogen gas, which may ignite
Ca, Mg	bubble rapidly releasing hydrogen
Al, Zn, Fe, Sn, Pb	bubble moderately to very slowly as hydrogen is released; reaction is faster in warm acid; lead stops reacting when coated with insoluble $PbCl_2$ or $PbSO_4$
Cu, Hg, Ag, Au	no reaction

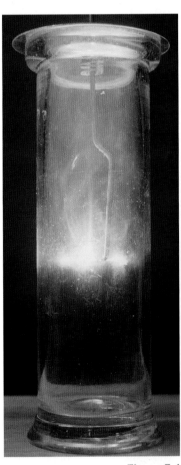

Figure 7.4
Calcium burns in oxygen with a bright white flame.

The reactive metals, such as potassium and sodium, often cause explosions because the reaction releases both heat and hydrogen. The surface of aluminium must be cleaned or the oxide coating will prevent reaction until it is dissolved away by the acid. Heating the acid increases the reaction rate.

The following equations illustrate some of the reactions in table 7.3.

- Sodium + dilute sulfuric acid
  Word equation:

sodium metal + sulfuric acid → sodium sulfate solution + hydrogen gas

Balanced chemical equation:

$$2Na(s) + H_2SO_4(aq) → Na_2SO_4(aq) + H_2(g)$$

- Zinc + dilute hydrochloric acid
  Word equation:

zinc metal + hydrochloric acid → zinc chloride solution + hydrogen gas

Balanced chemical equation:

$$Zn(s) + 2HCl(aq) → ZnCl_2(aq) + H_2(g)$$

The activity series of metals

The experiments described in the previous section reveal a common trend in the reactivity of metals. The order of metal reactivity is known as the *activity series of metals*. A more complete list is shown in table 7.4.

The activity series is the combined result of many other experiments including thermal decomposition reactions of compounds of these elements. Care must be taken in using this list as some metals can behave unexpectedly in different chemical environments. For example, aluminium is more reactive than iron yet it does not corrode as rapidly as iron. This is due to an impervious coating of aluminium oxide that exists as a microlayer on the surface of that metal.

Reactivity and electron transfer

The reaction between metals and acids or other chemicals involves *electron transfer*.

- The more reactive a metal, the more readily electron transfer occurs. Thus, magnesium rapidly reacts with dilute hydrochloric acid as magnesium rapidly transfers electrons to the hydrogen ions in the acid. This process can be summarised using *half-equations* that show the process of electron loss by the metal and electron gain by the hydrogen ion. The overall equation is found by summing the two half-equations and cancelling out the electrons.

Figure 7.5
Zinc reacts with hydrochloric acid producing bubbles of hydrogen gas.

Table 7.4 Activity series of metals

most active	potassium
	sodium
	barium
	calcium
	magnesium
	aluminium
	chromium
	zinc
	iron
	cobalt
	nickel
	tin
	lead
	copper
	mercury
	silver
	platinum
least active	gold

Electron loss:	$Mg(s) \rightarrow Mg^{2+}(aq) + 2e^-$
Electron gain:	$2H^+(aq) + 2e^- \rightarrow H_2(g)$
Ionic (overall) reaction:	$Mg(s) + 2H^+(aq) \rightarrow Mg^{2+}(aq) + H_2(g)$

7.1 PRACTICAL ACTIVITIES

The activity series of metals

Atoms of noble metals, such as gold, hold their valence electrons tightly and do not transfer them to the hydrogen ions of the acid. Thus, there is no reaction between these metals and dilute hydrochloric acid.

SYLLABUS FOCUS

11. WRITING HALF-EQUATIONS AND IONIC EQUATIONS
Half-equations help us understand the electron transfer process between metals and non-metals. Generally:
- metals lose electrons to form metal ions (cations)
- non-metals gain electrons to form non-metal ions (anions)
- hydrogen ions gain electrons to form hydrogen gas.

Using these generalisations, we can write half-equations for the reactions between metals and dilute acids. Half-equations must be balanced in terms of atoms and charges.

Ionic equations are created by summing two half-equations so that the number of electrons lost by the metal equals the number of electrons gained by the non-metal or hydrogen ion.

Example: Reaction of aluminium with hot sulfuric acid
Aluminium atoms will lose three electrons and the hydrogen ions will gain two electrons.

Electron loss:	$Al(s) \rightarrow Al^{3+}(aq) + 3e^-$	(1)
Electron gain:	$2H^+(aq) + 2e^- \rightarrow H_2(g)$	(2)

To balance the electrons, multiply half-equation (1) by 2 and half-equation (2) by 3, and then add the two half-equations. Check that the atoms and charges balance.

Electron loss:	$2Al(s) \rightarrow 2Al^{3+}(aq) + 6e^-$
Electron gain:	$6H^+(aq) + 6e^- \rightarrow 3H_2(g)$
Ionic equation:	$2Al(s) + 6H^+(aq) \rightarrow 2Al^{3+}(aq) + 3H_2(g)$

7.1 QUESTIONS

1. Identify the least active metal in the following list.
   A   Calcium
   B   Tin
   C   Iron
   D   Aluminium

2. Identify the univalent metal in the following list that reacts with air, water and dilute acid.
   A   Barium
   B   Silver
   C   Lead
   D   Sodium

3. Identify the metal from the following list that does not react with steam at red heat but does react slowly with hot, dilute acids.
   A   Tin
   B   Gold
   C   Iron
   D   Silver

4. Use the activity series to identify the most active metal in each of the following lists:
   (a) silver, calcium, aluminium
   (b) nickel, cobalt, gold
   (c) barium, calcium, potassium
   (d) gold, mercury, platinum
   (e) lead, zinc, magnesium.

5. Write balanced chemical equations for the following reactions involving metals.
    (a) Steam is passed over red-hot zinc.
    (b) Magnesium powder is heated in a jar of oxygen.
    (c) Potassium metal is added to dilute hydrochloric acid.
    (d) Magnesium metal is added to dilute sulfuric acid.

6. Write half-equations and ionic equations for the following:
    (a) calcium + dilute sulfuric acid
    (b) zinc + dilute hydrochloric acid
    (c) potassium + dilute sulfuric acid.

7. A silvery, divalent metal X reacts with steam only if the metal is red-hot. The surface of the metal gradually becomes covered in a black powder. A gas is evolved in the reaction. This gas explodes in the presence of a flame.
    (a) Identify the gas evolved.
    (b) Write a balanced equation for the reaction of red-hot X with steam.
    (c) Identify X from the following list: Al, Mg, Fe, Ca, Ag. Justify your answer.

7.2 REACTIVITY AND USES OF METALS

Remember

Before beginning this section, you should be able to:
• explain the relationship between the reactivity of an element and the likelihood of it existing as an uncombined element
• describe observable changes when metals react with dilute acid, water and oxygen.

Key content

By the end of this section, you should be able to:
• outline examples of the selection of metals for different purposes based on their reactivity, with a particular emphasis on current developments in the use of metals
• identify the importance of first ionisation energy in determining the relative reactivity of metals
• outline the relationship between the relative activities of metals and their positions in the periodic table
• present information clearly and succinctly using a variety of pictorial representations to show relationships.

Relating reactivity to use

Knowledge of a metal's reactivity is important in designing ways to use it. If a metal readily oxidises (corrodes), it is unsuitable as a structural material unless it can be protected from the environment. New metals and alloys are constantly being investigated. Titanium is one example. It has an activity similar to aluminium but it has greater tensile strength. It can withstand shearing forces for a longer time than many conventional metals.

Titanium alloys are used in the engines of commercial jets. The chemical industry makes increasing use of titanium because of its resistance to corrosion. Pumps, pipes and reaction vessels made of titanium are used in some chemical industries.

Figure 7.6
The fuel tanks on Skylab space station were made of titanium.

Figure 7.7
A worker inspects hot, galvanised, sheet steel at a steelworks. The zinc layer prevents the steel from rusting even if the surface is scratched.

galvanised: describes a metal (such as iron) coated with zinc to protect it from corrosion

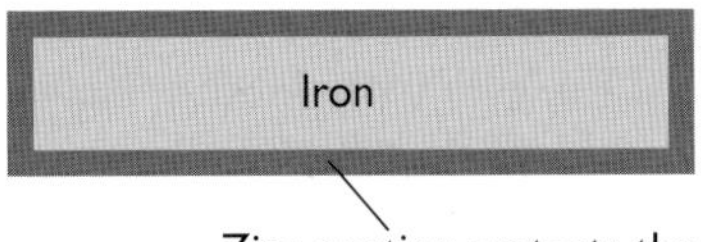

Zinc coating protects the iron from rusting.
Figure 7.8
The zinc coating on galvanised iron protects the metal from corrosion.

Table 7.5 lists some common uses of metals that are related to their chemical reactivity. Other uses are related to their physical properties.

Table 7.5 Uses of metals related to their chemical reactivity

Metal	Property	Use related to property
Mg, Al	high reactivity with oxygen producing a very bright, white light	fireworks
Ti	high corrosion resistance	surgical implants
Zn	more readily oxidised than iron or steel	• **galvanised** iron. Iron sheeting is protected from rusting by the more active zinc. • sacrificial anodes. Zinc anodes protect ship propellers and hulls.
Sn	not as readily oxidised as iron or steel	tin plating of steel cans. If no iron is exposed, the less reactive tin protects the iron.
Cu	high corrosion resistance	water pipes, electrical wires and wrapping for optic fibre cables. Copper does not corrode readily in the environment.

SAMPLE PROBLEM 7.1

Account for the use of calcium rather than copper as a dehydrating agent for some petroleum solvents.

SOLUTION

Calcium is a very active metal that reacts with water and removes it from the organic solvent. Copper is very unreactive and does not remove water from the solvent.

$$Ca(s) + 2H_2O(l) \rightarrow Ca(OH)_2(s) + H_2(g)$$

Ionisation energy

The reactivity of metals is related to their tendency to lose valence electrons to form ions that have a stable electron configuration. The tendency of gaseous atoms to lose electrons is measured by a quantity called the **ionisation energy** (I). This energy must be supplied to overcome the attractive force that binds the electrons to the nucleus.

ionisation energy: the minimum energy required to remove an electron completely from a gaseous atom

Electrons can be removed sequentially according to the strength of the force that binds them to the nucleus. The energy required to remove the most loosely bound electron is called the *first ionisation energy* (I_1). The successive ionisation energies (I_1, I_2, I_3 etc.) reflect the positions of the electrons in their shells.

Ionisation energies are measured in the gaseous state as the symbol (g) indicates in the following examples for an element E.

First ionisation (I_1): $\quad E(g) \rightarrow E^+(g) + e^-$

Second ionisation (I_2): $\quad E^+(g) \rightarrow E^{2+}(g) + e^-$

Third ionisation (I_3): $\quad E^{2+}(g) \rightarrow E^{3+}(g) + e^-$

An element such as sodium ($Z = 11$) has 11 electrons arranged in 3 electron shells. The total number of ionisations for sodium is 11. The successive ionisation energies increase as each electron is removed.

The factors that affect the ease of removal of electrons from atoms are the:

- size of the nuclear charge
- distance of the electrons from the nucleus
- presence of shielding inner electrons.

Example 1: Lithium ($Z = 3$)

Figure 7.9 relates the ionisation energy for each electron in a lithium atom to its position within the electron shells.

Lithium atoms have three electrons. There is one valence electron in the L shell. This electron is the easiest to remove as the L shell is further from the electrostatic attraction of the positive nucleus. The L shell electron is also shielded from the nucleus by the inner K shell electrons. The second ionisation energy (I_2) is greater than the first (I_1) as the electron has to be removed from a positive ion (Li$^+$) rather than a neutral atom (Li). The electrons in the K shell are harder to remove as they are closer to the nucleus so there is a greater electrostatic attraction. Lithium typically exhibits a +1 valency in all its compounds, such as LiBr and Li_2O, because of the ease of removal of the L shell electron.

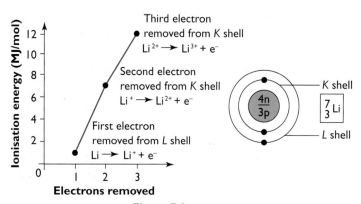

Figure 7.9
Ease of removal of electrons from the K and L shells in lithium

Example 2: Nitrogen ($Z = 7$)

Nitrogen has an electron configuration of 2, 5. The five valence electrons in the L shell are easier to remove from the atom than the inner K shell electrons, as shown by the data in table 7.6. Plotting this data shows that the first five ionisation energies increase fairly regularly, but the last two are significantly higher.

Table 7.6 Successive ionisation energies for nitrogen (MJ/mol)

I_1	I_2	I_3	I_4	I_5	I_6	I_7
1.4	2.9	4.6	7.5	9.5	53.3	64.4

Comparing the ionisation energy of metals

Electron transfer reactions occur when metals react with acids. In this case, however, the electron transfer occurs in an aqueous solution and not

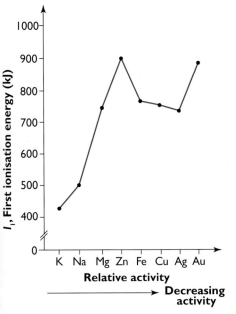

Figure 7.10

Relationship between first ionisation energy and relative activity of selected metals

in the gaseous state. We now need to consider the possibility that the ionisation energy of a gaseous metal atom may be related to the activity series. Table 7.7 shows the first ionisation energy data for selected metals.

Table 7.7 First ionisation energy of selected metals

Metal	K	Na	Mg	Zn	Fe	Cu	Ag	Au
I_1 (kJ)	425	502	744	913	766	752	737	896

This table shows that very reactive metals, such as potassium and sodium, have very low ionisation energies and that magnesium and zinc, which are less reactive than sodium, have higher ionisation energies. Beyond this, however, the data does not show a simple relationship between the activity series and ionisation energy. Other factors come into play when determining the relative reactivity of metals.

Reactivity and the periodic table

Figure 7.11 compares the positions of the metals in the activity series with their locations in the periodic table. The following observations can be made:

- The most active metals, such as potassium and sodium, are in group I on the left side of the table. In general, their reactivity increases down the group. Thus, caesium and francium are highly reactive metals.
- The next most active metals, such as calcium and magnesium, belong in group II. Again, reactivity increases down the group.
- Metals of moderate reactivity, such as zinc and iron, lie at the edge of the metal zone of the periodic table.
- There is no general pattern for the remaining elements, except that the least reactive, such as gold and mercury, are located in the lower central region called the *transition metals*. Other metals in this region, such as osmium, iridium and platinum, are also quite unreactive.

Figure 7.11

Metal reactivity and the periodic table

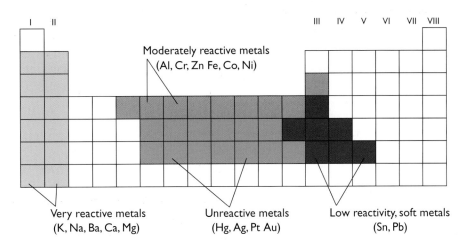

As previously stated, the reactivity of metals in groups I and II increases down the group. This is related to the decreasing first ionisation energies down each group. This, in turn, is related to the increasing distance of the valence shell from the nucleus. Figure 7.12 shows the decrease in first ionisation energy with increasing reactivity for group I metals.

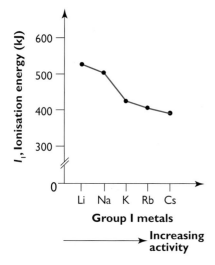

Figure 7.12
Relationship between first ionisation energy of group I metals and reactivity

Figure 7.13
Copper is an unreactive metal that is highly ductile and has a high electrical conductivity.

7.2 QUESTIONS

1. Select the correct statement about metal reactivity and the periodic table.
   A   The most reactive metals are the transition metals.
   B   Group III metals are less reactive than group II metals.
   C   Soft metals in group IV are more reactive than soft metals, such as aluminium, in group III.
   D   The least reactive metals in the periodic table are found at the bottom of groups V and VI.

2. Identify the number of valence electrons in a multi-electron metal atom with the successive ionisation energies (measured in MJ/mol) given in table 7.8.
   A   1
   B   2
   C   3
   D   4

3. Titanium and titanium alloys are being used increasingly in many industries and applications because
   A   titanium is a lightweight metal with high tensile strength and high resistance to corrosion.
   B   they are more reactive than magnesium and can be used to protect other metals.
   C   titanium is very cheap to manufacture.
   D   titanium is inert, dense and strong.

4. Tin is suitable for plating steel can because
   A   tin is less dense than iron.
   B   tin is less reactive than iron and protects it from corrosion.
   C   tin is more reactive than iron and corrodes sacrificially.
   D   it is a non-toxic metal that is resistant to corrosion in a marine environment.

Table 7.8 Successive ionisation energies (MJ/mol)

I_1	I_2	I_3	I_4	I_5	I_6	I_7
0.584	1.823	2.751	11.584	14.837	18.384	23.302

5. Which of the following metals has the smallest first ionisation energy?
   A Magnesium
   B Sodium
   C Aluminium
   D Rubidium

6. Gallium is chemically similar to aluminium.
   (a) Gaseous gallium atoms can be ionised in three successive steps to form the stable $Ga^{3+}(g)$ ion. Write each of the half-equations for the stepwise ionisation.
   (b) Identify the ionisation step that requires the greatest amount of energy. Justify your response.
   (c) Gallium metal also ionises when placed in dilute hydrochloric acid. Write a half-equation for the ionisation of gallium in this case.
   (d) Write the net ionic equation for the reaction of gallium with dilute hydrochloric acid.

7. The successive ionisation energies (in MJ/mol) for two multi-electron elements X and Y are shown in table 7.9:
   (a) Use this data to determine the number of valence electrons for each element.
   (b) Classify X and Y as metals or non-metals. Justify your answer.
   (c) Predict the chemical formula of a compound formed between X and Y.

Table 7.9 Successive ionisation energies (MJ/mol)

X	0.60	1.15	4.92	6.48	8.15	10.50	12.33	14.21	18.19	20.39	57.06	63.34
Y	1.26	2.30	3.83	5.16	6.55	9.37	11.03	33.61	38.61	43.97	51.07	57.10

eBook *plus*

Weblinks

SUMMARY

- Metals react with dilute hydrochloric or sulfuric acid to release hydrogen gas and form ionic salts.

- The order of the activity of metals can be determined by the rate at which they react with other substances including oxygen, water and dilute acids.

- The ease or difficulty of thermal decomposition of metallic compounds can be related to the activity series.

- The most reactive metals are located in groups I and II of the periodic table. The least reactive metals are located in the lower periods of the transition metals.

- The reactivity of metals can be understood in terms of the ease with which they lose electrons. The reactivity of metals is related to their uses.

- Ionisation energy is the energy required to remove successive electrons from gaseous atoms.

PRACTICAL ACTIVITIES

7.1 PRACTICAL ACTIVITIES

THE ACTIVITY SERIES OF METALS

Aim

To gather first-hand data and use supplied second-hand data to rank metals in order of their activity

Safety issues

- Wear safety glasses throughout this experiment.
- Identify other safety issues relevant to this experiment by reading the method.

Materials

- 4 test tubes
- hot-water bath
- hotplate
- 250 mL of 2 mol/L sulfuric acid
- small strips of each of selected metals: Cu, Zn, Mg and Fe

Method

Gathering first-hand data

Part A: Reaction with dilute hydrochloric acid

1. Place a small sample of each metal in a separate test tube.
2. Add about 2–3 mL of dilute acid and observe any reactions.
3. Repeat the experiment at a higher temperature by placing the tubes in a hot water bath and note any changes after 10–15 minutes. (The water in the bath can be boiled and then the heat turned off. There is no need to continue boiling.)

Part B: Reaction with water

1. Use water instead of acid to test the reactivity of each metal as in part A.
2. After observing reactions at room temperature, place the tubes in a hot-water bath and note any further changes.

Analysing second-hand data

The following second-hand data is supplied for you to analyse.

Part C: Reaction with oxygen (air)

Table 7.10 shows the effect of heating a strip of each metal in air in a Bunsen burner flame.

Table 7.10 Effect of heating metal strips in a Bunsen burner flame

Metal	Observations
Cu	surface of strip darkens slowly on heating
Zn	surface becomes covered in a white powder
Mg	strip burns with a brilliant white flame, forming white, crumbly powder
Fe	strip glows and changes colour to a dull grey

Part D: Thermal decomposition of metal carbonates

Table 7.11 shows the effect of heating carbonates of the selected metals to 1000 °C.

Table 7.11 Effect of heating metal carbonates to 1000 °C

Metal carbonate	Observations
$CuCO_3$	green powder rapidly turns black; a colourless gas evolves rapidly; gas gives a positive limewater test
$ZnCO_3$	white powder does not change colour; colourless gas evolves; gas gives a positive limewater test
$MgCO_3$	white powder does not change colour; colourless gas evolves slowly; gas gives a positive limewater test
$FeCO_3$	grey-green powder turns black; colourless gas evolves quickly; gas gives a positive limewater test

Two other metal carbonates were also tested for thermal decomposition. The results are listed below:

- sodium carbonate — no changes observed; no gases evolved
- silver carbonate — yellow powder turns black on heating; gases evolved that give a positive limewater test and rekindles a glowing splint.

PRACTICAL ACTIVITIES

Results and analysis

1. Use your tabulated results of parts A and B to rank (where possible) the selected metals from most reactive to least reactive.

2. Process the data from part C and explain whether it is consistent with your ranked order established in parts A and B.

3. Examine the data in table 7.11.

   (a) Identify the gas that produces a positive limewater test.

   (b) Explain whether the data is consistent with the following generalisation:

   "The more active the metal, the more thermally stable its carbonate."

4. (a) Identify the gas that produces a positive glowing splint test.

   (b) Use the data on sodium carbonate and silver carbonate as well as your experimental results to establish an activity series for Cu, Zn, Mg, Fe, Na and Ag.

   (c) Write a balanced chemical equation for the thermal decomposition of silver carbonate based on the experimental data.

Conclusions

Write a brief conclusion for this experiment.

Chapter 8

THE PERIODIC TABLE

Introduction

As more metals and other elements were discovered, scientists recognised that patterns in their physical and chemical properties could be used to organise and classify the elements. The periodic table is a useful way of classifying elements.

In this chapter

Figure 8.1

The French chemist Antoine Lavoisier (1743–1794) is often called the 'father of chemistry'. He first defined the term 'element'. In this 1890s artwork, he is shown conducting an experiment on water. Lavoisier was executed by guillotine during the French Revolution.

8.1 *THE HISTORICAL DEVELOPMENT OF THE PERIODIC TABLE*

quantum: a fixed amount of energy. Quantum theory states that objects can possess only certain discrete amounts of energy.

cloud model of the atom: a model of the atom in which quantum theory uses mathematical probability functions to describe electrons as waves

Developing a model of the atom

In 1803, *John Dalton* proposed that matter was composed of atoms. The earliest models of atoms were very simple. Dalton visualised atoms as solid particles without any structure. Dalton proposed that one element differed from another because they had different atomic weights.

The discovery of the electron by *J. J. Thomson* in 1897 led to a new model of the atom. This model, formulated in 1904–09, is often called the plum pudding model as Thomson visualised the atom as a positive sphere in which negative electrons were embedded. The model has an unfortunate name as Thomson did not envisage the electrons to be arranged randomly but that there would be some pattern to their arrangement.

Ernest Rutherford developed the planetary model of the atom in 1911. His discovery of the nucleus led him to propose a model in which electrons orbited the central positive nucleus as planets orbit the Sun.

The Bohr model of the atom followed in 1913. *Niels Bohr* realised that the electrons must occupy stable, non-radiating orbits about the nucleus. He proposed that electrons occupy stable *shells* or *energy levels* around the central positive nucleus. Bohr was able to calculate the energies of an electron in each orbit of the hydrogen atom. He realised that electrons could move from one energy level to another by the absorption or emission of a **quantum** of energy.

An *octet* of electrons in the outer shell was shown to confer stability to an atom. Thus, the stability of the noble gases was related to the presence of these stable octets.

The currently accepted model is sometimes called the **cloud model of the atom**. In this model, developed by *Erwin Schrodinger* in 1927–35, the electrons are visualised as probability waves. The probability cloud is denser where there is greater chance of finding a particular electron at a specific location around the nucleus.

The development of an atomic model was influenced by the work being done to construct a periodic table of the elements. In the next section, we will see how these two developments led to a deep understanding of elements and matter.

Figure 8.2
Niels Bohr (1885–1962) proposed the shell model of the atom.

(a) Dalton's atomic theory (1803)

Solid sphere

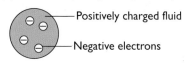

(b) Thomson's plum pudding model (1909)

Positively charged fluid

Negative electrons

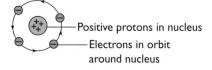

(c) Rutherford's planetary model (1911)

Positive protons in nucleus

Electrons in orbit around nucleus

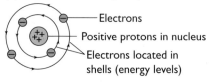

(d) Bohr's shell model (1913)

Electrons

Positive protons in nucleus

Electrons located in shells (energy levels)

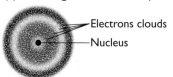

(e) Schrodinger's cloud model (1935)

Electrons clouds

Nucleus

Figure 8.3
Models of the atom

The evolution of the periodic table

Our knowledge of elements and their properties was very limited up to the middle of the seventeenth century. Before that time, chemists (or alchemists as they were known) were busy in their laboratories trying to understand the chemical nature of matter. They hoped to find a way of turning base metals such as lead into gold. They also sought to discover chemicals or elixirs that could prolong youth and prevent old age. Through their experiments, some new substances and chemical techniques were developed.

The initial stumbling block was the lack of understanding of what constituted a pure substance. In 1660, Robert Boyle took the first steps by clearly defining the terms 'element' and 'compound'. Some substances (such as water and salt) that were believed to be elements were eventually found to be compounds, as they could be broken down into simpler substances.

By the late eighteenth century, about 33 elements had been identified. Chemists now had sufficient information about the properties of these elements to begin to classify them.

Antoine Lavoisier (1743–1794)

Antoine Lavoisier (figure 8.1) is often called the father of modern chemistry as he established that elements were the fundamental building blocks of chemical substances. He examined their physical and chemical properties and classified materials into four groups or 'elements'. Lavoisier defined 'element' as a substance that could not be decomposed into simpler substances. His classification scheme of 1789 identified four groups of 'elements': *metals*, *non-metals*, *elastic fluids* (gases) and *earths*. Some of these 'elements' (earths) were much later shown to be compounds. Lavoisier also established the importance of accurate gravimetric analysis and the concept of mass conservation in a chemical change.

Johann Dobereiner (1780–1849)

Between 1817 and 1829, Johann Dobereiner observed the chemical similarity between certain groups of three elements, which he called *triads*. Dobereiner arranged the elements of each triad in order of their atomic weights. He noted that not only were the properties (such as density) of the middle element of each triad intermediate between the first and last, but also the atomic weight of the middle member was close to an average of the atomic weights of the other two. One such triad consisted of the elements lithium, sodium and potassium. Dobereiner pointed out that lithium reacted slowly with water while sodium reacted rapidly. Potassium, however, reacted violently. Table 8.1 provides examples of Dobereiner's triads.

Table 8.1 Two examples of Dobereiner's triads

Triad	Atomic weight	Density (g/cm³)	Sodium salt formula
Cl	35.45	1.56	NaCl
Br	79.90	3.12	NaBr
I	126.90	4.93	NaI
S	32.06	2.07	Na_2S
Se	78.96	4.81	Na_2Se
Te	127.60	6.25	Na_2Te

John Newlands (1837–1898)

Following the work of Dobereiner, the classification of elements made little progress until the early 1860s due to the lack of accurate atomic weight data. In 1864, John Newlands published a new classification of the elements. He arranged the elements in tabular form in order of increasing atomic weight, with spaces left for undiscovered elements. Newlands' 1866 table was divided into eight columns and seven rows with some elements occupying the same position. Later versions of this table omitted the undiscovered elements. Table 8.2 shows a portion of Newlands' table of the elements. The elements in each column are listed in order of increasing atomic weight.

Table 8.2 The first three columns of Newlands' periodic table

(1)	(2)	(3)
H	F	Cl
L*	Na	K
G*	Mg	Ca
B	Al	Cr
C	Si	Ti
N	P	Mn
O	S	Fe

*Newlands used these old symbols; L = Li; G = Be

Newlands noted that 'every eight element starting from a given one possessed similar physical and chemical properties'. Thus, the shaded elements (lithium, sodium and potassium) were chemically similar and were described as a family of elements. Newlands described this repeating pattern as the *law of octaves*. Unfortunately, his law often seemed to break down. For example, nitrogen and phosphorus are non-metals and not similar to manganese. Despite these problems, Newlands laid the foundations for the modern periodic table. In1887, his contributions were recognised by the Royal Society as being of great significance. He was awarded the prestigious Davy Medal.

Dmitri Mendeleev (1834–1907)

Dmitri Mendeleev, a Russian chemist, used the similarities in the physical and chemical properties of elements to produce his own classification of the elements. Like Newlands, he based his table of elements on their order of atomic weights. Where the atomic weight of the element was not accurately known, he placed the element in a position consistent with its properties. He left spaces for undiscovered elements in the belief that the properties of these undiscovered elements could be predicted by trends across the rows and down the columns of the table. A table published in 1871 consisted of eight columns (*groups*) and twelve rows (*series*). A portion of this table is shown in Figure 8.4.

Elements with similar chemical properties occupied the vertical groups of Mendeleev's table. Mendeleev noted that there was a gradation in physical properties down the groups. Today we recognise these vertical groupings as families of elements.

Series	Group							
	I	II	III	IV	V	VI	VII	VIII
1	H = 1							
2	Li = 7	Be = 9.4	B = 11	C = 12	N = 14	O = 16	F = 19	
3	Na = 23	Mg = 24	Al = 27.3	Si = 28	P = 31	S = 32	Cl = 35.5	
4	K = 39	Ca = 40	[ ] = 44	Ti = 48	V = 51	Cr = 52	Mn = 55	Fe = 56
								Co = 59
								Ni = 59
								Cu = 63
5		Zn = 65	[ ] = 68	[ ] = 72	As = 75	Se = 78	Br = 80	
12				Th = 231	U = 240			

Figure 8.4 A portion of Mendeleev's periodic table

Mendeleev also recognised that the pattern of properties repeated in each row or series. These repeating patterns or *periodic relationships* became expressed in Mendeleev's periodic law.

Periodic law (1869)
The properties of the elements vary periodically with their atomic weights.

Figure 8.5
Mendeleev arranged the elements according to increasing atomic weight, and left spaces for undiscovered elements.

The Royal Society awarded Mendeleev the Davy Medal in 1882, following the general acceptance of his table. However, the Society made no mention in its citation of the predictive ability of Mendeleev's table. Mendeleev spent the rest of his life promoting his periodic table. One of his most important contributions was to use the predictive ability of his table to help identify the properties of undiscovered elements. He made predictions about the properties of an undiscovered element by considering the properties of its neighbouring elements. An example of this is shown in table 8.3 for the then undiscovered element germanium. Mendeleev called this missing element 'eka-silicon', as it was expected to be 'like' the previously known member of the family, silicon. When germanium was discovered in 1886, its properties closely paralleled those predicted by Mendeleev in 1871.

Table 8.3 A comparison of the properties of germanium observed in 1886 with those predicted by Mendeleev in 1871 before its discovery

Property	1871 prediction for 'eka-silicon', Es	1886 observed properties of germanium, Ge
atomic weight	72	72.3
atomic volume (cm³/mol)	13	13
oxide formula	EsO_2	GeO_2
oxide density (g/cm³)	4.7	4.7
chloride formula	$EsCl_4$	$GeCl_4$
chloride boiling point (°C)	90	86

Lothar Meyer (1830–1895)

Mendeleev was not the only chemist who developed a periodic system of classification at this time. Lothar Meyer's periodic table (1864–70), which consisted of 56 elements, was similar to Mendeleev's. The periodic nature of the properties of the elements was revealed graphically when Meyer published graphs of the physical properties of the elements as a function of their atomic weights. Figure 8.6 shows a typical Meyer plot of atomic volume versus atomic weight.

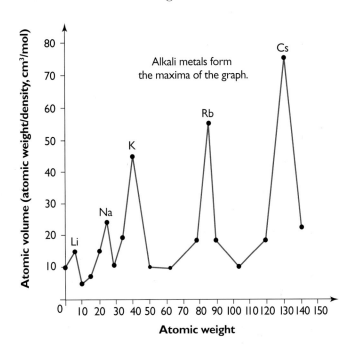

Figure 8.6
Meyer's periodic properties: atomic volume as a function of atomic weight

Mendeleev's table was superior to Meyer's in that it was based on chemical properties so generalisations could be made more readily. Both Meyer and Mendeleev were honoured with the Davy Medal in 1882 for their contributions to the periodic table.

William Ramsay (1852–1916)

Between 1893 and 1898, the English chemist William Ramsay and his team discovered a family of unreactive gases, including helium, neon and argon. Ramsay believed that this new family should be added to the right-hand end of Mendeleev's periodic table to create a new group. Mendeleev eventually added this new family (group VIII), which was called the *inert gases* and, more recently, the *noble gases.*

Henry Moseley (1887–1915)

In 1913, the Dutch physicist Anton van den Broek suggested that the elements of the periodic table be arranged according to the charge on their nucleus rather than according to their atomic weight. To test this idea, Henry Moseley undertook a series of experiments in 1912 and 1913 in which he investigated the X-ray spectra of ten consecutive elements of the periodic table. He discovered a mathematical relationship between the X-ray frequency and a 'fundamental quantity' for each element. In his paper published in 1913, Moseley states:

> "*There is in the atom a fundamental quantity, which increases by regular steps as we pass from one element to the next.*"

Moseley's 'fundamental quantity' was first called the atomic number (Z) by Ernest Rutherford in 1920. As a result of Moseley's work, the modern periodic table arranges elements in order of increasing atomic number (Z). The periodic law is now reframed.

Figure 8.8
Henry Moseley investigated the X-ray spectra of elements in the periodic table. He was killed in action at Gallipoli during World War I at 27 years of age.

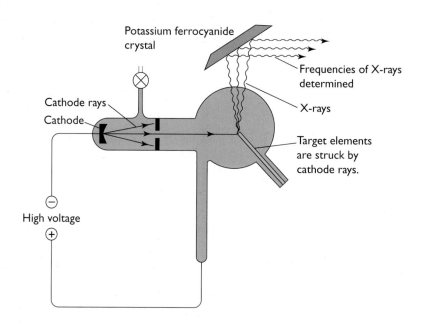

Potassium ferrocyanide crystal

Frequencies of X-rays determined

Cathode rays

Cathode

X-rays

Target elements are struck by cathode rays.

High voltage

Figure 8.7
Moseley's X-ray tube

Periodic law (present)

The properties of elements vary periodically with their atomic numbers.

J. J. Thomson (1856–1940)

J. J. Thomson discovered the electron in 1897 in his classic experiments with gas discharge tubes. He proposed that each element contained a unique number of electrons arranged in concentric rings within the atom.

Thomson suggested that those elements that belonged to the same family had similar properties because of similar arrangements of electrons. His plum pudding model of the atom (1904–09) was influenced by the periodic properties of the elements.

Niels Bohr (1885–1962)

Niels Bohr (figure 8.2) produced his model of the atom in 1913 (see pages 141–2). In this model, the electrons occupied concentric energy levels or shells around the nucleus. Bohr proposed that elements in the same group of the periodic table should have the same number of electrons in the outer shell (the valence shell). This same number of valence electrons gave these family members similar chemical properties.

Bohr's shell model also explained the properties of the noble gases. The presence of eight electrons in the outer shell of all the noble gases (except helium with a filled *K* shell) was responsible for the chemical inertness of these elements.

Wolfgang Pauli (1900–1958)

Wolfgang Pauli was able to explain the length of each period of the periodic table using his quantum theory discoveries. He reasoned that no two electrons could exist in the same 'quantised states'. As a consequence, Pauli was able to show that the quantum theory could predict the number of elements that would occupy each of the periods of the periodic table. Thus, he showed that period 1 should contain only two elements while period 2 could accommodate eight elements.

8.1 DATA ANALYSIS
Modelling the periodic table

8.1 QUESTIONS

1. Dobereiner identified sets of three elements with similar properties. He called these sets triads. Identify which of the following sets of elements that Dobereiner would have recognised as a triad.
   A   S, Se, Te
   B   Li, Be, B
   C   O, S, As
   D   Al, Ga, Ge

2. Newlands developed a periodic table in 1864. This table
   A   classified elements according to the number of electrons in their valence shells.
   B   arranged elements in order of their increasing atomic weights.
   C   turned out to be identical to Mendeleev's table.
   D   is identical to Dobereiner's periodic table.

3. Mendeleev's periodic table
   A   arranged elements according to the number of neutrons in an atom's nucleus.
   B   consisted of eighteen families of elements.
   C   created families of elements in each column.
   D   was based on the law of octaves.

4. Between 1864 and 1870, Lothar Meyer developed a periodic table containing 56 elements, which was similar to Mendeleev's table. Another major contribution that he made to the classification of elements was
   A   demonstrating periodicity by drawing graphs of the physical properties of each element as a function of atomic weight.
   B   providing data for Newlands to use in his periodic table.
   C   arranging the elements according to similarities in their chemical properties.
   D   writing a book in which he described the properties of the known 56 elements.

5. In the period 1893–98, William Ramsay and his team discovered the noble gases. Their discovery posed a problem for the classification of the elements because
   A   their proton numbers did not fit into the existing pattern.
   B   the trend in their ionisation energies did not fit the existing periodic pattern.
   C   their zero valence suggested that they should occupy a period of their own.
   D   Mendeleev's periodic table had not allocated space for this new family of elements.

6. The following lines of a poem were written by E. H. Lewis in 1925 in remembrance of Henry Moseley and his important contribution to our understanding of the atom and the arrangement of elements in the periodic table.

"He numbers the charge on the centre for each of the elements,
That we named for gods and demons, colours, tastes and scents."

Explain how these lines of the poem relate to Moseley's contributions.

7. Outline the contributions of J. J. Thomson and Niels Bohr to the development of the periodic table.

8. Four years before the metal gallium was discovered, Mendeleev predicted some of its properties. He called the unknown element 'eka-aluminium', Ea. Table 8.4 compares some of these properties.

Table 8.4

Property	Predictions about 'eka-aluminium', Ea	Observed properties of gallium, Ga
atomic weight	68	69.7
density	5.9	5.9
oxide formula	Ea_2O_3	Ga_2O_3

(a) Explain the meaning of the prefix 'eka'.
(b) Explain how Mendeleev could make such predictions about an undiscovered element.
(c) Predict the formula that Mendeleev would have written for the chloride of 'eka-aluminium'.

8.2 PERIODIC TRENDS

Structure of the modern periodic table

The modern periodic table uses the atomic number (Z) to arrange and classify the elements into vertical groups and horizontal periods. The current table consists of seven horizontal periods and eighteen vertical groups. The last two periods contain the subseries known as the *lanthanoid* and *actinoid* series. For convenience, these are located below the main part of the table. Each vertical group represents a family of chemically related elements.

The position of the first element, hydrogen, is different in different versions of the table. In periodic table on the HSC datasheet (see inside front cover), hydrogen is placed at the top of group I, above lithium and sodium, as it has one valence shell electron. Its chemical properties, however, are unlike the rest of the group. The atomic weight listed for each element is the weighted average of all its natural isotopes.

The seven periods

Each horizontal row represents a period. Hydrogen and helium are the only two elements in period 1. The K shell of helium is full with two electrons.

Periods 2 and 3 are short, with only eight elements each. From left to right across each of these periods, the elements change from strongly metallic to non-metals, and finally noble gases. Neon and argon, with their stable octets, complete periods 2 and 3 respectively.

Figure 8.9
Gallium is chemically similar to aluminium — both are members of group III of the periodic table. Gallium is liquid at room temperature so it melts in a person's hand.

There are eighteen elements in each of periods 4 and 5. The *transition metals* are a special subseries of elements located in these periods between the active metals on the left and the soft metals on the right. The *M* shell at the end of period 3 is not full so the transition metals of period 4 represent a series in which the *M* shell is progressively filled. In the transition metals of period 5, the electrons are progressively added to the *N* shell.

The two subseries called the lanthanoids and actinoids, which have similar physical and chemical properties, make periods 6 and 7 very long. The actinoid series contains radioactive and synthetic elements. As elements beyond element 118 are synthesised, an eighth period will be added to the table.

Groups of the periodic table

There are eighteen vertical groups of the periodic table. These groups are numbered from left to right using either Roman numerals or the numbers 1 to 18. The Roman numeral scheme is still quite commonly used, although the trend is to number the groups from 1 to 18. Thus, group V is also referred to as group 15. Group VII is also called group 17.

- Group I or group 1 (Li, Na, K, Rb, Cs, Fr) — This group is known as the *alkali metals*. They are highly reactive, low-density metals with a valency of +1. Their oxides and hydroxides dissolve in water to produce strongly alkaline solutions.
- Group II or group 2 (Be, Mg, Ca, Sr, Ba, Ra) — This group is commonly known as the *alkaline earth metals*. They are reactive metals but not as reactive as group I metals. They have a valency of +2. Their oxides and hydroxides produce alkaline solutions.

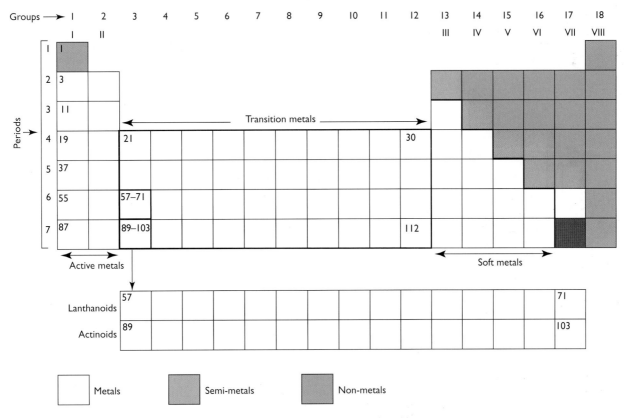

Figure 8.10 The annotated periodic table

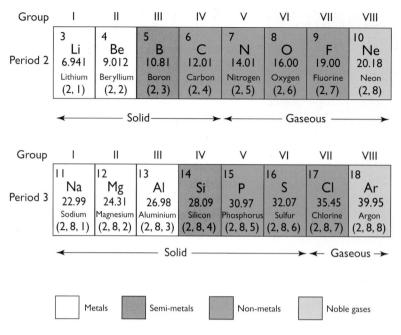

Group	I	II	III	IV	V	VI	VII	VIII
Period 2	3 Li 6.941 Lithium (2, 1)	4 Be 9.012 Beryllium (2, 2)	5 B 10.81 Boron (2, 3)	6 C 12.01 Carbon (2, 4)	7 N 14.01 Nitrogen (2, 5)	8 O 16.00 Oxygen (2, 6)	9 F 19.00 Fluorine (2, 7)	10 Ne 20.18 Neon (2, 8)

← Solid → ← Gaseous →

Group	I	II	III	IV	V	VI	VII	VIII
Period 3	11 Na 22.99 Sodium (2, 8, 1)	12 Mg 24.31 Magnesium (2, 8, 2)	13 Al 26.98 Aluminium (2, 8, 3)	14 Si 28.09 Silicon (2, 8, 4)	15 P 30.97 Phosphorus (2, 8, 5)	16 S 32.07 Sulfur (2, 8, 6)	17 Cl 35.45 Chlorine (2, 8, 7)	18 Ar 39.95 Argon (2, 8, 8)

← Solid → ← Gaseous →

☐ Metals ▨ Semi-metals ▨ Non-metals ▨ Noble gases

Figure 8.11 Periods 2 and 3

- Groups 3 to 12 (transition metals) — Many common metals used in industry (such as iron, nickel and copper) are transition metals. These metals are typically hard with a high density with valencies from +1 to +4. They tend to form coloured ionic salts with non-metals and negative radicals. They have incomplete inner electron shells.

- Group III or group 13 (B, Al, Ga, In, Tl) — Boron is a semi-metal and the remaining elements are increasingly metallic down the group. These are soft metals with low melting points and a valency of +3.

- Group IV or group 14 (C, Si, Ge, Sn, Pb) — Carbon is a non-metal while silicon and germanium are semi-metals. Both tin and lead are soft metals. All these elements have a valency of +4. Tin and lead also form ionic compounds in which the metals have a valency of +2 or +4.

- Group V or group 15 (N, P, As, Sb, Bi) — Both nitrogen and phosphorus are non-metals while arsenic and antimony are semi-metals. Bismuth is a soft metal. The common valencies of this group are +3 and +5. Bismuth forms ionic compounds in which its valency is +3.

- Group VI or group 16 (O, S, Se, Te, Po) — The first three elements are non-metals. Tellurium is a semi-metal and polonium is a radioactive, soft metal. The common valencies of this group are −2, +4 and +6. In binary ionic salts, the non-metals have a valency of −2.

- Group VII or group 17 (F, Cl, Br, I, At) — This group is commonly known as the *halogens* ('salt formers') as they combine with metals to form ionic salts. All members are non-metals, although astatine is sometimes classified as a semi-metal. Astatine is also radioactive. The common valency of this group is −1 although, in some compounds, they exhibit a valency of +7. In ionic salts, these elements have a valency of −1.

- Group VIII or group 18 (He, Ne, Ar, Kr, Xe, Rn) — This group is called the *noble gases*. They are generally inert, although some compounds of krypton and xenon have been prepared. Radon is a radioactive noble gas. These non-metals have a stable valence shell.

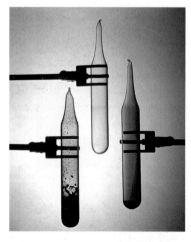

Figure 8.12

The group VII elements are known as the halogens. The flasks (left to right) contain iodine I_2, a grey-black solid that readily sublimes; chorine Cl_2, a greenish-yellow gas; and bromine Br_2, a red-brown liquid that readily forms a vapour of the same colour.

13	14	15	16	17
III	IV	V	VI	VII
5 B Semi-metal	6 C Non-metal	7 N Non-metal	8 O Non-metal	9 F Non-metal
13 Al Metal	14 Si Semi-metal	15 P Non-metal	16 S Non-metal	17 Cl Non-metal
31 Ga Metal	32 Ge Semi-metal	33 As Semi-metal	34 Se Non-metal	35 Br Non-metal
49 In Metal	50 Sn Metal	51 Sb Semi-metal	52 Te Semi-metal	53 I Non-metal
81 Tl Metal	82 Pb Metal	83 Bi Metal	84 Po Metal	85 At Non-metal

Some semi-metallic properties

Figure 8.13
Metallic trends for groups III to VII

metallic character: the tendency of an element to have the properties of metals. The presence of mobile electrons in the lattice is indicative of metals.

- The main block is the grouping of elements that excludes the transition metals.
- *Lanthanoid series* — These are all soft, grey metals that react vigorously with water to release hydrogen gas and produce alkaline solutions. Their most common valency is +3, although valencies of +2 and +4 exist.
- *Actinoid series* — These are all radioactive metals. Some are naturally occurring but others have been synthesised in nuclear reactors or in particle accelerators. They react vigorously with water to release hydrogen gas and produce alkaline solutions. The typical valencies of these metals are +3, +4, +5 and +6.

Trends in the periodic table

The periodic table is a wonderful predictive tool. There are many physical and chemical properties that show distinct trends across a period or down a group. It is important to be able to explain these trends in terms of atomic structure.

Electrical conductivity

Generally the electrical conductivity is related to the **metallic character** of an element. The trend in this property is not uniform across the periodic table. Silver, copper, gold and aluminium have the highest electrical conductivities.

Table 8.5 Trends in electrical conductivity in the periodic table

Trends	Electrical conductivity
across a period	generally *decreases* as elements become less metallic. Non-metals do not have free mobile electrons in their crystal lattice.
down a group	generally *increases* as elements become more metallic (except group III). Down a group, the valence shell electrons become further away from the nucleus and can more easily escape into the lattice.

Atomic radius

The radius of an atom depends on the number of electron shells and the size of the nuclear charge. Electron shells are attracted inwards as the charge on the nucleus increases.

Table 8.6 Trends in atomic radius in the periodic table

Trends	Atomic radius
across a period	*decreases* as the valence shell moves closer towards the increasingly positive nucleus
down a group	*increases* as the number of electron shells increases

Ionisation energy

Valence shell electrons are more readily removed if they are further from the nucleus, or if the nucleus has a smaller positive charge. The presence of shielding inner electron shells also reduces the energy required to ionise an atom.

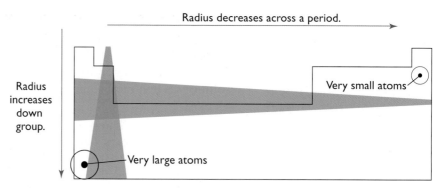

Figure 8.14 Diagrammatic trend of atomic radius

Table 8.7 Trends in ionisation energy in the periodic table

Trends	Ionisation energy
across a period	*increases* because the atomic radius decreases across a period so the valence electrons are closer to the nucleus
down a group	*decreases* because the atomic radius increases as there are more electron shells. The outershell electrons are not as strongly attracted to the nucleus in atoms with more shells.

Melting and boiling points

The strength of the bonding in the crystal lattice affects the melting and boiling points of the element. Metallic lattices vary considerably in the strength of the metallic bond. The metallic bond is at its strongest in the transition metals. In covalent network crystals (such as carbon and silicon), the binding forces are very strong and the melting and boiling points are very high. In covalent molecular crystals (such as sulfur and phosphorus), the intermolecular forces are weak and the elements have low melting and boiling points.

Table 8.8 Trends in melting and boiling points in the periodic table

Trends	Melting and boiling points
across a period	• *increases* initially (from group I to group IV) and then *decreases* as the lattice changes from metallic to covalent network and then covalent molecular
down a group	• *decreases* in groups I to IV • *increases* in groups V to VIII • generally *increases* for transition metals

Electronegativity

Apart from the noble gases, non-metals have high **electronegativity** as they attract electrons to complete their valence shell. Fluorine has the highest electronegativity. In contrast, metals tend to lose electrons from their valence shell and so have very low electronegativity. Francium has the lowest electronegativity.

electronegativity: a measure of the electron-attracting ability of an element. Non-metals are very electronegative while metals are electropositive.

Table 8.9 Trends in electronegativity in the periodic table

Trends	Electronegativity
across a period	*increases* as the metallic character decreases
down a group	*decreases* as the metallic character increases

Valency

The group number indicates the maximum valency of an element. Group VIII elements, however, have a valency of zero. Elements in the same group tend to have the same valency, although several valencies are common for elements in groups V, VI and VII (see table 3.8 and pages 65–6).

Table 8.10 Trends in valency (combining power) in the periodic table

Trends	Valency
across a period	Maximum valency *increases* from groups I to VII, in which group number equals maximum valency.
down a group	Maximum valency is *constant* and equal to the group number (except for group VIII with a valency of 0).

Reactivity

There are no simple trends in reactivity of elements across periods or down groups (table 8.11). The noble gases are very unreactive. The heavy metals in the lower central region of the transition metals are the least reactive. The most reactive metals are found at the bottom of groups I and II.

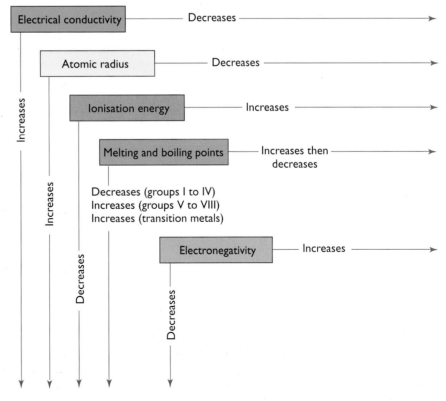

Figure 8.15 Diagrammatic summary of periodic trends

Table 8.11 Trends in reactivity in the periodic table

Trends	Reactivity
across a period	Each period starts with a reactive metal and ends with an unreactive noble gas.
down a group	• *increases* down groups I and II. • *decreases* down the group of transition metals. • *decreases* down groups III and IV for soft metals. • generally *decreases* down groups V to VII for non-metals. • *increases* down the group of noble gases.

Sodium is a highly reactive, soft, silvery-white metal at room temperature.

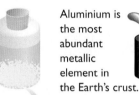

Aluminium is the most abundant metallic element in the Earth's crust.

Phosphorus is a highly reactive element that is essential to life.

Argon is an inert (noble) gas used in electric light bulbs.

| 11
Sodium
Na | 12
Magnesium
Mg | | 13
Aluminium
Al | 14
Silicon
Si | 15
Phosphorus
P | 16
Sulfur
S | 17
Chlorine
Cl | 18
Argon
Ar |

Magnesium metal does not occur naturally. Because of its strength and low density, alloys of magnesium are used in the aircraft industry.

Pure silicon is a hard, grey solid with a crystalline structure similar to diamond.

Sulfur is a yellow, crystalline solid at room temperature.

Chlorine is a toxic greenish-yellow gas at room temperature. It is used for bleaching and disinfecting.

Figure 8.16 The elements of period 3 have a variety of different uses.

SAMPLE PROBLEM 8.1

Figure 8.17 shows the trend in property X of the elements with increasing atomic number. Identify which of the following properties is consistent with the trends shown in the graph.

A Boiling point
B First ionisation energy
C Valency
D Electrical conductivity

SOLUTION

The graph shows that property X increases across a period (left to right) and decreases down a group (note that the maxima decrease in size as Z increases). Thus, the answer is B (first ionisation energy). Electrons are harder to remove as the nuclear charge increases across a period. Down a group, the ionisation energy decreases as the atomic radius increases and the valence shell moves further away from the nucleus. Although the maximum valency increases across a period, it remains constant within a group.

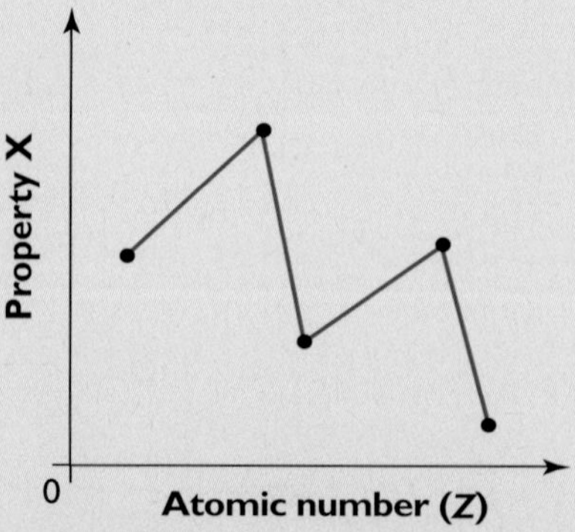

Figure 8.17
Graph of property X versus atomic number

12. COMPUTER SPREADSHEETS: TABULATING AND GRAPHING

A computer spreadsheet, such as Microsoft Excel®, allows numerical data to be tabulated, sorted and graphed. Spreadsheet applications also allow you to use formulae to calculate new data.

1. **Tabulating data**
   (a) A spreadsheet consists of columns (A, B, C etc.) and rows (1, 2, 3 etc.).
   (b) Decide how many columns and rows your table will require. For example, if you are tabulating data on the trend in ionisation energy versus atomic number for the first 10 elements of the periodic table, you will need two columns and eleven rows. The first row is used for the headings of each column.
   (c) Use cells A1 and B1 for the column headings as shown in table 8.12.
   (d) Enter the values 1 to 10 for the atomic numbers in cells A2 to A11. Enter the following values of the ionisation energy for each element in cells B2 to B11: 1.32, 2.38, 0.53, 0.91, 0.81, 1.09, 1.41, 1.32, 1.69, 2.09.

Table 8.12

	A	B
1	Atomic number (Z)	Ionisation energy (MJ)
2	1	1.32
3	2	2.38

2. **Graphing data**
   (a) Drawing an XY graph for a data series: Draw an XY graph of the data in table 8.12.
   (b) Drawing an XY graph for two data series: You may wish to compare the values for the ionisation energy of two vertical groups of the periodic table. Table 8.13 shows two such series of data in spreadsheet format.

8.2 **DATA ANALYSIS**
Computer graphing — periodic trends

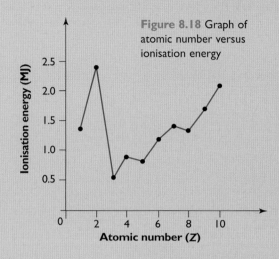

Figure 8.18 Graph of atomic number versus ionisation energy

Table 8.13

	A	B	C	D
1	Atomic number (Z)	Group II ionisation energy (MJ)	Atomic number (Z)	Group VI ionisation energy (MJ)
2	4	0.91	8	1.32
3	12	0.74	16	1.01
4	20	0.60	34	0.95
5	38	0.56	52	0.89
6	56	0.51	84	0.82

Draw an XY graph of the two data series in table 8.13.

Name the first series 'Group II' and the new series 'Group VI'.

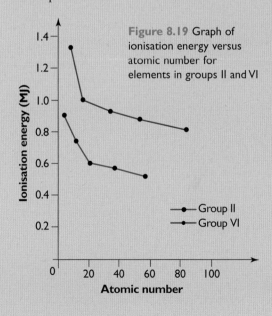

Figure 8.19 Graph of ionisation energy versus atomic number for elements in groups II and VI

8.2 QUESTIONS

1. Identify the elements in the following set that are transition metals: Mo, Sn, Y, Be, Sb, V, Au, Os, Cs.

2. Identify the elements in the following set that are (a) lanthanoids (b) actinoids: Er, Lr, Sn, Ce, Pu, Np, Fr, Ag, Dy.

3. Recall a characteristic property of the elements in the following groups or series.
   (a) Group II
   (b) Group VI
   (c) Group VIII
   (d) Actinides

4. Describe the trend in the following properties across a period and down a group.
   (a) Valency
   (b) Ionisation energy
   (c) Electronegativity
   (d) Electrical conductivity

5. Element A is a member of group VI. It forms an ionic salt with calcium with the formula CaA. It forms a covalent compound with chlorine with the formula ACl_2. It also forms two molecular oxides with formulae AO_2 and AO_3.
   (a) Identify the valency of A in each of the compounds described.
   (b) Explain which elements of group VI would have the properties exhibited by element A.

6. Explain why the melting points of the halogens increase down the group.

7. Figure 8.20 shows the relationship between property P and atomic number for the elements of period 3.

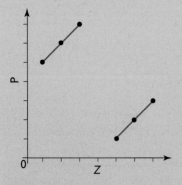

Figure 8.20
Relationship between property P and atomic number

Identify which of the following properties could correspond with P.
A Melting point
B Electrical conductivity
C Valency of the most common ion
D Electronegativity

8. Sketch a graph showing the number of valence shell electrons versus atomic number for the first 20 elements of the periodic table.

9. Consider the following data for successive ionisation energies (MJ/mol) for elements P, Q and R. Use these data to identify the periodic group to which each element belongs.

Table 8.14

P:	0.50	4.57	6.92	9.55	13.36	16.62	20.12	25.50
Q:	1.01	2.26	3.37	4.57	7.02	8.50	27.11	31.68
R:	0.79	1.58	3.24	4.36	16.10	19.8	23.79	29.26

10. The first ionisation energies (MJ/mol) for four consecutive elements (B, C, D, E) of the periodic table are: B, 1.257; C, 1.527; D, 0.425; E, 0.596. Identify the periodic groups to which each element belongs. Justify your answer.

11. The following data was collected for the first four elements (D, E, F and G) of a group of the periodic table.

   • All elements are diatomic.
   • D_2 is a pale, yellow-green gas.
   • E_2 is a green-yellow gas.
   • F_2 is a red-brown, fuming liquid.
   • G_2 has black-violet, shiny crystals.
   • E reacts with sodium to form white crystals with the formula NaE.
   (a) Identify the periodic group to which these elements belong.
   (b) Use the correct symbol for element E to write a balanced chemical equation for its reaction with sodium.

12. The following compounds are formed by the elements of group V: Na_3N, H_3N, PCl_3, H_3AsO_4, SbF_3, $BiBr_3$. Determine the valencies exhibited by the group V elements in these compounds.

13. The numerical values of a physical property X of the first six elements of period 3 are 98, 650, 660, 1410, 44 and 113. Identify a physical property that shows such a trend. Justify your answer.

13. USING INSTRUCTION TERMS CORRECTLY

When answering questions, it is important to know what the instruction terms (verbs) require you to do. Here are some examples.

'Assess'

This instruction term requires you to make a judgement of value, quality, outcome, results or size. A balanced judgement is important.

Example:

Assess the safety issues involved in heating magnesium metal in dilute hydrochloric acid in a school laboratory.

Answer:

The reaction of magnesium metal in dilute acid is an exothermic reaction in which a small amount of heat is released. This would not normally be a problem as long as the magnesium is in ribbon rather than powdered form. In ribbon form, it will react slowly and the heat will be dissipated. Heating the acid, however, means that the reaction rate will increase, even with a magnesium ribbon. It is important, therefore, not to heat the reaction tube too strongly. In addition, the hydrogen evolved creates an explosive mixture. This process is best done in a hot-water bath over an electric hotplate so that no naked flame is present to ignite the hydrogen. When heating metals in a test tube of acid, there is always the risk of violent boiling so safety glasses are essential.

'Recall'

This instruction term requires you to present remembered facts, ideas or experiences.

Example:

Recall the common group name of the elements of group I of the periodic table.

Answer:

The alkali metals

eBookplus

Weblinks

eBookplus

Checkpoint
Revision 4

eBookplus

Checkpoint
Revision 4 Answers

SUMMARY

- Chemists such as Dalton, Thomson, Rutherford, Bohr and Schrodinger proposed various atomic models.

- Lavoisier and Dobereiner were the early pioneers involved in classification of the elements.

- Newlands developed a periodic table in which elements were arranged in order of increasing atomic weight.

- Mendeleev improved on Newlands' table by considering similarities in chemical and physical properties as well as leaving spaces for undiscovered elements.

- Thomson, Bohr and Pauli provided a theoretical basis for the structure of the periodic table.

- The periodic law is the basis of the predictive nature of the periodic table.

- The modern periodic table arranges elements in periods and groups according to increasing atomic number.

- Elements belonging to a particular group exhibit a pattern of electronic configuration.

- Most physical and chemical properties of the elements and their compounds show trends across periods and down groups.

DATA ANALYSIS

8.1 DATA ANALYSIS

MODELLING THE PERIODIC TABLE

Part A: The elements of period 2

Table 8.16 shows the eight elements of period 2 (*A* to *H*) represented randomly on eight 'cards' with a list of properties of that element. Table 8.16 provides the key to the properties. (*Note:* Some of the data for elements *A* and *G* is missing.)

1. Place the eight cards in a logical order based on trends in the data and properties listed on the cards. The first card should be the most metallic element and the last card should be a noble gas.

2. Once you have determined the correct order of the cards, try to predict the missing data for elements *A* and *G*.

Table 8.15 Properties listed in table 8.16

X	code symbol for element
s	state at 25 °C
c	metal/semi-metal/non-metal
mp	melting point (°C)
I_1	first ionisation energy (MJ)
El	electronegativity
HC	heat conductivity (J/s/m/K)
OF	oxide formula
OB	oxide bonding
CF	chloride formula
CB	chloride bonding

Table 8.16 Elements of period 2

X	*A*		**X**	*B*		**X**	*C*		**X**	*D*
s	solid		**s**	gas		**s**	solid		**s**	gas
c	non-metal		**c**	non-metal		**c**	metal		**c**	non-metal
mp	3974		**mp**	−249		**mp**	1278		**mp**	−220
I_1	1.1		I_1	2.1		I_1	0.9		I_1	1.3
El	2.55		**El**	0		**El**	1.57		**El**	3.44
HC	2000		**HC**	0.049		**HC**	200		**HC**	0.026
OF	AO_2		**OF**	–		**OF**	CO		**OF**	DO
OB	covalent		**OB**	–		**OB**	partly ionic		**OB**	covalent
CF	–		**CF**	–		**CF**	CCl_2		**CF**	DCl_2
CB	–		**CB**	–		**CB**	partly ionic		**CB**	covalent

X	*E*		**X**	*F*		**X**	*G*		**X**	*H*
s	solid		**s**	solid		**s**	gas		**s**	gas
c	semi-metal		**c**	metal		**c**	non-metal		**c**	non-metal
mp	2300		**mp**	180		**mp**	−220		**mp**	−210
I_1	0.8		I_1	0.5		I_1	1.7		I_1	1.4
El	2.04		**El**	0.98		**El**	3.98		**El**	3.04
HC	27		**HC**	85		**HC**	0.028		**HC**	0.026
OF	E_2O_3		**OF**	F_2O		**OF**	–		**OF**	H_2O_5
OB	covalent		**OB**	ionic		**OB**	–		**OB**	covalent
CF	ECl_3		**CF**	FCl		**CF**	–		**CF**	HCl_3
CB	covalent		**CB**	ionic		**CB**	–		**CB**	covalent

DATA ANALYSIS

Part B: Properties of an unknown element

Table 8.18 shows a section of the periodic table containing elements *A*, *B*, *C*, *D*, *F*, *G*, *H* and *I* and their properties. An unknown element *E* is also shown. Table 8.17 provides the key to the properties.

1. Use this data to predict the properties of the unknown element *E*. (*Hint:* See the periodic table on the inside front cover.)

2. Use a book of published chemical data to identify the unknown element *E* and compare your predictions with the measured data.

Table 8.17 Properties listed in table 8.18

X	code symbol for element
d	density (g/cm³)
mp	melting point (°C)
bp	boiling point (°C)
HC	heat conductivity (J/s/m/K)
EC	electrical conductivity (MS/m)
I_1	first ionisation energy (kJ)
OF	oxide formula

Table 8.18 Elements in a section of the periodic table

X	*A*	*B*	*C*
d	5.32	5.72	4.80
mp	937	817	217
bp	2830	sublimes at 613	685
HC	60	50	3
EC	10^{-4}	3.9	10^{-4}
I_1	768	953	947
OF	AO_2	B_2O_3	CO_2

X	*D*	*E*	*F*
d	7.30		6.24
mp	232		450
bp	2602		990
HC	67		3
EC	8.7		10^{-4}
I_1	715		876
OF	DO_2		FO_2

X	*G*	*H*	*I*
d	11.3	9.8	9.4
mp	327	271	254
bp	1740	1560	962
HC	35	7.9	20
EC	4.8	0.84	0.7
I_1	722	710	818
OF	GO_2	H_2O_3	IO_2

DATA ANALYSIS

8.2 DATA ANALYSIS

COMPUTER GRAPHING: PERIODIC TRENDS

Part A: Trend in electronegativity across a period

The following data and information is provided for the elements of period 3.

1. Open a spreadsheet application, such as Microsoft Excel.

2. Copy the following headings and data into the first two columns.

Table 8.19

Atomic number (Z)	Electronegativity
11	0.93
12	1.31
13	1.61
14	1.90
15	2.19
16	2.58
17	3.16

3. Construct an XY graph and draw a smooth line through the data points.

4. Describe the trend in electronegativity across period 3.

5. Explain the trend in electronegativity across period 3.

6. Explain why electronegativity data was not provided for element 18.

Part B: Trend in density down selected groups

The following density data is provided for the elements of groups I and IV.

1. Open a spreadsheet application, such as Microsoft Excel.

2. Copy the following headings and data into the first four columns.

Table 8.20

Atomic number (Z)	Density (group I)	Atomic number (Z)	Density (group IV)
3	0.53	6	2.26
11	0.97	14	2.33
19	0.86	32	5.32
37	1.53	50	7.30
55	1.87	82	11.3

3. Construct an XY graph of these two data series.

4. Describe the trend in density down (a) group I and (b) group IV.

5. Identify any anomalies in these trends for either group.

6. Compare the densities of group I elements with group IV elements.

Chapter 9 CHEMICAL ANALYSIS

Introduction

Chemical industries across the world employ analytical chemists to investigate the composition of materials. These days, analytical chemists use instrumental methods to more accurately determine the composition of a material. However, older methods (often called 'wet' methods) are still used in chemical analysis.

In this chapter

Figure 9.1

There is now a wide range of sensitive instruments for many types of chemical analysis.

9.1 ATOMIC WEIGHT AND THE MOLE THEORY

relative atomic mass: another name for atomic weight, which is now the IUPAC standard terminology

isotopes: atoms with the same atomic number but different mass numbers due to the presence of different numbers of neutrons

Mass and chemical change

The law of mass conservation in a chemical reaction is the first and most fundamental law of chemistry.

> *Law of mass conservation*
> In a chemical change, there is no gain or loss of mass.

Another way of expressing this law is:

mass of reactants = mass of products

English chemist John Dalton (1764–1844) explained the law of mass conservation using his atomic model. He realised that, in a chemical reaction, the atoms were rearranged into new substances but that there was no net loss or gain of atoms. Dalton also realised that the atoms of each element had their own unique mass, and he developed a table of relative atomic weights for many elements.

H	C	S	Fe	Ag
Hydrogen	Carbon	Sulfur	Iron	Silver
1	12	32	56	108

Figure 9.3 Each element has atoms of unique mass.

Atomic weight

Dalton established a table of the atomic weights of the atoms of different elements. He did this by determining the mass of one element that would react with another. In some cases, his calculations of atomic weight (or **relative atomic mass**) were wrong but, over the next 50 years and through the work of many chemists, these tables of atomic weight improved in accuracy. The early tables of atomic weights used hydrogen as a reference as it was the lightest atom. Atoms of hydrogen were assigned an atomic weight of 1. Other elements then had atomic weights that were greater than 1. Since then, however, other elements have been used as reference standards. The current standard is the carbon-12 **isotope**.

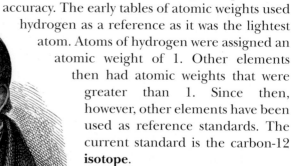

Figure 9.2 English chemist John Dalton (1764–1844) introduced modern atomic theory and used this theory to explain the conservation of mass in a chemical change.

A sample of water was electrolysed in electrolysis apparatus to produce hydrogen and oxygen. The hydrogen and oxygen formed were collected separately and weighed.

$$\text{water} \rightarrow \text{hydrogen} + \text{oxygen}$$

Use the following data for the electrolysis of water to verify the law of mass conservation.

Initial mass of apparatus including water = 187.271 g
Final mass of apparatus after electrolysis = 187.126 g
Mass of hydrogen collected = 0.016 g
Mass of oxygen collected = 0.129 g

SOLUTION

Mass of water electrolysed = 187.271 – 187.126
= 0.145 g
Mass of hydrogen + oxygen formed = 0.016 + 0.129
= 0.145 g

Thus, the mass of water that decomposed equals the mass of hydrogen and oxygen formed.

The term 'atomic weight' rather than 'atomic mass' is the current convention used by IUPAC (International Union of Pure and Applied Chemistry).

There has been much controversy in the last 30–40 years over the use of these terms. Physicists measure mass in grams or kilograms and weight in newtons. For many years, chemists used 'atomic mass' so that its unit of measurement (gram) would be consistent with physics.

In more recent times, IUPAC proposed that the historical term 'atomic weight' be used instead. 'Atomic weight' is used in the HSC examination, in the periodic table and in standard chemistry data books.

Table 9.1 shows the relative atomic masses or atomic weights (A_r) of selected elements. For example, atoms of gold, Au, are much heavier than atoms of magnesium, Mg.

Table 9.1 Atomic weights of selected elements

Element	H	C	N	O	Mg	S	Cl	Zn	Au
Atomic weight (A_r)	1.008	12.01	14.01	16.00	24.31	32.07	35.45	65.39	197.0

Molecular weight

The relative molecular mass of any compound is correctly referred to as the molecular weight (M_r). The term 'formula weight' is sometimes used. For any compound,

molecular weight = sum of atomic weights

$$M_r = \Sigma(A_r)$$

SAMPLE PROBLEM 9.2

Equal masses (5.0 g) of powdered magnesium and zinc were allowed to burn in oxygen to produce their oxides. The solid products were collected and weighed. The mass of magnesium oxide, MgO, produced was 8.29 g and the mass of zinc oxide, ZnO, was 6.22 g.

(a) Calculate the mass of oxygen that reacted with 5.0 g of each metal.

(b) Calculate the ratio of metal to oxygen for each reaction, and compare it with the ratio of their atomic weights.

(c) Account for the difference in mass of the two products.

SOLUTION

(a) Using the law of mass conservation, the mass of oxygen that combined with 5.0 g of:
Mg = 8.29 – 5.0 = 3.29 g
Zn = 6.22 – 5.0 = 1.22 g

(b) The mass ratio of Mg to O
$$= 5.0 : 3.29 = 1.52 : 1.$$
The ratio of atomic weights $A_r(Mg)$ to $A_r(O)$
$$= 24.31 : 16 = 1.52 : 1.$$
These ratios are the same.
The mass ratio of Zn to O
$$= 5.0 : 1.22 = 4.09 : 1.$$
The ratio of atomic weights $A_r(Zn)$ to $A_r(O)$
$$= 65.39 : 16.00 = 4.09 : 1$$
These ratios are the same.

(c) Magnesium atoms are much lighter than zinc atoms and much closer in mass to oxygen atoms. Thus, the mass of products and their mass ratios differ.

SAMPLE PROBLEM 9.3

Use the data in table 9.1 to calculate the molecular weight of:
(a) nitrogen dioxide
(b) gold (III) oxide.

SOLUTION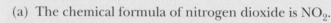

(a) The chemical formula of nitrogen dioxide is NO_2.
$$\therefore M_r = \Sigma(A_r)$$
$$= 14.01 + (2 \times 16.00)$$
$$= 46.01$$
(b) The chemical formula of gold (III) oxide is Au_2O_3.
$$\therefore M_r = \Sigma(A_r)$$
$$= (2 \times 197.0) + (3 \times 16.00)$$
$$= 442.00$$

Percentage composition of compounds

The table of atomic weights allows chemists to calculate the percentage by weight of each element in a compound. These results can then be compared with those obtained experimentally. If a compound is pure, it has a constant percentage composition. If it is impure due to small amounts of contaminants, this will alter its percentage composition.

SAMPLE PROBLEM 9.4

A 10.00 g sample of silver oxide was decomposed by heating. The mass of silver formed was 9.10 g.
(a) Assuming the sample was pure, calculate the percentage composition of the silver oxide.
(b) The formula for silver oxide is Ag_2O. The atomic weight of Ag = 107.9 and O = 16.00. Use this information to determine whether the sample was pure.

SOLUTION

(a) The silver oxide decomposes to form silver and oxygen.
$$\text{silver oxide} \rightarrow \text{silver} + \text{oxygen}$$
The 10.00 g sample produced 9.10 g of silver. Assuming the rest is oxygen, the mass of oxygen is 0.90 g.

$$\therefore \% \text{ silver} = 9.10/10.00 \times 100$$
$$= 91.0\%$$
$$\% \text{ oxygen} = 0.90/10.00 \times 100$$
$$= 9.0\ \%$$

(b) The molecular weight of Ag_2O
$$= 2 \times 107.9 + 16.00$$
$$= 231.80$$

Therefore, in pure Ag_2O,
$$\% \text{ silver} = 2 \times 107.9/231.80 \times 100$$
$$= 93.1\%$$
$$\% \text{ oxygen} = 16.00/231.80 \times 100$$
$$= 6.9\%$$

Thus, the sample is slightly impure as the experimental results show a lower percentage of silver.

Using atomic models to explain changes in mass

John Dalton's atomic theory explained the conservation of mass in a chemical change in terms of the conservation of atoms. Because the atoms of each element had a fixed mass, the rearrangement of atoms in a chemical change did not result in a net change in mass. Figure 9.4 illustrates Dalton's ideas about mass and atom conservation using the reaction between carbon and sulfur.

Figure 9.4 Conservation of mass and atoms in the reaction between carbon and sulfur

Mass of reactants = 12 + 32 + 32 = 76   Mass of product = 76

Volume changes in gaseous reactions

When Dalton was developing his atomic theory, French chemist Joseph Gay-Lussac (1778–1850) was conducting experiments on the reacting volumes of gases. His research showed that gas-phase reactions obeyed a simple law, which is now called the *law of combining gas volumes*.

> ### *Law of combining gas volumes*
> The ratios of the volumes of gases involved in a chemical reaction are expressed by small, whole numbers.

Examples:
Gay-Lussac discovered the following relationships between the volumes of the reacting and product gases at constant temperature and pressure. In each case, the volumes of the combining gases were in a simple, whole number ratio.

1. Hydrogen + chlorine
When hydrogen gas and chlorine gas reacted, they formed hydrogen chloride gas.

hydrogen gas + chlorine gas → hydrogen chloride gas
   1 litre   1 litre   2 litres
$$\therefore \text{ Volume ratio} = 1 : 1 : 2$$

2. Hydrogen + oxygen

When hydrogen gas and oxygen gas were sparked, they combined to produce water. If the temperature was maintained above 100°C, the water formed water vapour. Gay-Lussac found that 2 litres of hydrogen was required to react completely with one litre of oxygen.

$$\text{hydrogen gas} + \text{oxygen gas} \rightarrow \text{water vapour}$$

$$\begin{array}{ccc} 2 \text{ litres} & 1 \text{ litre} & 2 \text{ litres} \end{array}$$

$$\therefore \text{ Volume ratio} = 2 : 1 : 2$$

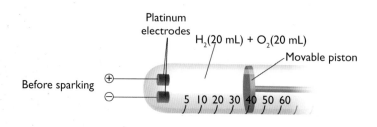

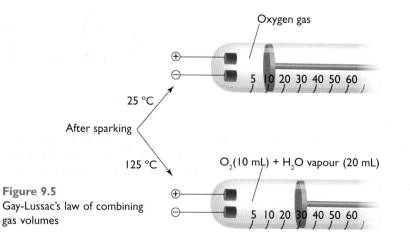

Figure 9.5
Gay-Lussac's law of combining gas volumes

Avogadro's law

Some results of Gay-Lussac's many experiments posed a problem because they seemed inconsistent with Dalton's atomic theory. Dalton tried to explain Gay-Lussac's results using the assumption that equal volumes of gases contained equal number of atoms. For example, in the reaction of hydrogen with oxygen, the volume data implied that 2 atoms of hydrogen combined with 1 atom of oxygen to form 2 'compound atoms' of water.

According to Dalton, however, an atom of oxygen could not split in two to produce two 'compound atoms' of water. Dalton refused to accept the idea that atoms could split and so he rejected Gay-Lussac's data.

The dilemma was ultimately solved in 1811 by the Italian physicist Amedeo Avogadro (1776–1856) by proposing the existence of *molecules* or atomic aggregates. Avogadro reasoned that many gases consist of molecules, and that it was the molecule that split, rather than the atom, in a chemical change. His explanation is expressed as Avogadro's law.

> **Avogadro's law**
> Equal volumes of gases, at the same temperature and pressure, contain equal numbers of particles (molecules).

Thus, the reaction between hydrogen and oxygen could be explained in terms of a model in which both gases existed as *diatomic molecules*. These molecules split and the atoms recombined to form water, which must consist of a *triatomic molecule*, H_2O. Note that the ratio of molecules is the same as the coefficients in the balanced chemical equation.

hydrogen	+	oxygen	$\rightarrow$	water vapour
2 molecules		1 molecule		2 molecules
$2H_2(g)$	+	$O_2(g)$	$\rightarrow$	$2H_2O(g)$

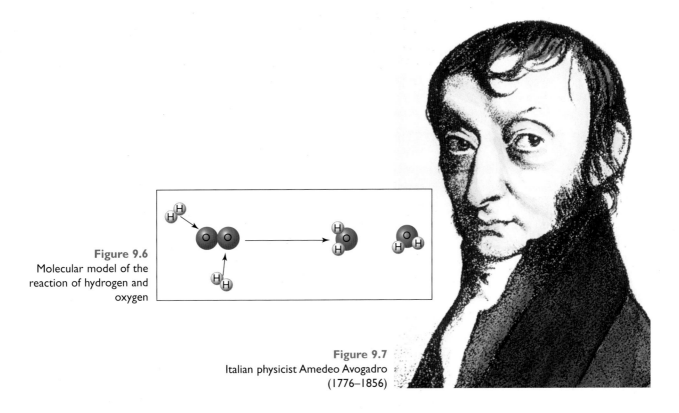

Figure 9.6
Molecular model of the reaction of hydrogen and oxygen

Figure 9.7
Italian physicist Amedeo Avogadro (1776–1856)

SAMPLE PROBLEM 9.5

Hydrogen and nitrogen can be made to react under high temperature and pressure to form a gas with the formula N_xH_y. The following initial and final volume data was collected at constant temperature and pressure.

Table 9.2

Gas	nitrogen, N_2	hydrogen, H_2	N_xH_y
Initial volume (L)	10	10	0
Final volume (L)	8	4	4

Use this data to:

(a) show that it is consistent with Gay-Lussac's law of combining gas volumes

(b) determine the values of x and y and thus the chemical formula of the product.

SOLUTION

(a) Calculate the volume of reacting nitrogen and hydrogen.

Volume of nitrogen reacted = 10 − 8 = 2 L

Volume of hydrogen reacted = 10 − 4 = 6 L

Calculate the volume ratio.

$$V(N_2) : V(H_2) : V(N_xH_y) = 2 : 6 : 4 = 1 : 3 : 2$$

This is a simple, whole number ratio, which is consistent with Gay-Lussac's law of combining gas volumes.

(b) According to Avogadro's law, the volume ratio equals the ratio of molecules.

$$\text{Molecule ratio} = N_2 : H_2 : N_xH_y = 1 : 3 : 2$$

This molecular ratio (1 : 3 : 2) provides the coefficients in the balanced chemical equation:

$$N_2 + 3H_2 \rightarrow 2N_xH_y$$

Thus, to balance atoms, the values of x and y are 1 and 3, respectively. Therefore, the chemical formula of this compound is NH_3 (ammonia).

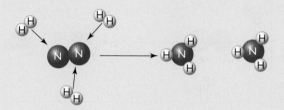

Figure 9.8 Model of the formation of ammonia from nitrogen and hydrogen

The mole

As previously stated, the reference standard for atomic weight is the carbon-12 isotope. This is an atom of carbon that has 6 protons and 6 neutrons in its nucleus and 6 electrons surrounding the nucleus. Its mass is defined as exactly 12 units on the relative atomic mass scale.

Chemists, however, do not normally weigh individual atoms; they weigh much larger amounts of matter. Therefore, they needed to establish a reference standard for mass using the more convenient unit of grams. The scale that was devised is called the *mole scale*, and was based on the carbon-12 isotope. Chemists used a variety of experimental techniques to determine that the number of atoms in exactly 12 g of carbon-12 is 6.022×10^{23}. This large number was called the **Avogadro constant** (N_A) in honour of Amadeo Avogadro and is used to define the mole.

Avogadro constant: the number of elementary particles (atoms) in exactly 12 g of carbon-12. This number is equal to 6.022×10^{23}.

Figure 9.9
One mole each of sodium chloride, iron (III) chloride, copper sulfate, potassium iodide, cobalt nitrate and potassium manganate (VII)

One mole (exactly 12 g) of carbon-12 contains 6.022×10^{23} atoms.

One mole of any substance is that quantity of the substance that contains an Avogadro number of elementary particles. This definition applies to atoms, molecules or any object. Thus, one mole of eggs is equal to 6.022×10^{23} eggs! The mole is a very useful chemical concept. Avogadro's law is consistent with mole theory. Equal volumes of gases at the same temperature and pressure contain not only equal numbers of molecules, but also equal numbers of moles of molecules.

Molar weight (*M*)

The mass of one mole of any element or compound is called its molar weight, and is measured in g/mol. This is the mass in grams that is equivalent to its atomic weight or molecular weight. Here are some examples.

Elements

One mole of any element contains 6.022×10^{23} atoms of that element. This is equivalent to the atomic weight of the element expressed in grams.
- One mole of magnesium weighs 24.31 g. Thus, M = 24.32 g/mol.
- One mole of gold weighs 197.0 g. Thus, M = 197.0 g/mol.

Compounds

One mole of any compound contains 6.022×10^{23} molecules or formula units of that compound. This is equivalent to the molecular weight expressed in grams.
- One mole of water weighs 18.016 g. Thus, M = 18.016 g/mol.
- One mole of carbon dioxide weighs 44.01 g. Thus, M = 44.01 g/mol.

> The relationship between the number of moles (*n*) of a substance of mass (*m*) and molar weight (*M*) is:
> $$n = m/M$$
> where *n* is measured in moles (mol), *m* in grams (g) and *M* in grams/mole (g/mol).

SAMPLE PROBLEM 9.6

SOLUTION

Calculate the number of moles of sulfuric acid, H_2SO_4, present in 4.9 g of the compound.

Calculate the molar weight of sulfuric acid.
$$M(H_2SO_4) = (2 \times 1.008) + 32.07 + (4 \times 16.00)$$
$$= 98.086 \text{ g/mol}$$
$$m = 4.9 \text{ g}$$
$$\therefore n = m/M$$
$$= 4.9/98.086$$
$$= 0.050 \text{ mol (2 significant figures)}$$

SAMPLE PROBLEM 9.7

Calculate the mass of 3.5 mol of hexane, C_6H_{14}.

SOLUTION

Calculate the molar weight of hexane.

$$\begin{aligned} M(C_6H_{14}) &= (6 \times 12.01) + (14 \times 1.008) \\ &= 86.172 \text{ g/mol} \\ n &= 3.5 \text{ mol} \\ \therefore\ m &= nM \\ &= 3.5 \times 86.172 \\ &= 301.6 \text{ g} \end{aligned}$$

SAMPLE PROBLEM 9.8

Calculate the number of:

(a) oxygen molecules

(b) oxygen atoms

in 96 g of oxygen gas.

SOLUTION

Calculate the molar weight of oxygen gas, O_2.

$$\begin{aligned} M(O_2) &= 2 \times 16.00 \\ &= 32.00 \text{ g/mol} \end{aligned}$$

Calculate the number of moles of O_2.

$$\begin{aligned} n(O_2) &= m/M \\ &= 96/32.00 \\ &= 3.0 \text{ mol} \end{aligned}$$

(a) 1 mole of O_2 contains 6.022×10^{23} molecules of O_2.
Thus, 3.0 moles of O_2 contains $3.0 \times 6.022 \times 10^{23}$
$= 1.807 \times 10^{24}$ molecules.

(b) 1 molecule of oxygen is composed of 2 oxygen atoms.
Thus, 1.807×10^{24} molecules contains $2 \times 1.807 \times 10^{24}$
$= 3.613 \times 10^{24}$ atoms.

Mole relationships in chemical reactions

A balanced chemical equation summarises the mole relationship between reactants and products. Consider each of the following examples.

Example 1: Combustion of calcium

Calcium burns in oxygen to form calcium oxide. The balanced chemical equation for this reaction is:

$$2Ca(s) + O_2(g) \rightarrow 2CaO(s)$$

This equation can be interpreted in terms of mole theory as follows:

> 2 moles of calcium reacts with 1 mole of oxygen to form 2 moles of calcium oxide.

C
Carbon
Al
Aluminium
C6H12O6
Glucose
12 g
27 g
180 g

Figure 9.10
A mole each of various substances

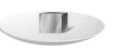

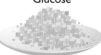

SAMPLE PROBLEM 9.9

SOLUTION

A mixture of 2 moles of calcium metal and 100 g of oxygen is placed in a container and heated till the calcium burns to form calcium oxide. Determine whether there is sufficient oxygen to burn all the calcium.

Calculate the number of moles of oxygen in the container.

$$M(O_2) = 2 \times 16.00$$
$$= 32.00 \text{ g/mol}$$
$$m(O_2) = 100 \text{ g}$$
$$\therefore n(O_2) = m/M$$
$$= 100/32.00$$
$$= 3.125 \text{ mol}$$

The balanced equation (in example 1 on page 170) shows that each 2 moles of calcium requires 1 mole of oxygen to react completely. The 3.125 mol of oxygen in the container is, therefore, in excess of that required. There will be more than enough oxygen needed for complete combustion.

Example 2: Thermal decomposition of silver carbonate

Silver carbonate decomposes on heating to form silver, oxygen and carbon dioxide. The balanced equation for this reaction is:

$$2Ag_2CO_3(s) \rightarrow 4Ag(s) + O_2(g) + 2CO_2(g)$$

This equation can be interpreted in terms of mole theory as follows:

2 moles of silver carbonate decomposes to form 4 moles of silver, 1 mole of oxygen gas and 2 moles of carbon dioxide gas.

SAMPLE PROBLEM 9.10

SOLUTION

Calculate the number of moles of oxygen that would evolved if 100 g of silver carbonate is thermally decomposed.

Step 1: Convert the mass data to moles. Calculate the molar weight of silver carbonate.

$$M(Ag_2CO_3) = (2 \times 107.9) + 12.01 + (3 \times 16.00)$$
$$= 275.81 \text{ g/mol}$$

Step 2: Calculate the number of moles of silver carbonate.

$$n(Ag_2CO_3) = m/M$$
$$= 100/275.81$$
$$= 0.363 \text{ mol}$$

9.2 DATA
ANALYSIS
Moles and volumes
of gases

Step 3: Use the mole ratios of the balanced equation (in example 2 above) to determine the number of moles of oxygen formed. From the balanced equation:

2 moles of Ag_2CO_3 form 1 mole of O_2.

Thus, 0.363 mol of Ag_2CO_3 will produce $0.363/2 = 0.182$ mol of O_2.

14. USING INSTRUCTION TERMS CORRECTLY

When answering questions, it is important to know what the instruction terms (verbs) require you to do. Here is an example.

'Demonstrate'

This instruction term requires you to show, by example or calculation, that a statement, concept or data is true or consistent.

Example:

Demonstrate that Dalton's atomic theory is consistent with the law of mass conservation.

Answer:

Dalton's atomic theory states that the atoms of each element have a unique atomic weight and that, during a chemical reaction, the atoms of the elements rearrange into new patterns. For example:

$$\text{carbon} + \text{oxygen} \rightarrow \text{carbon dioxide}$$
$$C + O_2 \rightarrow CO_2$$

Each carbon atom has an atomic weight of 12.01 and each oxygen atom has an atomic weight of 16.00. Therefore, the masses of the reactants are:

Reactants: $\quad \Sigma(A_r(C) + M_r(O_2)) = 12.01 + (2 \times 16.00)$
$$= 44.01$$
Product: $\quad \therefore M_r(CO_2) = 44.01$

The total mass of reactants equals the mass of the product, so the conservation of atoms is consistent with the law of mass conservation.

SAMPLE PROBLEM 9.11

Hydrated sodium carbonate is represented by the formula $Na_2CO_3 \cdot xH_2O$, where x is an integer. When 100.00 g of this compound was heated strongly to drive off the water, the anhydrous compound left behind had a mass of 37.04 g.

$$Na_2CO_3 \cdot xH_2O(s) \rightarrow Na_2CO_3(s) + xH_2O(g)$$

Calculate the number of moles of water molecules, x, in one mole of hydrated sodium carbonate.

SOLUTION

Step 1: Calculate the mass of water evolved.
$$m(H_2O) = 100.00 - 37.04$$
$$= 62.96 \text{ g}$$

Step 2: Calculate the molar weights of sodium carbonate and water.
$$M(Na_2CO_3) = 105.99 \text{ g/mol}$$
$$M(H_2O) = 18.016 \text{ g/mol}$$

Step 3: Calculate the number of moles of sodium carbonate and water.
$$n(Na_2CO_3) = m/M$$
$$= 37.04/105.99$$
$$= 0.349 \text{ mol}$$
$$n(H_2O) = m/M$$
$$= 62.96/18.016$$
$$= 3.495 \text{ mol}$$

Step 4: Determine the ratio of moles.
$$n(H_2O) : n(Na_2CO_3) = 3.495 : 0.349$$
$$= 10 : 1$$

Step 5: Determine the value of x.
Thus $x = 10$.

Therefore, there are 10 moles of water in one mole of hydrated sodium carbonate.

9.1 QUESTIONS

1. Mercury (II) oxide is thermally decomposed to form mercury and oxygen.
   (a) Write a balanced chemical equation for this reaction.
   (b) During the reaction, 100 g of mercury (II) oxide was completely decomposed and 92.6 g of mercury was formed. Calculate the mass of oxygen released.

2. Equal masses of calcium and magnesium are completely combusted in air.
   (a) Identify the products of each combustion reaction.
   (b) Explain why the mass of each solid product is different.

3. Use the atomic weights in the periodic table to calculate the molecular weight of each of the following compounds.
   (a) $CuSO_4$
   (b) Calcium carbonate
   (c) Ammonia

4. Use the atomic weights in the periodic table to calculate the percentage by weight of oxygen in each of the following compounds.
   (a) $CaCO_3$
   (b) CH_3CO_2H

5. A total of 3.0 L of gaseous carbon dioxide is formed by the reaction of 3.0 L of carbon monoxide gas and 1.0 L of ozone gas, O_3.
   (a) Demonstrate that this data is consistent with Gay-Lussac's law of combining gas volumes.
   (b) Demonstrate that the data is consistent with the balanced equation for the reaction.

6. Methane, CH_4, burns in oxygen, O_2, to form carbon dioxide gas and water vapour. When mixed and ignited, 40 mL of methane reacted with 100 mL of oxygen (an excess) at 120 °C and 100 kPa pressure.

   When the system was returned to the original temperature and pressure, the final mixture had 0 mL of methane, 20 mL of oxygen, 40 mL of carbon dioxide and 80 mL of water vapour. Demonstrate that this data is consistent with Gay-Lussac's law of combining gas volumes.

7. At 1000 °C, 5 mL of sulfur vapour reacts with 10 mL of oxygen gas to form 10 mL of sulfur dioxide gas. Use this data to determine the number of atoms in the sulfur molecule in the vapour state at that temperature.

8. Calculate the number of moles of carbon dioxide present in 4.4 g of carbon dioxide.

9. Sodium chloride is an ionic compound.
   (a) Calculate the molar weight of sodium chloride.
   (b) Calculate the number of moles of sodium chloride in 10 g of the compound.
   (c) Calculate the number of chloride ions in 10 g of the compound.

10. Calculate the number of hydroxide ions in 10 g of zinc hydroxide.

11. Calcium carbonate reacts with hydrochloric acid to form calcium chloride, water and carbon dioxide.
    (a) Write a balanced equation for the reaction.
    (b) Calculate the mass of carbon dioxide formed when 10 g of calcium carbonate dissolves in excess acid.
    (c) Calculate the number of carbon dioxide molecules formed.

12. Calculate the mass of magnesium metal required to react completely with 3.011×10^{21} molecules of oxygen to form magnesium oxide.

13. Nitrogen monoxide gas reacts with oxygen gas to form brown nitrogen dioxide gas.
    (a) Write a balanced equation for this reaction.
    (b) In a reaction vessel, 60 g of nitrogen monoxide and 60 g of oxygen are mixed together. Calculate the number of nitrogen dioxide molecules formed, assuming the reaction is complete.

14. Hydrogen gas reduces copper (II) oxide to copper and water.
    (a) Write a balanced equation for the reaction.
    (b) Calculate the number of hydrogen molecules required to completely reduce 10g of copper (II) oxide.

15. Hydrated copper (II) sulfate contains 5 molecules of water per crystal unit. Its formula is $CuSO_4.5H_2O$. If 50g of hydrated copper (II) sulfate is completely dehydrated by heating, calculate:
    (a) the mass of water vapour evolved.
    (b) the number of water molecules evolved.

9.2 *EMPIRICAL AND MOLECULAR FORMULAE*

Empirical formulae

The concept of empirical formulae was introduced on pages 96–7. The empirical formula of a compound represents its atomic composition expressed as the simplest whole number ratio. Consider the ball-and-stick models of various molecules shown in figure 9.12.

Hydrogen peroxide

Hydrogen peroxide is a colourless liquid, and is a useful antiseptic and bleach. The ball-and-stick model shows that this molecule is composed of two hydrogen atoms and two oxygen atoms. The ratio of atoms is:

$$H : O = 2 : 2 = 1 : 1$$

Thus, the empirical formula is HO.

Ethylene

Ethylene is a faintly sweet-smelling gas that stimulates fruit to ripen. It is also present in petroleum gas and is the basis of the polymer industry. The ball-and-stick model shows that this molecule is composed of two carbon atoms and four hydrogen atoms. The ratio of atoms is:

$$C : H = 2 : 4 = 1 : 2$$

Thus, the empirical formula is CH_2.

(a)

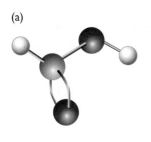

(b)

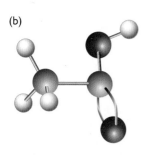

Figure 9.11
(a) The molecular and empirical formulae of formic acid (methanoic acid) are both CH_2O_2. (b) The molecular formula and empirical formula of acetic acid (ethanoic acid, bottom) are $C_2H_4O_2$ and CH_2O, respectively.

Hydrogen peroxide

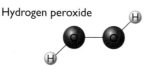

Ethylene

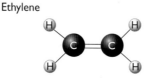

Ethyl acetate

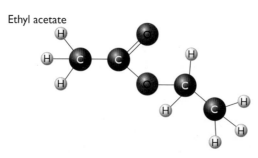

Figure 9.12
Ball-and-stick models of hydrogen peroxide, ethylene and ethyl acetate

Ethyl acetate

Ethyl acetate is a colourless liquid that is a useful industrial solvent. The ball-and-stick model shows that this molecule is composed of four carbon atoms, eight hydrogen atoms and two oxygen atoms. The ratio of atoms is:

$$C : H : O = 4 : 8 : 2 = 2 : 4 : 1$$

Thus, the empirical formula is C_2H_4O.

Gravimetric analysis allows chemists to determine the empirical formula of a compound. Sample problems 9.12 and 9.13 show how this is done.

SAMPLE PROBLEM 9.12

Magnesium chloride

Gravimetric analysis of 100 g of magnesium chloride yields the following data:

$$\text{Magnesium} = 25.53 \text{ g}$$
$$\text{Chlorine} = 74.47 \text{ g}$$

Use this data to determine the empirical formula.

SOLUTION

Calculate the number of moles of magnesium and chlorine in the 100 g sample of the compound.

$$n(\text{Mg}) = m/M$$
$$= 25.53/24.31$$
$$= 1.050 \text{ mol}$$
$$n(\text{Cl}) = m/M$$
$$= 74.47/35.45$$
$$= 2.101 \text{ mol}$$

The empirical formula can now be calculated by determining the simplest mole ratio.

$$n(\text{Mg}) : n(\text{Cl}) = 1.050 : 2.101$$

Divide each number in the ratio by the smaller number (1.050).

$$n(\text{Mg}) : n(\text{Cl}) = 1 : 2$$

Therefore, the empirical formula is $MgCl_2$.

SAMPLE PROBLEM 9.13

Acetic acid

Gravimetric analysis of acetic acid yields the following percentage composition data:

40.01% carbon, 6.72% hydrogen, 53.27% oxygen

Calculate the empirical formula of acetic acid.

SOLUTION

Calculate the number of moles of each element in a 100 g sample. Each 100 g of acetic acid contains 40.01 g of carbon, 6.72 g of hydrogen and 53.27 g of oxygen.

$$\therefore n(\text{C}) = m/M$$
$$= 40.01/12.01$$
$$= 3.33 \text{ mol}$$
$$n(\text{H}) = m/M$$
$$= 6.72/1.008$$
$$= 6.67 \text{ mol}$$
$$n(\text{O}) = m/M$$
$$= 53.27/16.00$$
$$= 3.33 \text{ mol}$$

The empirical formula can now be calculated by determining the simplest mole ratio.

$$n(\text{C}) : n(\text{H}) : n(\text{O}) = 3.33 : 6.67 : 3.33$$

Divide each number in the ratio by the smallest number (3.33)

$$n(\text{C}) : n(\text{H}) : n(\text{O}) = 1 : 2 : 1$$

Therefore, the empirical formula of acetic acid is CH_2O.

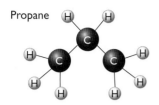

Propane

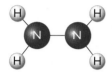

Hydrazine

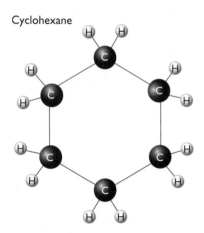

Cyclohexane

Figure 9.13
Ball-and-stick models of propane, hydrazine and cyclohexane

Molecular formulae

The molecular formula of a compound represents the actual number of atoms of each element in the molecule. Ball-and-stick models can help in determining molecular formulae.

Propane

Propane is a hydrocarbon gas and a useful fuel. The ball-and-stick model (figure 9.13a) shows that propane is composed of three carbon atoms and eight hydrogen atoms. The ratio of atoms is:

$$C : H = 3 : 8$$

Therefore, the molecular formula of propane is C_3H_8. The empirical formula is also C_3H_8 as 3 : 8 is the simplest ratio.

Hydrazine

Hydrazine is colourless liquid that is very soluble in water. It is used as a high-performance fuel. The ball-and-stick model (figure 9.13b) shows that hydrazine is composed of two nitrogen atoms and four hydrogen atoms. The ratio of atoms is:

$$N : H = 2 : 4$$

Therefore, the molecular formula of hydrazine is N_2H_4. However, the empirical formula is NH_2 as the simplest atom ratio is 1 : 2.

Cyclohexane

Cyclohexane is a hydrocarbon derived from petroleum. The ball-and-stick model (figure 9.13c) shows that it is composed of six carbon atoms and twelve hydrogen atoms. The ratio of atoms is:

$$C : H = 6 : 12$$

Therefore, the molecular formula is C_6H_{12}. However, the empirical formula is CH_2 as the simplest atom ratio is 1 : 2.

To determine the molecular formula of a compound, its composition and molecular weight must be known. The molecular weight of many molecules can be obtained using an instrumental technique called *mass spectrometry*. Sample problem 9.14 shows such an analysis.

SAMPLE PROBLEM 9.14

A straight chain hydrocarbon is gravimetrically analysed and found to contain 85.63% carbon and 14.37% hydrogen. Mass spectrometry shows that its molecular weight is 42.1. Determine the (a) empirical formula and (b) molecular formula of the hydrocarbon.

SOLUTION

(a) For 100 g of the hydrocarbon:
$$m(C) = 85.63 \text{ g}$$
$$m(H) = 14.37 \text{ g}$$

Calculate the number of moles of each element.
$$n(C) = 85.63/12.01$$
$$= 7.13 \text{ mol}$$
$$n(H) = 14.37/1.008$$
$$= 14.26 \text{ mol}$$

Calculate the mole ratio.

$$n(C) : n(H) = 7.13 : 14.26$$
$$= 2 : 1$$

Thus, the empirical formula is CH_2.

(b) The molecular formula is a multiple of the empirical formula. The molecular weight of CH_2 is 14.016. The number of CH_2 units in the molecule

$$= 42.1/14.016$$
$$= 3$$

Thus, the molecular formula of the hydrocarbon is C_3H_6.

9.1 PRACTICAL ACTIVITIES

The empirical formula of magnesium oxide

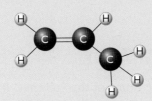

Figure 9.14 Ball-and-stick model of C_3H_6

9.2 QUESTIONS

1. Use the periodic table or a table of atomic weights to determine the percentage by weight of each element in the following compounds.
   (a) H_2SO_3
   (b) P_4O_{10}
   (c) $Ca(OH)_2$

2. Identify which of the following are examples of empirical formulae.
   A $ZnCl_2$
   B P_4O_{10}
   C UF_6
   D $K_2C_2O_4$

3. Determine the (a) empirical formulae and (b) molecular formulae for the molecules shown in figure 9.15.

4. Determine the empirical formula for each compound using the following percentage composition data:
   (a) 11.640% nitrogen, 88.360% chlorine
   (b) 36.51% sodium, 25.39% sulfur 38.10% oxygen
   (c) 16.4% magnesium, 18.9% nitrogen, 64.7% oxygen
   (d) 72.03% manganese, 27.97% oxygen.

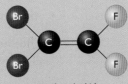

molecule W

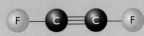

molecule X

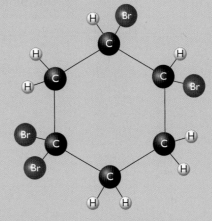

molecule Y

Figure 9.15
Ball-and-stick models of molecules

5. After heating 3.972 g of an oxide of mercury, and driving off the oxygen, the mercury remaining had a mass of 3.678 g. Determine the empirical formula of this oxide of mercury.

6. A hydrocarbon molecule has a molecular weight of 54.09. The percentage composition of this hydrocarbon is 88.81% carbon and 11.19% hydrogen. Use this data to determine the (a) empirical formula and (b) molecular formula of the hydrocarbon.

7. A compound of silicon and oxygen is analysed and found to have 87.45% Si and 12.55% O by weight. Calculate the empirical formula of the compound.

8. A metal M is trivalent. Common trivalent metals include chromium, aluminium, iron and gallium. The sulfate of M is an ionic salt with a percentage composition by weight of 27.93% M, 24.06% S and 48.01% O.
   (a) Use this data to calculate the atomic weight of M.
   (b) Use the periodic table to identify M.

SUMMARY

- The ratios of the volumes of gases involved in a chemical reaction are expressed by small, whole number ratios (Gay-Lussac's law).

- Equal volumes of gases at the same temperature and pressure contain equal numbers of molecules (Avogadro's law).

- Exactly 12 g of the carbon-12 isotope contains 6.022×10^{23} atoms (the Avogadro constant).

- An Avogadro number of atoms is referred to as 1 mole.

- The molar weight (M) of an element or compound is the weight of 1 mole of that substance.

- The amount of a substance (n) is measured in moles. The relationship between n and the mass (m) of the substance is expressed by the equation: $n = m/M$.

- The empirical formula of a compound is the simplest ratio of its atoms. The molecular formula shows the true number of atoms in the molecule.

PRACTICAL ACTIVITIES

9.1 PRACTICAL ACTIVITIES

THE EMPIRICAL FORMULA OF MAGNESIUM OXIDE

Aim

To determine the empirical formula of magnesium oxide and to investigate how repetition affects reliability. Students should work in groups and combine their results.

Safety issues

- Wear safety glasses throughout this experiment.
- Avoid looking at burning magnesium as the bright light can damage the eyes.
- Identify other safety issues relevant to this experiment by reading the method.

Materials

- porcelain crucible and lid
- electronic balance
- pipeclay triangle
- tripod and heatproof mat
- Bunsen burner
- tongs
- 25 cm clean magnesium ribbon

Method

1. Determine the mass of the shiny magnesium ribbon supplied.
2. Weigh a clean porcelain crucible and lid.
3. Fold the ribbon into a loose spiral and place it in the crucible. Support the crucible on the pipeclay triangle.

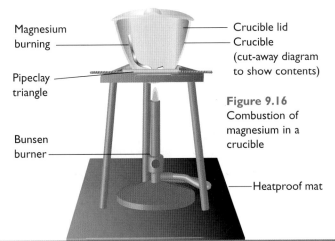

Magnesium burning

Pipeclay triangle

Bunsen burner

Crucible lid

Crucible (cut-away diagram to show contents)

Figure 9.16 Combustion of magnesium in a crucible

Heatproof mat

4. Heat the crucible slowly using a blue Bunsen flame. The lid should be ajar to allow air to enter. Increase the heating until the magnesium begins to ignite. Use the tongs to place the lid over the crucible to prevent the oxide powder escaping.
5. Continue to heat until all the magnesium has combusted. You may need to open the lid slightly using the tongs to let in fresh air.
6. Turn off the Bunsen burner and allow the crucible and contents to cool to room temperature.
7. Reweigh the crucible and contents.

Results

Record the following quantities in a table: mass of magnesium; mass of magnesium oxide; and mass of oxygen combined into the oxide.

Questions

Answer the following questions in your report on this experiment.

1. Use your experimental results to calculate the mass ratio, $m(\text{Mg}) : m(\text{O})$.
2. Compare this mass ratio with the ratio of atomic weights of these two elements.
3. Use your results to calculate the percentage by weight of magnesium and oxygen in magnesium oxide.
4. Repeat the calculation in question 4 using the data from other groups, and then find the average.
5. Use your answer to question 2, and an appropriate mole calculation, to calculate the empirical formula of magnesium oxide using the average percentage composition data from all groups.
6. Discuss several ways of improving the accuracy of the experimental procedure.
7. Discuss whether repetition has improved the reliability of your investigation.
8. As magnesium burns, it may react with nitrogen in the air to form magnesium nitride. Magnesium nitride decomposes to form magnesium oxide when a little water is added. Explain how you would alter the experimental method to ensure the final product contains only dry magnesium oxide.

Conclusion

Briefly describe the outcome of your investigation.

DATA ANALYSIS

9.2 DATA ANALYSIS
MOLES AND VOLUMES OF GASES

In these two activities, you will process second-hand data to relate the mole relationships in reactions involving metals and gases.

Part A: Magnesium and sulfuric acid

Samples of 2.0 g of pure magnesium were reacted separately with a slight excess of either dilute or concentrated sulfuric acid. In each case, the metal dissolved, and the gases evolved were collected and their volumes determined in separate dry vessels at 25 °C and 100 kPa pressure. The results are summarised in table 9.3.

Table 9.3

Reaction	Volume of gas collected (mL)	Products identified
1. Magnesium + dilute sulfuric acid	2039	magnesium sulfate, hydrogen
2. Magnesium + concentrated sulfuric acid	2039	magnesium sulfate, water, sulfur dioxide

1. Use table 9.3 to write balanced chemical equations for reactions 1 and 2.
2. Use the balanced equations to determine the mole ratio of:
   (a) magnesium to hydrogen for reaction 1.
   (b) magnesium to sulfur dioxide for reaction 2.
3. Explain how your answer to question 2 is consistent with the gas volume data in table 9.3.
4. Separate experiments have shown that 24.79 L of any gas at 25 °C and 100 kPa pressure contains one mole of the gas. Use this information to calculate the number of moles of each gas formed in reactions 1 and 2.
5. Use the mass of magnesium to calculate the number of moles of magnesium that reacted in each experiment.
6. Explain how your answers to questions 4 and 5 are consistent with the mole relationship in the balanced equations.

Part B: Oxidation of mercury

In 1774, Antoine Lavoisier conducted an experiment in which he heated a weighed sample of mercury in a closed, long-necked flask for 12 days. The sample of mercury was connected to a fixed volume of air in a bell jar. He observed that the mercury was slowly converted to a red solid (mercury oxide), and that the volume of air in the bell jar decreased (by about 20%) as the mercury reacted. Lavoisier found that the red product weighed more than the original mercury, and that this increase in weight was equal to the loss in weight of the air. He also noted that the air remaining in the bell jar no longer supported combustion of a glowing splint of wood and extinguished a lit candle.

Lavoisier's experiment was repeated in a modern laboratory. All the mercury was converted to a red solid. The data in table 9.4 was collected at 25 °C and 100 kPa. Answer the following questions, remembering that 24.79 L of any gas at 25 °C and 100 kPa pressure contains one mole of the gas.

Table 9.4

Mass of mercury used (g)	100.000
Mass of red product (g)	107.976
Original volume of air (L)	20.000
Final volume of air (L)	13.821

1. Identify the gas removed from the air during the reaction with mercury.
2. The red product is mercury (II) oxide. Write its chemical formula.
3. Write a balanced equation for this reaction.
4. Demonstrate that this data is consistent with the mole relationship in the balanced equation.

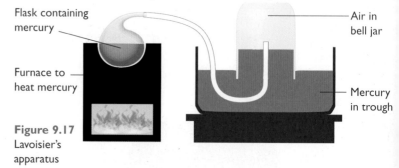

Flask containing mercury

Furnace to heat mercury

Air in bell jar

Mercury in trough

Figure 9.17 Lavoisier's apparatus

Chapter 10

EXTRACTION AND RECYCLING OF METALS

Introduction

Economic considerations dictate that minerals in an ore body must be sufficiently concentrated to ensure a profitable mining operation. The extraction of copper illustrates the important chemical, economic and environmental principles involved in conversion of an ore into the final metal product.

In this chapter

Figure 10.1
Iron ore is an important natural resource.

10.1 ORES AND RESOURCES

Australia's minerals and ores

Australia supplies many different types of metal, as well as refined and unrefined **ores**, to the world markets. Many of the ores found in the lithosphere originate in the hot, melted, mineral mixture called magma. As the magma cools, crystals of certain heavy, metallic minerals form and sink under gravity to the bottom of the magma chamber. This causes the minerals to become concentrated in a particular zone. The minerals may also move into fissures in the surrounding bedrock. Massive ore bodies containing sulfides of nickel, copper and iron have been formed in this way.

Some mineral deposits are of hydrothermal origin. Hydrothermal fluids rise through rock fractures and deposit minerals as they cool. Gold, silver, zinc sulfide (*sphalerite*), lead sulfide (*galena*) and iron sulfide (*pyrite*) form mineral veins in this way. Other mineral deposits, such as bauxite, are of sedimentary origin.

Ores are examples of *non-renewable resources*. Ore bodies take thousands or millions of years to form. Many ore bodies have been extensively mined until it is no longer economically viable to operate the mine. New mineral deposits are discovered but this cannot continue indefinitely. We must, therefore, be careful not to waste our mineral and metal supplies. Recycling is vital to extend the life of these supplies.

Common metallic ores

Metallic ores can be classified according to the anion present in their minerals. Table 10.1 gives some examples, while figure 10.3 shows where some of the common minerals and metals are mined in Australia.

Table 10.1 Classification of common metallic ores

Classification group	Examples
sulfides	chalcocite, Cu_2S; chalcopyrite, $CuFeS_2$; sphalerite, ZnS; galena, PbS; pentlandite, $(FeNi)_9S_8$
oxides	boehmite, $Al_2O_3.H_2O$; haematite, Fe_2O_3; magnetite, Fe_3O_4; spodumene, $Li_2O.Al_2O_3.4SiO_2$; rutile, TiO_2; ilmenite, $FeTiO_3$; uraninite, UO_2; cassiterite, SnO_2; cuprite, Cu_2O
carbonates/hydroxides	calcite, $CaCO_3$; magnesite, $MgCO_3$; dolomite, $CaCO_3.MgCO_3$; malachite, $CuCO_3.Cu(OH)_2$; azurite, $2CuCO_3.Cu(OH)_2$

Figure 10.2
A smelter where aluminium is obtained from bauxite

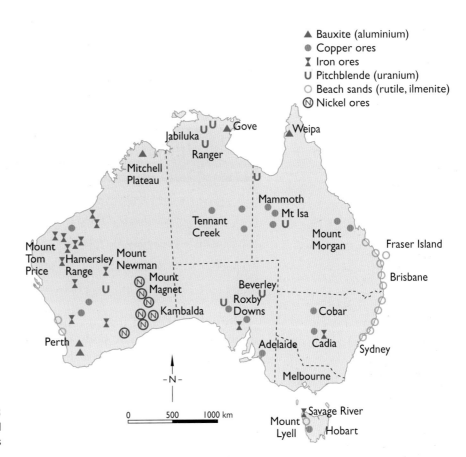

Legend:
▲ Bauxite (aluminium)
● Copper ores
Ⴆ Iron ores
U Pitchblende (uranium)
○ Beach sands (rutile, ilmenite)
Ⓝ Nickel ores

Figure 10.3
Australia's mineral and metal mining sites

Economics of metal production

Australia ranks as one of the world's leading mineral resource nations. Our reserves of bauxite, lead, zinc, uranium and silver minerals are among the highest in the world.

Before an ore body can be commercially developed, various economic decisions must be made. Here are some examples.

Location and size of the ore body

Ore bodies at various depths beneath established cities and towns are difficult to mine. For example, coal seams beneath Sydney can be mined only at more shallow depths outside the suburban fringes. In other parts of Australia, ore bodies are located in protected areas such as national parks and Aboriginal lands. Ore bodies may be close to ecologically sensitive areas, so mining permits may be issued only if the ecosystem is protected.

The ore body must be large enough to ensure that profits can eventually be made. If the ore body is too small, the start-up costs may never be recovered.

Concentration of metal in the ore body

A large, high-grade ore body is economical to mine because there is a high concentration of the metal in the ore. Some low-grade deposits may still be economical to mine if they are large enough and suitably located. As new technologies are developed that minimise costs, deposits that were once considered low-grade and uneconomical may become viable. This has occurred in the Mount Gordon copper mine in Queensland.

The concentration of metal in an economically viable ore body varies from one metal to another. Table 10.2 compares the percentage of metal in a pure mineral with the percentage present in several Australian ore bodies.

Table 10.2 Examples of metal content in Australian ore bodies

Metal extracted	Mineral present in ore body	Location of ore body	% metal in pure mineral	Average % metal in ore body
iron	haematite, Fe_2O_3	Pilbara, WA	70	60
	limonite, $Fe_2O_3.H_2O$	Pilbara, WA	63	58
aluminium	boehmite, $Al_2O_3.H_2O$	Weipa, Qld	45	30
copper	chalcocite, Cu_2S	Mount Gordon, Qld	80	9
zinc	sphalerite, ZnS	Century, Qld	67	12

More than 90% of iron ore from the Pilbara is exported rather than smelted in Australia. A body of iron ore should contain a minimum of 50% iron. It should be noted that some ore bodies can be mined economically with much lower metal concentrations (some as low as 20% iron) if they are readily accessible, while inaccessible deposits often require even higher concentrations. At Mount Tom Price, concentrators have been constructed to raise the percentage of iron in low-grade ores to allow them to be exported as high-grade ores.

SAMPLE PROBLEM 10.1

A 5.0 g sample of limonite was analysed gravimetrically. In Western Australia, this type of ore body requires a minimum of 58% iron to be economically viable. The mass of pure iron extracted during the analysis was 2.25 g. Determine whether the ore would be economical to mine.

SOLUTION

% iron in iron ore = 2.25/5.0 x 100
　　　　　　　　 = 45%

This value is less than 58% so the ore would not be economical to mine unless enrichment-processing costs could be reduced.

yield: the amount of product (e.g. a metal) derived from a chemical extraction process (often expressed as a percentage of the maximum theoretical amount)

Yield of metal

Mining companies maximise their profits by ensuring a high **yield** of metal. Losses occur during the mining and extraction processes so the actual yield of metal is less than the theoretical yield. By improving efficiencies and extraction methods, the yield of metal can be increased.

SAMPLE PROBLEM 10.2

A sample of chalcocite ore from Mount Gordon (Esperanza) in Queensland gave an assay of 15.3 % chalcocite, Cu_2S.

(a) Determine the theoretical yield of pure copper from 10 tonnes of chalcocite ore.

(b) Calculate the theoretical yield of copper as a percentage of the mass of ore.

(a) *Step 1:* Calculate the mass of chalcocite in 10 tonnes of ore.
$$m(Cu_2S) = 15.3/100 \times 10$$
$$= 1.53 \text{ t}$$
Step 2: Determine the percentage of copper in Cu_2S.
$$\% \text{ Cu} = M(Cu)/M(Cu_2S) \times 100$$
$$= (2 \times 63.55)/(159.17 \times 100)$$
$$= 79.9\%$$
Step 3: Calculate the theoretical mass of copper.
$$m(Cu) = 79.9/100 \times 1.53$$
$$= 1.22 \text{ t}$$

(b) theoretical % yield of copper $= 1.22/10 \times 100$
$$= 12.2\%$$

Costs of exploration and establishment of mine and extraction plant

Australia leads the world in mineral exploration. In 2001, the cost of mineral exploration in Australia was $683 million; these costs must be recovered. Once an economically viable ore body is discovered and characterised, a large amount of money must be raised to set up the mining operation. Expenses include buildings, smelters, machinery, sites for the safe disposal of waste, miners' salaries and housing for each miner's family.

Figure 10.4
(a) This iron ore train is over 7 km long and pulls over 600 wagons as it snakes through Western Australia on the Newman-to-Port Hedland track (b) Loading an iron ore train in Western Australia

Transportation costs

Various types of transport, including truck, rail and shipping, are involved in mining and marketing of metals and ores. Mining companies may need to build a railway line from the mine to the coast so that bulk carriers can transport the product overseas. The more remote the mine, the greater the transport costs.

World metal prices

The price of metals varies daily on the world market. Low prices affect profitability and continued decline in prices may lead to mine shutdowns if no profit can be made. Mining and metal production cannot continue if the costs are larger than the sales. Various economic factors, including the fluctuating value of the Australian dollar, as well as the changing demand for various metals, influence metal prices. Table 10.3 shows an example of changing metal prices.

10.1 DATA ANALYSIS
The viability of mining a vanadium ore deposit

Table 10.3 World metal prices (US dollars)

Metal	December 2002 price/kg	June 2005 price/kg
copper	$1.57	$3.45
aluminium	$1.37	$1.71

10.1 QUESTIONS

1. Many metal ores are formed in magma chambers. A mineral that forms in this way is
   A   aluminium oxide.
   B   silver.
   C   copper sulfide.
   D   gold.

2. Metallic ores are non-renewable resources because they
   A   were formed millions of years ago and they cannot be renewed in our lifetimes.
   B   are too expensive to renew.
   C   are too deep in the lithosphere to extract.
   D   are formed only in hydrothermal regions.

3. A metal that is commonly found as an oxide ore is
   A   calcium.
   B   zinc.
   C   nickel.
   D   tin.

4. In Australia, the greatest amounts of iron ores are mined in
   A   Western Australia.
   B   Tasmania.
   C   Queensland.
   D   New South Wales.

5. A 50 g sample of an ore containing sphalerite was obtained from the Century Zinc mine in Queensland. The sample was dissolved in acid and the zinc extracted. The mass of zinc recovered was 5.5 g. Determine the zinc content of the ore sample.

6. Iron is extracted from haematite ore using a blast furnace. A 200-tonne sample of haematite ore from the Pilbara was reduced to iron in a blast furnace. Calculate the theoretical yield of iron if the ore has 63% iron by weight.

7. Use the following headings to discuss the issues in establishing a viable mine to extract and refine metals.
   (a) Exploration
   (b) World metal prices
   (c) Yield

10.2 EXTRACTION AND RECYCLING

Remember
Before beginning this section, you should be able to:
• explain why ores are non-renewable resources
• discuss the importance of predicting yield in the identification, mining and extraction of commercial ore deposits.

Extraction of copper from its ores

Copper forms many different minerals. The earliest copper minerals to be mined and smelted were those that were brightly coloured and rich in copper, such as malachite, $CuCO_3.Cu(OH)_2$, and azurite, $2CuCO_3.Cu(OH)_2$. Over time, the high-grade surface ores became depleted. We now need to mine ores with lower copper content to provide the copper for our technological society.

Australia is the world's third largest copper-producing nation, with major mines and smelters at Olympic Dam in South Australia and Mt Isa

Key content

By the end of this section, you should be able to:
- describe the separation processes, chemical reactions and energy considerations involved in the extraction of copper from one of its ores
- recount the steps taken to recycle aluminium
- justify the increased recycling of metals in our society and across the world
- analyse information to compare the cost and energy expenditure involved in the extraction of aluminium from its ore and the recycling of aluminium

in Queensland. By the beginning of the twenty-first century, Australia was spending over $28 million a year on copper ore exploration. In 2001, Australia produced 869 kilotonnes of copper, while $2.3 billion flowed into the Australian economy from sales of copper and copper concentrates. Current mining ventures at Mt Isa include deep-drilling operations to depths of 2 kilometres.

Figure 10.5
Chalcopyrite is an important mineral from which copper can be extracted. Chalcopyrite's colour varies from golden to blue-violet.

Copper ores

The main copper ores mined in Australia are:
- chalcopyrite, $CuFeS_2$
- bornite, Cu_5FeS_4
- covellite, CuS
- chalcocite, Cu_2S
- cuprite, Cu_2O.

Other minerals are usually associated with these ores, including gold, silver sulfide, lead sulfide and zinc sulfide.

Extraction of copper from chalcopyrite

The conventional extraction of copper from the chalcopyrite ore body involves both physical and chemical separation procedures. These are summarised in the following steps.

Step 1: Crushing and grinding the mined ore

The mined ore (which may contain as little as 0.25% copper) is placed in a crusher and converted to pebbles less than 10mm in size. The pebbles are placed in a ball mill where they are rolled and ground to a fine powder (<0.3 mm) to liberate the mineral crystals from the unwanted rock (gangue). These processes occur near the mine site.

Figure 10.6
The roasted ore is smelted to produce a copper matte.

Step 2: Concentration

The chalcopyrite mineral is separated from the gangue of silicate minerals using the process of froth flotation. The chalcopyrite minerals are removed from the gangue because they stick to the froth. The copper concentrate, containing 25–36% copper by weight, is pumped to the smelter. The gangue slurry is pumped into a tailings pond for disposal. Alternatively, the gangue may be used to refill the exhausted mine pit.

Step 3: Extraction and casting

(a) Roasting — The initial roasting process converts chalcopyrite to: chalcocite, Cu_2S; iron (II) oxide; and sulfur dioxide. This roasting process involves heating the chalcopyrite concentrate in a current of air. Some of the sulfur in the mineral is oxidised to sulfur dioxide; volatile oxides of arsenic and antimony impurities are removed during roasting.

$$2CuFeS_2(s) + 4O_2(g) \rightarrow Cu_2S(l) + 2FeO(s) + 3SO_2(g)$$

(b) Smelting — The roasted ore is placed in a furnace, and sand (silica) and coal (carbon) are added. The coal burns as oxygen-enriched air is blown through the furnace via a lance. The temperature increases to 1000 °C as the coal burns. At this temperature, the chalcopyrite undergoes a complex series of reactions forming a molten *copper matte*, which is a mixture of Cu_2S (chalcocite), and Cu_2O (cuprite). The iron in the chalcopyrite forms iron oxide, FeO. The iron oxide combines with the fused silica to form a *slag* of iron silicate. The slag floats on the matte and can be discarded. The copper matte contains 50–70% copper. Sulfur dioxide gas is released, collected and converted to sulfuric acid using the Contact Process. This sulfuric acid is sold to reduce the overall costs of the operation.

The smelting processes can be summarised by the following equations:

$$2Cu_2S(s) + 3O_2(g) \rightarrow 2Cu_2O(l) + 2SO_2(g)$$

$$FeO(s) + SiO_2(s) \rightarrow FeSiO_3(l)$$

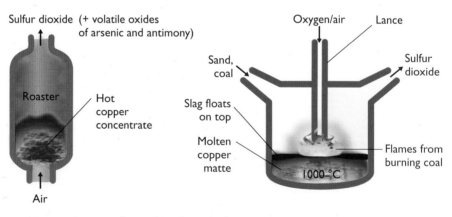

Figure 10.7
Copper ore is roasted and smelted.

(c) Converting — Additional sand is added to the molten copper matte, which reacts with the air blown into the converter to form molten copper. Sulfur is removed as sulfur dioxide gas by blowing air through

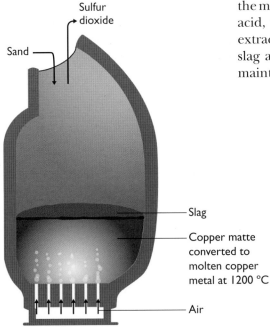

Figure 10.8
A copper converter

oxidation: loss of electrons

reduction: gain of electrons

the molten copper at 1200 °C. The sulfur dioxide is converted to sulfuric acid, which may be sold or used in associated hydrometallurgical extractions of copper from mine wastes and low-grade ores. Some slag also forms. This reaction is exothermic so no fuel is needed to maintain the temperature of the converter.

$$2Cu_2S(l) + 3O_2(g) \rightarrow 2Cu_2O(l) + 2SO_2(g)$$

$$2Cu_2O(l) + Cu_2S(l) \rightarrow 6Cu(l) + SO_2(g)$$

(d) Casting — The melted copper (98% pure) is run off into moulds and cast into blocks for further refining. The cast copper is called *blister copper* because of the bubbled surface caused by escaping sulfur dioxide gas. It contains about 2% impurities, which include iron, arsenic, nickel, silver, gold and sulfur.

Step 4: Electrolytic refining

The process of *electrolysis* is used to refine (purify) the blister copper produced in the smelter. Electrolytic refining involves **oxidation** of blister copper, which forms the *anode* (positive electrode) in the electrolytic cell, and **reduction** of copper ions to metallic copper, which is deposited at the *cathode* (negative electrode). The electrolyte is a warm, acidified solution of copper sulfate. In modern plants, the cathode is composed of stainless steel, rather than sheets of pure copper used in older plants. The copper deposited on the surface of the cathode is 99.9% pure.

Anode: $Cu(s) \rightarrow Cu^{2+}(aq) + 2e^-$

Cathode: $Cu^{2+}(aq) + 2e^- \rightarrow Cu(s)$

Figure 10.9
Blister copper is about 98% pure.

Some impurities in the copper anodes remain in solution as the anode disintegrates. Other impurities such as gold, platinum and silver sink to the bottom of the tank to form a sludge. This sludge is recovered and the valuable metals extracted from it.

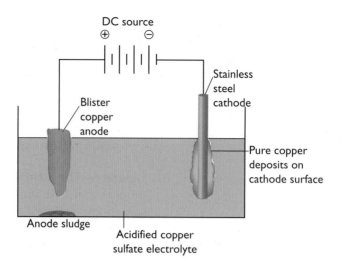

Figure 10.10
Electrolytic refining of crude copper

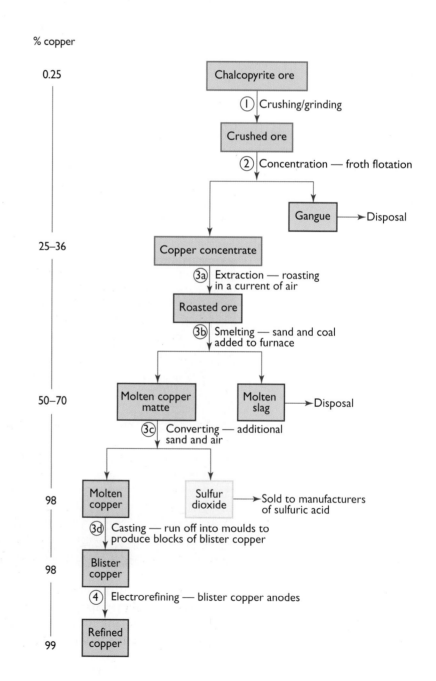

Figure 10.11
Summary of copper extraction and recycling

Energy issues and new technologies

The conventional method of copper smelting and refining was developed between 1865 and 1909. Since then, more efficient, automated equipment has allowed companies to maintain profits in the face of increased costs due to environmental protection legislation. The conventional method requires large amounts of energy per tonne of metal produced. By the mid-twentieth century, newer technologies such as *flash smelting* halved the energy usage. This technique is used at Olympic Dam in South Australia. The furnace is heated until it is so hot that the copper concentrate immediately ignites with the oxygen and silica flux as it enters the furnace. Impure liquid copper (the copper matte) and sulfur dioxide are formed during combustion. Large amounts of heat are released, which keep the furnace at the correct temperature. The molten copper matte is collected by a ladle and poured into the converter furnace where iron and sulfur are burnt away. The matte is then ladled into the final anode furnace where natural gas is used to burn off excess oxygen in the copper. From there, it is poured and cast into moulds to form anodes for electrolytic refining.

In the mid 1980s, the SX/EW (solvent extraction/electrowinning) process was widely adopted as an important adjunct to smelting. This is a hydrometallurgical process in which sulfuric acid and iron (III) sulfate solutions are used to leach copper from oxidised ores, mine wastes and low-grade ores that would not normally be economical to mine. Solvent extraction techniques, using organic solvents and strong acid solutions, eventually produce a concentrated aqueous solution of copper for eltro-winning. Electrowinning is similar to electrolytic refining, except that copper is not transported from anode to cathode. The copper deposited on the cathode comes directly from the solution of copper ions.

No rock needs to be mined for electrowinning. The acid solution is pumped into the ore body and allowed to dissolve the copper mineral, and the dissolved metal is pumped out. By extracting the copper on site, the copper ore does not have to be mined conventionally. This is a huge energy saving as considerable energy is used in mining an ore body and in removing the unwanted rock from the copper minerals. Compared to conventional smelting methods, where 65 MJ of energy is expended to extract one kilogram of copper, hydrometallurgical methods use only 15–36 MJ of energy.

Environmental issues

In the nineteenth and early twentieth centuries, copper smelting resulted in the release of *sulfur dioxide* into the atmosphere. This caused extreme environmental damage. Sulfur dioxide is one of the gases responsible for the production of acid rain. Large areas of Europe and the USA have been damaged in the past by these acidic emissions. Sulfur dioxide was the curse of the Mount Lyell operation in Queenstown, Tasmania. The forests and shrubs around Mount Lyell were destroyed, leaving a highly eroded landscape, which is now starting to recover as smelting operations have ceased. Environmental legislation now requires copper producers to treat exhaust gases being emitted to the atmosphere so that the maximum sulfur dioxide content is 1000 ppm. The exhaust gases pass through **scrubbers** and the sulfurous acid produced can be collected and catalytically oxidised to sulfuric acid, which can be sold or used to extract copper using newer hydrometallurgical techniques.

scrubbers: devices that spray water through gaseous and particle emissions to prevent toxic gases and particles escaping to the environment

Waste water from the primary stages of copper ore concentrating, and from exhaust stack scrubbers, and spent electrolytes from electrolytic baths contain dissolved and suspended solids. These include many heavy metals, such as mercury, lead, cadmium and arsenic, which are retained in lined ponds to prevent them from contaminating the environment. Precipitation and filtration processes remove most of these toxic wastes from effluents before discharge. However, the pH of the effluents must be increased to between 6 and 9 to avoid acidification of lakes, streams and soil. These effluents must also be passed through heat exchangers so that they are discharged at no more than 3 °C above the ambient temperature. Unchecked thermal pollution can significantly damage aquatic ecosystems.

Figure 10.12
The effects of copper pollution on the King River in Tasmania, near the former Mount Lyell plant

Strategies to conserve our metal resources

Metals are important non-renewable resources. Along with their alloys, they have a wide variety of uses including coinage, electrical wires, containers, structural metals and alloys and piping. Consequently, metals must continue to be mined and recycled to supply the demand.

As society continues to use metals, we must also continue to fund the search for new ore bodies. There is not a limitless supply of metals in the world so various strategies must be adopted, including:

- *replacing scarce metals* with metals in plentiful supply. For example, copper could be replaced by aluminium. This already happens in high-tension electrical wires.

- *preventing corrosion.* Metals such as iron need to be protected from corrosion; this is cheaper than replacing the metal.

- *recycling steel.* The basic oxygen steelmaking (BOS) process recycles scrap steel during the production of new steel. If the scrap comes from its own previous castings, the steel company knows the composition of the steel and it can be reused quickly. Some scrap steel, however, comes from recycled cars and appliances, and the chemical composition of this steel varies considerably. This type of scrap must be sorted before reuse. Tin cans, which are really steel cans lined with tin, are also recycled. The cans are shredded and the tin removed by dissolving it in a hot, oxidising, alkaline solution. The steel that emerges at the end of this detinning process is then recycled.

- *recycling aluminium.* Before 1960, aluminium drink cans were unknown; most drink containers were made of glass or steel. Since then, aluminium has been used extensively because it is readily rolled, lightweight, odourless, tasteless and conducts heat away from the drink so it can be chilled rapidly. However, the huge use of aluminium has led to the problem of waste disposal. Rather than rely on landfill sites, Australia now recycles about 70% of its aluminium drink cans. How does this help the environment? Obviously, if more aluminium is recycled, fewer mines are needed, so less pollution from fluoride compounds is released during its manufacture.

Recycling also saves energy. Melting and recycling aluminium uses less than 5% of the total energy required to convert bauxite ore to aluminium. Thus, recycling is not only energy efficient, but also conserves our metal supplies. Over 40% of the global demand for aluminium is met through recycling.

10.2 DATA ANALYSIS
Recycling aluminium and steel

Figure 10.13
Only 5% of the energy required to convert bauxite to aluminium is used to recycle aluminium.

10.2 QUESTIONS

1. Malachite is a green copper mineral that was mined by Egyptians in ancient times. Its chemical formula is $CuCO_3.Cu(OH)_2$. Today, chalcopyrite, $CuFeS_2$, is more commonly mined to supply the world's need for copper metal. This mineral is mined at Mt Isa to depths of 2 km.
   (a) Calculate the percentage of copper in each mineral.
   (b) Explain why copper mining at Mt Isa is being conducted at great depths.

2. A low-grade chalcopyrite ore body contains 0.5% copper. Calculate the percentage by weight of chalcopyrite in the ore.

3. The following steps in the extraction of copper from chalcopyrite ore are jumbled. Determine the correct sequence.
   (a) Roasting
   (b) Concentrating
   (c) Electrolytic refining
   (d) Casting
   (e) Crushing and grinding
   (f) Smelting
   (g) Converting

4. Identify the reactions that occur at each of the following stages of copper extraction from chalcopyrite. Include relevant equations in your answers.
   (a) Roasting
   (b) Smelting
   (c) Converting

5. Explain how the sulfur in chalcopyrite can cause environmental pollution during the roasting, smelting and converting processes.

6. When copper is cast into moulds, the final product is called cast copper, which contains 2–3% of impurities.
   (a) Identify the impurities normally present in a sample of cast copper.
   (b) A power company wishes to purchase pure copper to make electrical wiring. Cast copper has too high a resistance to be used for this purpose. Explain how the copper is purified so that it can be used for electrical wiring.
   (c) Illustrate your answer to (b) by writing appropriate half-equations.

7. In the last sixty years, there has been a large increase in the use of metals generally. However, the percentage increase in demand for copper and iron has not been as large as for aluminium.
   (a) Explain why copper and iron production has been outstripped by aluminium production.
   (b) Metals are non-renewable resources. Identify the strategies needed to ensure continuity of future supplies.

8. (a) Compare the energy requirements to produce aluminium from its raw materials with the production of ingots of recycled aluminium.
   (b) Identify an atmospheric benefit of recycling aluminium.

SUMMARY

- Metallic ores are materials derived from the lithosphere that contain commercial quantities of a metal.

- Copper can be extracted from its common ores by roasting, smelting and electrolytic refining.

- The extraction of metals from ores requires a consideration of economic and non-economic factors.

- Considerably more energy is required to extract aluminium electrically from bauxite than to extract iron and copper from their ores.

- The price of metals on the world market is related to their cost of production and their abundance.

- Metals need to be recycled because ores are non-renewable resources.

DATA ANALYSIS

10.1 DATA ANALYSIS

THE VIABILITY OF MINING A VANADIUM ORE DEPOSIT

Read the following information about the establishment of an oil shale and vanadium mine at Julia Creek* and answer the questions that follow.

Location:

Julia Creek is located in northwest Queensland, 165 km east of Cloncurry. The Fimiston Mining Company owns the Julia Creek project area. The area was bought in 1998 following geological research and metallurgical testing that suggested economically viable deposits of vanadium oxide and shale oil existed there.

Exploration and development:

Geological exploration began in the Julia Creek area in 1968 with a successful search for uranium ores. Instead, the exploration discovered oil shale and vanadium deposits. In 1969, a 6 km grid east and west of Julia Creek was established and 55 test drill holes were made. The drill cores showed consistent mineralisation. Between 1970 and 1973, research aimed to find the best methods for extracting vanadium from the ore body. By 1982, it was established that shallow, open-cut mining would be the best option. Initial exploration in three pit sites showed that this part of the ore body consisted of 1798 megatonnes; preliminary analysis showed that 64 L of oil and 3.5 kg of V_2O_5 could be obtained from each tonne. To this point, $15 million had been spent.

Further research and development between 1983 and 1988 showed that the market price of oil would make the extraction of shale oil uneconomical. Between 1988 and 1996, the project was sold to many different mining companies, which failed to proceed to production. Fimiston Mining acquired the site in 1998.

Mineralogy research:

Mineralogy research had found that the vanadium in the oil shale is mixed with clay, hydrated pyrite and silicate compounds. Some of the vanadium had been incorporated into the clay minerals. Some vanadium was also bound to organic molecules such as porphyrins. The amount of vanadium in the hydrated iron oxide minerals was about three times higher than in the clay.

Resource estimates:

The oil shale covers an area of 500 000 square km with an average thickness of 7 m. This is estimated to contain 4252 megatonnes of ore. From this ore body, it is estimated that 60 L/tonne of oil could be extracted. In total, 2400 billion barrels of oil could be mined.

It is estimated that the ore body will also produce large amounts of vanadium. This vanadium resource consists of two ore types. The upper oxide layer totals 160 megatonnes with 0.25% V_2O_5 content. The lower oil shale contains 180 megatonnes with 0.40% V_2O_5 content.

Beneficiation:

Metallurgical tests show that the vanadium oxide content of the oxide ore body can be increased from 0.25% to 1.4% by scrubbing and cycloning to remove some of the clay material. Leaching tests on this enriched ore to produce soluble vanadium showed that acid leaching is rapid but very expensive and uneconomical, due to the high levels of calcite in the ore body. Alkaline leaching with a sodium carbonate solution showed that at least 75% of the vanadium oxide was converted to soluble vanadium. Further research continues to find ways to minimise the high consumption of sodium carbonate in the leaching process.

Conclusions:

In May 2000, it was recommended to Fimiston Mining that further development work continue on this project. The likelihood of metallurgical breakthroughs and the use of new oil shale technologies being developed elsewhere could make the Julia Creek deposit economically viable in the future. It is suggested that income from the sale of the vanadium would make the oil shale extraction more attractive to investors.

(*based on Coxhell, S & Fehlberg, B, 'Julia Creek vanadium and oil shale deposit', *AIG Journal*, May 2000. Click on the Julia Creek weblink in your eBookPLUS.)

DATA ANALYSIS

Questions

1. Identify the type of ore body at Julia Creek that the early exploration geologists were seeking.
2. State the conclusions that had been reached about this site in 1982.
3. Suggest a reason why the ownership of the Julia Creek site has changed many times since 1968.
4. Outline the findings of the mineralogy research for vanadium in the ore body.
5. State the meaning of the term 'beneficiation'.
6. Outline the conclusions made from the leaching tests carried out.
7. Summarise the conclusions and recommendations made by Coxhell and Fehlberg in their report for Fimiston Mining.
8. Discuss the importance of predicting yield in the identification, mining and extraction of commercial ore deposits.

10.2 DATA ANALYSIS

RECYCLING ALUMINIUM AND STEEL

Read the following information and answer the questions that follow.

The costs of mining, concentrating, extracting and transportation make metals expensive to produce. Metal recycling is an important industry as the cost of producing recycled metals is much lower, and it saves non-renewable resources.

Aluminium:

All aluminium products (such as foil, window frames and beverage cans) can be recycled repeatedly, which extends the useful life of the metal. Scrap aluminium is a valuable commodity around the world. Recycling centres for aluminium cans have been established in Australia and worldwide. This process is very efficient, and the time between collection and the production of new cans is as short as six weeks. Countries such as Sweden recycle over 90% of their aluminium cans. Australia's recycling rate is about 70%. Twenty aluminium cans can be made from recycled aluminium for the same energy expenditure as making one aluminium can from raw materials.

The steps in recycling process aluminium cans are:

- Aluminium cans are collected and stored temporarily at local collection centres.
- At a centralised sorting centre, the cans are screened to remove steel cans. The cans are then crushed.
- Following weighing, the cans are crushed into large blocks before transportation to the furnace.
- The cans are melted, poured into moulds and cooled to produce ingots of solid aluminium.
- Aluminium ingots are then rolled thinly by manufacturers and made into new cans.

Other aluminium scrap is sorted into pure aluminium and alloys. Alloys are melted separately and the alloy composition adjusted before casting into ingots.

DATA ANALYSIS

Aluminium recycling saves considerable energy and materials. For every 1 kg of aluminium recycled:

- 14–21 kW/h less electricity is required for electrolysis
- 5–8 kg of bauxite does not have to be mined
- 20 kg of greenhouse gases are not emitted into the atmosphere.

Recycling also reduces the use of landfill sites in cities and towns. Over the last 30 years, the aluminium industry has designed lighter cans that require less aluminium. This means that about 40% less metal needs to be produced to make these cans so less ore needs to be mined and less energy is used.

The use of aluminium in the automobile industry also helps to reduce greenhouse gas emissions. The reduction in car weight, by the use of aluminium alloys, leads to lower fuel consumption. Recovering and remelting aluminium scrap for use in cars also leads to a 95% saving in greenhouse emissions over using newly smelted aluminium.

Steel:

There is a 75–80% energy saving in making steel cans using recycled steel over production from raw materials. However, the recycling rate (40%) for steel cans in Australia is lower than that for aluminium. As steel cans are coated in tin to prevent corrosion, they need to be de-tinned before the steel is recovered. In Australia, most recycled steel is used as steel reinforcement bars in concrete and in steel wires. Scrap steel makes up about 15% of all new steel produced in Australia.

Worldwide, steel is the most recycled material and the annual savings in electrical energy are equivalent to the power needed for 18 million homes per year. Every kilogram of steel that is recycled saves:

- 1.5 kg of iron ore from being mined
- 0.5 kg of coal being mined
- 40% of the water used in producing new steel
- 2 kg of greenhouse gases being emitted into the atmosphere.

The benefits of recycling aluminium and steel also apply to other metals. However, the extent of recycling other metals, such as copper and lead, varies considerably. In Australia, over 20% of copper and 60% of lead is recycled. Most recovered lead comes from car batteries. In some cases, the costs involved in recycling are higher than the price obtained by selling the recycled metal.

Questions

1. Explain why scrap aluminium is a valuable commodity worldwide.
2. Outline the energy and environmental savings from recycling aluminium.
3. Recount the steps in recycling aluminium drink cans.
4. Explain the benefits of using aluminium in the car industry.
5. Describe the benefits of recycling steel.
6. Explain why the recycling of some metals is relatively low.

WATER

CORE MODULE 3

Chapter **11** *WATER IN NATURE*

Figure 11.1
Water is essential for all forms of life.

Introduction

Earth is often called the 'water planet'. Much of the Earth's surface is covered in water and no life form can survive entirely without water. Although water is abundant in many places, water is scarce in many parts of the world, such as deserts. Fresh water is a resource needed by humans for drinking, cooking, gardening and washing. It is also needed in agriculture for crop production; large storage dams are constructed to collect fresh water for irrigating marginal land in low-rainfall areas. Seventy-five per cent of all the fresh water used in Australia is used for irrigation. Humans use water not only for drinking, but also as a means of transport and for recreation. Liquid water can be used for swimming, sailing and waterskiing, while solid water (ice) can be used for skating and snowskiing. In industry, water can be used as a solvent, reactant or coolant, and also to assist waste disposal into drains. Water is essential for life on this planet.

In this chapter

solvent: a substance (present in the larger amount) that dissolves a solute to form a solution

solution: a homogeneous mixture of two or more substances. Solutions may exist as solids, liquids or gases.

solute: a substance (present in the smaller amount) that is dissolved in a solvent to produce a solution

Solvents and water

In simple terms, **solvents** are commonly (but not always) liquids in which different substances dissolve to form homogeneous mixtures or **solutions**. In industry and in our homes, various liquids are used as solvents. Water is a very common solvent for many household products such as ammonia floor cleaners, liquid soaps and soft drinks. Some medicines use a mixture of water and alcohol to dissolve the active ingredients. Kerosene, turpentine and methylated spirits are other useful solvents. They are often used to dissolve materials that do not dissolve in water. For example, oil paints can be removed from paintbrushes using kerosene or turpentine a solvent. Steel is a solid solution of carbon atoms in solid iron. Table 11.1 lists some more examples of **solutes**, solvents and solutions.

Table 11.1 Solutes, solvents and solutions

Solution	Solute	Solvent
salt water	sodium chloride	water
soda water	carbon dioxide	water
methylated spirits	methanol	ethanol
tincture of iodine	iodine	ethanol
clear furniture glaze	oils and waxes	polyurethane
cupronickel	nickel	copper

Solutions are not always substances dissolved in liquids. The definition of the term 'solution' is much broader. Solutions are simply homogeneous mixtures of two or more substances. Thus, an alloy such as bronze can be classified as a solution as it is a uniform mixture of tin in copper. Filtered air can be considered a solution of different gases (oxygen, carbon dioxide, water vapour etc.) in nitrogen.

Figure 11.2
Icebergs consist of frozen fresh water floating in salt water.

• Solute particle
• Solvent particle

Solute particles evenly dispersed through the solvent to produce a single phase.

Figure 11.3
Particle model of solution

Water is sometimes called the 'universal solvent'. Some substances, such as salt and sugar, are very soluble in water. Oxygen is much less soluble than salt but some dissolved oxygen is vital to aquatic life. In general, water is an excellent solvent for many ionic compounds and some low-molecular-weight, covalent molecular compounds, such as organic acids and sugars. The solubility of various biochemical solutes in our body fluids is essential for the normal functioning of the body. Here are some examples of the importance of water as a solvent.

• Oxygen and carbon dioxide dissolve in water in the bloodstream and are then carried to different parts of the body.

• Various nitrogenous waste products of metabolism (e.g. urea) can dissolve in water and be eliminated from the body as urine.

• Carbon dioxide dissolves in the cellular water of leaf cells and is then available as a raw material for photosynthesis.

• Solutions of acids in water are used by our body to digest food.

• Hormones produced by our glands can be transported to various organs because they are soluble in the aqueous body fluids.

• Oceans and rivers dissolve atmospheric oxygen, which makes it available to aquatic organisms.

States and distribution of water

Water is a vital chemical for a living planet. From space, our planet has been called the 'blue planet' because of the vast oceans that cover its surface. Without liquid water, life as we know it cannot exist. On Earth, water is widely distributed in the hydrosphere, atmosphere, biosphere and even in the lithosphere, as shown in table 11.2.

Table 11.2 Distribution of water on Earth

Sphere of the Earth	Classification according to physical state	% of sphere that is water
hydrosphere	*solid:* polar ice, glaciers *liquid:* oceans, inland seas, lakes, rivers, billabongs	95–99
biosphere	*liquid:* cell protoplasm, extracellular water, transport systems *gas:* water vapour in intercellular and some organ spaces	60–95
lithosphere	solid: frozen soil, hydrated minerals liquid: aquifers, groundwater, hydrothermal solutions	less than <10
atmosphere	*solid:* ice crystals at high altitude, hail *liquid:* water droplets in clouds *gas:* water vapour	0.5–5, depending on latitude and altitude

About 97% of all the water on the Earth is present in the oceans. Another 2% is locked up as ice in glaciers and polar icecaps. The remainder is distributed in the lithosphere, biosphere and atmosphere.

Although water moves from place to place, the strong pull of gravity ensures that water is not lost to space. The water cycle (figure 11.4) summarises how water moves from place to place. This cycle is powered by the

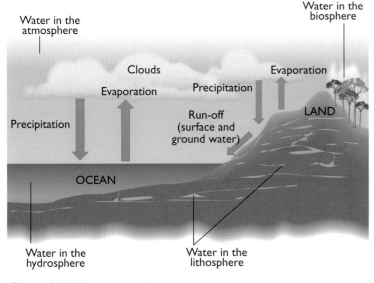

Water in the atmosphere

Clouds

Evaporation

Precipitation

Evaporation

Water in the biosphere

LAND

Precipitation

Run-off (surface and ground water)

OCEAN

Water in the hydrosphere

Water in the lithosphere

Figure 11.4 The water cycle

energy from the Sun. Water returns to the atmosphere by evaporation from oceans, lakes and streams, and when released by living things, especially plants in their transpiration stream. Water also sublimes directly from the solid to vapour states. The rate of evaporation and sublimation of water to form water vapour depends on the temperature. Warm water evaporates faster than cold water. Sublimation from ice is much slower as the temperature is lower, so the molecules are held more firmly within the crystal lattice of the ice.

A water flow budget is an accounting of the total amount of water entering and leaving various spheres. This shows that there is a mass balance of water as it moves between the hydrosphere, atmosphere, biosphere and lithosphere.

The role of the different states of water

Let us consider the different roles that water has on Earth.

Cellular water and metabolism

Water is an essential component of living cells. There is a high percentage by weight of water in plants and animals. Tomatoes, for example, are 95% water by weight while humans are about 67% water. In most life forms, water comprises about 70% of the weight of cells. Humans, like other living things, need to maintain a daily balance between water intake and loss. Table 11.3 summarises some of the important physical and chemical roles water has in living cells and in metabolism.

Table 11.3 Physical and chemical roles of water in living cells and metabolism

Physical	Chemical
• *Water is a transport medium and provides support.* The vascular system of plants and animals is a network of vessels that transports nutrients to and wastes from all the cells of a multicellular organism. Water keeps plant cells turgid and prevents wilting. Organisms that live in water are supported by the buoyancy of the water. • *Water is a solvent.* Water dissolves many salts and small molecules. Many life processes, such as digestion and respiration, can occur only if solute molecules and ions are dissolved in a solvent. • *Water is required for reproduction.* Sex cells, such as sperm, require a liquid in which to swim as they seek out an egg to fertilise. This process is common in both the plant and animal kingdoms. The embryos of animals grow in a watery medium.	• *Metabolic water is produced by respiration.* Water is produced when carbohydrates, fats and proteins undergo cellular respiration. $$C_6H_{12}O_6 + 6O_2 \rightarrow 6CO_2 + 6H_2O$$ This metabolic water is an important source of water in living organisms. • *Water is required for photosynthesis.* Water is absorbed through the roots of terrestrial plants and finds its way into photosynthetic cells. Water is needed by green plants to produce food and oxygen by photosynthesis. $$6CO_2 + 6H_2O \rightarrow C_6H_{12}O_6 + 6O_2$$ • *Water is required to digest dietary fat.* fat + water $\rightarrow$ glycerol + organic acids

Water moderates the temperature of the Earth

Water can absorb large amounts of heat without causing a large rise in temperature. Thus, oceans and large bodies of water reduce temperature fluctuations, which benefits the living things that use these habitats. In inland, terrestrial environments, such as deserts, the ambient temperature can vary much more than along the coast, where the cooling effects of sea breezes produce more moderate temperatures. Our Earth would be a much more hostile environment for life forms without the moderating effects of water in its various states.

Water as an agent of weathering and erosion

Weathering and erosion of the landscape is often caused by water. Rain or waves can physically wear away rocks. When water freezes in rock crevices, the huge pressures that result can cause rocks to split. This process, called *ice wedging*, occurs because water expands as it freezes, producing expansive forces strong enough to crack steel pipes as well as rocks. In many cold regions of the world, ice in the form of moving glaciers can also wear away rocks. Glaciers carry large quantities of rocky debris as they move slowly downhill under the force of gravity.

Water can also chemically weather minerals present in rocks. *Feldspar*, $KAlSi_3O_8$, is a common mineral found in rocks. It weathers chemically to form a clay called *kaolinite*, $Al_2Si_2O_5(OH)_4$. The presence of aqueous solutions of acids (e.g. carbonic acid produced by carbon dioxide dissolving in water) hastens the weathering process. Other acids in soil include organic acids produced by bacterial decay of plant and animal remains.

Various minerals in the ground are dissolved by ground or surface water. Limestone caves are formed when the mineral calcite, $CaCO_3$, in the limestone is dissolved by dilute solutions of carbonic acid in rainwater or surface water. The acid dissolves the limestone to produce calcium ions and hydrogen carbonate ions.

$$CaCO_3(s) + H_2CO_3 \rightarrow Ca^{2+} + 2HCO_3^-$$

The dissolved calcium ions may re-precipitate to produce stalactites or stalagmites, or they may precipitate when they reach the ocean.

(b)

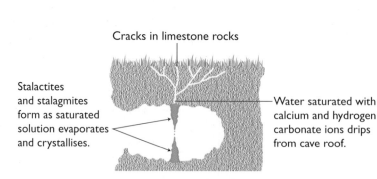

Figure 11.5
(a) Stalagmites (growing up from the cave floor) and stalactites (hanging down from the cave ceiling) in Tasmania (b) Weathering of limestone caves

Water as a natural resource

The *Sydney Water Corporation* supplies billions of litres of *potable water* each day to the residents of Sydney. The water that is collected in the catchment must be treated to ensure that the final product is clear, tasteless and odourless and does not contain harmful microbes that may cause disease.

National potable water guidelines have been established by the National Health and Medical Research Council (NHMRC). Potable water has a maximum of 500 ppm (500 mg/L) of soluble minerals. Water tastes salty if the salinity is greater than 200 ppm.

Figure 11.6
Aerial view of Warragamba Dam outside Sydney showing low water levels in 2004 due to drought

Rain that falls on the ground either soaks into the ground to become part of the groundwater or runs off into rivers, lakes and seas. Ultimately, it finds its way back to the oceans. Much of the groundwater stays in the ground for long periods. Some sandy soils are porous and absorb large amounts of water while others, such as clay, absorb very little. Permeable rocks such as sandstone can carry water underground. These are called *aquifers* and they are important in supplying bore water to many outback communities. Groundwater moves slowly, about 0.5–100 cm/day in these aquifers. Most people wrongly believe that lakes and rivers are our major sources of fresh water. In fact, about 90% of all fresh water is located underground.

Farmers use river or dam water to *irrigate* their crops and to provide water for their livestock. Large rivers in Australia were once used extensively to transport goods and livestock; rail and road transport have reduced their use. Waterways are used recreationally for skiing, swimming and boating. *Hydro-electric* power stations use the kinetic energy of falling water to generate electricity. Water is also essential in coal-fired power stations. The heat from coal combustion is used to boil water and generate steam that turns the turbines to generate electricity.

Figure 11.7
The kinetic energy of falling water is used to generate electricity.

SYLLABUS FOCUS

15. USING INSTRUCTION TERMS CORRECTLY

When answering questions it is important to know what the instruction terms (verbs) require you to do. Here are some examples.

'Select'
This instruction term requires you to make the correct choice from a number of possible answers.

Example:
Select from table 11.4 the method by which the human body loses the greatest amount of water vapour from the body each day.

Table 11.4

Method	faeces	urine	perspiration	exhalation
% loss	4	60	12	24

Answer:
Exhalation and perspiration are the processes in which water is lost in the form of a vapour. The larger of these is exhalation.

'Extrapolate'
This instruction term requires you to make an inference from what is known.

Example:
Table 11.5 shows the concentration of water in the atmosphere as a function of altitude. Extrapolate the data to determine the concentration at an altitude of 80 km.

Table 11.5

Altitude (km)	30	50	60	70	80
Concentration of water (molecules/m³)	10^{21}	10^{20}	10^{19}	10^{18}	

Answer:
It can be inferred from table 11.5 that water concentration drops by 10 molecules/m³ for each 10 km increase in altitude above 50 km. The extrapolated value for 80 km is 10^{17} molecules/m³.

The melting and boiling points of water

Water's different physical states are related to the ambient temperature. The melting and boiling points of water are very high for a molecule of such low molecular weight.

At 0 °C (and normal atmospheric pressure), ice and liquid water can exist in equilibrium with one another. This is expressed in the equation:

$$H_2O(s) \rightleftharpoons H_2O(l)$$

This phase change equilibrium can be demonstrated by measuring the temperature of melting ice blocks in a beaker. As long as some ice exists in the water, the temperature of the system stays constant at 0 °C. When all the ice has melted, the temperature will rise.

At 100 °C, liquid water and water vapour exist in equilibrium with one another as expressed in the equation:

$$H_2O(l) \rightleftharpoons H_2O(g)$$

This phase change equilibrium (at 100 °C) can be demonstrated by measuring the temperature of the surface of boiling water where steam is in contact with the thermometer bulb. The temperature remains at 100 °C as long as liquid water and water vapour are present.

The boiling point of any liquid, including water, depends on the local air pressure. The normal boiling point of water is 100 °C but this rises if the air pressure rises. Hydrothermal water at depths of several kilometres may reach temperatures of up to 260 °C and still not boil. As the water rises towards the surface, the pressure drops and the water boils explosively in the form of a geyser.

Figure 11.8
A geyser releases steam.

You may be surprised to know that water can boil at temperatures much lower than 100 °C. This occurs when the atmospheric pressure is lower than that at sea level. At altitudes of 3–5 kilometres, the water may boil at about 80–90 °C. At even higher altitudes, where the air is very thin, the water may boil at temperatures as low as normal room temperature. So, boiling water is not always hot!

The effect of solutes

Figure 11.9 shows the effect of the presence of different solutes or impurities on the freezing and boiling points of water. The data reveals that the freezing point of the water decreases as the concentration of solute increases. Thus, salt water freezes at a lower temperature than pure water.

11.1 PRACTICAL ACTIVITIES

The effect of salt on the boiling point of water

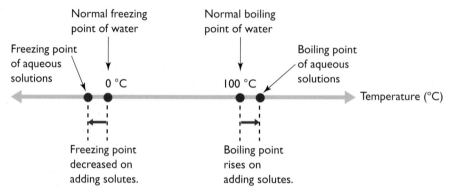

Figure 11.9 Effect of solutes on the freezing and boiling points of water

A commercial liquid called *antifreeze* (or ethylene glycol) is commonly added to the water in car radiators to ensure that the water in the radiator and pipes does not turn to ice when the ambient temperature drops below 0 °C. At concentrations of about 20% ethylene glycol, the freezing point is reduced by about 8 °C. Antifreeze increases the boiling point of water by several degrees, so it is also useful in preventing the radiator water boiling.

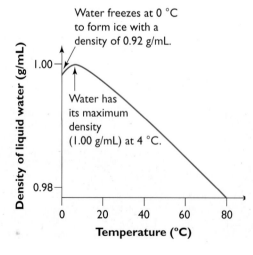

Figure 11.10
Structure of ethylene glycol (1,2-ethanediol)

The density of water

Density is a measure of the mass per unit volume of a material. Mathematically, density can be calculated using the formula:

$$D = m/V$$

where D = density (g/mL),
m = mass (g)
and V = volume (mL).

Figure 11.11 shows the density of water as a function of temperature. The maximum density occurs at 4 °C, which suggests that the density of ice (at 0 °C) is less than that of liquid water at 4 °C. When most other liquids freeze, they produce a solid that is more dense and sinks in the liquid. Because ice is less dense than water, it floats rather than sinks.

Figure 11.11
Density of water as a function of temperature

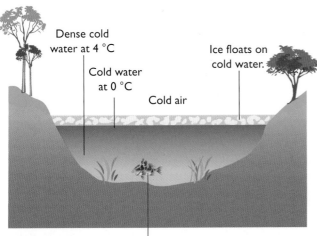

Figure 11.12
Life continues in a frozen pond.

Dense cold water at 4 °C

Cold water at 0 °C

Cold air

Ice floats on cold water.

Fish and other aquatic organisms survive in the liquid water.

The high density of water at 4 °C has important implications in the biosphere. In cold climates, such as the alpine areas of eastern Australia, lakes start to cool as winter approaches. As the water temperature drops at the surface, the density of the surface water increases until it reaches its maximum density at 4 °C. This dense surface water sinks and sets up convection currents within the lake. These convection continues until *all* the water is at 4 °C. As the temperature at the surface continues to drop, the density of the water rises again and, when the temperature reaches 0 °C, ice starts to form at the surface. The ice that forms floats on the surface providing an insulating layer for the water below. Therefore, aquatic organisms can survive in frigid lakes in liquid water below the icy surface layer.

SAMPLE PROBLEM 11.1

Use the following data to calculate the change in volume of a 250.0 g sample of ice at –10 °C when heated to 20 °C.
Density of ice at –10 °C = 0.9182 g/mL
Density of water at 20 °C = 0.9982 g/mL

SOLUTION

Use $D = m/V$ to calculate the volume of the ice and the water.

Volume of ice $(V) = m/D$
$= 250.0/0.9182$
$= 272.27$ mL

Volume of water $(V) = m/D$
$= 250.0/0.9982$
$= 250.45$ mL

Change in volume $= 272.27 – 250.45$
$= 21.82$ mL

10.2 DATA ANALYSIS
The density of water and ice

Figure 11.13
Mount Thetis, Tasmania. The lake is partly iced over in winter. The less dense ice floats on the water surface.

11.1 QUESTIONS

1. Identify the solute in lawnmower fuel.
   A   Petrol
   B   Oil
   C   Fuel mixture
   D   Natural gas

2. The solvent in brass is
   A   tin.
   B   zinc.
   C   copper.
   D   chromium.

3. Select the example that best shows the importance of water in the biosphere.
   A   Acid rain dissolves the surface of marble statues.
   B   Ground water dissolves limestone rocks to create caves.
   C   Water acts as a transport medium in the cells and organ systems of plants and animals.
   D   Moving glaciers wear away rocks.

4. Table 11.6 data shows the density of aqueous solutions of sulfuric acid at 25 °C.

Table 11.6

% sulfuric acid	10	20	30	40	50
Density (g/cm³)	1.06	1.14	1.22	1.30	

Extrapolate the data to determine the density of a 50% solution of sulfuric acid.
   A 1.32 g/cm^3
   B 1.38 g/cm^3
   C 1.40 g/cm^3
   D 1.42 g/cm^3

5. Table 11.7 shows the solubility of a number of atmospheric gases in water at 25 °C. Of those gases that are important in biochemical processes in the biosphere, select the one with the greatest solubility in water.
   A   Argon
   B   Ammonia
   C   Carbon dioxide
   D   Oxygen

Table 11.7

Gas	Ar	Cl_2	CO_2	N_2		O_2
Solubility in water (g/kg)	0.053	6.41	1.45	0.018	480	0.039

6. (a) Explain why water boils at less than 100 °C on high mountains.
   (b) Food can be cooked faster using a pressure cooker. Explain how raising the pressure inside the sealed cooker can cause food to cook faster.

7. Table 11.8 gives the percentage by weight of water in a human.

Table 11.8

Organism	Mass of organism (kg)	% water (w/w)
human	50	67

   (a) Identify the ways in which water is important to a human.
   (b) Calculate the weight of water present in the tissues and bodily fluids of a 50 kg human.
   (c) Explain why water is important in the respiratory system of a human.

8. (a) The average concentration of dissolved solids in the ocean is about 35 times greater than that in artesian water. Explain why the oceans have such a high concentration of dissolved solids compared with artesian water.
   (b) Hydrothermal water is in contact with hot rocks underground. This hot water can be used by humans to generate power. Explain why hydrothermal water contains a greater concentration of dissolved minerals than surface waters in lakes and streams.

9. A student dissolved some salt in tap water and measured the mass and volume of the resulting salt water. Use the following information to calculate the density of the salt water.

   Mass of sample = 18.84 g
   Volume of sample = 15.375 mL

10. Gerry's father asked him to top up the car radiator with antifreeze solution. He noticed on the bottle in the garage that the radiator antifreeze solution consisted of an aqueous solution of ethylene glycol.
   Gerry decided to investigate this solution further. He prepared aqueous solutions of ethylene glycol and measured their freezing points. Table 11.9 shows the data he collected in his experiments.

Table 11.9

% ethylene glycol in water (w/w)	5	10	15	20	25
Freezing point of solution (°C)	−1.6	−3.3	−5.3	x	−10.0

(a) Plot a line graph of this data. Plot the dependent variable on the vertical axis.

(b) Use your graph to interpolate a value for x, the freezing point of a 20% ethylene glycol solution.

(c) Explain the purpose of using ethylene glycol solutions in car radiators.

(d) Predict the freezing point of a mixture of 4 kg of ethylene glycol and 32 kg of water.

11. (a) Water is essential for photosynthesis in green plants and aquatic algae. Write a balanced chemical equation to show that water is a reactant in photosynthesis.

(b) Calculate the mass of water required to react with 11 kg of carbon dioxide to form glucose during the photosynthetic process.

(c) Calculate the mass of oxygen that is liberated in the reaction in (b).

12. (a) Quartz, feldspar and mica are three common rock-making minerals. One type of feldspar has the formula $KAlSi_3O_8$. Identify the element in this mineral that has the greatest percentage by weight.

(b) Clay is formed by chemical weathering of feldspar. This clay is called kaolinite, $Al_2Si_2O_5(OH)_4$. Write a balanced equation for this chemical weathering process.

(c) Natural acids assist in the chemical weathering of rocks. Explain how the acids that assist this chemical weathering are formed in nature.

SUMMARY

- Water is present in the hydrosphere, lithosphere, atmosphere and biosphere. It is present in different physical states (solid, liquid and gas) and in different percentages.

- Water has high melting and boiling points and it expands on freezing to produce a solid (ice), which is less dense than the liquid.

- The freezing point and boiling points of water are affected by solutes such as salt and ethylene glycol.

- Water is an agent of weathering and erosion.

- Water has a great influence on the climate as it absorbs and stores vast amounts of heat.

- Water is required by all living things. It has physical as well as chemical roles.

- Potable water is an important natural resource.

PRACTICAL ACTIVITIES

11.1 PRACTICAL ACTIVITIES

THE EFFECT OF SALT ON THE BOILING POINT OF WATER

Part A: First-hand investigation

Aim

To determine the effect of salt on the boiling point of water

Safety issues

- Wear safety glasses throughout this experiment.
- Ensure all glassware is securely clamped.
- Identify other safety issues relevant to this experiment by reading the method.

Materials

- thermometer (110 °C)
- conical flask (250 mL)
- Bunsen burner
- tripod and gauze mat
- clamps, bosshead and stand
- pure water
- salt water (~15%w/w)

Method

1. The first step in this investigation is to calibrate your thermometer to determine the boiling temperature of pure water. Set up the apparatus as shown in figure 11.14. Use about 120 mL of water.

2. Ensure the bulb of the thermometer is kept just under the water surface as it boils but not near the hot glass at the base. Record the constant temperature of the boiling water. If the thermometer does not read 100 °C in the boiling water, determine the adjustment needed for future readings for salt water.

3. When cool, remove the flask and replace the pure water with salt water and repeat the

experiment. Ensure the bulb remains in the solution as before. Record the temperature each minute after the temperature reaches 90 °C. Cease heating once salt crystals start to form in the boiling liquid as the water evaporates.

Results

Record your observations in a suitable table.

Questions

Answer the following questions in your report on this experiment:

1. Explain why calibration of the thermometer was necessary to validate the experimental results.

2. Describe the effect of dissolved salt on the boiling point of water.

3. Explain how the reliability of this experiment could be improved.

Conclusion

Briefly describe the outcome of your investigation.

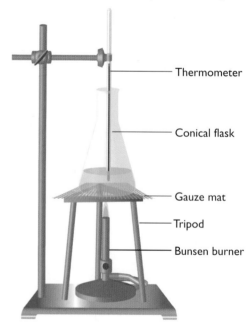

Figure 11.14
Apparatus for measuring boiling point of a liquid

Thermometer

Conical flask

Gauze mat

Tripod

Bunsen burner

DATA ANALYSIS

Part B: Processing supplied data

Table 11.10 provides information on the boiling point of pure water and salt water over a period of 18 minutes.

Table 11.10

Time (minutes)	Temperature of pure water (°C)	Temperature of salt water (°C)
0	95.0	95.0
2	96.1	96.5
4	97.3	98.0
6	98.7	99.5
8	99.9	101.0
10	100.0	101.9
14	100.0	103.3
16	100.0	104.1
18	100.0	105.1

Questions

1. Use grid paper to plot line graphs for each data set. Plot both graphs on the same grid.
2. Use the graphs to describe the effect of salt on the boiling point of water.
3. Explain why the temperature of the pure water remained at 100 °C after boiling began.
4. Suggest a hypothesis to explain why the temperature of the boiling salt water increased with time.
5. Crystals of salt eventually form in the boiling salt water. Once this happens, the temperature does not rise any further. Suggest a reason for this observation.

11.2 DATA ANALYSIS

THE DENSITY OF WATER AND ICE

Part A

Apparatus was set up to investigate the change in volume of 10.000 g of water over a range of temperatures from 1 °C to 6 °C (figure 11.15). A syringe was used to introduce and expel water from a calibrated glass tube of uniform cross-sectional area. Graduations on the tube were used to measure the volume of the water at each temperature. The graduations were viewed through a high-powered microscope placed above the apparatus. The temperature of the circulating water was monitored by a thermocouple connected to a data logger. The results of the experiment are shown in table 11.11.

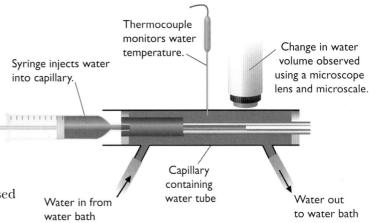

Thermocouple monitors water temperature.

Syringe injects water into capillary.

Change in water volume observed using a microscope lens and microscale.

Capillary containing water tube

Water in from water bath

Water out to water bath

Figure 11.15 Apparatus for measuring the effect of the temperature of water on its volume

Questions

1. Use 2 mm grid paper to plot a line graph of this data (table 11.11). Temperature is the independent variable so should be plotted on the horizontal axis.
2. Use your graph to determine the temperature at which 10.000 g of water has the smallest volume.

3. Calculate the density of water at each temperature using the formula: $D = m/V$, where D = density (g/mL), m = mass (g) and V = volume (mL). Tabulate your calculated data.

4. Use your density data to determine the temperature when water has its greatest density.

Part B

Table 11.12 shows the density of ice as a function of temperature.

1. Plot a line graph of density of ice versus temperature, with temperature on the horizontal axis.

2. Explain whether ice expands or contracts as it is cooled.

3. Calculate the volume of 10.00 g of ice at –4 °C.

4. Explain why ice floats on melted ice water.

5. Explain how this data is relevant to the survival of aquatic organisms in frozen lakes.

6. Figure 11.16 shows diagrams of the arrangement of water molecules in an ice crystal and in liquid water. Use these diagrams to account for the differing densities of ice and water at 0 °C.

Table 11.11

Temperature (°C)	1	2	3	4	5	6
Volume of water (mL)	10.0009	10.0003	10.0002	10.0000	10.0002	10.0005

Table 11.12

Temperature (°C)	0	–1	–2	–3	–4
Density of ice (g/mL)	0.91700	0.91710	0.91720	0.91728	0.91737

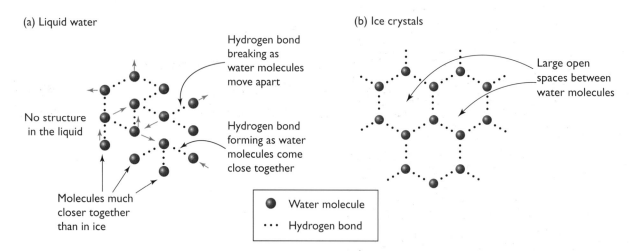

(a) Liquid water

Hydrogen bond breaking as water molecules move apart

No structure in the liquid

Hydrogen bond forming as water molecules come close together

Molecules much closer together than in ice

(b) Ice crystals

Large open spaces between water molecules

● Water molecule

⋯ Hydrogen bond

Figure 11.16 Particle diagrams of liquid water and ice

Chapter *12* STRUCTURE AND BONDING IN WATER

Introduction

Water is classified as a covalent molecular compound. Its importance and distribution are related to its molecular structure and physical properties. In this section, we will examine the structure and bonding of water molecules. We will then compare these properties with those of other types of molecular compounds.

In this chapter

Figure 12.1

The surface tension of water helps to support this insect on the water surface.

12.1 INTERMOLECULAR FORCES AND POLARITY OF MOLECULES

Remember

Before beginning this section, you should be able to:
- describe the physical properties used to classify compounds as ionic, covalent molecular or covalent network.

Key content

By the end of this section, you should be able to:
- construct Lewis electron dot structures of water, ammonia and hydrogen sulfide to identify the distribution of electrons
- compare the molecular structures, molecular shapes and melting and boiling points of water, ammonia and hydrogen sulfide
- describe hydrogen bonding between molecules
- identify the water molecule as a polar molecule
- describe the attractive forces between polar molecules as dipole–dipole forces
- explain the following properties of water in terms of its intermolecular forces: surface tension, viscosity, boiling and melting points
- process information from secondary sources to graph and compare the boiling and melting points of water with other similar-sized molecules
- identify data and process information from secondary sources to model the structure of the water molecule and effects of forces between water molecules
- choose equipment and perform first-hand investigations to demonstrate the following properties of water: surface tension, viscosity.

Electronegativity and the polarity of molecules

Non-metallic elements have incomplete valence shells and tend to attract electrons to produce a stable valence shell. This electron-attracting ability of non-metals is called *electronegativity*. Metals, however, prefer to lose valence shell electrons to achieve stable outer shells so are called *electropositive*.

When *covalent bonds* form between atoms of the same element, the electrons are shared equally. Electrons are not equally shared between atoms when different non-metals bond together. The non-metal with the higher electronegativity has the greater share of the electrons. Table 12.1 lists the electronegativities of some non-metals.

Table 12.1 Electronegativities of some non-metals

Element	F	O	Cl	N	Br	I	S	C	H
Electronegativity	3.98	3.44	3.16	3.04	2.96	2.66	2.58	2.55	2.20

Bond polarity

A covalent bond is said to be *non-polar* if the electron pairs are shared equally. If the electron pairs are not shared equally, the bond is said to be **polar** (see figure 12.2).

Examples:

1. The chlorine–chlorine bond in Cl_2 and the hydrogen–hydrogen bond in H_2 are non-polar as the atoms that form the bonds are identical.
2. The iodine–chlorine bond is polar as the chlorine has greater electronegativity than the iodine atom. Therefore, the chlorine atom has a greater share of the electron pair. The iodine atom is thus slightly positively charged and the chlorine atom is slightly negatively charged. The polar I—Cl bond is an example of a bond **dipole**. Figure 12.3 shows how this bond dipole is represented.

Partial ionic character of polar covalent bonds

If one of the two atoms linked by a covalent bond gains a 100% share of the electron pair, the bond becomes purely ionic. Very few bonds are purely ionic or purely covalent. Therefore, in molecular compounds, covalent bonds typically have some partial ionic character.

In the I—Cl bond, the electronegativity difference ($3.16 - 2.66 = 0.56$) corresponds approximately to a covalent bond with 10% ionic character. When the electronegativity difference reaches 1.55 units (e.g. in the Al—Cl bond), the bond is highly polar and has approximately 40% ionic character. The Cs—F bond in caesium fluoride is purely ionic as the electronegativity difference of 3.19 is very high.

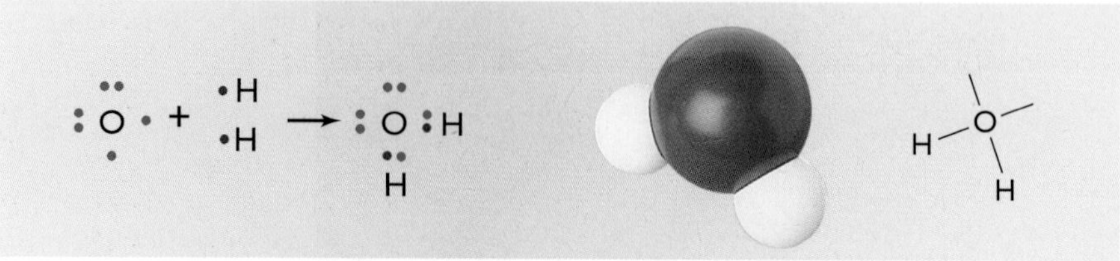

Figure 12.2
Lewis electron dot structures, a space-filling molecular model and the structural formula of water. The oxygen end of the water molecule is slightly more negative than the hydrogen end of the molecule. This makes the water molecule polar.

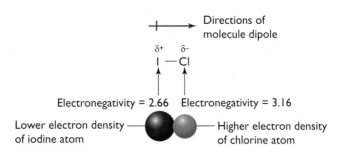

Directions of molecule dipole

$\delta+$ $\quad\delta-$

I — Cl

Electronegativity = 2.66   Electronegativity = 3.16

Lower electron density of iodine atom —————   Higher electron density of chlorine atom

Figure 12.3 Polarity of the iodine–chlorine bond

dipole: an asymmetric charge distribution within a molecule such that there is a distance between the centres of positive and negative charge

polar: describes a covalent bond in which there is an asymmetric charge distribution due to one atom having greater electronegativity than the other

SAMPLE PROBLEM 12.1

SOLUTION

Determine which of the following bonds is the most polar.

N—Cl, H—F, O—Cl, Br—I, C—H

Use table 12.1 to determine the differences in electronegativity between the elements that form each bond.

N—Cl: 3.16 – 3.04 = 0.12
H—F: 3.98 – 2.20 = 1.78
O—Cl: 3.44 – 3.16 = 0.28
Br—I: 3.16 – 2.96 = 0.20
C—H: 2.55 – 2.20 = 0.35

Thus, the H—F bond is very much more polar than the others.

Polar and non-polar molecules

Molecules can also be classified as **polar molecules** and non-polar molecules. The shape and symmetry of the molecule are the critical factors that determine overall polarity.

polar molecule: a molecule with a permanent dipole. One end of the molecule is partially positive and the other end is partially negative.

- Molecules are non-polar if the sum of their bond dipoles in three dimensions is zero. Thus, perfectly symmetrical molecules are non-polar.

- Molecules are polar if the sum of their bond dipoles in three dimensions is non-zero. Thus, asymmetrical molecules are polar.

Figure 12.4
Chlorine molecules are non-polar. They can be represented as Lewis electron dot structures, 3-D space filling models or a structural formula.

Figure 12.5 shows models of common non-polar molecules. Carbon dioxide and boron trichloride are non-polar molecules as the sums of their molecular dipoles are equal to zero. The C=O and B—Cl bonds are polar bonds, but the arrangement of these bond dipoles in space leads to an overall zero dipole for the whole molecule. The symmetry of these molecules cancels the bond dipoles.

Simple diatomic molecules composed of different elements are polar as one atom always has a higher electronegativity. In larger molecules, the symmetry or asymmetry of the molecule determines whether the whole molecule is polar or non-polar (see figure 12.6). Both linear hydrogen cyanide and pyramidal ammonia molecules are polar as their bond dipoles sum to produce a non-zero molecular dipole.

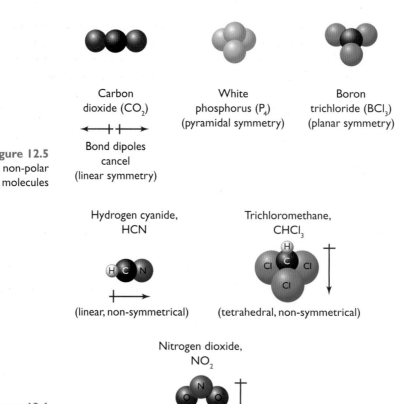

Carbon
dioxide (CO₂)

White
phosphorus (P₄)
(pyramidal symmetry)

Boron
trichloride (BCl₃)
(planar symmetry)

Bond dipoles
cancel
(linear symmetry)

Figure 12.5
Models of some non-polar
molecules

Hydrogen cyanide,
HCN

Trichloromethane,
CHCl₃

(linear, non-symmetrical)

(tetrahedral, non-symmetrical)

Nitrogen dioxide,
NO₂

Figure 12.6
Models of some polar molecules

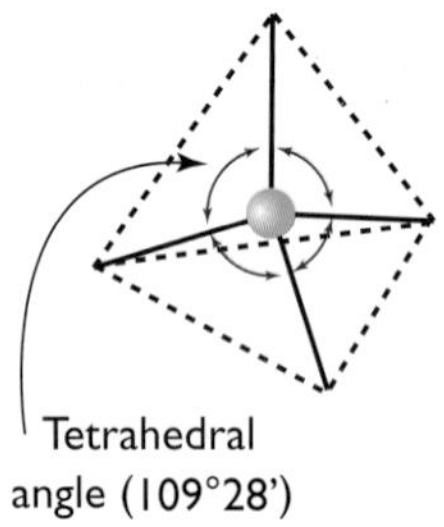

(bent, non-symmetrical)

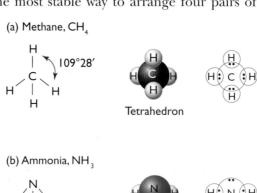

Tetrahedral
angle (109°28')

Figure 12.7
Bond angles in a tetrahedron

Lewis electron dot structures

The Lewis electron dot structures of molecules help us visualise the arrangement of electron pairs in the valence shells of each bonding atom. Some electron pairs are involved in bond formation; others that are not involved are known as non-bonding or lone pairs. Electron pairs repel each other and move as far apart as possible to achieve greater stability. The most stable way to arrange four pairs of valence electrons is in the shape of a *tetrahedron*. In this symmetrical three-dimensional shape, the bond angles are 109°28', as shown in figure 12.7.

Methane, ammonia and water are molecules with molecular shapes based on the tetrahedron, as shown in figure 12.8. Methane is a perfect tetrahedron as four bonding pairs of electrons surround the central carbon atom. In ammonia, there are three bonding electron pairs and one non-bonding pair (lone pair).

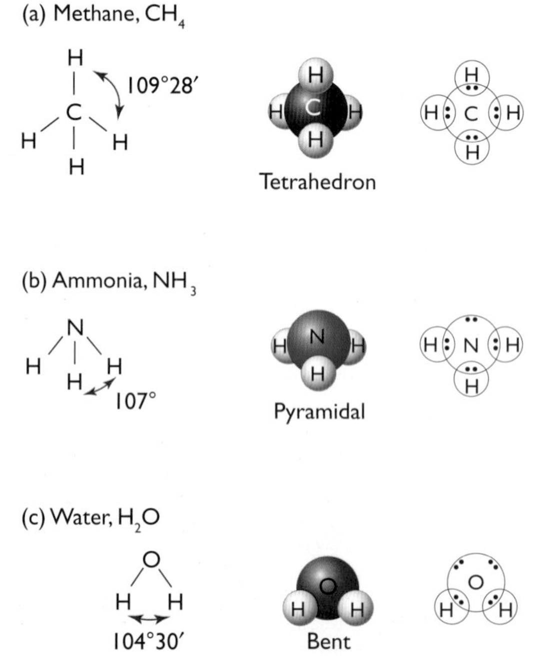

(a) Methane, CH₄

Tetrahedron

(b) Ammonia, NH₃

Pyramidal

(c) Water, H₂O

Figure 12.8
Space-filling models and Lewis
electron dot structures for methane,
ammonia and water

Bent

Differences in repulsion lead to the formation of a trigonal pyramid-shaped molecule. The H—N—H bond angle is 107°. In water, with two bonding electron pairs and two non-bonding pairs, the molecule takes on a bent shape. The H—O—H bond angle is 104°.

A molecule similar to water is hydrogen sulfide. Its H—S—H bond angle is 92°, as shown in figure 12.9.

Figure 12.9
Space-filling model and Lewis electron dot structure for hydrogen sulfide

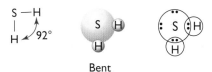

Bent

Testing the polarity of molecular liquids

Figure 12.10 shows a simple method that can be used in the school lab-oratory to test for the presence of a molecular dipole in molecular liquids. If water and hexane, for example, are tested with charged perspex rods, only the water stream is attracted to the charged rod. This experiment confirms that water is a polar molecule while hexane is non-polar.

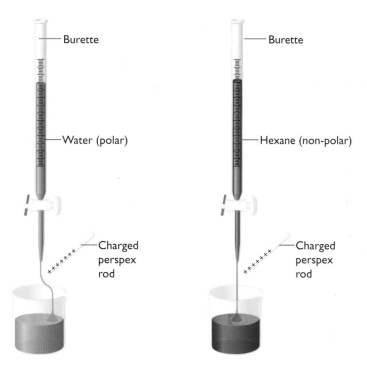

Figure 12.10 Testing polarity of molecular liquids

eBook plus

Testing molecular polarity

eBook plus

Weblinks

SYLLABUS FOCUS

16. USING WEBSITES TO VISUALISE AND CONSTRUCT MOLECULES

There are many web-based programs that help chemists to visualise the shapes and bonding interactions between molecules. Some are interactive and allow you to rotate molecules in three dimensions or to construct Lewis electron dot structures. You will find useful websites in your eBookPLUS; web searches will reveal many more.

Intermolecular forces

Attractive intermolecular forces exist between all molecules. The physical properties of covalent molecular substances depend on the strength of these forces. Figure 12.11 shows how intermolecular forces can be classified.

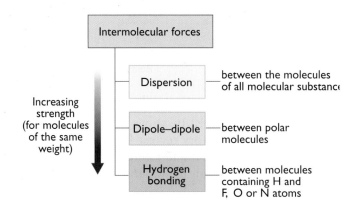

Figure 12.11
Classification of intermolecular forces

dispersion force: an intermolecular attractive force caused by a temporary dipole inducing a temporary dipole in a nearby molecule.

Dispersion forces

Electrons are not always evenly distributed around the nucleus. **Dispersion forces** are weak attractive forces that result from an uneven electron distribution around the nucleus and between neighbouring atoms. One side of the atom can temporarily become more positive than the other side due to the motion of the outershell electrons. Dipoles are, therefore, created in atoms due to these asymmetric charge distributions. These temporary dipoles continuously break down and reform. The creation of temporary dipoles in one atom can induce dipoles in adjoining atoms. Another way of describing dispersion forces is to consider them as the attraction between temporary dipoles and induced temporary dipoles. In visual terms, a model of these events at the atomic level would show that the locations of the negative and positive ends of the dipoles move constantly from one atomic surface to another.

Generally, the larger an atom or molecule, the larger the dispersion forces between it and its neighbours. This generalisation has been verified experimentally. Large molecules have large numbers of electrons, which become available to form temporary dipoles. Table 12.2 illustrates this with the noble gases by showing that boiling point is directly related to the molecular weight of the gas. For example, helium, with quite weak dispersion forces, has a low boiling point.

Table 12.2 Boiling points of the noble gases

Noble gas	He	Ne	Ar	Kr	Xe	Rn
Molecular weight	4.0	20.2	39.95	83.8	131.3	222
Boiling point (°C)	−269	−246	−186	−152	−108	−62

The *surface area* of a molecule also affects the size of the dispersion force. For example, some hydrocarbon molecules with identical molecular weights have different shapes due to chain branching. This creates differences in effective surface area of the molecules and affects how closely the molecules can pack together, causing differences in melting and boiling points.

Dipole–dipole forces

Molecules with permanent dipoles attract one another. The negative end of one dipole attracts the positive end of the neighbouring dipole. **Dipole–dipole forces** are stronger than dispersion forces in molecules of similar molecular weight. Table 12.3 compares the melting and boiling points of nitrogen (a non-polar molecule) with nitrogen monoxide (a polar molecule). These molecules have similar molecular weights and, thus, similar dispersion forces. The higher melting and boiling points of nitrogen monoxide are due to dipole–dipole interactions.

dipole–dipole force: a force caused by the positive end of one dipole attracting the negative end of another dipole

Attraction between dipoles

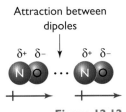

Figure 12.12
Dipole–dipole forces between nitrogen monoxide molecules

Table 12.3 Comparing the melting and boiling points of a polar and a non-polar molecule

Molecule	Molecular formula	Molecular weight	Melting point (°C)	Boiling point (°C)
nitrogen	N_2	28.0	–210	–196
nitrogen monoxide	NO	30.0	–164	–152

In a series of related molecules (such as the hydrides of group VI), the increase in boiling point with increasing molecular weight is mainly due to the increasing contribution of dispersion forces and the decreasing contribution of dipole–dipole attraction. This is shown in table 12.4. The *dipole moment* is a measure of the dipole attraction of the molecule. The table shows that hydrogen sulfide is a significantly more polar molecule than hydrogen telluride.

Table 12.4 Comparison of the boiling points of some hydrides of group VI

Molecule	Molecular weight	Dipole moment ($\times 10^{-30}$ C m)	Boiling point (°C)
H_2S	34.1	3.2	–60
H_2Se	81.0	0.8	–41
H_2Te	129.6	<0.7	–2

Hydrogen bonding

hydrogen bonding: a strong type of polar attraction caused by the interaction of a highly electropositive hydrogen atom with the lone pairs of electrons of fluorine, oxygen or nitrogen atoms bonded to hydrogen atoms in another molecule. (Hydrogen bonds have some covalent character due to delocalisation of electrons.)

Hydrogen bonding is the attraction between a partially positive hydrogen atom in one molecule and a non-bonding electron pair in a fluorine, oxygen or nitrogen atom bonded to hydrogen atoms in a neighbouring molecule. Recent X-ray diffraction studies suggest that the hydrogen bond is not wholly electrostatic in origin. It has been suggested that the hydrogen bond has about 10% covalent character. This helps to account for the strength of this bond compared with other intermolecular forces.

Hydrogen bonding raises the melting and boiling points of covalent molecular substances much more than dispersion or dipole–dipole forces. Hydrogen bonding is an important force between the chains of natural polymers such as proteins and DNA. Figure 12.13 illustrates the extensive hydrogen bonding in HF compared with other hydrogen halides. The boiling point of HF is significantly higher than would be expected for such a small molecule.

Water and ammonia both exhibit strong hydrogen bonding. Their melting and boiling points are much higher than those of molecules of comparable molecular weight. Hydrogen sulfide does not exhibit hydrogen bonding. Its molecules are attracted mainly by dipole–dipole forces and dispersion forces. Table 12.5 compares the melting and boiling points of these three molecules. The absence of hydrogen bonding in hydrogen sulfide is shown by its low melting and boiling points.

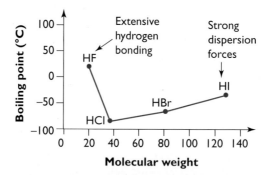

Figure 12.13
Relationship between molecular weight and boiling point of hydrogen halides

Table 12.5 Comparison of melting and boiling points

Molecule	Molecular weight	Dipole moment ($\times 10^{-30}$ C m)	Melting point (°C)	Boiling point (°C)
NH_3	17.0	5.7	−78	−33
H_2O	18.0	6.2	0	100
H_2S	34.1	3.2	−86	−60

Highly electronegative oxygen atom

Hydrogen bonding between O and H

Hydrogen bonding between N and H

Highly electronegative nitrogen atom

Strong hydrogen bonding

Figure 12.14
Hydrogen bonding in water and ammonia

Water   Ammonia   Hydrogen fluoride

The properties of water

Water is a unique compound. An examination of its physical properties reinforces this statement.

Surface tension

surface tension: a measure of the attractive tensional forces in the surface of a liquid. These elastic forces hold the water molecules together, preventing the water from spreading out to increase its surface area.

cohesion: the attraction between like molecules or like materials

Elastic forces exist in the surface layers of a liquid; the **surface tension** of a liquid is a measure of these elastic forces. Water molecules are held together by strong **cohesive** forces. All polar liquids (including water) with strong cohesive forces have high surface tensions. You may have observed insects walking on a water surface (see figure 12.1 on page 215). They can do this because of the high surface tension of the water that creates a 'skin' on the surface. The surface tension is a measure of the energy required to increase the surface area of the liquid.

The surface tension of water is compared with that of other liquids in table 12.6. Water, ethanol and glycerine all exhibit hydrogen bonding, but hydrogen bonding is strongest in water. Mercury has a very high surface tension as demonstrated by its inability to 'wet' or **adhere** to glass. When water drips from a tap, the detached water droplets are almost spherical in shape. In the absence of gravity, they would form a perfect sphere. Figure 12.15b helps to explain why drops of water are spherical. Water molecules at the surface of the drop experience unbalanced attractive forces compared with those in the interior of the drop. These unbalanced forces cause the droplet to assume a spherical shape to minimise the surface energy.

adhere: stick by the force of attraction between unlike molecules or unlike materials

(a)

(b) Inside the drop, water molecules are pulled equally in all directions.

At the surface, water molecules are pulled unequally.

◯ water molecule

Figure 12.15
(a) Intermolecular forces are responsible for the spherical shape of drops of water.
(b) Forces at the surface of a drop of water

Figure 12.16
A sphere has the smallest surface area for a given volume. Because of its high surface tension, mercury beads tend to form small spherical shapes when dropped. When resting on a surface, the larger spheres are flattened by their own weight.

Table 12.6 Surface tension and viscosity

Molecule	Molecular formula	Surface tension (mJ/m²) at 20 °C	Viscosity (mPa/s)
Water	H_2O	73	1.01
Ethanol	C_2H_5OH	23	1.20
Glycerine	$C_3H_5(OH)_3$	63	1490
Benzene	C_6H_6	29	0.63
Mercury	Hg	490	1.55
Ethylene glycol	$C_2H_4(OH)_2$	48	19.9

Viscosity

Viscosity is a measure of a liquid's resistance to flow. Because they have a high viscosity, heavy motor oils, honey and sugary molasses flow very slowly out of a burette. Water runs out of a burette because it is much less viscous. Viscosity depends on the structure of molecules and the intermolecular forces between molecules. Long chain molecules often have high viscosity because their long chains can become entangled as they flow. This is why grease and tar are very viscous but petrol and kerosene are not.

A device called a *viscometer* is used to measure the flow rate of a liquid (figure 12.17). The viscosity of a liquid is determined by measuring the time taken for a fixed quantity of the liquid to flow through a narrow-bore (or capillary) tube. When liquids are heated, their viscosity tends to decrease. Molasses and honey are viscous and flow slowly when cold but flow more readily when warmed. Table 12.6 compares the viscosities of some common liquids. Water has a higher viscosity than benzene, as benzene has no hydrogen bonding between its molecules. Glycerine molecules contain three OH groups per molecule; the strong hydrogen bonding between its molecules leads to a much higher viscosity than water at the same temperature.

12.2 PRACTICAL ACTIVITIES

Investigating viscosity and surface tension

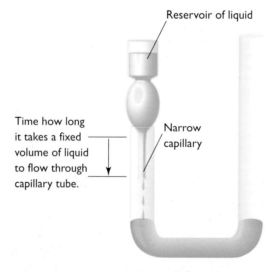

Reservoir of liquid

Time how long it takes a fixed volume of liquid to flow through capillary tube.

Narrow capillary

Figure 12.17 Measuring viscosity with a viscometer

Melting and boiling points

On pages 207–8, we investigated the melting and boiling points of water. Water is a very small molecule with much higher melting and boiling points than other molecules of comparable size. This difference is due to the strong hydrogen bonding between water molecules. Table 12.7 illustrates this difference.

Table 12.7 Comparison of the melting and boiling points of water with molecules of similar molecular weight

Molecule	Molecular weight	Melting point (°C)	Boiling point (°C)
H_2O	18.0	0	100
CH_4	16.0	−182.5	−161.5
NH_3	17.0	−78	−33
Ne	20.2	−249	−246

12.1 PRACTICAL ACTIVITIES

Comparison of the melting and boiling points of molecules

When water is cooled, molecular clusters form; the density of the water increases and reaches a maximum at 4 °C. Between 4 °C and 0 °C, the density of water decreases until ice crystals begin to form. In ice, five neighbouring water molecules bind to form tetrahedral clusters that are stabilised by hydrogen bonding (figure 12.18a). A three-dimensional network of these clusters forms the open cage-like structure of ice (figure 12.18b). This open structure explains the expansion of water as it freezes and the low density of ice (0.92 g/mL) compared with the maximum density of liquid water (1.0 g/mL).

(a)

Water molecule at centre of tetrahedron

(b)

Open-cage structure

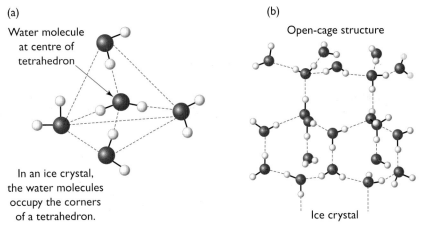

In an ice crystal, the water molecules occupy the corners of a tetrahedron.

Ice crystal

Figure 12.18
(a) Tetrahedral cluster of water molecules in ice and (b) crystal structure of ice

Ice crystals are examples of covalent molecular crystals. Such crystals are softer than ionic or covalent network crystals. Molecular crystals such as ice and sulfur are brittle. When they are hammered, they shatter into tiny, irregularly shaped fragments. Ionic crystals such as sodium chloride are also brittle but, when hammered, they shatter into tiny crystals of uniform shape. These observations demonstrate the differences between molecular and ionic crystals. Ice crystals also differ from sulfur crystals in the presence of hydrogen bonding in the ice crystal's lattice. Only dispersion forces hold sulfur's lattice together. Electron diffraction studies have shown that water molecules at the surface of ice vibrate rapidly due to reduced hydrogen bonding. This behaviour of water at the surface of ice crystals gives the surface a semi-liquid property.

12.1 QUESTIONS

1. Classify each of the following molecules as polar or non-polar.
   (a) HBr (linear)
   (b) Cl₂CO (trigonal planar)
   (c) PH₃ (pyramidal)
   (d) CCl₄ (tetrahedral)
   (e) CHClF (tetrahedral)
   (f) CS₂ (linear)

2. Use table 12.1 of electronegativities to rank the following covalent bonds from the most polar to the least polar.

   H—S, O—F, Br—Cl, C—N, C—O, S—S

3. (a) Draw Lewis electron dot structures for the following molecules.
    (i) OF₂ (bent)
    (ii) NF₃ (trigonal pyramidal)
    (iii) CCl₄ (tetrahedral)
   (b) For each molecule in (a), identify the number of bonding and non-bonding electron pairs around the central atom.
   (c) Classify each molecule in (a) as polar or non-polar.

4. (a) Define the term 'viscosity'.
   (b) Table 12.8 shows the variation in the viscosity of water with temperature. Account for the trend in this data.

Table 12.8

Temperature (°C)	Viscosity (mPa/s)
20	1.01
40	0.65
60	0.47
80	0.36
100	0.28

5. The synthetic polymer polyethylene can be manufactured in two forms. One form, called HDPE (high density polyethylene), has long linear chains of CH₂ groups with an average molecular weight of 3 000 000. Another form, called LDPE (low density polyethylene), has branched chains and an average molecular weight of 1 000 000. Explain why the melting point of HDPE (135 °C) is higher than the melting point of LDPE (80 °C).

6. Account for the trend in boiling points (b.p.) of the following hydrogen halide molecules.

   HCl (b.p. = –85 °C), HBr (b.p. = –66 °C), HI (b.p. = –35 °C)

7. The following molecules have similar molecular weights. Account for the differences in their boiling points (b.p.) in terms of structure and bonding.

   CH₃OH (b.p. = 65 °C), H₂S (b.p. = –62 °C), C₂H₆ (b.p. = –89 °C)

8. Figure 12.19 shows the bonding between the helical protein strands that make up human hair. The 'R' groups represent hydrocarbon side-chains. Identify the strongest bonding forces between the chains as shown in the diagram.

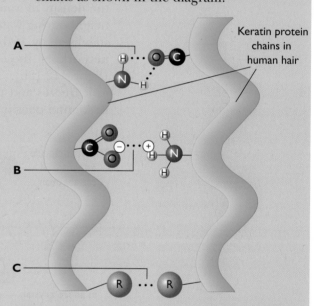

Figure 12.19 Bonding between helical keratin chains in human hair

9. Figure 12.20 shows a model of the cross-linking between chains in the cellulose polymer. Identify the type of bonding involved in this cross-linking of cellulose chains.

10. Drops of water are placed on the surface of a block of paraffin wax. They are observed to form small round drops. When the experiment is repeated with detergent solution, the water spreads rather than forming drops. Account for these observations.

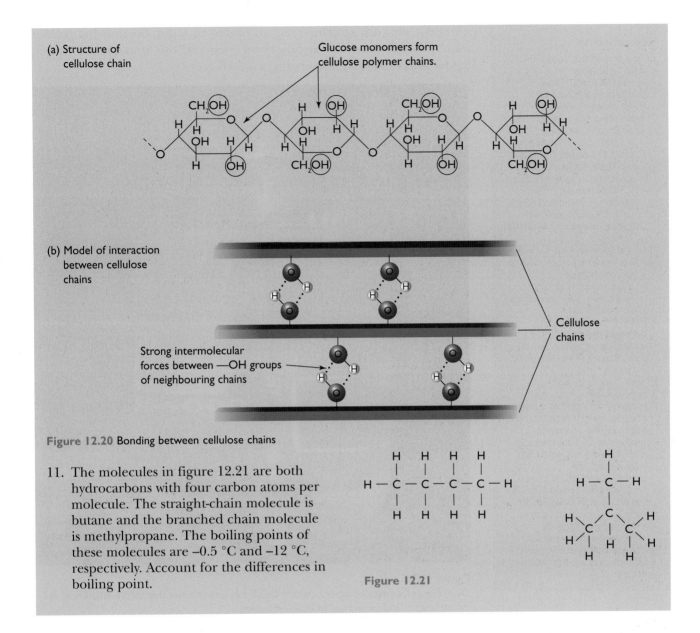

(a) Structure of cellulose chain

Glucose monomers form cellulose polymer chains.

(b) Model of interaction between cellulose chains

Strong intermolecular forces between —OH groups of neighbouring chains

Cellulose chains

Figure 12.20 Bonding between cellulose chains

11. The molecules in figure 12.21 are both hydrocarbons with four carbon atoms per molecule. The straight-chain molecule is butane and the branched chain molecule is methylpropane. The boiling points of these molecules are –0.5 °C and –12 °C, respectively. Account for the differences in boiling point.

Figure 12.21

12.2 *INTERACTIONS WITH WATER*

Bonding and solubility

Whether or not a solute will dissolve in a solvent depends on whether it can establish strong interactions with the solvent particles. We are familiar with the high solubility of sodium chloride (an ionic salt) and glucose (a molecular solid) in water. These are highly soluble because both these solutes establish strong interactions with the water solvent: ion–dipole attractive forces between sodium and chloride ions and water; and hydrogen bonding interactions between glucose and water. In some cases, molecular compounds can become ionised by their reaction with water. For example, hydrochloric acid forms hydrogen and chloride ions, and these bind strongly to the water dipoles. Non-polar molecules, such as hexane, tend to dissolve in non-polar solvents, such as kerosene. In these cases, the dispersion forces stabilise the solute particles in the solvent.

Key content
By the end of this section, you
should be able to:
- explain changes, if any, to
  particles and account for
  those changes when the
  following types of chemicals
  interact with water:
  - a soluble ionic compound,
    such as sodium chloride
  - a soluble molecular
    compound, such as sucrose
  - a soluble or partially
    soluble molecular element
    or compound, such as
    iodine, oxygen or hydrogen
    chloride
  - a substance with a covalent
    network structure, such as
    silicon dioxide
  - a substance with large
    molecules, such as cellulose
    or polyethylene
- analyse the relationship
  between the solubility of
  substances in water and the
  polar nature of the water
  molecule
- perform a first-hand
  investigation to test the
  solubility in water of a range
  of ionic, soluble molecular
  and insoluble molecular
  substances, and substances
  with covalent networks and
  large molecules
- process information from
  secondary sources to visualise
  the dissolution in water of
  various types of substances,
  and solve problems by
  using models to show the
  changes that occur in particle
  arrangement as dissolution
  occurs.

Covalent network structures are insoluble in water because the solvent cannot break down the strong bonds between the atoms in the crystal lattice and establish a low-energy, solvated state.

Figure 12.22
Oil and water molecules do not readily dissolve in one another due to the differences in the structures and properties of their molecules.

The following generalisation applies to most solute–solvent interactions:
This generalisation is sometimes simplified to 'like dissolves like'. Thus, a non-polar and a polar substance do not generally dissolve in each other. This is observed when kerosene is mixed with water; kerosene does not dissolve and floats on the surface of the water. Similarly, sodium chloride is not very soluble in kerosene.

The greater the structural similarity and properties between solute and solvent, the greater the solubility.

Let us examine the solubility in water of the major groups of crystalline materials.

Ionic lattices

The formation of strong ion–dipole attractions between water molecules and ions explains the generalisation that many ionic compounds are soluble in water. This interaction assists the ions to break away from the crystal lattice. Salts such as potassium iodide, calcium nitrate and sodium chloride readily dissolve in water to form aquated sodium and chloride ions. The term 'dissociation reaction' is used to describe the process in which an ionic solid breaks up into its ions in water.

$$Ca(NO_3)_2(s) \rightarrow Ca^{2+}(aq) + 2NO_3^-(aq)$$

$$NaCl(s) \rightarrow Na^+(aq) + Cl^-(aq)$$

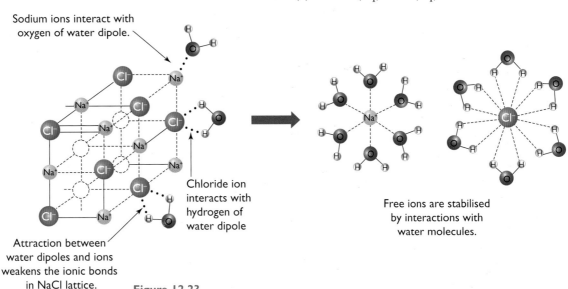

Sodium ions interact with oxygen of water dipole.

Chloride ion interacts with hydrogen of water dipole

Attraction between water dipoles and ions weakens the ionic bonds in NaCl lattice.

Free ions are stabilised by interactions with water molecules.

Figure 12.23
Dissolution and aquation of sodium chloride

dissolution: disintegration or breaking apart of the particles of a solid when dissolving in a solvent

Some ionic compounds are not soluble in water. Ionic compounds such as copper (II) oxide and iron (II) sulfide have such strong ionic bonds in the crystal lattice that the energy required to break down the lattice is not compensated for by the aquation of the ions.

Covalent molecular lattices

Small polar molecules, such as ammonia and ethanol, are readily soluble in water due to the strong hydrogen bonding between the solute and the water solvent. Table 12.9 compares the solubilities of various substances in water at room temperature. It shows that polar molecules are much more soluble in water than non-polar molecules.

Table 12.9 Solubility of molecules in water at 25 °C

Molecule	Molecular formula	Molar weight (g/mol)	Polarity	Solubility (g/100 g water)
Hydrogen	H_2	2.0	non-polar	0.00015
Oxygen	O_2	32.0	non-polar	0.004
Nitrogen	N_2	28.02	non-polar	0.0017
Iodine	I_2	253.8	non-polar	0.034
Carbon dioxide	CO_2	44.0	non-polar	0.145
Hydrogen chloride	HCl	36.5	polar	70

(continued)

Table 12.9 (continued)

Molecule	Molecular formula	Molar weight (g/mol)	Polarity	Solubility (g/100 g water)
hydrogen bromide	HBr	80.9	polar	2.7
sulfur dioxide	SO_2	64.1	polar	9.4
ammonia	NH_3	17.0	polar	48
methanol	CH_3OH	32.0	polar	completely miscible

Methanol is miscible in all proportions with water. There is strong hydrogen bonding between the hydroxyl (—OH) groups of the methanol and water molecules.

Simple sugars such as glucose and fructose can be transported through plant vascular tissue in aqueous solutions. The strong hydrogen bonding between the sugar and water molecules ensures the high solubility of these sugars in water.

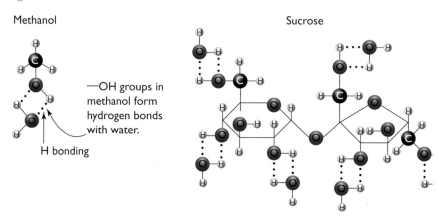

Figure 12.24
Hydrogen bonding in methanol and glucose solutions

Hydrogen chloride is highly water soluble (70 g/100 g water at 25 °C) because the hydrogen chloride molecule becomes ionised when the covalent bond breaks. Hydrogen ions are transferred to water molecules to form acidic hydronium ions. This solution is called hydrochloric acid. Water is often called an *ionising* solvent for this reason.

$$HCl(g) + H_2O(l) \rightarrow H_3O^+(aq) + Cl^-(aq)$$

Iodine is only partially soluble (0.034 g/100 g) in water at 25 °C. It is a non-polar solute and can bond to the water solvent only through dispersion interactions. Adding ethanol to the water increases iodine's solubility as the iodine has greater dispersion interactions with the ethanol solvent. Oxygen, a non-polar molecule, has an even lower solubility in water than iodine, and the dispersion interactions are even weaker.

Many covalent molecular compounds are insoluble in water. These include hydrocarbons such as hexane and octane. Hydrocarbon liquids are said to be **immiscible** with water.

WATER: AN IONISING SOLVENT

immiscible: describes two liquids that do not mix, but form separate layers

Polymers

Insoluble molecular substances include cellulose, a natural polymer, and synthetic polymers, such as polyethylene and PVC. Polymers are long-chain molecules made up of repeating subunits called *monomers*.

Cellulose is made up of smaller glucose sugar monomers. The plastics polystyrene and polyethylene are synthetic polymers made from styrene and ethylene monomers, respectively.

The high molecular weight of polymers usually makes them too large to dissolve in water. Many of them, such as polyethylene, are said to be *hydrophobic* or literally 'water hating'. Cellulose, on the other hand, has many polar hydroxyl groups along the cellulose chain. These groups are *hydrophilic* ('water loving') and form hydrogen bonds with water molecules, producing strong adhesive forces. This force is important in plant tissue for conduction of water through cellulose xylem vessels.

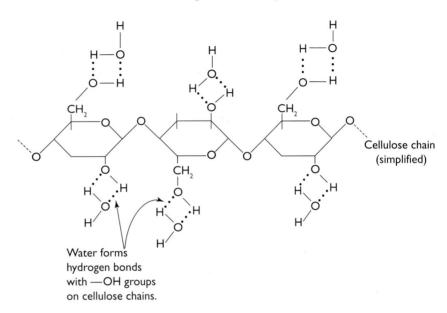

Figure 12.25
Water and cellulose interactions

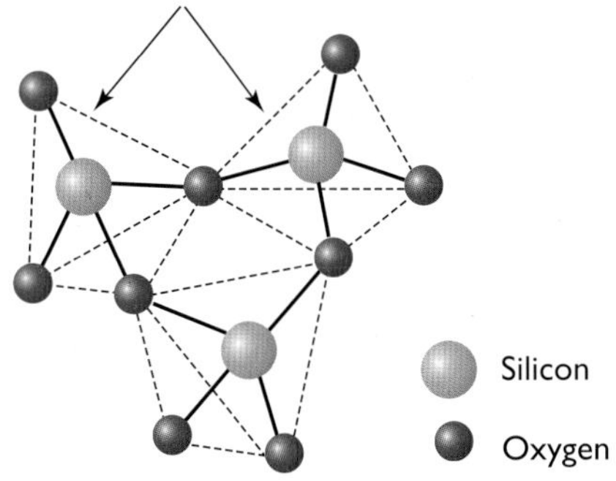

Water forms hydrogen bonds with —OH groups on cellulose chains.

Cellulose chain (simplified)

Tetrahedral arrangement of oxygen atoms around silicon atoms

Silicon

Oxygen

Figure 12.26
Structure of silica

12.3 PRACTICAL ACTIVITIES

Investigating solubility in water

Covalent network lattices

Covalent network crystals are very stable due to the strong chemical bonds that extend throughout the lattice. These crystals do not dissolve in common solvents such as water (a polar solvent) or kerosene (a non-polar solvent). One of the most common rock-making minerals is silica, which is the compound called silicon dioxide. Silica is the main mineral present in sand grains. Its low solubility in water (0.012%w/w) means that the chemical weathering of sand is very slow. Figure 12.26 shows the three-dimensional structure of a portion of the silica crystal.

Solubility generalisations

The previous discussion about solubility in water leads to the following generalisations.

- Many ionic compounds dissolve in water due to strong interactions between the ions and the water dipole.
- Many small polar molecules dissolve in water due to strong dipole–dipole interactions.
- Small non-polar molecules have low solubility in water due to weak dispersion interactions.
- Large molecules, such as polymers, and covalent network lattices do not dissolve in water as the solute–solvent interaction is too weak.

12.2 QUESTIONS

1. Select the substance that is most likely to dissolve in water.
   A Graphite
   B Silica
   C Octane
   D Sodium nitrate

2. Select the substance that is most likely to dissolve in a hydrocarbon solvent, such as kerosene.
   A Water
   B Sodium chloride
   C Pentane, C_5H_{12}
   D Copper (II) sulfate pentahydrate

3. Select the correct statement.
   A Kerosene is a suitable solvent for both ionic and covalent molecular solids.
   B Not all ionic crystals dissolve in water.
   C All oxides are water-soluble.
   D Sucrose is very soluble in organic solvents because of the strong hydrogen bonding that occurs.

4. Water can act as an ionising solvent for some covalent molecular compounds. Identify the compound that ionises strongly in solution with water.
   A Hydrogen chloride
   B Sodium chloride
   C Sucrose
   D Polyethylene

5. Strong adhesive forces exist between cellulose and water due to the presence of
   A strong dispersion forces between molecules.
   B hydrogen bonds between hydroxyl groups.
   C ion–dipole attractions.
   D covalent bonding between water and cellulose.

6. Write balanced equations for:
   (a) dissolution of magnesium sulfate in water
   (b) ionisation of hydrofluoric acid, HF, in water to form hydronium ions, H_3O^+, and fluoride ions
   (c) dissolution of sucrose, $C_{12}H_{22}O_{11}$, in water.

7. The experimental data in table 12.10 (on the next page) was collected by a student to determine the relative solubility of various substances in a variety of solvents.

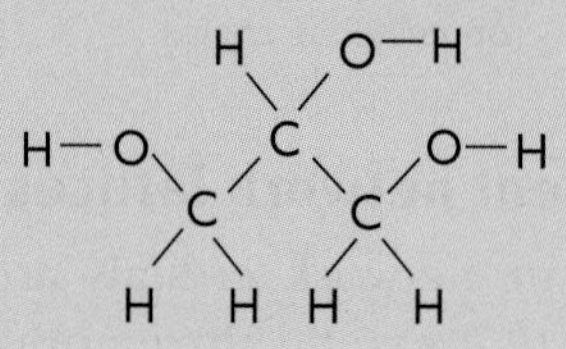

Glycerine

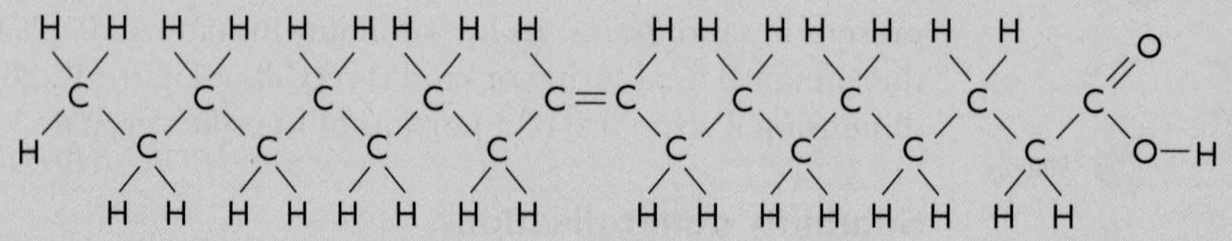

Oleic acid

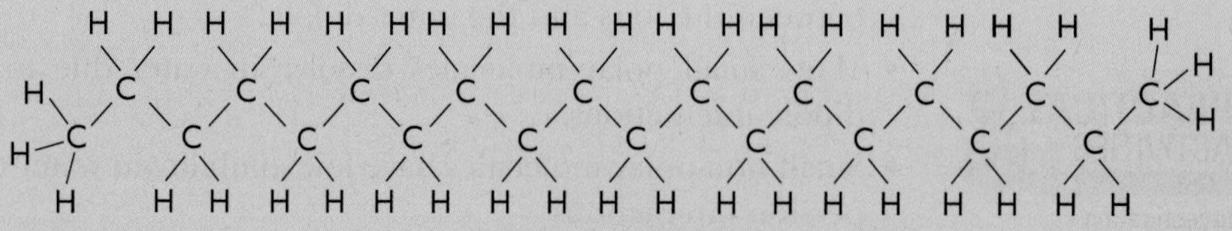

Paraffin constituent (Eicosane)

Figure 12.27 Structures of glycerine, oleic acid and a constituent of paraffin

Figure 12.27 shows the structure of glycerine, oleic acid and a typical molecule found in paraffin wax.

(a) Explain why sucrose, sodium chloride and glycerine were soluble in water but not in kerosene.

(b) Explain why paraffin, silica and oleic acid were insoluble in water.

(c) Explain why silica did not dissolve in any of the solvents.

(d) Compare and explain the solvent properties of ethanol with those of water and kerosene.

Table 12.10

| | Solvent | | |
Substance	Water	Ethanol	Kerosene
sucrose	S	I	I
sodium chloride	S	SS	I
glycerine	S	S	I
paraffin wax flakes	I	I	S
silica	I	I	I
oleic acid	I	SS	S

S = soluble, SS = slightly soluble, I = insoluble

8. Figure 12.28 shows the solubility of carbon dioxide in water as a function of temperature.

(a) Identify whether carbon dioxide becomes more or less soluble if the temperature of the solution is changed from 20 °C to 40 °C.

(b) Calculate the mass of carbon dioxide that dissolves in 1 kg of water at 40 °C.

(c) Explain the change in carbon dioxide solubility with temperature.

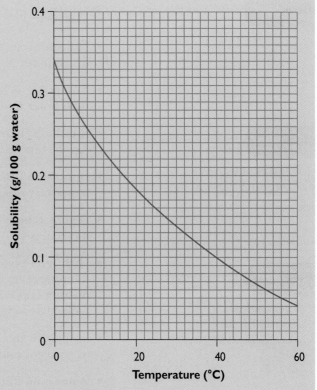

Figure 12.28 Relationship between solubility of carbon dioxide and temperature

9. A molecule with the structural formula shown in figure 12.29 is tested for its solubility in water and in kerosene. Predict its solubility in each solvent. Justify your answer.

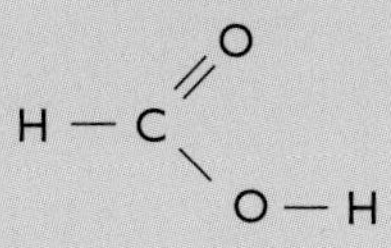

Figure 12.29 Structure of HCOOH

10. Octadecanoic acid, $CH_3(CH_2)_{16}COOH$, is added to water and the large molecule moves to the surface, as shown in figure 12.30. Account for the orientation of the octadecanoic acid at the water–air boundary.

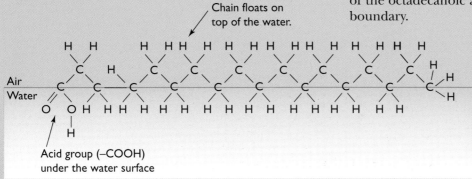

Figure 12.30 Octadecanoic acid at a water surface

eBook *plus*

Weblinks

eBook *plus*

Checkpoint
Revision 5

eBook *plus*

Checkpoint
Revision 5 answers

SUMMARY

- Molecules can be polar or non-polar depending on the distribution of electrons. Water is a polar molecule.

- Non-polar molecules have much lower melting and boiling points than polar molecules of similar molecular weight.

- Intermolecular forces can be classified as dispersion forces, dipole–dipole forces and hydrogen bonding.

- Dispersion forces are caused by temporary dipoles inducing temporary dipoles in nearby atoms and molecules.

- Dipole–dipole forces are attractive interactions between polar molecules.

- Hydrogen bonding in water has a significant role in determining the properties of water and the structure of ice. Water has higher melting and boiling points than other molecules of similar molecular weight.

- Properties such as surface tension and viscosity can be explained in terms of intermolecular forces.

- Water is an important solvent in biological systems. Ions and molecules have different solubilities in water, which can be related to the polarity of water.

- Water is an ionising solvent. Some molecules dissolve in water and react with it to release ions.

PRACTICAL ACTIVITIES

12.1 PRACTICAL ACTIVITIES

COMPARISON OF THE MELTING AND BOILING POINTS OF MOLECULES

Aim

To compare the melting and boiling points of molecules with similar molecular weights

Method

Part A

You are provided with several data sets.

1. For data set A in table 12.11, plot column graphs of melting and boiling point. Arrange the data in order of molecular weight.

2. Plot column graphs for each of data sets B (table 12.12) and C (table 12.13), arranging the data in order of increasing melting or boiling point.

3. Use a molecular model kit and the diagrams provided to construct these molecules.

Table 12.11 Data set A: Water and similar-sized molecules

Molecule	Molecular weight	Melting point (°C)	Boiling point (°C)
H_2O	18.0	0	100
CH_4	16.0	−183	−162
NH_3	17.0	−78	−33
Ne	20.2	−249	−246
HF	20.0	−83	20

Table 12.12 Data set B: Non-polar hydrocarbons

Molecule	Molecular weight	Melting point (°C)	Boiling point (°C)
hexane, C_6H_{14}	86.2	−95	69
2-methylpentane, C_6H_{14}	86.2	−154	60
3-methylpentane, C_6H_{14}	86.2	−163	63
2,2-dimethylbutane, C_6H_{14}	86.2	−100	50
2,3-dimethylbutane, C_6H_{14}	86.2	−129	58

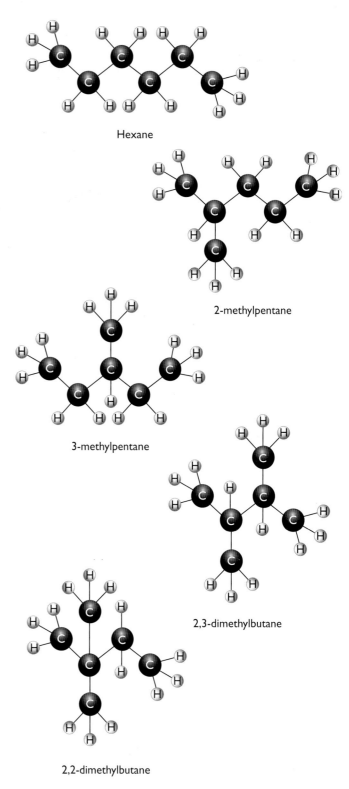

Hexane

2-methylpentane

3-methylpentane

2,3-dimethylbutane

2,2-dimethylbutane

Figure 12.31 Models of non-polar hydrocarbons for data set B

PRACTICAL ACTIVITIES

Table 12.13 Data set C: Polar and non-polar organic molecules

Molecule	Molecular weight	Melting point (°C)	Boiling point (°C)
1-butanol, $C_4H_{10}O$	74.1	–90	118
2-methylpropan-2-ol, $C_4H_{10}O$	74.1	26	83
pentane, C_5H_{12}	72.1	–130	36
propanoic acid, $C_3H_6O_2$	74.1	–21	141

Part B: Modelling water and ice

Use the information in figure 12.18 to construct models of a water molecule and a section of an ice crystal.

Questions

1. For data set A, explain the differences in melting and boiling points in terms of differences in intermolecular forces.

2. For data set B, account for the differences in melting and boiling points for the unbranched and branched hydrocarbons.

3. For data set C, account for differences in melting and boiling points in terms of structure and bonding.

4. Use your model for the structure of ice (part B) to explain why ice floats on liquid water at 0 °C.

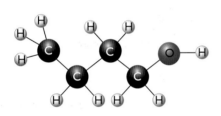

Butan-1-ol (1-butanol)

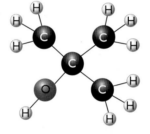

2-methylpropan-2-ol (2-methyl-2-propanol)

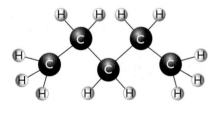

Pentane

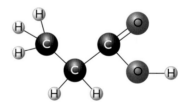

Propanoic acid

Figure 12.32 Models of polar and non-polar molecules for data set C

PRACTICAL ACTIVITIES

12.2 PRACTICAL ACTIVITIES

INVESTIGATING VISCOSITY AND SURFACE TENSION

Part A: Viscosity

Aim

To compare the viscosity of water and other liquids

Safety issues

- Wear safety glasses throughout this experiment.
- Ensure no flames or sparks come near the organic liquids.
- Identify other safety issues relevant to this experiment by reading the method.

Materials

- flow tubes with capillaries
- Pasteur pipettes
- burette, clamp and stand
- 150 mL beaker
- 1.5 m tubes filled with test liquids
- stoppers
- stopwatch
- glass marbles
- hexane
- glycerine

Method

Part 1: Flow through a capillary

1. The flow tube consists of a 15 cm long, wide-bore glass tube (the reservoir) attached via a short length of rubber hose to a 10 cm long capillary tube (see figure 12.33). Clamp the flow tube vertically and place a beaker underneath. Mark two lines, 5 cm apart, on the side of the reservoir tube with a marker pen. Flush the flow tube with the test liquid before each measurement.
2. Start with water as the test liquid. Use a Pasteur pipette to fill the reservoir and allow the water to flow through into the beaker below. Place your fingertip or a stopper over the end of the capillary to stop the flow when the water level is at the top mark. Remove your finger (or stopper) and record the time taken for the liquid to flow down to the second mark. Repeat this measurement five times.
3. Repeat step 2 for hexane and glycerine.
4. Collect and average results from different groups.

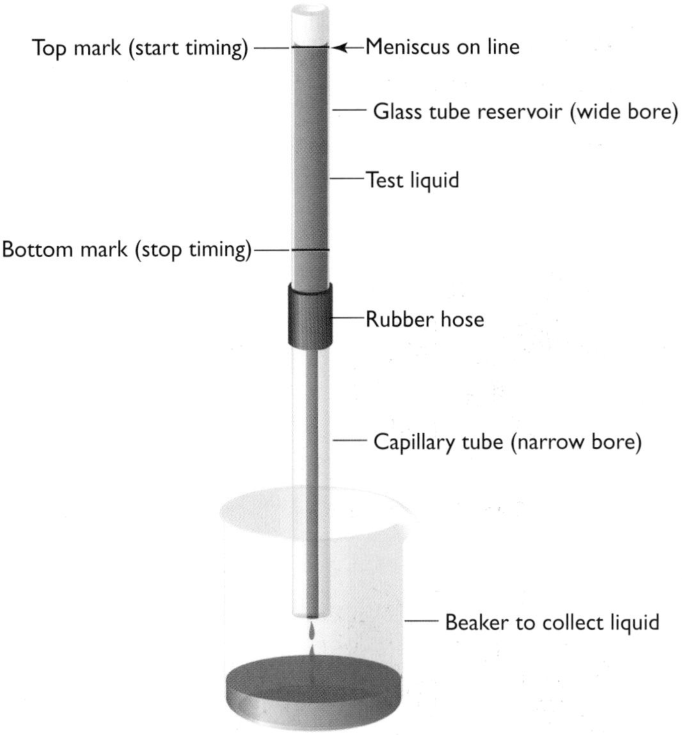
Top mark (start timing)
Meniscus on line
Glass tube reservoir (wide bore)
Test liquid
Bottom mark (stop timing)
Rubber hose
Capillary tube (narrow bore)
Beaker to collect liquid

Figure 12.33 Flow tube and capillary

Part 2: Marbles falling through liquids

The time for a marble to fall through a column of liquid is (see figure 12.34) related to its viscosity.

1. Prepare 1.5 m long tubes (~2.5 cm diameter) containing the test liquids (water, hexane and glycerine) and one identical glass marble per tube. Stopper the ends of each tube securely and use masking tape to secure the stoppers. Ensure that no air is trapped in the tubes.

PRACTICAL ACTIVITIES

2. Tip the tube to the vertical position and record the time for the marble to fall to the end of the tube. Repeat the measurement at least 5 times for each tube. Average the results.

3. At the end of the experiment, recover the hexane and store it away safely.

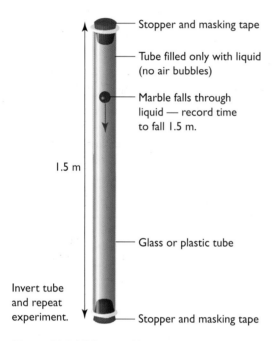

Figure 12.34 Falling marbles

Results

Record your observations in a suitable table.

Questions

Answer the following questions in your report on this experiment.

1. Compare the flow times in part 1 and rank the liquids from least viscous to most viscous.

2. Compare the falling times of the marbles through the test liquids. Rank the liquids from least viscous to most viscous.

3. Compare the results from each experiment and explain the differences in viscosity of the liquids in terms of structure and bonding.

Conclusion

Briefly describe the outcome of your investigation.

Part B: Surface tension

Aim

To compare the surface tension of water with other liquids

Safety issues

• Wear safety glasses throughout this experiment.
• Identify other safety issues relevant to this experiment by reading the method.

Materials

• capillary tubes (with identical bores)
• bossheads, clamps and stand
• 150 mL beakers
• test tubes
• sewing needles
• paperclips
• wide plastic or glass dishes
• toothpicks
• detergent solution
• glycerine
• hexane

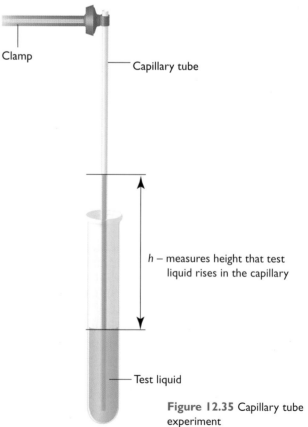

Figure 12.35 Capillary tube experiment

PRACTICAL ACTIVITIES

Method

Part 1: Capillarity

The height to which liquids rise in narrow-bore, capillary tubes is related to their surface tension. Liquids that adhere to or 'wet' the glass form a film on the inner surface of the tube. The film contracts due to its surface tension, drawing the surface of the liquid up the capillary tube. This process continues until the weight of liquid balances the surface tension force pulling the liquid upwards.

1. Clean the internal surfaces of the capillary tubes thoroughly with the liquid (water, hexane, glycerine) to be tested in it.

2. For each test liquid, clamp a capillary tube in a test tube containing the liquid.

3. Measure the final height of each column of liquid above the surface of the liquid in the test tube. Tabulate these results.

Part 2: Floating sewing needles on water

1. Bend a dry paperclip to act as a support for the sewing needle. Ensure that the needle is dry and not greasy.

2. Partially fill a shallow dish of water. Lower the needle, supported on the paperclip, onto the water surface. Lower the paperclip under the surface of the water and remove it, leaving the needle floating.

3. Reduce the surface tension of the water by adding a drop of detergent solution to the water surface near the side of the dish. What happens to the floating needle?

4. Try floating needles on the surfaces of other liquids, such as glycerine and hexane.

Part 3: Toothpick circle on water

1. Arrange toothpicks on the surface of water in a large dish so that they form a circle.

2. Very carefully, and without splashing, place a drop of liquid detergent or soap solution in the centre of the circle and observe the toothpicks.

Results

Record your observations in a suitable table.

Questions

1. For part 1, rank the heights of liquids in the capillary tubes from highest to lowest.

2. Does the order for question 1 agree with the known relative surface tensions of these liquids?

3. Describe and explain the results for parts 2 and 3.

Conclusion

Briefly describe the outcome of your investigation.

PRACTICAL ACTIVITIES

12.3 PRACTICAL ACTIVITIES

INVESTIGATING SOLUBILITY IN WATER

Aim

To investigate the solubility of various substances in water

Safety issues

- Wear safety glasses throughout this experiment.
- Identify other safety issues relevant to this experiment by reading the method.

Materials

- test-tube rack
- test tubes and stoppers
- spatulas
- substances to test:
  - ionic salts — copper (II) sulfate, copper (II) oxide, copper (II) chloride, magnesium sulfate, magnesium oxide, magnesium chloride, sodium sulfate, sodium carbonate, sodium chloride
  - covalent molecular substances — sucrose, iodine, paraffin wax shavings, ethanol, butan-1-ol, hexane, polyethylene, cellulose, starch
  - covalent network substances — graphite, silica
- ball-and-stick model of NaCl

Part A: Testing solubility

Method

Control your variables as much as possible by using the same amounts of water and solutes in each experiment. Use only a few grains of each of the solid solutes, equal to the size of a grain of rice. Use 3–5 drops of the liquid solutes.

1. Set up your stoppered test tubes, half filled with water, in a test-tube rack.
2. Add the substance to be tested. Stopper and shake the tube for a minute and return it to the rack. Determine whether all, some or none of the substance has dissolved.

Results

Record your observations in a suitable table.

Questions

1. Tabulate your experimental results for each group of substances. Identify those that are soluble, partially soluble or insoluble.
2. Account for your experimental results in terms of structure and bonding.
3. Discuss how the accuracy of your investigation could be improved.

Part B: Modelling dissolution in water

Method

1. Use the molecular model kit to construct 10 molecules of water. Place them in a small tray.
2. Compare the dissolution of iodine and hydrogen chloride molecules in water by making models of I_2 and HCl and mixing them into the water models. I_2 remains as molecules; the covalent bond in HCl breaks and forms H^+ and Cl^- ions that interact with the water dipoles.
3. (a) With the aid of a ball-and-stick model of NaCl, draw a diagram of the edge of a sodium chloride lattice in water. Show how the water dipoles orient themselves around the positive sodium ions and the negative chloride ions.

   (b) Draw a second diagram in which some of the ions on the edge have broken away from the crystal and been solvated by water molecules. Show how the water dipoles cluster around these free ions.

Conclusion

Briefly describe the outcome of your investigation.

Chapter 13

SOLUTIONS AND SOLUBILITY

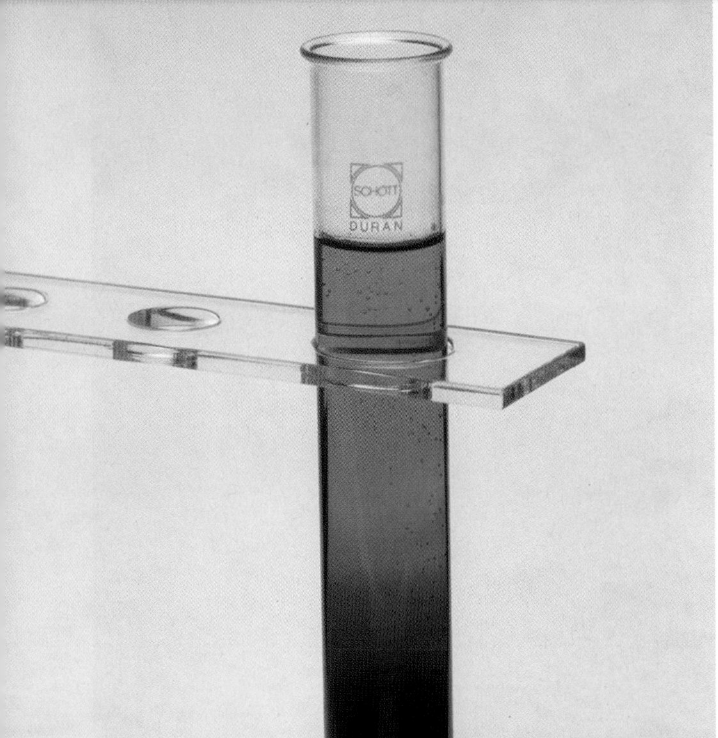

Introduction

In chapter 12, we saw that the solubility of a solute varies from one solvent to another. In this chapter, we will examine the conditions that lead to the precipitation of ionic compounds when solutions of ions are mixed. We will also examine how chemists calculate the concentration of solutions.

In this chapter

Figure 13.1

Potassium permanganate, $KMnO_4$, dissolves readily in water to produce a pinkish purple solution.

13.1 SOLUTIONS AND PRECIPITATION

Remember

Before beginning this section, you should be able to:
• recall a first-hand investigation in which you tested the solubilities in water of a range of ionic substances.

Key content

By the end of this section, you should be able to:
• identify some combinations of solutions that will produce precipitates, using solubility data
• describe a model that traces the movement of ions when solution and precipitation occur
• identify the dynamic nature of ion movement in a saturated solution
• construct ionic equations to represent the dissolution and precipitation of ionic compounds in water
• present information in balanced chemical equations and identify the appropriate phase descriptors, (s), (l), (g), and (aq), for all chemical species
• perform a first-hand investigation, using micro-techniques, to compare the solubility of appropriate salts in solution through precipitation reactions.

electrolyte: substance that releases ions into solution, which then is capable of conducting an electric current

Precipitation reactions

In 1887, Svante Arrhenius proposed the ionic theory of **electrolytes**. He realised that aqueous solutions of different soluble salts conducted electricity because these solutions contained ions. Such solutions are called electrolytes. The following equations illustrate dissolution reactions that produce electrolyte solutions.

Dissolution of barium nitrate:

$$Ba(NO_3)_2(s) \rightarrow Ba^{2+}(aq) + 2NO_3^-(aq)$$

Dissolution of ammonium sulfate:

$$(NH_4)_2SO_4(s) \rightarrow 2NH_4^+(aq) + SO_4^{2-}(aq)$$

Figure 13.2 Yellow lead iodide is very insoluble. It precipitates when a solution of lead ions is mixed with a solution of iodide ions.

Figure 13.3 provides a particle model of a typical electrolyte solution. Notice that water dipoles cluster around the positive and negative ions.

When electrolyte solutions are mixed, the new ion combinations that result may lead to a chemical change. One common result of mixing electrolyte solutions is the **precipitation** of an insoluble ionic solid. Figure 13.4 shows a particle model of this precipitation process.

precipitation: formation of a solid in a chemical reaction when liquids, solutions or gases are mixed

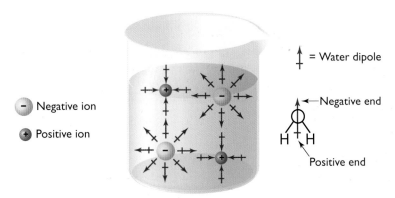

Figure 13.3
Model of electrolyte solutions showing water dipoles

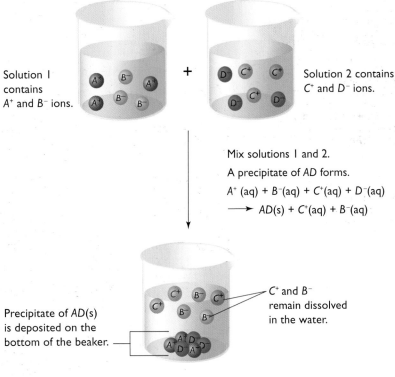

Mix solutions 1 and 2.
A precipitate of AD forms.
A^+ (aq) + B^-(aq) + C^+(aq) + D^-(aq)
$\longrightarrow$ AD(s) + C^+(aq) + B^-(aq)

Solution 1 contains A^+ and B^- ions.

Solution 2 contains C^+ and D^- ions.

Precipitate of AD(s) is deposited on the bottom of the beaker.

C^+ and B^- remain dissolved in the water.

Figure 13.4
Model of precipitation

solubility: the concentration of a saturated solution of a given substance at a particular temperature. Solubility is normally measured in grams/100 mL.

Chemists have developed tables of **solubility** to allow us to predict which combinations of electrolytes form precipitates. Table 13.1 provides generalisations about solubility for common ionic compounds. The salts are classified according to the anion present. In this table, the term 'insoluble' is applied when less than 0.1 g of a substance dissolves in

100 mL (100 g) of water at 25 °C; the term 'soluble' is applied when at least 1 g of the substance dissolves in 100 mL of water. Substances between these extremes are termed 'slightly soluble'. The following generalisations can be made from table 13.1:

- All nitrate salts are soluble.
- All group I and ammonium salts are soluble.
- Most chloride and sulfate salts are soluble.
- Most carbonate salts and hydroxides are insoluble.

Table 13.1 Solubility of some ionic salts in water at 25 °C

Anion	Soluble	Slightly soluble	Insoluble
nitrate	all	none	none
chloride	most	$PbCl_2$	AgCl
sulfate	most	$CaSO_4$, Ag_2SO_4	$BaSO_4$, $PbSO_4$
carbonate	Na_2CO_3, K_2CO_3, $(NH_4)_2CO_3$	none	most
hydroxide	NaOH, KOH, NH_4OH, $Ba(OH)_2$	$Ca(OH)_2$	most

The following sample problems show how a table of solubility can be used to predict precipitation.

SAMPLE PROBLEM 13.1

SOLUTION

Predict whether or not a precipitate will form when the following aqueous solutions are mixed.

(a) Barium chloride solution and potassium sulfate solution
(b) Copper (II) sulfate solution and ammonium nitrate solution
(c) Nickel sulfate solution and sodium hydroxide solution
Name the precipitate that forms.

(a) The ions present on mixing are Ba^{2+}, Cl^-, K^+, SO_4^{2-}. Table 13.1 shows that Ba^{2+} and SO_4^{2-} can produce a precipitate of insoluble barium sulfate.

(b) The ions present on mixing are Cu^{2+}, SO_4^{2-}, NH_4^+, NO_3^-. Table 13.1 shows that no ion combinations can form precipitates as all nitrates and ammonium salts are soluble.

(c) The ions present on mixing are Ni^{2+}, SO_4^{2-}, Na^+, OH^-. Table 13.1 shows that Ni^{2+} and OH^- can produce a precipitate of insoluble nickel hydroxide.

Precipitation equations

Whole formula equations and ionic equations can be written for precipitation reactions. Consider the reaction when colourless silver nitrate and colourless sodium chloride solution are mixed. A white precipitate of silver chloride forms (see figure 13.5). The whole formula equation is:

$$AgNO_3(aq) + NaCl(aq) \rightarrow AgCl(s) + NaNO_3(aq)$$

This equation shows that aqueous sodium nitrate is present in the final mixture. However, the ions are not associated but move independently in the solution, just as the ions in the original electrolyte solutions that were mixed. This can be shown by the next equation (an ionic equation) where

Figure 13.5
A precipitation reaction occurs when colourless silver nitrate is mixed with sodium chloride, producing silver chloride.

all dissolved salts are shown as independent ions. Only the silver chloride precipitate is shown as associated ions.

$$Ag^+(aq) + NO_3^-(aq) + Na^+(aq) + Cl^-(aq) \rightarrow AgCl(s) + Na^+(aq) + NO_3^-(aq)$$

It can be seen that sodium ions and nitrate ions appear on both sides of the equation. They can be cancelled out, as they are only *spectator* ions; they are not involved in the precipitation process. These ions associate again only if the filtered solution is crystallised.

After cancelling the spectator ions, we are left with the *net ionic equation* for precipitation.

$$Ag^+(aq) + Cl^-(aq) \rightarrow AgCl(s)$$

SAMPLE PROBLEM 13.2

When colourless lead (II) nitrate and potassium iodide solutions are mixed, a bright yellow precipitate of lead (II) iodide forms. Write a whole formula balanced equation and a net ionic equation for this precipitation reaction.

SOLUTION

The word equation is:
lead (II) nitrate (aq) + potassium iodide (aq) →
lead (II) iodide(s) + potassium nitrate (aq)

The whole formula balanced equation is constructed by inserting the correct formula for each compound. The equation is then balanced as usual by inserting coefficients.

$$Pb(NO_3)_2(aq) + 2KI(aq) \rightarrow PbI_2(s) + 2KNO_3(aq)$$

Convert this equation into ionic form and cancel the spectator ions.

$$Pb^{2+}(aq) + 2NO_3^-(aq) + 2K^+(aq) + 2I^-(aq) \rightarrow$$
$PbI_2(s) + 2K^+(aq) + 2NO_3^-(aq)$

The net ionic equation is:

$$Pb^{2+}(aq) + 2I^-(aq) \rightarrow PbI_2(s)$$

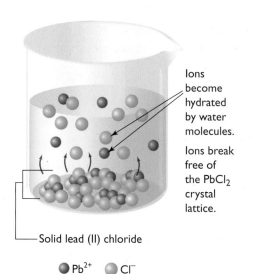

Ions become hydrated by water molecules.

Ions break free of the PbCl$_2$ crystal lattice.

Solid lead (II) chloride

● Pb^{2+} ● Cl$^-$

Figure 13.6
Lead (II) chloride precipitate dissolving in hot water

Effect of temperature

The solubility rules apply to reactions at room temperature (25 °C). If the solutions are heated before mixing, precipitation may not occur. This is particularly true for substances on the borderline of insolubility (i.e. those that are partially soluble). A good example of this is the precipitation of lead (II) chloride. Lead (II) chloride is slightly soluble (1.0 g/100 g water) at room temperature, but becomes more soluble as the temperature increases. The precipitate dissolves in hot water. At 100 °C, its solubility is 3.3 g/100 g H$_2$O. As the hot solution cools, the white precipitate gradually reappears. This process of dissolution and precipitation can be represented by the following equation:

$$PbCl_2(s) \rightleftharpoons Pb^{2+}(aq) + 2Cl^-(aq)$$

In this equation, the *reversible arrows* indicate that the reaction can move in either direction, depending on the conditions. In fact, this is true of all precipitation reactions. Even the most insoluble compounds dissolve to a small extent and dissolution increases as the temperature rises.

Effect of ion concentration

The concentration of the reacting ions also affects whether a precipitate will form. If the two solutions are very dilute, the dissolution process may counteract the tendency to precipitate and no precipitate will form.

Consider the example of lead (II) chloride once more. Chemists have measured its solubility at 25 °C and know that a maximum of 1.0 g dissolves in 100 g of water. If dilute solutions of lead (II) nitrate and sodium chloride are mixed, and the mass of lead (II) chloride that forms is less than 1.0 g per 100 g of water, no precipitate is produced. The lead ions and chloride ions remain dissolved.

SAMPLE PROBLEM 13.3

In separate beakers, 0.001 mole of lead (II) nitrate and 0.002 mole of sodium chloride are each dissolved in 50 mL (50 g) of water. The two solutions (at 25 °C) are mixed. The solubility of lead (II) chloride is 1.0 g/100 g water. Predict whether a precipitate of lead (II) chloride forms.

SOLUTION

The balanced equation for the reaction is:
$$Pb(NO_3)_2(aq) + 2NaCl(aq) \rightarrow PbCl_2(s) + 2NaNO_3(aq)$$

Therefore, the mole ratio of Pb(NO$_3$)$_2$: NaCl required for complete reaction is 1 : 2. The mole ratio of the reactants is 0.001 : 0.002 = 1 : 2. Theoretically, the amount of lead (II) chloride that can form is 0.001 mol.

$$M(PbCl_2) = 278.1 \text{ g/mol}$$

Therefore,

mass of 0.001 mol of lead (II) chloride (m) = nM

= 0.001 × 278.1

= 0.278 g

The total mass of water on mixing is 50 + 50 = 100 g. Thus, 0.278 g of lead (II) chloride is present in 100 g of water. As 1.0 g will dissolve in 100 g of water, all the lead (II) chloride produced in the reaction will remain in solution. Therefore, no precipitate will form.

Monitoring precipitation using conductivity measurements

As ions associate to form a precipitate, there is a change in the electrical conductivity of the solution. An interesting example of this conductivity change is the reaction between dilute solutions of barium hydroxide and sulfuric acid. The reactions involved are:

Whole formula equation:

$$Ba(OH)_2(aq) + H_2SO_4(aq) \rightarrow BaSO_4(s) + 2H_2O(l)$$

Ionic equations:

$$Ba^{2+}(aq) + SO_4{}^{2-}(aq) \rightarrow BaSO_4(s)$$

$$H^+(aq) + OH^-(aq) \rightarrow H_2O(l)$$

We can see that this reaction involves precipitation of barium ions and sulfate ions, as well as neutralisation of hydrogen ions and hydroxide ions to form water. As barium sulfate is very insoluble and water is not an electrolyte, the mixture that forms is a non-conductor. Consequently, the electrical conductivity drops as sulfuric acid is added gradually to the barium hydroxide solution. The conductivity of the mixture will increase again only if excess acid is added. This is shown in figure 13.7, where the minimum conductivity occurs when the maximum amount of barium sulfate precipitate has formed.

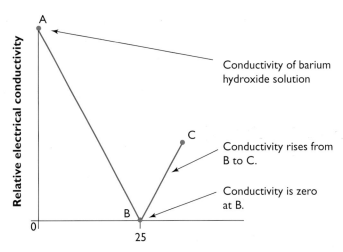

Figure 13.7
Conductivity of barium hydroxide solution as sulfuric acid is added

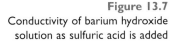
saturated solution: a fixed volume of solution at a particular temperature in which no more solute can dissolve

Saturated solutions

Sodium chloride is quite soluble in water. If sodium chloride crystals are stirred into water, the concentration of salt increases. Stirring increases the speed at which the salt dissolves. Eventually, a point is reached where no more salt dissolves, despite stirring, and any excess remains undissolved. At this point, the solution is said to be a **saturated solution**. Its maximum solubility can be measured by experiment. One way of measuring the maximum solubility is to add a weighed excess of salt to 100 g of water in a beaker at 25 °C. If the mixture is heated to dissolve the salt and then cooled back to 25 °C, any salt in excess of the saturation limit will crystallise. This excess salt can be recovered, dried and weighed. The mass of salt dissolved in the saturated solution can then be calculated. For sodium chloride, this mass is 35.9 g per 100 g of water.

13.1 PRACTICAL ACTIVITIES

Investigating solubility using precipitation reactions

A saturated solution in contact with its solute crystals is an example of **dynamic equilibrium**. Detailed experimental studies have shown that dissolution reactions and recrystallisation (or precipitation) reactions still occur at the molecular level in such heterogeneous mixtures. Time-lapse photography shows that the crystals on the base of the beaker are constantly changing shape as some surfaces of the crystals dissolve and others grow larger by ion association and crystallisation (precipitation). These processes are balanced and the system is said to be in dynamic equilibrium. Thus, in a saturated solution:

rate of dissolution = rate of precipitation (crystallisation)

The following equation represents this dynamic equilibrium. Note the use of reversible arrows.

$$NaCl(s) \rightleftharpoons Na^+(aq) + Cl^-(aq)$$

Figure 13.8 shows a particle model of this dynamic equilibrium in a saturated salt solution.

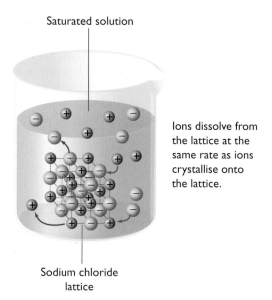

Saturated solution

Ions dissolve from the lattice at the same rate as ions crystallise onto the lattice.

Sodium chloride lattice

Figure 13.8
Particle model of a dynamic equilibrium in a saturated salt solution

Radioactive tracers can be used to prove that a saturated solution is in dynamic equilibrium. Radioactive sodium can be converted into radioactive sodium chloride by reaction with chlorine. These radioactive crystals are chemically identical to normal crystals. When a radioactive sodium chloride crystal is added to a saturated sodium chloride solution, the water gradually becomes radioactive, showing that the system is dynamic.

Ionic salts vary in their solubilities in water at 25 °C so that different masses are required to produce saturated solutions. Table 13.2 shows the maximum solubility of a range of ionic compounds.

Table 13.2 Solubility of ionic compounds in water at 25 °C

Salt	NH_4Br	KBr	$NaNO_3$	KNO_3	$Ba(NO_3)_2$	NaF	BaF_2
Solubility (g/100 g H_2O)	78	68	92	38	10	4	0.2

Solubility and temperature

As most salts are more soluble in hot water, the mass of salt required to produce a saturated solution rises with temperature. This is illustrated by figure 13.9, which shows the solubility of sodium chloride as a function of temperature. Below the line, solutions are unsaturated; above the line, solutions are saturated.

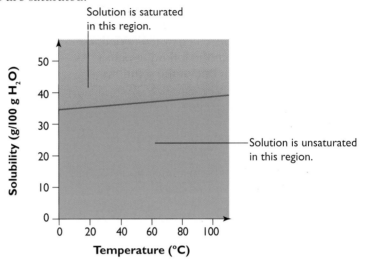

Figure 13.9
Solubility of sodium chloride as a function of temperature

13.1 QUESTIONS

Use table 13.1 as needed to answer these questions.

1. Identify which of the following compounds produce highly conductive solutions when mixed with water.
   A Sodium nitrate
   B Sucrose
   C Barium sulfate
   D Calcium carbonate

2. Identify which of the following mixtures form a precipitate.
   A Calcium chloride solution + ammonium nitrate solution
   B Sodium nitrate solution + copper (II) sulfate solution
   C Barium nitrate solution + sulfuric acid solution
   D Copper (II) nitrate solution + potassium chloride solution

3. The salt solution that produces a precipitate when added to iron (III) nitrate solution is
   A sodium sulfate.
   B potassium hydroxide.
   C ammonium nitrate.
   D sodium chloride.

4. The net ionic equation that best describes the precipitation action that occurs when potassium sulfate solution is mixed with calcium nitrate solution is
   A $K_2SO_4(aq) + Ca(NO_3)_2(aq) \rightarrow CaSO_4(s) + 2KNO_3(aq)$.
   B $K^+(aq) + NO_3^-(aq) \rightarrow KNO_3(s)$.
   C $Ca^{2+}(aq) + 2NO_3^-(aq) \rightarrow Ca(NO_3)_2(s)$.
   D $Ca^{2+}(aq) + SO_4^{2-}(aq) \rightarrow CaSO_4(s)$.

5. An unknown solution is believed to contain one of the following anions: Cl^-, SO_4^{2-}, CO_3^{2-}, NO_3^-.

   The solution was tested first with silver nitrate solution and then with barium chloride solution and no precipitate formed in either case. The unknown solution contained
   A chloride ions.
   B sulfate ions.
   C carbonate ions.
   D nitrate ions.

6. Identify whether a precipitate forms when 1 molar solutions of the following salts are mixed. If a precipitate forms, name the precipitate.
   (a) Calcium chloride solution and silver nitrate solution
   (b) Potassium carbonate solution and silver nitrate solution
   (c) Sodium chloride solution and ammonium nitrate solution
   (d) Sodium hydroxide solution and lead (II) nitrate solution

Table 13.3

Solution 1	Solution 2	Net ionic equation	Spectator ions	Precipitate
$Ca(NO_3)_2$	K_2SO_4	(a)	K^+, NO_3^-	(b)
$AgNO_3$	BaI_2	(c)	(d)	AgI
K_2CrO_4	$CaCl_2$	$Ca^{2+}(aq) + CrO_4^{2-}(aq) \rightarrow CaCrO_4(s)$	(e)	(f)

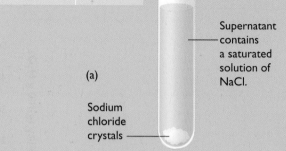

(a)

Stopper prevents loss of water from tube.

Supernatant contains a saturated solution of NaCl.

Sodium chloride crystals

7. Name one salt solution which, when added to each of the solutions in the following pairs, causes precipitation in one of the solutions but not in the other.
   (a) Calcium chloride, sodium chloride
   (b) Barium nitrate, calcium chloride
   (c) Sodium sulfate, sodium hydroxide
   (d) Silver nitrate, iron (III) nitrate

8. Identify two solutions that produce the following precipitates on mixing.
   (a) Silver bromide
   (b) Lead (II) chromate
   (c) Nickel (II) carbonate
   (d) Copper (II) sulfide
   (e) Barium phosphate

9. Write net ionic equations for each of the following reactions.
   (a) Calcium chloride solution + silver nitrate solution forms white silver chloride precipitate + calcium nitrate solution.
   (b) Barium nitrate solution + caesium sulfate solution forms white barium sulfate precipitate + caesium nitrate solution.
   (c) Copper (II) sulfate solution + potassium sulfide solution forms black copper (II) sulfide precipitate + potassium sulfate solution.

10. Copy and complete table 13.3 in your workbook. In each case, the net ionic equation is the reaction that occurs when solutions 1 and 2 are mixed.

11. A test tube containing 5.0 g of sodium chloride crystals and 10 mL (10 g) of water at 25 °C is stoppered and shaken vigorously until no more crystals dissolve. Figure 13.10b shows the test tube after shaking. Figure 13.10a shows the mass of NaCl dissolved as a function of time.
    (a) The solution becomes saturated when no more salt dissolves. Use figure 13.10b to determine when the solution first became saturated.
    (b) State when equilibrium was first established.
    (c) Write an ionic equation for the equilibrium in the saturated solution.

(b)

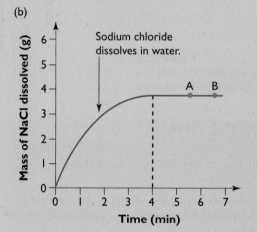

Sodium chloride dissolves in water.

Figure 13.10
(a) Equilibrium in an NaCl solution
(b) Amount of NaCl dissolved over time at 25 °C

   (d) Use figure 13.10b to calculate the solubility of sodium chloride in water. Express your answer in g/100 g water at 25 °C.
   (e) At time A in figure 13.10b, an additional crystal of NaCl is added to the tube and the stopper replaced. At time B, a sample of the salt solution is withdrawn and its concentration determined. Compare the concentration of dissolved salt at B with that at A.

12. Explain how a chemist could prove experimentally that the equilibrium in a saturated salt solution was dynamic.

13. Describe an experimental procedure to produce:
    (a) blue crystals of copper (II) sulfate from green crystals of copper (II) chloride
    (b) green crystals of copper (II) chloride from blue crystals of copper (II) sulfate.

13.2 CONCENTRATION OF SOLUTIONS

molarity: the concentration of a solution expressed in mol/L

Molarity of a solution

Chemists use a variety of methods to describe the strength or concentration (c) of a solution. One important unit of concentration is the unit of **molarity**.

Figure 13.11 Volumetric flasks are commonly used to prepare solutions of known volume or concentration.

The molarity of a solution is the number of moles of solute per litre of solution.

The formula for molarity is:

$$c = n/V$$

where, c = concentration of the solution (mol/L), n = moles of solute (mol) and V = volume of solution (L).

Many laboratory acid solutions are prepared with specific concentrations. Consider a 2 mol/L hydrochloric acid solution. The concentration of 2 mol/L tells us that 1 litre of the solution contains 2 moles of HCl, or that 200 mL of the solution contains 2 × 200/1000 or 0.4 moles.

Concentrated hydrochloric acid typically has a molarity of about 11 mol/L while concentrated sulfuric acid has a molarity of about 18 mol/L.

concentrated: describes a solution with a large amount of solute per litre

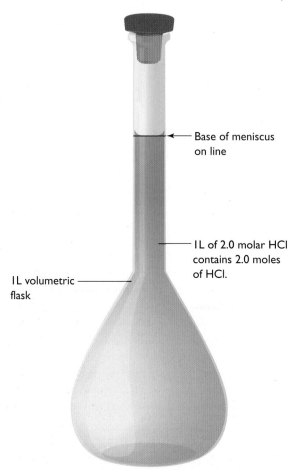

Base of meniscus on line

IL of 2.0 molar HCl contains 2.0 moles of HCl.

IL volumetric flask

Figure 13.12
Solution of HCl of known concentration

SAMPLE PROBLEM 13.4

A 250 mL solution is made by dissolving 8.0 g of glucose, $C_6H_{12}O_6$, in sufficient water.

(a) Calculate the number of moles of glucose that has been dissolved.

(b) Calculate the molarity of the solution.

SOLUTION

(a) Calculate the molar weight (M) of glucose by summing the atomic weights.

$$M = (6 \times 12.01) + (12 \times 1.008) + (6 \times 16.00)$$
$$= 180.16 \text{ g/mol}$$

Therefore, $n = m/M$
$$= 8.0/180.16$$
$$= 0.0444 \text{ mol}$$

(b) $c = n/V$
$$= 0.0444/0.250$$
$$= 0.18 \text{ mol/L}$$

SAMPLE PROBLEM 13.5

Calculate the volume of a 0.10 mol/L potassium iodide solution that contains 1.50 g of potassium iodide, KI.

SOLUTION

Step 1: Calculate the molar weight (M) of potassium iodide.

$$M = 39.10 + 126.90$$
$$= 166.00 \text{ g/mol}$$

Step 2: Calculate the number of moles in 1.50 g of KI.

$$n = m/M$$
$$= 1.50/166.0$$
$$= 9.036 \times 10^{-3} \text{ mol}$$

Step 3: Calculate the volume of the solution.

$$V = n/c$$
$$= 9.036 \times 10^{-3}/0.10$$
$$= 9.036 \times 10^{-2} \text{ L}$$
$$= 90.4 \text{ mL}$$

Dilution

It is quite common to dilute a more concentrated solution to prepare a dilute solution of a laboratory reagent. Consider a solution of sodium chloride of concentration c_1. If V_1 litres of this solution is measured using a pipette or burette and placed in a flask, you can calculate the number of moles of salt (n) present in the flask using the molarity formula:

$$n = c_1 V_1 \tag{1}$$

If sufficient water is then added to the flask so that volume of the **diluted** solution is V_2, the new concentration (c_2) can be calculated, as the number of moles of solute has not changed.

Thus,

$$c_2 = n/V_2 \tag{2}$$

Substituting equation 1 into equation 2 gives,

$$c_2 = c_1 V_1 / V_2$$

or,

> diluted: describes a solution with a small amount of solute per litre. It can be made by adding more solvent to a concentrated solution.

$$c_1 V_1 = c_2 V_2$$

This formula is very useful in problems involving dilution of solutions.

SAMPLE PROBLEM 13.6

After 100 mL of 10 mol/L hydrochloric acid is added to water, the final volume is adjusted to 2.5 L. Calculate the molarity of the diluted hydrochloric acid.

SOLUTION

$$c_1 = 10 \text{ mol/L} \qquad V_1 = 100 \text{ mL} = 0.1 \text{ L}$$
$$c_2 = ? \qquad V_2 = 2.5 \text{ L}$$

Substitute into the formula: $c_1 V_1 = c_2 V_2$

$$10 \times 0.1 = c_2 \times 2.5$$
$$c_2 = 0.40 \text{ mol/L HCl}$$

A mixture is made by adding 250 mL of 0.15 mol/L sodium chloride to 250 mL of 0.20 mol/L calcium chloride.
(a) Calculate the molarity of chloride ions in the final solution.
(b) Water is then added to the mixture until the total volume is 2 litres. Calculate the molarity of chloride ions in the diluted solution.

SOLUTION ▶▶▶▶▶

(a) *Step 1:* Calculate the number of moles of chloride ions in each solution before they are mixed:
$$n(NaCl) = cV$$
$$= 0.15 \times 0.250$$
$$= 0.0375 \text{ mol.}$$

Each mole of NaCl contains one mole of chloride ions. Thus,
$$n(Cl^-) = n(NaCl)$$
$$= 0.0375 \text{ mol}$$
$$n(CaCl_2) = cV$$
$$= 0.20 \times 0.250$$
$$= 0.050 \text{ mol}$$

Each mole of $CaCl_2$ contains 2 moles of chloride ions. Thus,
$$n(Cl^-) = 2n(CaCl_2) = 0.100 \text{ mol}$$

Step 2: Calculate the total number of moles of chloride ions by adding the number of moles in each solution. Thus, total moles of chloride ions = 0.0375 + 0.100
$$= 0.1375 \text{ mol}$$

Step 3: Total volume of solution = 250 + 250
$$= 500 \text{ mL}$$
$$= 0.500 \text{ L}$$

Thus, molarity of chloride ions $(c) = n/V$
$$= 0.1375/0.500$$
$$= 0.275 \text{ mol/L}$$

(b) $c_1 = 0.275$ mol/L $V_1 = 0.500$ L
$c_2 = ?$ $V_2 = 2.0$ L

Substitute these values into the dilution formula.
$$c_1 V_1 = c_2 V_2$$
$$0.275 \times 0.500 = c_2 \times 2.0$$
So, $c_2 = 0.0688$ mol/L

Calculate the volume of water that needs to be added to 100 mL of a 2.00 mol/L sodium chloride solution to produce a diluted solution with a molarity of 0.10 mol/L.

SOLUTION ▶▶▶▶▶

Use the dilution formula to calculate the volume of the final diluted solution.
$c_1 = 2.00$ mol/L $V_1 = 100$ mL = 0.100 L
$c_2 = 0.10$ mol/L $V_2 = ?$
$$c_1 V_1 = c_2 V_2$$
$$2.00 \times 0.100 = 0.10 \times V_2$$
$$V_2 = 2.0 \text{ L}$$
Therefore, the volume of water to be added = 2.0 − 0.1 = 1.9 L.

Molarity and precipitation reactions

Mole theory can be used to predict the mass of precipitate formed when two electrolytes are mixed. It can also be used to determine the volume of a solution of known concentration needed to completely precipitate an ion in another solution when the two solutions are mixed. These types of calculations are important to chemists conducting gravimetric analysis.

SOLUTION

If 100 mL of 0.10 mol/L sodium chloride is mixed with 100 mL of 0.10 mol/L silver nitrate, calculate the mass of silver chloride precipitate that will form.

Step 1: Write the balanced equation for the reaction.

$$AgNO_3(aq) + NaCl(aq) \rightarrow AgCl(s) + NaNO_3(aq)$$

Step 2: Calculate the number of moles of silver nitrate and sodium chloride used.

$$\begin{aligned} n(AgNO_3) &= cV \\ &= 0.10 \times 0.10 \\ &= 0.010 \text{ mol} \end{aligned}$$

$$\begin{aligned} n(NaCl) &= cV \\ &= 0.10 \times 0.10 \\ &= 0.010 \text{ mol} \end{aligned}$$

Thus, the reactants are added in a 1 : 1 mole ratio as required by the balanced equation for complete reaction.

Step 3: The balanced equation shows that 1 mole of silver chloride is formed from 1 mole of silver nitrate. Thus, the number of moles of silver chloride formed in this experiment is 0.010 mol.

Step 4: Calculate the molar weight of AgCl.

$$\begin{aligned} M(AgCl) &= 107.9 + 35.45 \\ &= 143.35 \text{ g/mol} \end{aligned}$$

Step 5: Calculate the mass of silver chloride precipitate formed.

$$\begin{aligned} m &= nM \\ &= 0.010 \times 143.35 \\ &= 1.43 \text{ g} \end{aligned}$$

SOLUTION

Calculate the volume of 0.20 mol/L barium chloride solution that needs to be added to 200 mL of 0.15 mol/L sodium sulfate solution to completely precipitate all the sulfate ions.

Step 1: Write the balanced equation for the precipitation reaction.

$$BaCl_2(aq) + Na_2SO_4(aq) \rightarrow BaSO_4(s) + 2NaCl(aq)$$

Step 2: Calculate the number of moles of sodium sulfate used.

$$\begin{aligned} n = cV &= 0.15 \times 0.200 \\ &= 0.0300 \text{ mol} \end{aligned}$$

Step 3: The balanced equation shows that, for complete precipitation of barium sulfate, 1 mole of barium chloride is needed to react with each mole of sodium sulfate. As 0.0300 moles of sodium sulfate is used, 0.0300 mol of barium chloride must be added.

Step 4: Calculate the volume of the barium chloride solution needed.

$$\begin{aligned} V(BaCl_2) &= n/c \\ &= 0.0300/0.20 \\ &= 0.150 \text{ L} \\ &= 150 \text{ mL} \end{aligned}$$

Alternative measurements of concentration

Molarity is only one way to express the concentration of a solution. Chemists use other measurements of concentration where the molarity unit is inconvenient. Let us examine some common examples.

Per cent by weight (%w/w)

A solution of known concentration can be prepared by weighing the solute and then adding the solvent until a known weight of solution is produced. The concentration is normally expressed as a percentage (%w/w).

$$c = \frac{\text{weight of solute}}{\text{weight of solution}} \times \frac{100}{1} \ \% \ \text{w/w}$$

For example, 4.0 g of sodium chloride can be weighed into a beaker and water added to dissolve the salt. If additional water is added until the total mass of solution is 200 g, the concentration of salt can be calculated as:

$$c(\text{NaCl}) = 4.0/200 \times 100/1$$
$$= 2.0\%\text{w/w}$$

This method of expressing concentration is also used in food and medicinal products. It can be used to show the percentage of sugar in a breakfast cereal or percentage of fluoride in a toothpaste.

Per cent by volume (%v/v)

This method of expressing concentration is commonly used when liquids are dissolved in other liquids. Medicines and alcoholic drinks often use this measure of concentration. The measurement of the volume of the solute and the volume of the final solution is used to calculate the concentration which is expressed as %v/v.

$$c = \frac{\text{volume of solute}}{\text{volume of solution}} \times \frac{100}{1} \ \% \ \text{v/v}$$

For example, 7.50 mL of methanol is dissolved in ethanol to make 150 mL of solution. The concentration of the methanol in the solution can be calculated as:

$$c(\text{CH}_3\text{OH}) = 7.50/150 \times 100$$
$$= 5.0\%\text{v/v}$$

Parts per million (ppm)

Sometimes, the concentration of solute in a solution is very small and the unit 'parts per million' is used. This unit can be expressed by weight or volume, or by weight per volume (mg/L).

(a) ppm by weight

$$c = \text{weight of solute (mg)}/\text{weight of solution (kg)}$$

Figure 13.13
Alcohol concentration in wine is measured as % by volume.

Alcoholic content 13%(v/v)

Wombat Wine

(b) ppm by volume

$$c = \text{volume of solute (mL)}/\text{volume of solution (kL)}$$

(c) ppm by weight per volume

$$c = \text{mass of solute (mg)}/\text{volume of solution (L)}$$

13.2 PRACTICAL ACTIVITIES

Preparing and diluting solutions

Examples:
1. A 200 ppm solution of copper ions in water contains 200 mg of copper for every kilogram of solution.
2. A 2 ppm mixture of ozone in air contains 2 mL of ozone in every kilolitre of air.
3. A 20 ppm solution of mercury ions in water is equivalent to 20 mg/L.

(*Note:* 1 ppm is also equal to 1 μg/g or 1 μL/L.)

SAMPLE PROBLEM 13.11

Sulfur dioxide is an antioxidant, commonly used in white wine and dried fruit to prevent spoilage by oxidation. The maximum sulfur dioxide concentration (2000 ppm) allowed in dried apricots is specified by weight. Determine whether a 500 g sample of export-quality dried apricots containing 0.700 g of sulfur dioxide is within the allowable range for export.

SOLUTION

Step 1: Convert the mass of sulfur dioxide to milligrams and the mass of dried apricots to kilograms.

$$m(\text{sulfur dioxide}) = 0.700 \text{ g} = 700 \text{ mg}$$
$$m(\text{dried apricots}) = 500 \text{ g} = 0.500 \text{ kg}$$

Step 2: Calculate the concentration of sulfur dioxide in the dried apricots.

$$c = 700/0.500 = 1400 \text{ ppm}$$

Thus, the level of sulfur dioxide in the dried apricots is within the allowable export range.

13.2 QUESTIONS

1. A bottle of nitric acid is labelled 4.0 mol/L. Select the correct statement about this solution.
   A   1 litre of the nitric acid solution contains 4 g of solute.
   B   4 litres of the nitric acid solution contains 1 mole of solute.
   C   1 litre of the solution contains 252 grams of solute.
   D   1 litre of the solution contains 63 grams of solute.

2. The number of moles of potassium nitrate in 25.00 mL of a 0.020 mol/L solution is
   A   0.020 moles.
   B   0.500 moles.
   C   0.0008 moles.
   D   0.0005 moles.

3. The molarity of the solution formed by dissolving 10 g of sodium bromide in sufficient water to make 200 mL of solution is
   A   0.49 mol/L.
   B   50 mol/L.
   C   0.050 mol/L.
   D   0.00049 mol/L.

4. The molarity of the diluted solution formed when 25 mL of 0.40 mol/L HCl is diluted with 75 mL of water is
   A   0.10 mol/L.
   B   0.20 mol/L.
   C   0.13 mol/L.
   D   1.20 mol/L.

5. The concentration of a solution in which 5.0 mL of acetone is dissolved in sufficient ethanol to produce 50.0 mL of solution is

   A   5.0%v/v.

   B   11.1%v/v.

   C   10.0%v/v.

   D   9.1%v/v.

6. Calculate the volume to which 30.0 mL of 0.500 mol/L sulfuric acid must be diluted so that the new concentration is 0.100 mol/L.

7. Calculate the volume of water required to produce a 0.10 mol/L sulfuric acid solution from 5.0 mL of concentrated (18.0 mol/L) sulfuric acid.

8. Element E forms a bromide with the formula EBr_2. If 20.0 g of EBr_2 is dissolved in water and the volume adjusted to 500 mL, the molarity of the solution is 0.20 mol/L. Calculate the atomic weight of element E.

9. One molar solutions of a metal sulfate and barium chloride were prepared and mixed in five test tubes in varying amounts according to table 13.4. The barium sulfate precipitated in each tube was filtered, dried and weighed, as shown in the table.

   (a) Plot a line graph of the mass of barium sulfate against the volume of barium chloride solution added to each tube.

   (b) Explain why the mass of barium sulfate was about the same in tubes 3, 4 and 5.

   (c) Determine the volume of barium chloride that reacts completely with 2 mL of the metal sulfate solution.

   (d) Calculate the number of moles of barium chloride that react with 1 mole of the metal sulfate.

   (e) Calculate the number of moles of sulfate ions in 1 mole of the metal sulfate.

   (f) Using the symbol M for the metal, write the chemical formula for the metal sulfate.

10. A 50 kg sample of steel from a blast furnace is found to contain 2.0%w/w carbon. Calculate the mass of carbon in the sample.

11. Environmentalists have linked measurable increases in carbon dioxide concentration in the atmosphere to global warming. Carbon dioxide data from 1960 and 1980 is listed below. Use this data to determine the increase in the concentration of carbon dioxide (in the units of parts per million, ppm) in this period.

   1960: Volume of air tested = 10 kL

     Volume of CO_2 in sample = 3.18 L

   1980: Volume of air tested = 500 mL

     Volume of CO_2 in sample = 169 μL

12. An environmental chemist determined the fluoride concentrations of two samples of potable water. She obtained the following data.

   Sample A: Volume of water sample = 2 mL

              Mass of fluoride present = 2.4 mg

   Sample B: Volume of water sample = 1.50 mL

              Mass of fluoride present = 1.125 mg

Determine whether the fluoride concentration (in ppm by weight) in each sample exceeds the 1000 ppm maximum level for fluoride in drinking water. (*Note*: density of water = 1.0 g/mL)

13. Oysters are filter feeders; they accumulate heavy metals in their tissues if they grow in contaminated water. In one sample, the contaminated oysters were found to contain 5 ppm of mercury, measured by dry weight

Table 13.4

Test tube	Volume of 1 mol/L metal sulfate (mL)	Volume of 1 mol/L barium chloride (mL)	Volume of water added (mL)	Mass BaSO₄ (g)
1	2	2	8	0.467
2	2	4	6	0.934
3	2	6	4	1.400
4	2	8	2	1.401
5	2	10	0	1.399

(a) The chemist who analysed the tissue dried it before analysing it. Explain why the concentration of mercury is based on the weight of dehydrated tissue rather than fresh tissue.

(b) Calculate how many milligrams of mercury would be present in 800 g of dried oyster tissue.

(c) If the tissue has concentrated the mercury 30 000 times, determine the concentration of mercury in the surrounding sea water.

14. Industries are constantly monitored by environmental chemists to ensure they do not contaminate waterways with waste water discharges. An environmental chemist collected a sample of industrial waste water prior to discharge. She tested the waste water and found it to have a cadmium concentration of 200 ppm.

(a) The company has stored 1500 kg of this waste water. Calculate the total mass of cadium present.

(b) If this waste water was discharged into a lake containing 2.5 megalitres, determine the diluted concentration of cadmium in the lake. (*Note:* 1 litre of water = 1 kg.) State whether this diluted concentration is above or below the acceptable limit of 10 ppm.

SUMMARY

- Solubility in water is different for different ionic compounds.

- All nitrate salts are soluble. All sodium and potassium salts are soluble.

- The solubility of an ionic compound in water is affected by temperature.

- Solutions are saturated when no more solute will dissolve.

- Some solutions of ions, when mixed, form precipitates.

- Solubility data can be used to predict the formation of precipitates.

- The molarity of a solution is the number of moles of solute per litre of solution.

- The concentration of a solution can be expressed in a variety of ways including: moles/litre, per cent by weight, per cent by volume and parts per million.

- Systematic dilution of solutions must be performed using accurate glassware.

PRACTICAL ACTIVITIES

13.1 PRACTICAL ACTIVITIES

INVESTIGATING SOLUBILITY USING PRECIPITATION REACTIONS

Aim

To develop solubility rules based on precipitation reactions using semi-microtechniques

Safety issues

- Wear safety glasses throughout this experiment.
- Identify other safety issues relevant to this experiment by reading the method.

Materials

- spot plate or acetate sheet
- dropper bottles containing 0.5 or 1.0 molar solutions of the following ions
- cations: Ag^+, Pb^{2+}, Cu^{2+}, Zn^{2+}, Mg^{2+}, Ca^{2+}, Ba^{2+} and K^+ as nitrate salts
- anions: Cl^-, CO_3^{2-}, SO_4^{2-} and OH^- as sodium salts

Method

In this experiment, the reactions are performed by combining drops of each reagent and observing any colour changes. Such small scale reactions are called semi-microtechniques.

1. Select the first cation to be tested. Place 1 drop of this solution in each of four wells in the spot plate or as four separate drops on an acetate sheet.
2. Test each of the four drops with 1 drop of a different anion solution. *Do not allow the tip of the dropper to touch the first drop.*

3. Record any colour changes or precipitate formation. You may need to view the drops against white or black backgrounds.
4. Repeat the procedure with other cations.

Results

Record your observations in a suitable table like table 13.5.

Table 13.5

	Cl^-	CO_3^{2-}	SO_4^{2-}	OH^-
Ag^+				
Pb^{2+}				
Cu^{2+}				
Zn^{2+}				
Mg^{2+}				
Ca^{2+}				
Ba^{2+}				
K^+				

Questions

1. Analyse your results for each anion tested and develop a series of solubility generalisations based on these results. These generalisations should take the format:

   Most … salts are soluble/insoluble except …

2. Compare your results with the solubility generalisation rules in table 13.1. Try to account for any discrepancies.
3. Write net ionic equations for all reactions that produced precipitates.

Conclusion

Briefly describe the outcome of your investigation.

PRACTICAL ACTIVITIES

13.2 PRACTICAL ACTIVITIES

PREPARING AND DILUTING SOLUTIONS

Aim

To prepare solutions of known concentration and to systematically dilute these solutions

Safety issues

- Wear safety glasses throughout this experiment.
- Identify other safety issues relevant to this experiment by reading the method.

Materials

- two 10 mL graduated pipettes
- pipette filler
- 25 mL bulb pipette
- 250 mL volumetric flask
- 150 mL beaker
- 150 mL flask
- wash bottle
- glass rods
- spatula
- electronic balance
- methylated spirits
- potassium dichromate

Method

Part A: Preparing and diluting a solution of methylated spirits

1. Rinse a 10 mL graduated pipette with small quantities of methylated spirits. Use the clean pipette and pipette filler to measure 5.0 mL of methylated spirits, and transfer this to a clean 150 mL flask.

2. Clean a 25 mL pipette with small volumes of water and fill it with water to the mark. Transfer the water to the flask containing methylated spirits.

3. Mix the methylated spirits and water to obtain a solution.

4. Calculate the concentration (c_1) of the methylated spirits solution as %v/v.

5. Devise and perform an experiment to systematically dilute the methylated spirits solution to produce 20 mL of a solution with a methylated spirits concentration (c_2) of 4.2%v/v.

Part B: Preparing and diluting a solution of potassium dichromate

1. Your aim is to prepare 250 mL of a 0.010 mol/L solution of potassium dichromate, $K_2Cr_2O_7$ using a 250 mL volumetric flask.

    (a) Calculate the mass of potassium dichromate that needs to be weighed on an electronic balance. Check your calculation with your teacher before proceeding.

    (b) Calculate the concentration of a 0.010 mol/L solution of potassium dichromate in g/L.

2. Weigh the required amount of potassium dichromate crystals into a clean 150 mL beaker.

3. Dissolve the crystals in a minimum of water. Stir the mixture with a glass rod.

4. Quantitatively transfer the solution to the clean, rinsed volumetric flask with the aid of a glass rod and wash bottle. Rinse the beaker many times and add the washings to the flask.

5. Add water until the base of the meniscus is on the mark. Stopper the volumetric flask and mix the solution thoroughly. Label the flask with the name and concentration of the solution.

6. Devise and perform an experiment to accurately dilute the potassium dichromate solution to produce 20 mL of a 0.5 g/L solution.

Questions

1. Describe the method you used to dilute the solutions in each experiment.

2. Explain why a measuring cylinder is unsuitable for quantitative dilution experiments.

Conclusion

Briefly describe the outcome of your investigation.

Chapter *14*

WATER AND ENERGY

Introduction

The large amounts of water on the Earth's surface play an important role in moderating the temperature of our planet. Water can absorb large quantities of heat without a large rise in temperature. This property of water is related to its structure and intermolecular bonding. In this section, we will investigate energy changes in aqueous systems.

In this chapter

Figure 14.1

Sand is hotter than the sea on a sunny day. The sand and the water have different capacities to absorb heat.

14.1 ENERGY CHANGES IN AQUEOUS SYSTEMS

Remember

Before beginning this section, you should be able to:
• visualise the dissolution in water of various types of substances.

Key content

By the end of this section, you should be able to:
• explain what is meant by the specific heat capacity of a substance
• compare the specific heat capacity of water with a range of other solvents
• explain and use the equation:

$$\Delta H = -mC\Delta T$$

• explain how water's ability to absorb heat is used to measure energy changes in chemical reactions
• describe dissolutions that release heat as exothermic and give examples
• describe dissolutions that absorb heat as endothermic and give examples
• explain why water's ability to absorb heat is important to aquatic organisms and to life on Earth generally
• explain what is meant by thermal pollution and discuss the implications for life if a body of water is affected by thermal pollution
• choose resources and perform a first-hand investigation to measure the change in temperature when substances dissolve in water and calculate the molar heat of solution
• process and present information from secondary sources to assess the limitations of calorimetry experiments and design modifications to equipment used.

Heat capacity

You will have noticed in the hot Australian summer how differently the solid Earth and ocean water absorb heat energy. A concrete path can be too hot to stand on while the nearby grass lawn is much cooler. The sand on the beach is much hotter underfoot than the nearby water. Different materials, therefore, have different capacities to absorb heat and change temperature.

Figure 14.2 A water–ice mixture remains at 0 °C while the ice melts.

To put these observations in a more quantitative light, let's consider a simple experiment, shown in figure 14.3, involving two different metals, such as silver and zinc. If 50 g of each metal is placed in a beaker of boiling water and left long enough, they will both reach a temperature of 100 °C. If we now transfer these hot lumps of metal to separate beakers, each containing 100 g of cold water at 20 °C, and monitor the rise in temperature of the water, we find that the water in the beakers does not rise to the same temperature.

Typical results of such an experiment are shown in table 14.1. We can infer from this type of experiment that zinc has a greater capacity to store heat than the same mass of silver. Conversely, if equal masses of these two metals (initially at room temperature) are heated, more heat is required to raise the temperature of the zinc by 1 degree than to raise the silver by the same temperature.

Table 14.1 Transfer of heat from hot metals to cold water

Metal (50 g)	Initial temperature of metal (°C)	Initial temperature of water (°C)	Highest temperature of water (°C)	Rise in temperature (°C)
silver	100	20	22.1	2.1
zinc	100	20	23.6	3.6

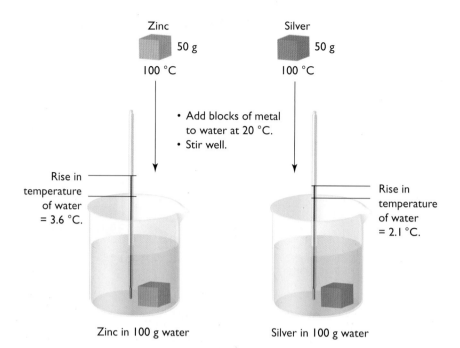

Zinc 50 g 100 °C

Silver 50 g 100 °C

- Add blocks of metal to water at 20 °C.
- Stir well.

Rise in temperature of water = 3.6 °C.

Rise in temperature of water = 2.1 °C.

Zinc in 100 g water

Silver in 100 g water

Figure 14.3
Heat capacity experiment

specific heat capacity: the amount of energy required to raise the temperature of 1 gram of a body by 1 Kelvin unit, expressed as J/K/g. Specific heat capacity is also measured in J/K/kg and J/K/mol.

joule: the SI unit of energy (heat)

Kelvin: unit (K) on the absolute temperature scale, where 0 °C = 273 K and 100 °C = 373 K. One degree Celsius is equal to 1 Kelvin unit.

These experiments can be applied to any material to determine a quantity called the **specific heat capacity** (C). This is defined as the amount of heat energy (in **joules**) that causes the temperature of 1 gram of the material to rise by 1 **Kelvin** unit. Table 14.2 lists some values of the specific heat capacity for some common materials.

Table 14.2 Specific heat capacities at 20 °C

Substance	Specific heat capacity (J/K/g)	Substance	Specific heat capacity (J/K/g)
aluminium	0.90	water	4.18
copper	0.39	ice	2.16
iron	0.45	ethanol	2.44
silver	0.23	acetone	2.17
zinc	0.39	hexane	2.26

The specific heat capacity of aluminium is significantly higher than that of the other metals listed in table 14.2. In general, reactive metals have higher heat capacities than less active metals. Silver has a very low heat capacity so its temperature rises much higher than that of an equal mass of aluminium when they are heated equally.

Heat capacity of water

Table 14.2 allows us to compare the heat capacities of water and three other solvents. Water has a significantly higher specific heat capacity (4.18 J/K/g) than ethanol, acetone and hexane. If we place 100 g of each of these four solvents in separate beakers at room temperature and supply them all with the same amount of heat energy, the temperature of water temperature will increase least. As temperature is a measure of the **kinetic energy** of particles in a liquid, more heat energy is required to increase the kinetic energy of water molecules than the other liquids. This is consistent with the strong hydrogen bonding between water molecules and the weaker intermolecular forces between particles in the other liquids.

kinetic energy: the energy of motion possessed by a particle. The higher the temperature of a substance, the greater the kinetic energy of its particles.

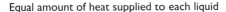
Equal amount of heat supplied to each liquid

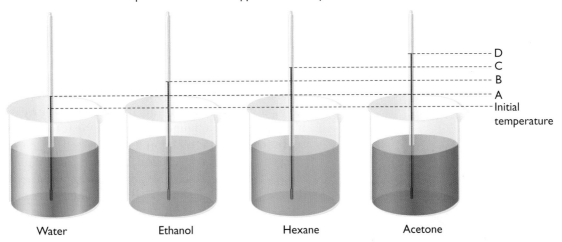

D
C
B
A
Initial temperature

Water   Ethanol   Hexane   Acetone

Figure 14.4
Measuring the temperature rise of four liquids when supplied the same amount of heat

Living things are composed of a high percentage of water. This ensures that their cells and bodies do not increase in temperature too much when exposed to high environmental temperatures. Terrestrial animals and plants also have elaborate cooling mechanisms, such as the transpiration stream or evaporation of sweat, to maintain a fairly constant body temperature.

Calorimetry and enthalpy changes

calorimeter: apparatus used to measure heat changes during a chemical reaction or change of state

A special device called a **calorimeter** is used to measure heat changes during a chemical reaction or a change of state. Figure 14.5 shows the features of an elaborate calorimeter (known as a 'bomb' calorimeter) used to measure the heat released when a fuel is burnt in oxygen. This type of calorimeter is composed of a sturdy metal vessel in which the fuel–oxygen mixture is ignited with a spark. The vessel is surrounded by well-stirred water in an insulated container. The metal of the reaction vessel and the surrounding water absorbs the heat liberated on combustion. A thermometer or temperature probe connected to a data logger measures changes in temperature.

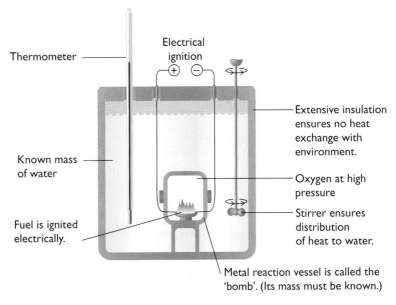

Thermometer

Electrical ignition

Extensive insulation ensures no heat exchange with environment.

Known mass of water

Oxygen at high pressure

Stirrer ensures distribution of heat to water.

Fuel is ignited electrically.

Figure 14.5
A calorimeter used to measure heat evolved on combustion of a fuel

Metal reaction vessel is called the 'bomb'. (Its mass must be known.)

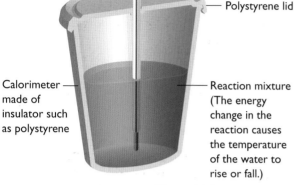

Thermometer or temperature probe is used to measure the initial and final temperatures.

Polystyrene lid

Calorimeter made of insulator such as polystyrene

Reaction mixture (The energy change in the reaction causes the temperature of the water to rise or fall.)

Figure 14.6
Polystyrene foam calorimeter

Simpler calorimeters are used in school laboratories. A polystyrene foam calorimeter is convenient for measuring energy changes in aqueous solutions. Polystyrene is an excellent insulator so little heat is lost to the polystyrene or the air during measurements. An alternative is a copper metal calorimeter surrounded by insulation (e.g. cotton fibre or beads of polystyrene) and housed in a wooden box. This type of calorimeter is also suitable for measuring energy changes involving changes of state. Both the copper and the water in the vessel absorb heat liberated in the change and release heat to the reactants if heat is absorbed in the reaction.

Let us consider a reaction in which a certain quantity of heat energy (q) is released to the surroundings. If the experiment is conducted in a perfectly insulated calorimeter, we can assume that:

heat released by reaction = heat gained by calorimeter

In this experiment, the material of the calorimeter (e.g. the water) increases from an initial temperature (T_i) to a maximum temperature (T_f). The following calorimetry equation allows us to calculate this quantity of heat from our experimental measurements.

$$q = mC\Delta T$$

where q is the quantity of heat (J) absorbed by the calorimeter, m is the mass (g) of the material absorbing the heat, C is the specific heat capacity (J/K/g) of the material absorbing the heat, and ΔT ($T_f - T_i$) is the change in temperature (K) of the material in the calorimeter.

SAMPLE PROBLEM 14.1

A polystyrene foam calorimeter contains 100 g of water at 22.0 °C. An electrical immersion heater supplies 2000 J of energy to heat the water. The maximum temperature recorded on the thermometer is 26.9 °C.

(a) Assuming all the heat released from the immersion heater is absorbed by the water, calculate the specific heat of the water.

(b) Explain how the accuracy of this experiment could be improved.

SOLUTION >>>>>

(a) $q = mC\Delta T$

$2000 = 100 \times C \times (26.9 - 22.0)$

$C = 4.1 \text{ J/K/g}$

(b) If more heat is delivered from the immersion heater to the water, there would be a smaller percentage error in the measurement of the temperature.

A temperature probe connected to a data logger would increase the experimental accuracy. It is essential to thoroughly insulate the calorimeter so that accuracy can be improved.

Enthalpy and enthalpy change

For elements and compounds, heat energy changes in chemical reactions or changes of state are often expressed by a quantity called the *heat content* or **enthalpy** (H).

enthalpy: the heat content of a system at constant pressure

The enthalpy of a substance is the sum of the kinetic and potential energies of one mole of the particles that comprise the material. It is not possible to measure the absolute enthalpy of a substance but we can experimentally measure the enthalpy change (ΔH) through calorimetry experiments. The enthalpy change for a reaction is defined as:

$$\Delta H = H(\text{products}) - H(\text{reactants})$$

If the quantity of heat (q) is measured under standard conditions of pressure and temperature, it can be equated to the enthalpy change for the reaction. The calorimetry equation then becomes:

$$\Delta H = -mC\Delta T$$

Note the negative sign in the equation. If there is a rise in temperature in the calorimeter due to heat liberation from the reaction, then ΔT is a positive quantity and ΔH is negative. If, however, the temperature of the calorimeter decreases, then ΔT is negative and ΔH is positive. Negative values of ΔH are associated, therefore, with **exothermic** processes and positive values of ΔH are associated with **endothermic** processes. For many chemical reactions, enthalpy changes are normally measured in kilojoules per mole (kJ/mol).

exothermic: describes a chemical reaction in which energy is released to the surroundings

endothermic: describes a chemical reaction in which energy is absorbed from the surroundings

SAMPLE PROBLEM 14.2

A polystyrene foam calorimeter contains 50 mL of 0.1 mol/L barium chloride and 50 mL of 0.1 mol/L sodium sulfate. The temperature was measured using a temperature probe connected to a data logger. The following data was collected.

Mass of solution = 100 g

Specific heat capacity of solution = 4.1 J/K/g

Initial temperature = 20.60 °C

Final (maximum) temperature = 21.65 °C

(a) Assuming that no heat was absorbed by the polystyrene, calculate the heat released during the precipitation reaction.

(b) Calculate the enthalpy change per mole of barium sulfate precipitated.

SOLUTION

(a) $\Delta H = -mC\Delta T$

$\qquad = -100 \times 4.1 \times (21.65 - 20.60)$

$\qquad = -430.5\,\text{J}$

Thus, 430.5 J of heat is released in this experiment.

(b)

Step 1: Calculate the number of moles of barium sulfate formed in this experiment.

$$n(\text{BaCl}_2) = cV$$
$$= 0.1 \times 50 \times 10^{-3}$$
$$= 5.0 \times 10^{-3}\,\text{mol}$$
$$n(\text{Na}_2\text{SO}_4) = cV$$
$$= 0.1 \times 50 \times 10^{-3}$$
$$= 5.0 \times 10^{-3}\,\text{mol}$$

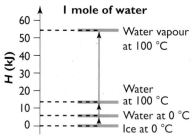

Figure 14.7
Enthalpy scale showing enthalpy changes during a change of state

Enthalpy changes during a change of state

Melting of ice and evaporation of liquid water involve a change of state. Both of these processes require energy, so they are classified as endothermic processes. The standard enthalpy change for these processes is positive.

$$H_2O(s) \rightarrow H_2O(l) \qquad \Delta H = +7\ \text{kJ/mol}$$
$$H_2O(l) \rightarrow H_2O(g) \qquad \Delta H = +44\ \text{kJ/mol}$$

Freezing of water into ice or condensation of water vapour to form liquid water droplets gives out heat energy, so these are exothermic processes. The standard enthalpy change for these processes is negative.

$$H_2O(l) \rightarrow H_2O(s) \qquad \Delta H = -7\ \text{kJ/mol}$$
$$H_2O(g) \rightarrow H_2O(l) \qquad \Delta H = -44\ \text{kJ/mol}$$

Enthalpy change varies with temperature. If we vaporise liquid water at 100 °C (rather than at the standard 25 °C), the amount of heat required is 40.7 kJ/mol. This is less than the 44 kJ/mol at 25 °C, as some energy is used to heat the liquid water from 25 °C to 100 °C. Similarly, the amount of heat required to melt ice at 0 °C is 6 kJ/mol, rather than 7 kJ/mol at 25 °C.

Endothermic and exothermic dissolution reactions

In this section, we will examine energy changes in some examples of dissolution reactions in water. Some substances dissolve in water and release energy in the form of heat. These dissolution reactions are exothermic. When other substances dissolve, the solution becomes cold as heat is removed and the kinetic energy of the water particles decreases. These dissolution reactions are endothermic.

The process of dissolution can be analysed in terms of the following three processes.

Step A: Endothermic process
Ions require energy to break free of their crystal lattice. This energy comes from the kinetic energy of the water molecules that is transferred to the crystal lattice as water molecules collide with it.

Step B: Endothermic process
Energy is needed to separate the water molecules to allow the ions to interact with the solvent. To break hydrogen bonds between water molecules requires 20 kJ/mol. The attraction of free ions for water dipoles helps the water molecules separate from each another.

Step C: Exothermic process

Energy is released as ion–dipole forces stabilise the ions in the solution. The ions are less free to move about and lose some of their kinetic energies.

Dissolution of sodium chloride

For sodium chloride, the energy released in step C is less than the energy required in steps A and B. Thus, the overall dissolution process for sodium chloride in water is endothermic. The enthalpy change is +4 kJ/mol.

$$NaCl(s) \rightarrow Na^+(aq) + Cl^-(aq) \qquad \Delta H = +4 \text{ kJ/mol}$$

Dissolution of sodium hydroxide

Great care must be taken in dissolving sodium hydroxide in water as the water can become very hot. The energy released on aquating the sodium and hydroxide ions (step C) is greater than the sum of the energies to dissociate the ions from the lattice (step A) and to overcome the inter-molecular forces in the solvent (step B). The equation for the exothermic dissolution is:

$$NaOH(s) \rightarrow Na^+(aq) + OH^-(aq) \qquad \Delta H = -44.5 \text{ kJ/mol}$$

The molar heat of solution for sodium hydroxide is therefore 44.5 kJ/mol. Note that positive and negative signs are used only when referring to enthalpy changes.

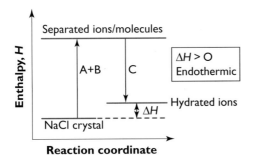

Figure 14.8
Enthalpy diagram for the dissolution of sodium chloride

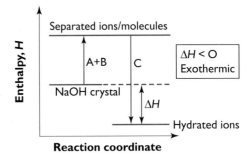

Figure 14.9
Enthalpy diagram for the dissolution of sodium hydroxide

Dissolution of concentrated sulfuric acid

The dissolution of concentrated sulfuric acid (a molecular liquid) in water is also highly exothermic. For this reason, it is an important safety practice to always add the concentrated acid slowly to the water with constant stirring. Allow time for the heat to dissipate and not boil the water. If water is added to the concentrated acid, the heat generated causes the solution to boil and splatter. This is highly dangerous. The equation for this exothermic dissolution is:

$$H_2SO_4(l) \rightarrow 2H^+(aq) + SO_4^{2-}(aq) \qquad \Delta H = -74.7 \text{ kJ/mol}$$

Dissolution of ammonium chloride

When ammonium chloride crystals are dissolved in water in a calorimeter, the temperature of the system is observed to decrease. In this case, the total energies required to separate the particles (steps A and B) is greater than the energy released on solvation (step C). The equation for the endothermic dissolution is:

$$NH_4Cl(s) \rightarrow NH_4^+(aq) + Cl^-(aq) \qquad \Delta H = +15.2 \text{ kJ/mol}$$

Table 14.3 lists the molar enthalpies of solution for some dissolution reactions.

Table 14.3 Enthalpy changes for various dissolution reactions

Ionic solute	ΔH(solution) (kJ/mol)
KF	−18
KOH	−55
$CaCl_2$	−83
$NaNO_3$	+21
NH_4NO_3	+26
KNO_3	+35

SAMPLE PROBLEM 14.3

A polystyrene foam calorimeter contained 50.0 g of water. When 1.0 g of dry ammonium chloride powder was added, the mixture dropped in temperature from 21.3 °C to 20.1 °C.

(a) Assuming that no energy was lost to the environment, calculate the molar enthalpy of solution for this dissolution reaction ($C = 4.2$ J/K/g).

(b) The accepted value in the literature for the enthalpy of solution of ammonium chloride is +15.2 kJ/mol. Account for any difference between this value and the experimental result.

SOLUTION

(a)

Step 1: Calculate the total mass of the mixture.

$$m = 50.0 + 1.0$$
$$= 51.0 \text{ g}$$

Step 2: Calculate the enthalpy change.

$$\Delta H = -mC\Delta T$$
$$= -51.0 \times 4.2 \times (20.1 - 21.3)$$
$$= 257.04 \text{ J}$$

Step 3: Calculate the molar weight of ammonium chloride.

$$M(NH_4Cl) = 14.01 + (4 \times 1.008) + 34.45$$
$$= 53.492 \text{ g/mol}$$

Step 4: Calculate the number of moles of ammonium chloride.

$$n(NH_4Cl) = 1.0/53.492$$
$$= 0.01869 \text{ mol}$$

Step 5: Calculate the molar enthalpy of solution.

$$\Delta H(\text{solution}) = 257.04/0.01869$$
$$= 13\ 753 \text{ J/mol}$$
$$= +13.8 \text{ kJ/mol}$$

(b) The experimental result is less than the accepted value, probably because some heat was gained or lost to the surroundings due to inadequate insulation. The temperature change is very small so the percentage error in its measurement is large. The thermometer may have absorbed some of the heat from the energy change. The accepted value applies to dissolution in a very large volume of water, which was not possible in this experiment.

Water in natural systems

Water's ability to absorb heat is important in all natural systems, but particularly in aquatic systems. The temperature of an ocean at any fixed latitude remains fairly constant. This is not true for the land, which heats up and cools down considerably. You notice this when you walk barefoot on concrete or beach sand in the heat of summer. As a consequence, aquatic organisms do not have to adapt to temperature extremes. The large masses of water covering the surface of the Earth help to reduce its temperature. Most Australians live on or near the coast because the climate is milder than areas further inland. As water evaporates, it absorbs energy and causes a cooling effect. You feel this effect when sweat evaporates from your skin.

Figure 14.10
The cooling effect of the ocean. When air is warmed by the land and rises, cool air from the ocean moves in to replace it. This creates a cooling cycle.

Table 14.4 Heat of fusion (melting)

Solid	Energy required to melt 1 mole (kJ)
ice	6
ethanol	5
methanol	3

Ice requires a considerable amount of heat to melt. The vibrational kinetic energy of the molecules in an ice lattice increases as heat is absorbed but the temperature of an ice–water mixture remains at $0\,°C$ until all the ice has melted. The solid states of most other solvents do not require as much energy to melt, as shown in table 14.4.

Very cold water at and just above $0\,°C$ contains hydrogen-bonded clusters of water molecules. As the clusters break up on warming, individual water molecules can come closer together until water reaches its maximum density at $4\,°C$. At temperatures higher than $4\,°C$, added heat causes an increase in kinetic energy of the molecules and, as more hydrogen bonds are broken, the molecules move apart and the density decreases.

Water's high specific heat capacity tells us that water can absorb much more heat for each degree rise in temperature than many other solvents.

When water reaches its boiling point, a large amount of energy is still required to vaporise the water. The steam produced stores considerable amounts of energy. This is why a steam burn is more dangerous than a hot water burn. Examine table 14.5, which compares the heat required to vaporise 1 mole of different solvents.

Table 14.5 Heat of vaporisation

Solvent	Energy required to vaporise 1 mole (kJ)
water	41
ethanol	38
methanol	35

SAMPLE PROBLEM 14.4

(a) Calculate the quantity of heat energy required to convert 2000 kg of ice at 0 °C into water vapour at 100 °C.

(b) Explain why the condensation of water vapour at 100 °C to liquid water at 100 °C is dangerous if it occurs on your skin.

SOLUTION

(a)

Step 1: Calculate the number of moles of water.

$$m = \text{mass of ice}$$
$$= 2 \times 10^6 \text{ g}$$
$$n(\text{ice}) = m/M$$
$$= 2 \times 106/18.016$$
$$= 1.11 \times 10^5 \text{ mol}$$

Step 2: Use the heat of fusion data in table 14.4 to calculate the heat required to melt the ice.

$$\text{Heat } (q) = n\Delta H$$
$$= 1.11 \times 10^5 \times 6$$
$$= 6.66 \times 10^5 \text{ kJ}$$

Step 3: Use the calorimetry equation to calculate the heat required to warm the ice water from 0 °C to 100 °C.

$$\text{Heat } (H) = mC\Delta T$$
$$= 2 \times 106 \times 4.2 \times (100 - 0)$$
$$= 8.4 \times 108 \text{ J}$$
$$= 8.4 \times 10^5 \text{ kJ}$$

Step 4: Use the vaporisation data in table 14.5 to calculate the heat required to vaporise water.

$$\text{Heat } (q) = n\Delta H$$
$$= 1.11 \times 105 \times 41$$
$$= 4.55 \times 106 \text{ kJ}$$

Thus, total heat $= 6.66 \times 105 + 8.4 \times 105 + 4.55 \times 106$
$$= 6.06 \times 10^6 \text{ kJ}$$

(b) The heat released is 41 kJ per 18 g (1 mole) of water vapour. This large amount of energy causes much more severe burns to the skin than the heat released as liquid water cools from 100 °C to body temperature.

Figure 14.11
Cooling towers of coal-fired power stations remove most excess heat to the atmosphere. The water is then returned to the lake.

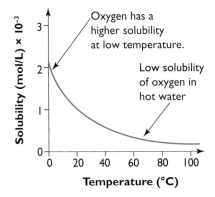

Oxygen has a higher solubility at low temperature.

Low solubility of oxygen in hot water

Figure 14.12
Solubility of oxygen in water as a function of temperature

Thermal pollution

In Australia, coal-fired power stations are usually located near lakes or coastal water so that cold water can be used to cool the hot gases produced during combustion. This process heats the coolant. To reduce *thermal pollution*, the heated water is cooled in special cooling towers before it is returned to the lake or ocean. Warm water is classified as a thermal pollutant because it alters physical and chemical equilibria in natural ecosystems.

Plants and animals that live in water rely on dissolved oxygen to survive. As the temperature of water rises, the amount of oxygen that dissolves in the water decreases. Figure 14.12 shows that even a small rise in temperature (10–15°C) causes a significant decrease in dissolved oxygen levels. Due to differences in density, poorly oxygenated warm water that is added to the surface of a lake does not mix readily with deeper, cooler water. Therefore, little oxygen diffuses or is transported to deeper water. In a short time, aquatic organisms on the lake floor can experience anoxic conditions due to the lack of dissolved oxygen.

If warmed water is released into a river rather than a lake, it becomes dispersed as the river flows along its course. This can affect the aquatic population downstream for quite some distance before the water cools sufficiently.

Levels of dissolved carbon dioxide also decrease with temperature. This has a significant impact on photosynthetic protists in aquatic ecosystems, which rely on dissolved carbon dioxide for photosynthesis. Any drop in the numbers of these producers affects other organisms higher in the food chain. Table 14.6 shows that a 5 °C rise in temperature from 20 °C to 25 °C causes the carbon dioxide solubility to drop by 14%.

Table 14.6 Change in solubility of carbon dioxide in water with temperature, at a constant pressure of 1 atmosphere

Temperature (°C)	0	20	25	30	35	40
CO_2 solubility (g/kg water)	3.35	1.69	1.45	1.26	1.10	0.97

17. LIMITATIONS OF CALORIMETRY MEASUREMENTS

To improve the accuracy of calorimetry measurements, various factors must be taken into account. The following examples refer to exothermic reactions.

Insulation

The calorimeter vessel must be insulated to avoid heat losses to the environment so that the measurement of temperature change is as accurate as possible. The usual approach is to use an insulator that absorbs little heat: one with a high specific heat capacity. Common materials used, along with their specific heat capacities (in J/K/g), include polystyrene (1.3), polyethylene (2.2), cork (2.0), paper (1.9), wool (1.4), and air (1.0). In comparison, glass has a specific heat capacity of 0.6 J/K/g.

Accurate temperature measurements

The use of thermocouples as temperature probes allows more accurate measurement of temperature as long as the probes are calibrated correctly. They are connected to data loggers to collect and display the data. However, mercury-in-glass thermometers can also be manufactured to a high degree of precision and accuracy.

Absorbing the heat into water

It is common to surround the reaction vessel in a bomb calorimeter with a very large mass (e.g. 2 kg) of well-stirred water. Water has a high specific heat capacity and can act as a good insulator. The heat released into the water causes only a small temperature rise. Such a small rise in temperature would normally make the error of measurement greater. However, measurement is accurate if electronic probes or precision thermometers are used.

Thermal capacity

When heat is liberated from a reaction, it is absorbed not only by the products, but also by the reaction vessel. Each of these has a different mass and specific heat capacity and, therefore, different thermal capacities. Accurate experimentation requires calculating the heat that each of these materials absorbs. For example, consider 50 g calorimeters made of glass or copper. If a reaction in these vessels causes a temperature rise in the water and the vessel of 1 °C, then the heat gained by these vessels is 30 J and 20 J, respectively.

Thermal conductivity

The previous example assumed that the reaction solution and vessel both reached the same temperature during the experiment. This is probably true for the copper calorimeter, with its high thermal conductivity of 401 J/s/K/m. However, other materials used, along with their low thermal conductivities (in J/s/K/m), include glass (1), polystyrene (0.08), polyethylene (0.3), water (0.6), air (0.02) and cork (0.05). Thus, a polystyrene foam calorimeter would absorb a negligible amount of heat during an experiment.

14.1 QUESTIONS

1. The specific heat capacities (in J/K/g) of four substances are: silver (0.23), water (4.18), ice (2.16), iron (0.45).
   All substances are initially at 20 °C and 100 J of heat energy is supplied to 10 g of each substance. Identify the substance that reaches the highest temperature.
   A Silver
   B Water
   C Ice
   D Iron

2. Calculate the final temperature of a 50 g sample of water, initially at 25 °C, when it absorbs 12 kJ of heat energy.
   A 25.1 °C
   B 82.4 °C
   C 25.2 °C
   D 265 °C

3. The high specific heat capacity of water compared with other solvents, such as kerosene, alcohol and acetone, is due to
   A stronger hydrogen bonding between the water molecules.
   B the low molecular weight of water.
   C weak dispersion forces between the molecules of all the other solvents.
   D water being the only polar molecule in this list of solvents.

4. The energy change required when water changes from liquid to vapour at 25 °C is
   $$H_2O(l) \rightarrow H_2O(g) \qquad \Delta H = +44 \text{ kJ/mol}$$
   Calculate the heat energy that must be absorbed to convert 54 g of water from liquid to vapour at 25 °C.
   A 44 kJ
   B 2.4 kJ
   C 2376 kJ
   D 131.9 kJ

5. The molar heat of solution of calcium chloride is 83 kJ/mol. The temperature of the water rises as calcium chloride dissolves. Select the equation that correctly summarises this dissolution information.

   A $CaCl_2(s) \rightarrow Ca^{2+}(aq) + 2Cl^-(aq)$
   $$\Delta H = -83 \text{ kJ/mol}$$

   B $CaCl_2(s) \rightarrow Ca^{2+}(aq) + 2Cl^-(aq)$
   $$\Delta H = +83 \text{ kJ/mol}$$

   C $CaCl(s) \rightarrow Ca^+(aq) + Cl^-(aq)$
   $$\Delta H = -83 \text{ kJ/mol}$$

   D $CaCl_2(aq) \rightarrow Ca^{2+}(aq) + 2Cl^-(aq)$
   $$\Delta H = +83 \text{ kJ/mol}$$

6. In a polystyrene calorimeter, 1.0 g of sodium hydroxide crystals was dissolved in 50 g of water. The initial temperature of the water was 21.5 °C. The maximum temperature of the mixture was 26.2 °C. Assuming the specific heat capacity of the mixture was 4.2 J/K/g, calculate the:
   (a) enthalpy change for the reaction
   (b) molar heat of solution for sodium hydroxide.

7. In a polystyrene foam calorimeter, 11 g of solid calcium chloride hexahydrate was dissolved in 100 g of water to produce 111 g of solution. The initial temperature was 25 °C. Given,

   $CaCl_2.6H_2O(s) \rightarrow$
   $Ca^{2+}(aq) + 2Cl^-(aq) + 6H_2O(l)$ $\Delta H = +18kJ$
   calculate the final temperature of the solution. Assume no heat loss and that the specific heat capacity of the solution is 4.1 J/K/g.

8. A 200 g sample of ice at −20 °C is warmed slowly to 0 °C without melting. Calculate the heat energy required for this process. (*Note*: C(ice) = 2.1 J/K/g.)

9. Use the data in tables 14.2, 14.4 and 14.5 to calculate the energy required to convert 100 g of solid ethanol at its melting point (−114 °C) to ethanol vapour at its boiling point (78 °C).

10. (a) Thermal pollution of waterways is a major problem. Define the term 'thermal pollution'.
    (b) A country town requires a new power station to supply electricity for its growing population. The state government decides to build a coal-fired power station on the shores of a large freshwater lake 10 km from the town. This lake is used for recreational fishing. Discuss the importance of preventing thermal pollution of the lake in relation to its use for fishing.

SUMMARY

- Dissolution reactions may be endothermic (heat absorbed) or exothermic (heat liberated).

- The enthalpy change in various reactions can be understood in terms of bond-breaking and bond-forming processes.

- Calorimetry can be used to measure the heat changes in chemical reactions.

- A calorimeter is a device that is used to measure energy changes in reactions.

- Calorimetric techniques can be used to measure the heat of solution of salts in water.

- Specific heat capacity is a measure of the capacity of a substance to absorb heat energy.

- Water's high specific heat capacity is important in moderating the temperature of the planet.

- Thermal pollution raises the temperature of water. The higher the temperature, the lower the concentrations of oxygen and carbon dioxide in the water. This is a problem for aquatic organisms.

14.1 PRACTICAL ACTIVITIES

CALORIMETRY: MEASURING THE HEAT OF SOLUTION

Aim

To determine the heat of solution of two ionic compounds

Safety issues

- Wear safety glasses throughout this experiment.
- Identify other safety issues relevant to this experiment by reading the method.

Materials

- 250 mL pyrex beaker
- 500 mL pyrex beaker
- pipette or burette
- polystyrene foam cups
- additional polystyrene sheeting
- shredded paper
- copper calorimeter, cotton fibre and wooden box
- cardboard
- copper wire stirrer
- temperature probe and data logger, or thermometer
- electronic balance
- potassium nitrate
- sodium hydroxide

Method

Part A: Investigating different salts

1. The calorimeter for this part consists of a polystyrene cup nested in a beaker for stability. Construct a foam lid to fit the cup and include a hole to insert the temperature probe and a hole for the stirrer.

2. Use a pipette or burette to measure 50.0 mL (50.0 g) of water into the calorimeter.

3. Insert the temperature probe and stirrer and record the temperature for five minutes.

4. Meanwhile, weigh out 2.00 g of potassium nitrate crystals using an electronic balance.

5. Add the salt to the calorimeter and replace the lid. Stir and record the temperature over the next 5 minutes. Ensure that all the salt dissolves and that the stirrer does not interfere with the temperature probe.

6. Repeat the experiment with the same mass of sodium hydroxide. In this case, take great care as this material is caustic and can damage the eyes severely. Work quickly as sodium hydroxide absorbs moisture from the air.

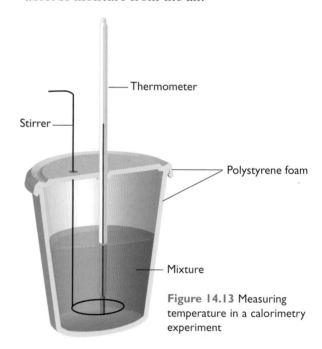

Figure 14.13 Measuring temperature in a calorimetry experiment

Labels: Thermometer, Stirrer, Polystyrene foam, Mixture

Results and calculations

1. Use the output from your data logger to determine the change in temperature (ΔT) due to the dissolution of the salt. Some data loggers present the information graphically, some in tabular format.

2. For each salt, calculate the total mass (m) of the solution (water + salt).

3. For each salt, use the calorimetry equation to calculate the heat liberated or absorbed. Assume that $C = 4.2\,\text{J/K/g}$.

4. For each salt, calculate the molar heat of solution.

PRACTICAL ACTIVITIES

Part B: Investigating different calorimeters

In this part, you will determine how the material used to construct the calorimeter affects your results. Use the following instructions and the steps in part A to compare copper and pyrex for either potassium nitrate or sodium hydroxide.

(a) Weigh a 250 mL pyrex beaker. Construct a calorimeter by putting the 250 mL beaker inside a 500 mL beaker, with shredded paper insulation between them. Make a cardboard lid. Calculate the heat of solution of the salt given that the specific heat capacity of pyrex is 0.75 J/K/g.

(b) Place a copper calorimeter of known mass inside a wooden box packed with cotton fibre. Calculate the heat of solution of the salt given that the specific heat capacity of copper is 0.39 J/K/g.

Compare your results with those obtained for the polystyrene calorimeter in part A.
(*Note:* The literature values for the molar heat of solution for potassium nitrate and sodium hydroxide are 35 kJ/mol and 45 kJ/mol, respectively.)

Questions

1. Explain why it is important to monitor the temperature of the system for 5 minutes before and 5 minutes after the reaction.

2. Discuss how the reliability of these measurements could be improved.

3. Explain why the use of a temperature probe connected to a data logger can provide more accurate results than a thermometer.

Conclusion

Briefly describe the outcome of your investigation.

ENERGY

CORE MODULE 4

Chapter 15 PHOTOSYNTHESIS AND FUELS

Introduction

Most life on Earth depends on the energy from the Sun. Over geological time, various organisms, such as green plants, have evolved to convert solar energy into useful chemical energy through a process known as photosynthesis. Some of these ancient plants were fossilised and converted to coal. Combustion of fossil fuels, such as coal, is important in our modern society as it is used to generate electricity. When we burn coal, we extract some of the Sun's energy in the form of heat.

In this chapter

Figure 15.1

Coal is an important fossil fuel. At Coppabella open-cut mine in Queensland, the mined coal is carried and poured onto the stockpile from a giant conveyor belt.

15.1 CHEMICAL ENERGY FROM FOSSIL FUELS

Remember

Before beginning this section, you should be able to:
• recall that energy changes are involved when reactants are converted into products.

Key content

By the end of this section, you should be able to:
• outline the role of photosynthesis in transforming light energy to chemical energy and recall the raw materials for this process
• outline the role of the production of high-energy carbohydrates from carbon dioxide as the important step in the stabilisation of the Sun's energy in a form that can be used by animals as well as plants
• identify the photosynthetic origins of the chemical energy in coal, petroleum and natural gas
• process and present information from secondary sources on the range of compounds found in coal, petroleum or natural gas, and on the location of deposits of the selected fossil fuel in Australia.

Photosynthesis

Many aquatic and terrestrial ecosystems use producers (phytoplankton, algae and green plants) to convert solar energy into chemical energy. **Photosynthesis** is an example of a photochemical process. Figure 15.3 summarises the major aspects of photosynthesis in a green plant. This diagram shows us that green leaves absorb sunlight and this energy is used to split water molecules to produce oxygen and to convert carbon dioxide into sugars and other **carbohydrates**.

Figure 15.2 Light energy is required for green plants to photosynthesise.

photosynthesis: the biochemical process in which chlorophyll molecules absorb solar energy to power an electron transfer reaction in which water and carbon dioxide are converted to oxygen and organic nutrients, such as sugar

carbohydrate: general name for a class of carbon compounds that includes sugars, starch and cellulose. Carbohydrates contain the elements carbon, hydrogen and oxygen.

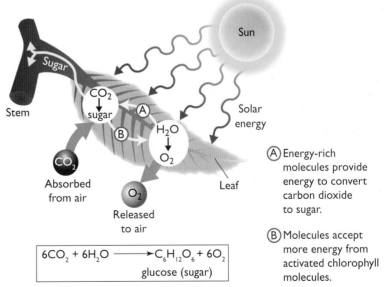

Ⓐ Energy-rich molecules provide energy to convert carbon dioxide to sugar.

Ⓑ Molecules accept more energy from activated chlorophyll molecules.

$$6CO_2 + 6H_2O \longrightarrow C_6H_{12}O_6 + 6O_2$$
glucose (sugar)

Figure 15.3 Photosynthesis is a photochemical process that occurs in green plants.

Only about 4% of the sunlight that shines on a green leaf is converted into chemical energy. In a typical food chain, some of the chemical energy stored in plants becomes available to consumers. As food is consumed, a large amount of chemical energy is converted to heat. The remainder is used to produce new tissue or to replace and repair old tissue. Further along the food chain, energy is lost progressively as heat energy.

Chlorophyll and the production of chemical energy

Chloroplasts are the cellular organelles where light energy is absorbed in a green leaf (see figure 15.4a). *Chlorophyll* molecules are arranged in layers within the chloroplast. A typical chlorophyll molecule is a complex organic ring in which four electronegative nitrogen atoms are bonded to a magnesium ion (figure 15.4b).

Chlorophyll molecules selectively absorb red and violet light. Figure 15.5 shows the absorption spectrum for chlorophyll. Note the weak absorption of green light. Green light is mainly reflected from leaves so most leaves look green.

The light that is absorbed is directed towards a reaction centre in a chlorophyll–protein matrix in which light energy is used to excite the chlorophyll molecules. This excitation results in the release of energised electrons, which react with water molecules. Chemical bonds are broken and the water is oxidised to release oxygen.

Oxidation of water:

$$2H_2O(l) \rightarrow O_2(g) + 4H^+(aq) + 4e^-$$

In another region of the chloroplast, electrons are involved in a reaction that converts carbon dioxide into simple carbohydrate molecules such as **glucose**.

Reduction of carbon dioxide:

$$6CO_2(g) + 24H^+(aq) + 24e^- \rightarrow C_6H_{12}O_6(s) + 6H_2O(l)$$

Photosynthesis is an *endothermic* process. For each mole of glucose formed, 2803 kJ of energy is required. The covalent bonds linking the atoms in the glucose molecule store chemical energy. Thus glucose, along with other carbohydrates, is a high-energy compound. We can think of carbohydrates as a means of stabilising solar energy for use by plants and animals within ecosystems. Without photosynthetic plants, animals could not use the Sun's energy.

The net equation for photosynthesis shows that water and carbon dioxide are the essential raw materials.

Photosynthesis:

$$6CO_2(g) + 6H_2O(l) \rightarrow C_6H_{12}O_6(s) + 6O_2(g) \qquad \Delta H = +2803 \text{ kJ/mol}$$

The glucose produced by photosynthesis is water soluble. It is transported in solution out of the leaf and around all parts of the plant via phloem tissue. Cells throughout the plant use glucose as a source of energy. Energy can be released by oxidising the glucose to carbon dioxide and water. This *exothermic* process is called *respiration*. Respiration also occurs in the cells of animals that eat plant tissue or animals that consume herbivores.

Respiration:

$$C_6H_{12}O_6(s) + 6O_2(g) \rightarrow 6CO_2(g) + 6H_2O(l) \qquad \Delta H = -2803 \text{ kJ/mol}$$

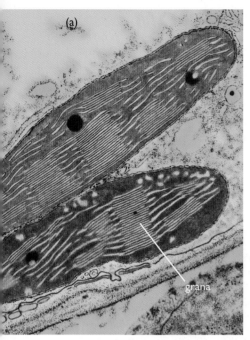

Figure 15.4
(a) Chloroplasts in a pea plant (x 16 000). The stacks of membranes known as grana contain chlorophyll molecules.
(b) Chlorophyll molecule

glucose: a simple sugar with the molecular formula $C_6H_{12}O_6$

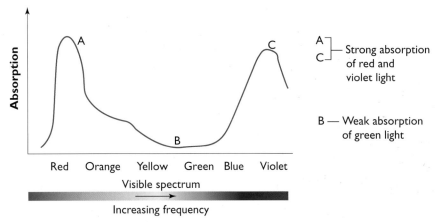

A ⌉
C ⌋ — Strong absorption of red and violet light

B — Weak absorption of green light

Figure 15.5
Absorption spectrum of chlorophyll

Storage of chemical energy

The glucose formed by photosynthesis may not need to be used immediately as an energy source. Plants can convert the excess glucose to various water-insoluble, polymeric molecules, such as *starch*, that can be stored (see the dark circles of starch visible in the chloroplasts in figure 15.4a, page 282). Starch molecules consist of chains of glucose molecules. Another important use of glucose, after its conversion to *cellulose*, is as a structural polymer for plant cell walls. The glucose molecules in cellulose are bonded in an arrangement different from that in starch.

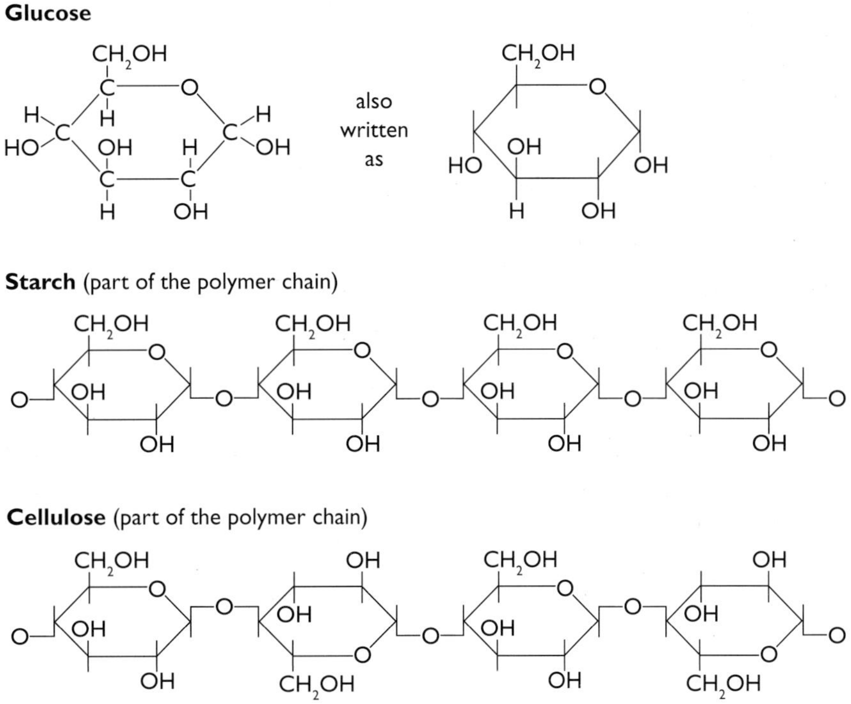

Glucose

also written as

Starch (part of the polymer chain)

Cellulose (part of the polymer chain)

Figure 15.6
Carbohydrates — glucose, starch and cellulose

fossil fuel: fuel formed from once-living organisms

petroleum: viscous, oily liquid composed of crude oil and natural gas that was formed by geological processes acting on marine organisms over millions of years

fuel: a substance that burns in air or oxygen to release useful energy

Fossil fuels

In Australia, **fossil fuels**, such as **petroleum**, natural gas and coal, are very important sources of chemical energy. Fossil fuels were formed from the burial and decomposition of ancient life forms. The energy stored in the chemical bonds of these **fuels** came from solar radiation from the Sun in the distant past. This energy is released when the fuels are burnt.

Table 15.1 shows that 95% of Australia's energy needs are derived from fossil fuels. The relative proportions will change over time as new oil and gas reserves are developed.

Table 15.1 Use of fossil fuels as energy sources in Australia

Energy source	%
coal	41
crude oil	38
natural gas	16
other (solar, wood, hydroelectricity, wind)	5

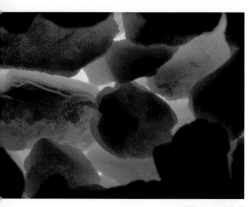

Figure 15.7
Burning fossil fuels, such as coal, releases energy

Figure 15.8
Strata are visible in this 7-metre coal seam at an open-cut mine near Singleton, New South Wales.

Figure 15.9
Stacks of cut peat logs in County Galway, Ireland, await collection and delivery to homes for burning as fuel.

Coal

Examination of coal strata reveals large numbers of plant fossils. These plants were once growing in freshwater swamps. As the plants died, they fell into the shallow swamp water. If they were buried rapidly by sediments and other debris, the material was deprived of oxygen so did not decay. This accumulated plant material eventually turned into coal.

There are four types or ranks of coal that are formed progressively over time. During the formation of coal, volatile matter including water is slowly removed due to pressure and heating. Gradually, the percentage of carbon in the coal rises.

1. *Peat* — Plant remains slowly turned into peat over a period of several thousand years. Peat is a porous, brown mass of partially decomposed roots, twigs and leaves. It has a high moisture content at 75–80%w/w. In some parts of the world (e.g. Ireland, England, Scotland and Russia), peat bogs are excavated and the dried peat is used as a low-grade fuel (see figure 15.9).

2. *Lignite* — If peat is buried under mud or sandy sediment, it becomes chemically altered due to heating and pressure until it forms lignite or *brown coal*. This process may take up to 40 000 years. Brown coal is found in the Latrobe Valley, Victoria. Its moisture content is lower than that of peat, but still quite high at 50–70%w/w.

3. *Black coal* — Over longer periods and greater depths of burial, brown coal is metamorphosed into *bituminous coal* or black coal with a low moisture content of 5–10%w/w. In Australia, black coal ranges in age from 65 million years to 260 million years. It is common in New South Wales and Queensland.

Figure 15.10
Anthracite is a hard, slow-burning coal that gives out intense heat. Anthracite has a very low moisture content.

4. *Anthracite* — Continued metamorphosis can turn black coal into a very dense form known as anthracite. This form of coal has the highest carbon content and the lowest percentage of volatile matter. Its moisture content is very low at 2–5%w/w. Anthracite coal can be found in Queensland.

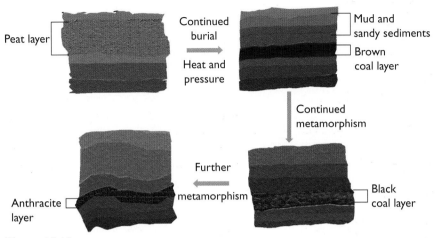

Figure 15.11
Formation of different ranks of coal

Table 15.2 shows the typical composition range for the four ranks of coal and a comparison of the energy released on their combustion.

Volatile materials are low molecular weight hydrocarbons that are evolved when coal is heated to 900 °C in the absence of air. The **specific energy** of a coal is the amount of energy released when it is burnt. It may be expressed on a wet or dry weight basis. The material left behind after such heating is called **coke**.

Various types of coal also have variable percentages of mineral matter due to the presence of shale. This material is left behind as *ash* after burning. High-ash black coals do not produce as much heat energy as low-ash black coals. Newcastle domestic steaming black coal has a high ash content (21%w/w) and produces 25 MJ/kg (wet weight) on combustion, while Gunnedah black coal (8%w/w ash) produces 30 MJ/kg (wet weight).

> specific energy: the amount of heat released from a fuel on combustion (usually measured in MJ/kg)
>
> coke: the solid formed by destructive distillation of coal. Coke is mainly composed of carbon.

Table 15.2 Characteristics of the different ranks of coal

Coal rank		peat	brown coal	black coal	anthracite
Moisture (%w/w)		75–80	50–70	5–10	2–5
Carbon (%w/w dry weight)		50–60	60–75	80–90	90–95
Volatile matter (%w/w dry weight)		60–65	45–55	20–40	5–7
Specific energy	MJ/kg dry weight	25	25–30	30–35	35–38
	MJ/kg wet weight	5	5–15	24–33	34–37

Coal contains a wide variety of organic compounds. The nature of these compounds depends on the temperatures and pressures that the coal has been subjected to during its formation. Figure 15.12 shows some of these compounds, which are very complex. Coal also contains some inorganic minerals, such as kaolinite (clay), pyrite, siderite, haematite, quartz, rutile, sphalerite and gypsum.

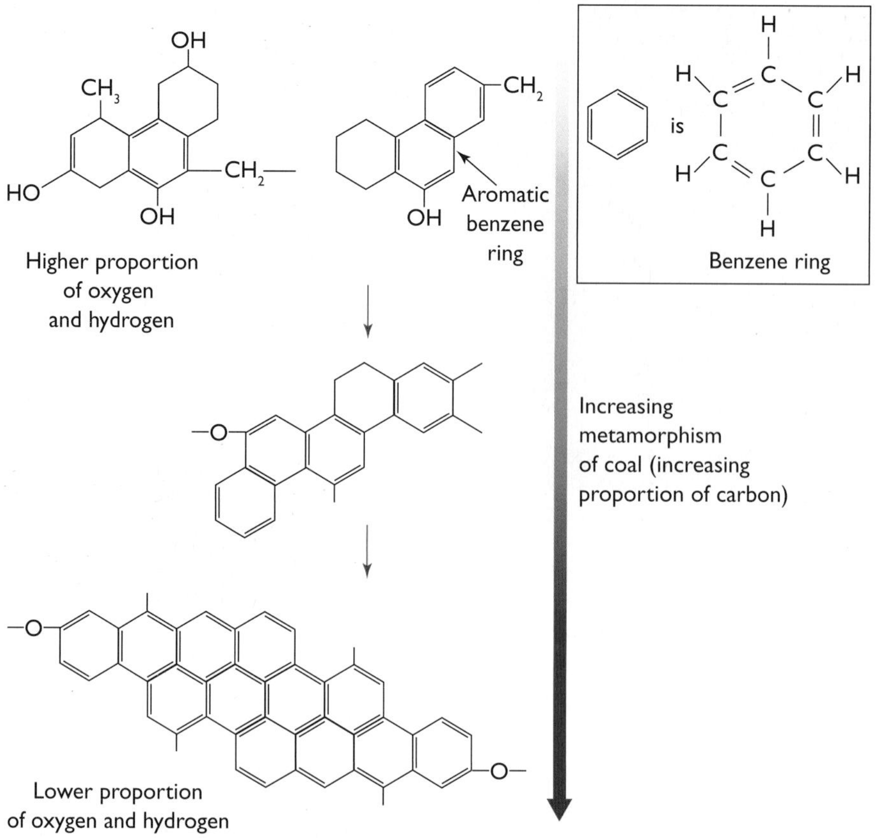
OH
CH3
HO
OH
CH2
CH2
OH
Aromatic benzene ring
Higher proportion of oxygen and hydrogen
is
Benzene ring
Increasing metamorphism of coal (increasing proportion of carbon)
Lower proportion of oxygen and hydrogen

Figure 15.12
Examples of organic compounds present in coal

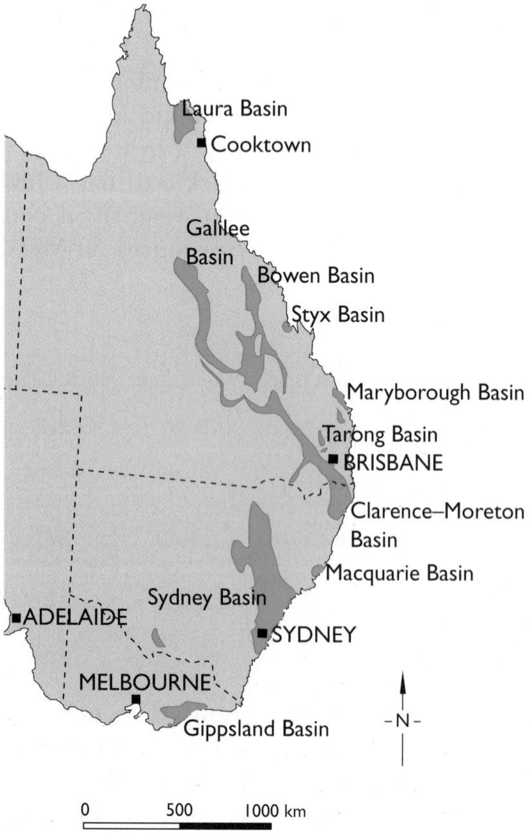
Laura Basin
Cooktown
Galilee Basin
Bowen Basin
Styx Basin
Maryborough Basin
Tarong Basin
BRISBANE
Clarence–Moreton Basin
Macquarie Basin
Sydney Basin
ADELAIDE
SYDNEY
MELBOURNE
Gippsland Basin
N
0
500
1000 km

Figure 15.13
Coal basins in eastern Australia

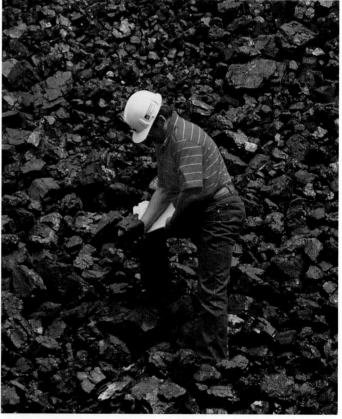

Figure 15.14
Coal is inspected for a range of qualities.

SAMPLE PROBLEM 15.1

SOLUTION

Compare the percentage by weight of carbon in dried wood to a sample of dried peat that contains 55%w/w carbon. Assume that dried wood consists predominantly of cellulose with the empirical formula $C_6H_{10}O_5$.

Calculate the percentage by weight of carbon in $C_6H_{10}O_5$.

$$\%C = 6M(C)/M(C_6H_{10}O_5) \times 100/1$$
$$= 72.06/162.14 \times 100/1$$
$$= 44\%$$

The percentage of carbon in dried wood is lower than that in dried peat. The process of coal formation has led to some loss of volatile material and, thus, a small increase in carbon content.

SAMPLE PROBLEM 15.2

New South Wales and Queensland have large reserves of black coal. In Victoria, lignite is the major rank of coal. Use tables 15.2 and 15.3 to compare the amount of heat produced by burning 10 kg of brown coal from the Latrobe Valley and the same mass of black coal from Blair Athol in Queensland.

Table 15.3

Coal, origin	Moisture content (%w/w)	Specific energy (MJ/kg dry weight)
Brown coal, Latrobe Valley	70	28
Black coal, Blair Athol	10	33

SOLUTION

Step 1: Calculate the mass of coal after drying.

Brown coal:	$30/100 \times 10 = 3$ kg
Black coal:	$90/100 \times 10 = 9$ kg

Step 2: Calculate the heat produced.

Brown coal:	$3 \times 28 = 84$ MJ
Black coal:	$9 \times 33 = 297$ MJ

The black coal produces much more heat than the brown coal.

Petroleum

Petroleum literally means 'rock oil' (from the Latin words *petra* meaning rock and *oleum* meaning oil). It is generally believed that petroleum was formed from the remains of unicellular marine organisms (such as algae and diatoms) that underwent anaerobic bacterial decay. Oil formed at 50–150 °C, at an early stage in the deposition of the sediment. However, as the layers became more compacted, it was forced out of the shale. The oil migrated upwards as an oily suspension in water until an impervious layer of rock prevented its further movement so that it became trapped and accumulated, as shown in figure 15.15. Oil and natural gas separated from water into layers in the oil trap.

The composition of the crude oil component of petroleum varies widely from one region to another. For example, crude oil from the Middle East has a higher proportion of straight-chain hydrocarbons than crude oil from Nigeria. Australian crude oil is low in sulfur compounds but this is higher in Mexican crude. Low-sulfur oils are referred to as 'sweet'. Table 15.4 compares the average composition of Bass Strait and Middle East crude oil. Australian crude is described as 'light' (low average molecular

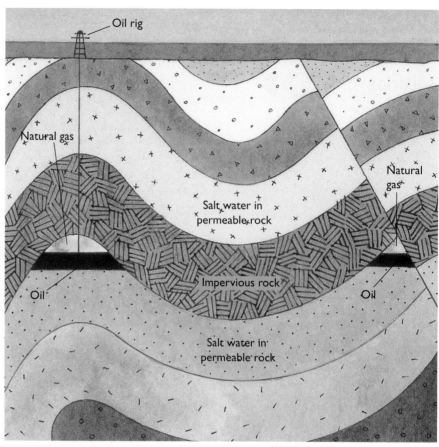

Figure 15.15
Oil was formed and then trapped by layers of impervious rock, often due to folding or faults in the rocks.

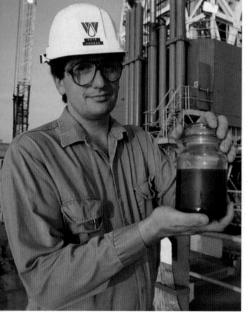

Figure 15.16
An example of the type of crude oil refined in Australia. The appearance of Australian crude oils varies from one location to another.

weight) in comparison with Middle East crude oil, which is 'heavy'. Australian oils have a high percentage of naphtha and petrol components. Middle East crude has a higher percentage of the heavier oils and solids than Australian crude.

Table 15.4 Composition of crude oil from Bass Strait and the Middle East

Fraction	Carbon atoms per hydrocarbon molecule	Bass Strait oil (%w/w)	Middle East oil (%w/w)
refinery gases	1–4	2	1
naphtha/petrol	5–12	30	13
kerosene	12–16	18	16
diesel oils	15–18	18	15
residue	18–40+	32	55

Natural gas may form in the presence or absence of crude oil. The petroleum wells in Bass Strait vary considerably in their relative percentages of crude oil and gas. Gas fields tend to form when the heat acting on the carbonaceous material produces temperatures in excess of 150 °C. The composition of natural gas varies from one gas field to another, although *methane* is the major component at about 89%.

Natural gas is commonly used as a fuel. Some of the propane and butane in natural gas is compressed and liquefied to produce liquefied petroleum gas (LPG). The petrochemical industry uses the ethane component to manufacture plastics and antifreeze for cars.

Figure 15.17
An oil rig off Australia's south coast, where rock is drilled to tap undersea petroleum wells

15.1 DATA ANALYSIS

Australian petroleum

Figure 15.18
About 30% of Australia's natural gas supplies come from this Moomba ethane plant in Cooper Basin, South Australia.

SYLLABUS FOCUS

18. USING INSTRUCTION TERMS CORRECTLY

When answering questions, it is important to know what the instruction terms (verbs) require you to do. Here are some examples:

'Compare'
This instruction term requires you to show how things are similar or different

Example
Compare coal and oil as sources of energy.

Answer:
Both coal and oil are fossil fuels. They are the remains of once-living organisms that have metamorphosed over long periods of geological time. They are both used to produce energy on combustion due to their high carbon or hydrocarbon content.

'Contrast'
This instruction term requires you to say how things are different or opposite.

Example:
Contrast the characteristics of peat and anthracite coal.

Answer:
Peat has a high moisture content while anthracite has a very low moisture content. Peat has a low specific energy while anthracite has a much higher specific energy.

15.1 QUESTIONS

1. The fossil fuel that currently provides the greatest proportion of energy in Australia is
   A coal.
   B crude oil.
   C natural gas.
   D wood.

2. Select the correct statement about photosynthesis.
   A Glucose and carbon dioxide are produced by photosynthesis.
   B Carbohydrates formed by photosynthesis are a means of stabilising solar energy for use by living things.
   C Photosynthesis occurs in all plant cells.
   D Starch is the first product of the photosynthetic process.

3. The type of coal with the highest moisture content is
   A peat.
   B brown coal.
   C black coal.
   D anthracite.

4. The region of Australia in which significant quantities of black coal is mined is
   A Tasmania.
   B Western Australia.
   C Victoria.
   D New South Wales.

5. Australian crude oil is described as light because it
   A is low in sulfur.
   B has a low percentage of bitumen.
   C contains a high percentage of low molecular weight hydrocarbons compared with Middle East crude.
   D contains a low percentage of low to average molecular weight hydrocarbons.

6. (a) Write a balanced chemical equation for the production of glucose by photosynthesis.
   (b) Classify photosynthesis as an endothermic or exothermic process.
   (c) Identify the raw material from which the oxygen produced in photosynthesis is originally derived.
   (d) Name the photosynthetic pigment present in the chloroplasts of green leaves.
   (e) Photosynthesis has been described as an electron transfer process. Explain.

7. (a) List the four ranks of coal in increasing order of their carbon content.
   (b) Anthracite coal has the highest specific energy of all the ranks of coal. Relate this observation to the geological processes that produce coal.

8. A sample of dried lignite has a specific energy of 30 MJ/kg.
   (a) Calculate the heat produced by the combustion of 50 kg of dried lignite.
   (b) The specific energy of bituminous (black) coal is higher than that of lignite. Explain.

9. Methane is a major component of natural gas. It has a specific energy of 56 MJ/kg.
   (a) Methane is classified as a hydrocarbon. Explain this classification.
   (b) Calculate the mass of methane that must be burnt to produce 100 kJ of energy.
   (c) Calculate the amount of energy released when 100 g of methane is burnt.

10. (a) Use the following information to compare the energy released on burning 1 litre of petrol and 1 litre of kerosene.
    Petrol: density = 0.7 kg/L
                  specific energy = 47 MJ/kg
    Kerosene: density = 0.8 kg/L
                  specific energy = 50 MJ/kg
    (b) Contrast the uses of coal and crude oil in Australia.

SUMMARY

- Green plants absorb sunlight and use this energy for photosynthesis.

- Photosynthesis is a photochemical process in which light energy is transformed into chemical energy. Water and carbon dioxide are converted to oxygen and food nutrients such as glucose.

- Carbon compounds produced by photosynthesis have been turned into fossil fuels, such as coal and petroleum, over millions of years of geological time.

- Fossil fuels include petroleum, coal and natural gas. They are important in our modern economy.

DATA ANALYSIS

15.1 DATA ANALYSIS
AUSTRALIAN PETROLEUM

Part A: Mapping the mining sites

About 80% of Australia's natural gas reserves are located in the Carnarvon and Bonaparte/Amadeus Basins of Western Australia and Northern Territory. The North West Shelf project is part of this Carnarvon Basin. In 2005, Western Australia achieved 25% of the world's production of liquefied natural gas (LNG), which is predominantly methane. By 2010, it is predicted that Australia will sell 160 million tonnes of LNG per year.

Questions

Crude oil is often, but not always, associated with natural gas fields. Oil and gas fields are located in many parts of Australia other than Western Australia. Table 15.5 lists some of Australia's major oil and gas basins.

Table 15.5

Basin	Location	Current reserves of oil and/or natural gas as % of Australia's total
Carnarvon	Western Australia (off shore)	
Browse	Western Australia (off shore)	
Gippsland		
Bonaparte/ Amadeus		
Cooper/ Eromanga		
Adavale/ Bowen/Surat		
Perth		
Bass		
Otway		

(a) Copy and complete table 15.5 in your workbook. Click on the Oil and Gas weblinks in your eBookPLUS.
(b) Gather the latest data concerning the known oil and/or gas reserves to complete column 3 of the table.
(c) Download the map of Australia from your eBookPLUS. Print this map and show and label the locations of the major oil- and gas-producing basins on your map.
(d) Identify whether any regions of Australia produce natural gas but not significant quantities of crude oil. If so, name these regions.

Part B: Compounds present in natural gas and crude oil

(a) Table 15.6 provides data on the typical composition of Australian natural gas, which can vary from one well to another by 1–2% of these values. The composition of natural gas from other countries often differs quite considerably from typical Australian natural gas. For example, New Zealand natural gas is only 45% methane.

Table 15.6

Component	% of component molecules
methane, CH_4	89
ethane, C_2H_6	5
carbon dioxide, CO_2	2
oxygen, O_2, and nitrogen, N_2	2
propane, C_3H_8	1
butane, C_4H_{10}	1

(i) Construct a column graph of this data.
(ii) Draw Lewis electron dot structures for methane and ethane.
(iii) Identify the components of natural gas that burn readily in air.

DATA ANALYSIS

(b) Table 15.4 on page 288 lists the common hydrocarbon fractions in crude oil. Each fraction is composed of paraffins, napthenes and/or aromatics. The proportions of these components vary considerably from one oil field to another throughout the world.

- *Paraffins*, also called *alkanes*, are hydrocarbon molecules with single covalent bonds between neighbouring carbon atoms. They are examples of saturated hydrocarbons. They are predominantly straight chained with a smaller amount of branched chained molecules.
- *Naphthenes* are ring-shaped, saturated molecules, also called *cycloalkanes* or *cycloparaffins*. Their boiling points are higher than paraffin molecules with the same number of carbon atoms.
- *Aromatics* are ring-shaped molecules based on C_6H_6 (benzene).

  (i) The 'medium naphtha' fraction of a crude oil was analysed and found to contain 44% paraffins, 42% naphthenes and 4% aromatics by volume. The boiling point range of this fraction was 80–120 °C. Select the compounds from table 15.7 that are likely components of this 'medium naphtha' fraction.
  (ii) Use the information in figure 15.19 to classify the compounds selected in (i) as paraffins, naphthenes or aromatics.
  (iii) Determine the range of numbers of carbon atoms per molecule in 'medium naphtha' fractions.
  (iv) Draw a Lewis electron dot structure for cyclopentane.

Table 15.7

Compound	Molecular formula	Boiling point (°C)
cyclopentane	C_5H_{10}	49
hexane	C_6H_{14}	69
benzene	C_6H_6	80
cyclohexane	C_6H_{12}	81
3,3-dimethylpentane	C_7H_{16}	86
heptane	C_7H_{16}	98
2,2,4-trimethylpentane	C_8H_{18}	99
methylcyclohexane	C_7H_{14}	101
2,2-dimethylhexane	C_7H_{18}	107
methylbenzene (toluene)	C_7H_8	110
cycloheptane	C_7H_{14}	118
2-methylheptane	C_8H_{18}	118
octane	C_8H_{18}	126
ethylcyclohexane	C_8H_{16}	130

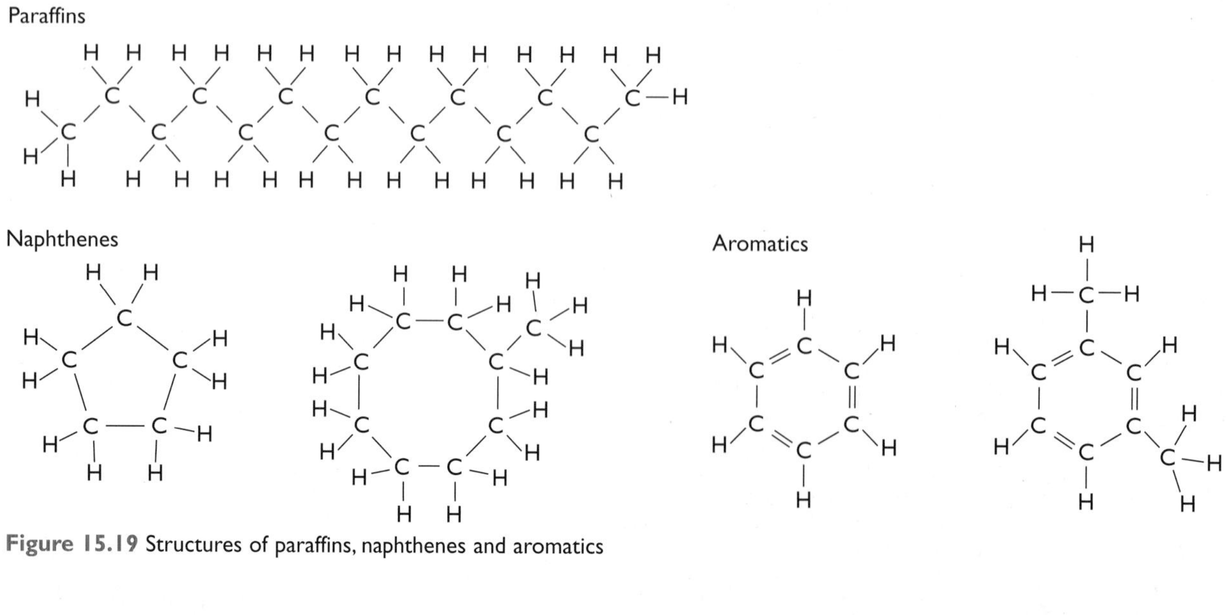

Paraffins

Naphthenes

Aromatics

Figure 15.19 Structures of paraffins, naphthenes and aromatics

Chapter 16

CARBON AND CARBON COMPOUNDS

Introduction

The element carbon is the basis of life. Organic chemistry is the branch of chemistry devoted to understanding the properties and reactions of carbon compounds. In this chapter, we will examine the properties of carbon and investigate its unique ability to bond covalently to itself and to other non-metals.

In this chapter

Figure 16.1

Oil is an important fossil fuel and a source of many carbon compounds. The distillation process is a crucial part of refining crude oil.

16.1   CARBON

Carbon and its allotropes

Carbon is classified as a non-metal. It is the first member of group IV of the periodic table and is located in period 2 between boron and nitrogen. The carbon atom has six electrons so its electron configuration is 2, 4. It tends to form covalent bonds with other atoms by sharing the four electrons in its valence shell. A unique feature of carbon is its ability to bond strongly to other carbon atoms. This tendency will be discussed further in the next section.

Carbon exists in three **allotropes** called diamond, graphite and the fullerene family.

Diamond

Diamond is a very valuable gemstone, prized for its brilliance and lustre. It is the hardest known natural material. For this reason, it is used in diamond saws and drill bits. Diamond is highly incompressible, and is a better thermal conductor than any metal. It is transparent to most frequencies of light from the far ultraviolet through the visible to the far infrared.

The carbon atoms in diamond are arranged tetrahedrally in a strong three-dimensional, covalent network lattice. All four valence electrons are involved in covalent bonding, so there are no free electrons in the lattice. Thus, diamond is a non-conductor of electricity.

Diamond was created deep underground under conditions of extreme temperature and pressure, where it was more stable than graphite. Over a period of millions of years, sedimentary deposits of carbonaceous materials slowly crystallised into diamonds.

Diamond is resistant to attack from most chemical substances. It burns in oxygen to form carbon dioxide, although this requires a very high temperature.

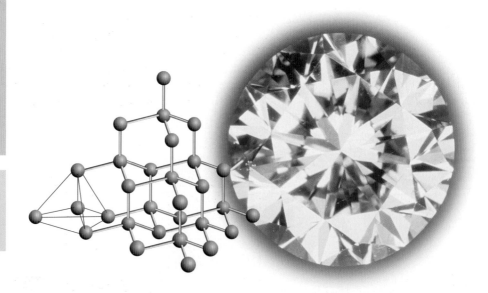

Figure 16.2 Diamonds are composed of pure carbon. Their properties of brilliance, durability and hardness are due to their ordered and rigid structure in which each carbon atom is covalently bonded to four other carbon atoms.

Graphite

Graphite is a soft, black solid. The carbon atoms are arranged in layers held together by weak dispersion forces; quite different from the arrangement in diamond. Within each layer, the carbon atoms are covalently bonded in interlocking hexagonal rings. These two-dimensional layers are very strong and rigid. However, the graphite lattice is weak between its layers, so layers slip when the lattice is subjected to shearing forces. This slippage plane makes powdered graphite a useful dry lubricant.

Within the hexagonal layers, only three of the four valence electrons are involved in covalent bonding to other carbon atoms. The remaining electron from each carbon atom is *delocalised*, and these electrons form an electrical conducting band in the lattice. Thus, graphite is a good electrical conductor.

Table 16.1 summarises the physical properties of diamond and graphite. Graphite has a higher thermal conductivity than diamond along the plane of hexagonal rings. This is due to the presence of a mobile electron cloud in the plane. Its thermal conductivity perpendicular to this plane is quite low.

Table 16.1 Physical properties of diamond and graphite

Allotrope	diamond	graphite
Melting point (°C)	<3550	3974 (under pressure)
Density (g/cm³)	3.51	2.26
Specific heat capacity (J/K/g)	0.51	0.71
Electrical conductivity (MS/m)	10^{-17}	0.07
Thermal conductivity (J/s/m/K)	1000	1950 (parallel to planes) 5.7 (perpendicular to planes)

Fullerenes

fullerenes: a family of carbon allotropes in which the carbon atoms are arranged in cage- or tube-like structures

The **fullerene** family of carbon allotropes was discovered in 1985. Fullerenes are ball- or rod-shaped structures (nanotubes) formed by the bonding of a large number of carbon atoms. The fullerenes are produced in laboratories in a variety of ways, including laser ablation, chemical vapour deposition and electric arc discharge.

The structures of carbon allotropes are shown in figure 16.3.

Diamond   **Fullerenes**   **Graphite**

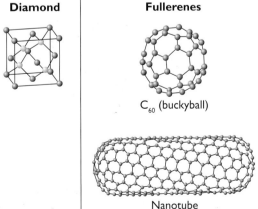

C_{60} (buckyball)

Nanotube

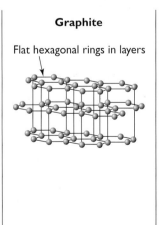

Flat hexagonal rings in layers

Figure 16.3
Structures of carbon allotropes
(*Note:* The carbon atoms shown light blue in the diamond structure are inside the unit cell cube.)

Clusters of 60 atoms (C_{60}) are the most abundant and named 'bucky-balls' after the architect R. Buckminster Fuller who had built similar structures. Other ball- and cage-like molecules from C_{32} to C_{84} have been isolated. Cage-like fullerenes may be used in the future as molecular lubricants because of the weak intermolecular forces between their ball-shaped molecules. At the moment, however, other lubricants are much cheaper to manufacture.

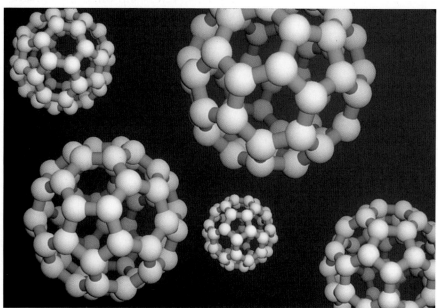

Figure 16.4
Molecules of 'buckyballs' consist of 60 carbon atoms

Another group of fullerenes are called 'buckytubes' or 'nanotubes', which consist of molecules with a long tubular shape (several hundred nanometres long) and an internal cavity with a diameter of about 15 nanometres. Nanotubes have high tensile strength. They are stronger than similar-sized steel wires and have potential for future engineering developments. These nanotubes can behave as conductors or insulators depending on their size and shape and the number of twists on the molecule. Nanotubes can also be single- or multi-walled.

In August 2005, Ken Atkinson of CSIRO and a team at the NanoTech Institute at the University of Texas announced the production of sheets of carbon nanotubes that are transparent, flexible, five times stronger than steel and electrically conductive. When these sheets are welded between two layers of acrylic glass, the composite material can be used as an electrically heated window. Due to its conductivity, it could also act as an antenna for a car radio.

Bonding in carbon compounds

Carbon compounds represent the largest group of compounds in the world. Most of these compounds are components of the living world, so the study of carbon compounds is usually called organic chemistry.

Carbon is a *tetravalent* element. Carbon atoms can link together to form long stable chains and rings, which can create vast numbers of natural and synthetic carbon compounds. Apart from hydrogen, oxygen and halogen atoms are a few of the common elements that bind to these carbon-based molecules.

single covalent bond: a covalent bond in which one electron pair is shared between neighbouring atoms

double covalent bond: a covalent bond in which two electron pairs are shared between neighbouring atoms

triple covalent bond: a covalent bond in which three electron pairs are shared between neighbouring atoms

Types of bond

Carbon atoms can bond covalently to each other in three different ways:

- **single covalent bonds**
- **double covalent bonds**
- **triple covalent bonds**.

Figure 16.5 shows the Lewis electron dot structures for single, double and triple covalent bonds between carbon atoms.

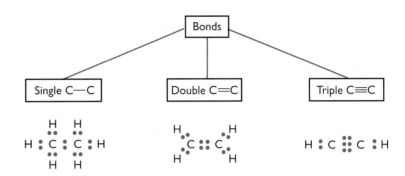

Figure 16.5
Lewis electron dot structures for single, double and triple covalent bonds

When showing the *structural formula* of an organic molecule, single, double and triple bonds are represented as follows:

- single bond: C — C
- double bond: C ═ C
- triple bond: C ≡ C.

Triple covalent bonds between carbon atoms are much stronger than double or single covalent bonds. Despite the greater strength of double and triple covalent bonds, they are much more chemically reactive than single carbon–carbon bonds. Thus, compounds containing multiple bonds undergo chemical reactions more readily that single-bonded carbon compounds.

The geometrical arrangement of electron pairs around carbon atoms depends on the type of bonding. Table 16.2 summarises this information.

Table 16.2 Geometry of electron pairs around carbon atoms in compounds

Carbon–carbon bond	Bond angles	Bond arrangement around the carbon atom
single	109°28'	tetrahedral
double	120°	planar
triple	180°	linear

Single bonds	Double bonds	Triple bonds

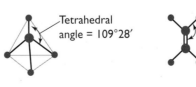

Figure 16.6
Bonding angles around carbon atoms in single, double and triple covalently bonded molecules

Types of molecule

The presence of single, double and triple covalent bonds in organic compounds produces a wide variety of molecular structures. These structures include:

- straight (unbranched) molecular chains
- branched molecular chains
- ring molecules.

Figure 16.7 shows the structural formulae of some examples of the variety of organic compounds.

Pentane   Methylbutane   Cyclohexane

Figure 16.7 Structural formulae of various types of chain and ring carbon compounds

16.1 QUESTIONS

1. Carbon
   A is a member of group V of the periodic table.
   B is a non-conductor of electricity in all its allotropic forms.
   C has an electron configuration of 2, 4.
   D is a semi-metal.

2. Allotropes are
   A different structural forms of an element.
   B compounds with the same molecular formula but different arrangements of atoms.
   C found only in the element carbon.
   D radioactive.

3. Select the statement that is true of diamond.
   A The diamond crystal is transparent to visible light only.
   B There are no free electrons in the crystal lattice.
   C The carbon atoms are arranged in layers within the lattice.
   D Diamond is inert and will not combust in oxygen.

4. Select the correct statement concerning graphite.
   A Graphite is a very hard crystal.
   B Graphite is a very poor electrical conductor.

   C Separate layers in a graphite lattice are held together by covalent bonds between carbon atoms.
   D Graphite is less dense than diamond.

5. Select the correct statement about the fullerene family.
   A All fullerenes are ball-shaped molecules.
   B Fullerenes are excellent electrical conductors.
   C Fullerenes can be produced in electric arc discharges between carbon electrodes.
   D Nanotubes are likely to be used in the future as lubricants.

6. Select the true statement about bonding between carbon atoms in hydrocarbon molecules.
   A A carbon–carbon single bond consists of one electron linking the two carbon atoms.
   B Double covalent bonds between carbon atoms consist of two electrons.
   C Triple covalent bonds between carbon atoms consist of three electron pairs.
   D A double carbon–carbon covalent bond is much weaker than a single carbon–carbon covalent bond.

7. Draw a Lewis electron dot structure for a hydrocarbon ring molecule with the molecular formula C_4H_8.

8. Figure 16.8 shows the Lewis electron-dot structure of a hydrocarbon molecule. Identify the number of single, double and triple carbon–carbon bonds in this molecule.

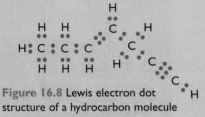

Figure 16.8 Lewis electron dot structure of a hydrocarbon molecule

9. Relate each of the following uses of carbon allotropes to a physical property or structure of the crystal.
   (a) Graphite powder is a useful dry lubricant.
   (b) Diamonds are used as drill tips.
   (c) Graphite blocks are used as electrodes in high-temperature electrolytic cells for the production of aluminium.

10. All allotropes of carbon react with excess oxygen at high temperatures. Write a balanced equation for this reaction.

16.2 *HYDROCARBONS*

Fractional distillation of petroleum

Hydrocarbons are compounds composed of carbon and hydrogen only. They are commonly found in fossil fuels such as *crude oil* and natural gas, which make up the natural product called *petroleum*. Petroleum formed gradually over long periods of geological time from the buried remains of marine organisms that lived about 500 million years ago.

Methane is the simplest hydrocarbon and the major component of natural gas, although the amount of methane varies considerably. Ethane is usually the next most abundant component. The hydrocarbons comprising crude oil include straight chains, branched chains and cyclic molecules, making it a highly viscous liquid. Petroleum is quite variable in its composition. Australian crude is lighter than many other crude oils from around the world. Therefore, Australia imports heavier crude oils (e.g. Arabian Heavy and Arabian Light) so that it provide the full range of petroleum products, particularly bitumen and greases. Arabian Heavy is more viscous than Arabian Light as it has a higher bitumen content.

Bass Strait, Queensland and the North West Shelf off the Western Australian coast are major locations for petroleum mining in Australia. The gaseous components of petroleum (methane, ethane, propane, butane and traces of pentane, as well as some non-hydrocarbon gases), which are dissolved in the crude oil, are extracted first. Apart from methane and some ethane, these gaseous hydrocarbons are liquefied and then fractionally distilled to obtain separate samples of each. The remainder is marketed as natural gas. The typical composition of natural gas from Australian gas wells is 89% methane, 5% ethane, 1% propane, 1% butane, 2% carbon dioxide and 2% air.

The remaining crude oil still contains some dissolved gaseous hydrocarbons. The crude oil is separated into *fractions* using a *fractionating column*. This separation is based on differences in boiling point (figure 16.10). The steps in this process are as follows.

• The crude oil is heated to about 370 °C at the bottom of a pipe still. This converts the viscous liquid to vapour and fluid, which then pass into the base of the fractionating column.

• Petroleum vapours and steam move up the column. The vapours cool and condense on baffles called bubble caps. This condensed liquid is richer in the least *volatile* components.

petrochemical feedstock: petroleum fractions used to manufacture other products such as plastics

naphtha: a component of the gasoline fraction that is used as a feedstock to manufacture ethylene for the plastics industry

• The liquids that form at a particular boiling point range are collected in trays. Some liquid overflows these trays and falls back to a hotter zone, where it meets hot ascending vapours that exchange heat and cause the more volatile components of the liquid to vaporise.

• This process repeats continuously so that the most volatile components rise higher in the column. The light (low molecular weight) components do not condense, so pass out of the top to be collected as refinery gas.

• The trays eventually collect liquids in a fairly narrow boiling range. The liquids are channelled out and collected.

Figure 16.9 Fractional distillation of crude oil is carried out in a fractionating column or tower.

• Liquids from the trays can be mixed to obtain the desired proportions of each component.

• The unvaporised (non-volatile) high molecular weight greases collect at the base of the column. Vacuum distillation is used to remove the heavy lubricating oils. Clear waxes are removed from the residue using solvent extraction. The solid residue that remains after this process is called *asphalt*.

Table 16.3 shows the typical fractions obtained from crude oil. The composition and boiling ranges of these fractions vary somewhat from one refinery to another.

Table 16.3 Typical crude oil fractions and uses

Boiling range (°C)	Carbon atoms per chain	Name of fraction	Common uses
<30	1–4	refinery gas	natural gas, bottled gas
30–125	5–8	gasoline (petrol fraction)	car fuel, **petrochemical feedstock**, solvent
90–220	7–13	gasoline (**naphtha** fraction)	conversion to petrol and alkenes by 'cracking' into smaller molecules
175–275	11–16	kerosene	home heating, aviation fuel, conversion to petrol ('cracking')
260–340	15–18	diesel oil	furnace fuel, diesel engines, conversion to petrol ('cracking')
>350	16–40	lubricating and fuel oils, paraffin waxes	lubrication, clear waxes and polishes
>400	>40	residue	asphalt (bitumen road surfaces)

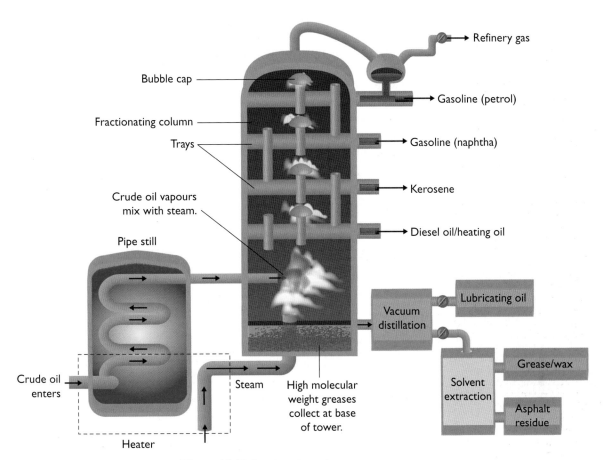

Figure 16.10 Fractionating column

The petrol derived from the gasoline fraction is insufficient to meet Australia's needs. Heavier fractions must be broken down ('cracked') into smaller hydrocarbon chains to produce sufficient quantities of petrol to supply the increasing number of vehicles on our roads.

Explain why molecules such as $C_{17}H_{36}$ are collected lower in the fractionating tower than molecules such as C_7H_{16}.

Hydrocarbons with high molecular weights (such as $C_{17}H_{36}$) have much higher boiling points than lower molecular weight hydrocarbons such as C_7H_{16}. The dispersion forces between heavier molecules are stronger than between lighter molecules. The lighter molecules move higher in the column before they are cool enough to condense back into liquids and become trapped in the trays. The heavier vapour molecules condense back to liquids much lower in the column as they do not require as much cooling to achieve a change in state.

16.2 PRACTICAL ACTIVITIES

Fractional distillation

homologous series: a family of compounds with similar chemical properties and a gradation of physical properties with increasing molar weight or chain length. A general formula describes all members of the series.

Alkanes and alkenes

Straight- and branched-chain hydrocarbons can be classified into groups or **homologous series** on the basis of the presence or absence of single, double or triple covalent bonds between carbon atoms. The presence of a carbon–carbon double bond in a hydrocarbon chain gives the molecule

functional group: a group of atoms attached to or part of a hydrocarbon chain that influence the physical and chemical properties of the molecule

alkane: a simple, saturated binary compound of carbon and hydrogen atoms with single bonds between the carbon atoms. The general formula for all members of this homologous series is C_nH_{2n+2}.

alkene: a simple, unsaturated binary compound of carbon and hydrogen atoms with a double bond between a pair of carbon atoms. The general formula for all members of this homologous series is C_nH_{2n}.

saturated hydrocarbon: hydrocarbon with only single C—C bonds and the maximum number of hydrogen atoms per carbon

unsaturated hydrocarbon: hydrocarbon with double or triple bonds between carbon atoms and fewer than the maximum number of hydrogen atoms per carbon

different physical and chemical properties from hydrocarbons with single covalent bonds only. The carbon–carbon double bond is, therefore, an example of a **functional group**.

Two important families or homologous series of hydrocarbons are the **alkanes** and **alkenes**. Alkanes are examples of **saturated hydrocarbons**; alkenes are examples of **unsaturated hydrocarbons**. Alkanes are commonly called paraffins (meaning 'little affinity' or 'unreactive'), while alkenes are sometimes called olefins (meaning 'oil-loving'). Alkenes are much more reactive than alkanes.

Alkanes

All molecules in the alkane homologous series have the general formula:

$$C_nH_{2n+2}, \text{ where } n = 1, 2, 3 \dots$$

In IUPAC nomenclature, the name of each alkane is a combination of a stem and a common suffix. The suffix used for all alkanes is *-ane*. The names for each stem are shown in table 16.4.

Table 16.4 Stems for naming hydrocarbons

n	1	2	3	4	5	6	7	8
Stem	*meth-*	*eth-*	*prop-*	*but-*	*pent-*	*hex-*	*hept-*	*oct-*

Thus, an alkane with $n = 6$ is named 'hexane'.

Figure 16.11 shows the structural formulae and space-filling models of some straight-chain alkanes.

Propane

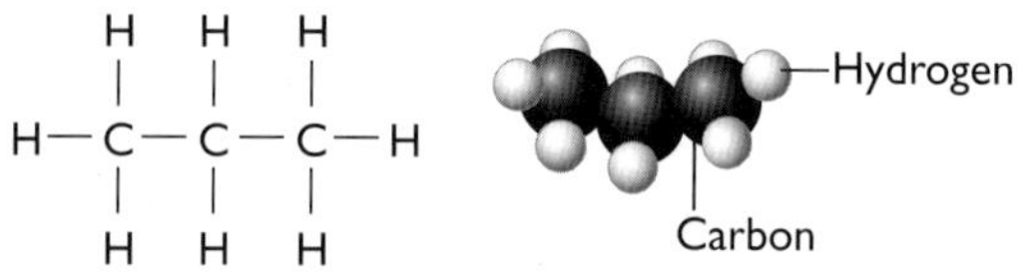

Hexane

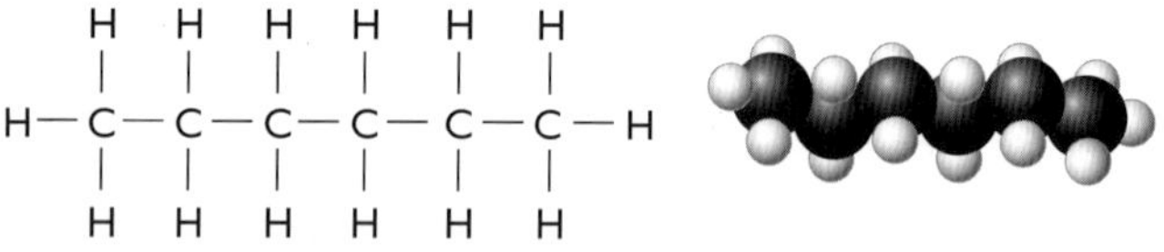

Figure 16.11
Structural formulae and space-filling models of two straight-chain alkanes

SAMPLE PROBLEM 16.2

Use the IUPAC rules for naming and determining the molecular formula of alkanes to complete table 16.5.

Table 16.5

n	Molecular formula	IUPAC name
1	CH_4	
3		propane
5		pentane
	C_8H_{18}	

Use the general formula to calculate the number of hydrogen atoms in each molecule. Thus, if $n = 2$, there are two carbon atoms and the number of hydrogen atoms is $2n + 2 = (2 \times 2) + 2 = 6$. So, the molecular formula is C_2H_6 and the name is 'ethane'. The complete table is shown below.

Table 16.6

n	Molecular formula	IUPAC name
1	CH_4	methane
3	C_3H_8	propane
5	C_5H_{12}	pentane
8	C_8H_{18}	octane

Alkenes

All molecules in the alkene homologous series have the general formula:

$$C_nH_{2n}, \text{ where } n = 2, 3, 4 \ldots$$

Note that it is not possible to have an alkene with $n = 1$ as a minimum of two carbon atoms are required for the double bond.

In IUPAC nomenclature, the suffix used for all alkenes is *-ene*. Thus, an alkene with $n = 3$ is named 'propene'.

IUPAC nomenclature specifies the location of the double bond in the hydrocarbon chain. The term 'locant' is used to describe the position of a functional group along the carbon chain. These rules are:

1. Number the longest chain from the end that gives the alkene functional group the lowest locant number possible.
2. The preferred IUPAC method (2005) of naming the alkene is to place the locant number of the first carbon of the double bond in front of the *-ene* suffix (e.g. hept-2-ene).

IUPAC also recognises the systematic method of placing the locant for the double bond in front of the name of the alkene (e.g. 2-heptene).

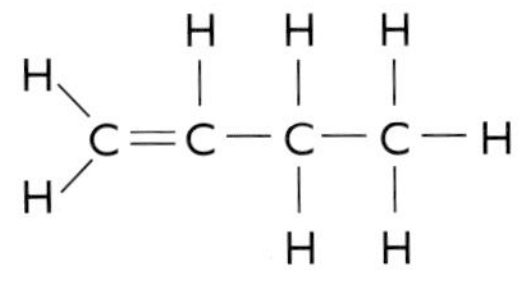

But-1-ene (1-butene)

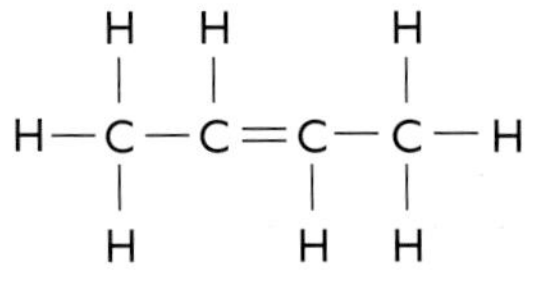

But-2-ene (2-butene)

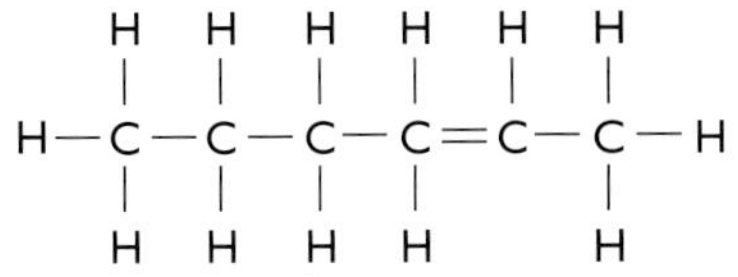

Hex-2-ene (2-hexene)

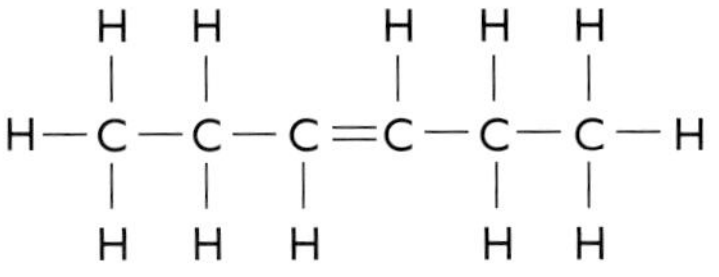

Hex-3-ene (3-hexene)

Figure 16.12
Examples of the naming rules for alkenes

Figure 16.12 provides some examples of these preferred IUPAC naming rules for straight chain alkenes, showing alternative systematic names. For alkenes with four or more carbon atoms, the location of the double bond can vary. For example, an alkene with molecular formula C_4H_8 can isomers: compounds with the same molecular formula but different structural formulae

have the double bond between the first and second carbon atoms or between the second and third carbon atoms in the chain. Thus, butene can exist as but-1-ene (1-butene) or but-2-ene (2-butene). These different structural forms of the alkene are called **isomers**. Their physical and chemical properties are similar but not identical.

SAMPLE PROBLEM 16.3

Determine the number of possible straight-chain isomers of the alkene with the molecular formula C_6H_{12}. Name these isomers using the IUPAC preferred nomenclature or another IUPAC recognised systematic nomenclature.

SOLUTION

The double bond can be located between C1 and C2, C2 and C3, or C3 and C4. Placing the double bond between C4 and C5 is the same as placing it between C2 and C3. Thus, there are only three straight-chain isomers.

$$CH_2{=}CH{-}CH_2{-}CH_2{-}CH_2{-}CH_3$$
hex-1-ene (1-hexene)

$$CH_3{-}CH{=}CH{-}CH_2{-}CH_2{-}CH_3$$
hex-2-ene (2-hexene)

$$CH_3{-}CH_2{-}CH{=}CH{-}CH_2{-}CH_3$$
hex-3-ene (3-hexene)

alkyl group: an alkane molecule with a missing hydrogen atom. An alkyl group is always attached to another molecule and cannot exist separately (e.g. —CH_3 is a methyl group).

Isomerism also exists when hydrocarbon chains are *branched*. Figure 16.13 shows some isomeric examples of alkanes and alkenes involving hydrocarbon (or alkyl) side chains or functional groups. The **alkyl groups** are named after their parent alkane. Thus a —CH_3 group is called a *methyl* group. The IUPAC nomenclature rules specify the position of these alkyl groups using a numbering system to allocate locants (positions) along the carbon chain. The numbering system requires the alkyl groups to have the lowest locant possible. Note, however, that the double bond in alkenes maintains its priority in being assigned the lowest locant. The alkyl groups are named alphabetically.

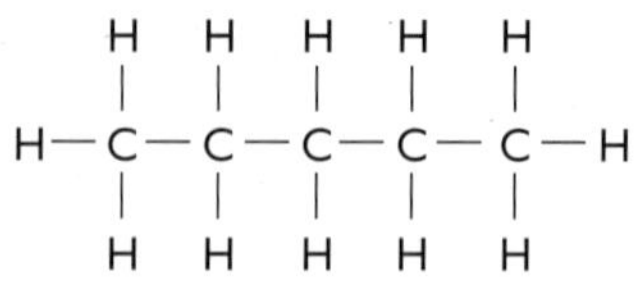

Pentane C_5H_{12}

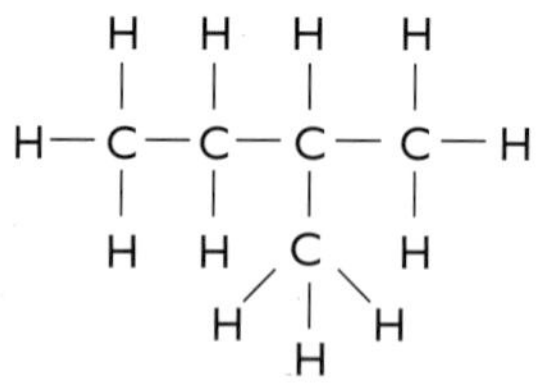

Methylbutane C_5H_{12}

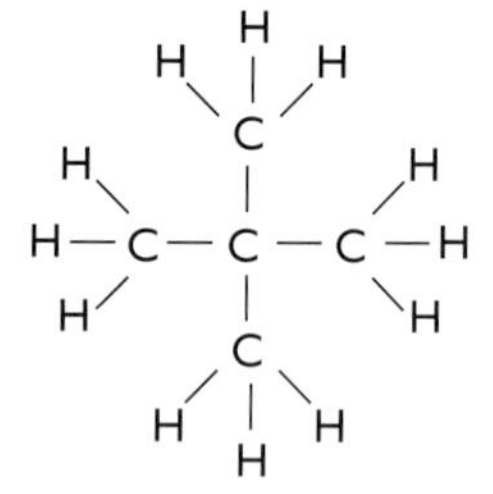

Dimethylpropane C_5H_{12}

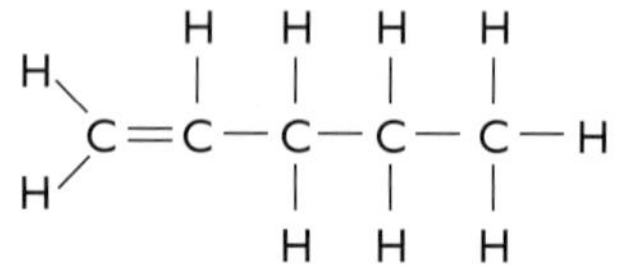

Pent-1-ene (1-pentene) C_5H_{10}

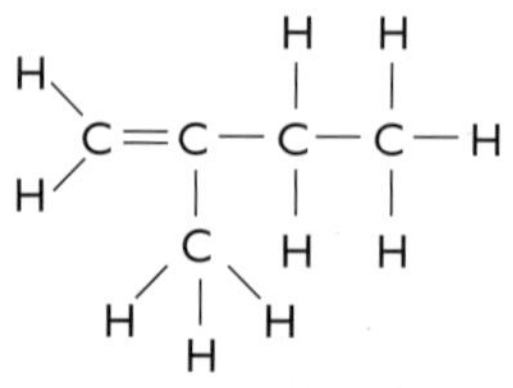

2-methylbut-1-ene (2-methyl-1-butene) C_5H_{10}

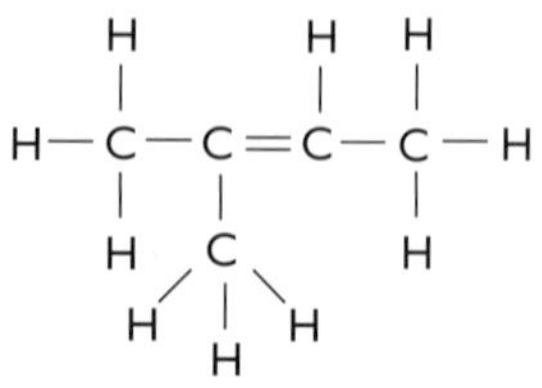

2-methylbut-2-ene (2-methyl-2-butene) C_5H_{10}

Figure 16.13 Examples of isomerism in branched-chain alkanes and alkenes

Properties of alkanes and alkenes

Alkanes and alkenes are *non-polar* molecules that dissolve readily in non-polar solvents such as kerosene (a mixture of liquid alkanes), but are insoluble in polar solvents such as water.

Melting and boiling points

The melting and boiling points of alkanes and alkenes increase with increasing chain length. This is consistent with the increasing dispersion forces between molecules as their molecular weight increases. Table 16.7 lists the melting and boiling points of various alkanes and alkenes. The first four members (C1–C4) of the alkanes are gases at 25 °C and the next twelve (C5–C16) are volatile liquids. All other alkanes are waxy solids.

Short-chain alkenes generally have slightly lower melting and boiling points than their corresponding alkanes. This indicates that the double bond in the short alkene chain reduces the extent of the dispersion forces between neighbouring chains when compared with short alkane chains of similar molecular weight.

Table 16.7 Melting and boiling points of alkanes and alkenes

Alkane	Melting point (°C)	Boiling point (°C)	Alkene	Melting point (°C)	Boiling point (°C)
C_3H_8	−188	−42	C_3H_6	−185	−48
C_5H_{12}	−130	36	C_5H_{10}	−165	30
C_6H_{14}	−95	69	C_6H_{12}	−140	64
C_7H_{16}	−91	98	C_7H_{14}	−119	94

Volatility

equilibrium vapour pressure: the pressure in a closed system when the rate of vaporisation of a substance (normally a pure liquid or a solution) equals the rate of condensation; also called 'vapour pressure'

Volatile substances readily vaporise at room temperature to produce a high concentration of vapour above the liquid or solid substance. This high concentration is measured by a quantity called the **equilibrium vapour pressure**. Some alkanes and alkenes vaporise readily at room temperature while others (such as solid waxes) produce little vapour. Generally, the lower the molecular weight of the hydrocarbon, the greater its rate of evaportion and the higher its volatility. This can be understood in terms of the weaker dispersion forces between hydrocarbon molecules with shorter chains. The boiling point of a hydrocarbon is a good indicator of its volatility. The volatility and, therefore, the vapour pressure of a hydrocarbon increase with increasing temperature, as shown in table 16.8 for octane.

Table 16.8 Vapour pressure of octane as a function of temperature

Temperature (°C)	0	20	40	60	80
Vapour pressure (kPa)	0.4	1.3	4.1	10.4	23.3

Flash point and safety issues

flash point: the minimum temperature at which the vapour pressure of a fuel (e.g. a hydrocarbon such as octane) is just high enough to form a combustible mixture with air

The **flash point** of a liquid hydrocarbon or other volatile liquid is the minimum temperature at which the vapour pressure of the substance is just sufficient to form a combustible mixture of the vapour with air. A combustible fuel–air mixture is dangerous as a spark or a flame can readily ignite it.

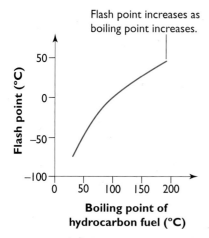

Flash point increases as boiling point increases.

Figure 16.14
Flash point as a function of the boiling point of hydrocarbon fuels

Figure 16.15
A lighter or other flame must never be lit near a petrol pump as petrol has a very low flash point.

16.3 DATA ANALYSIS

Alkanes and alkenes

Flash point varies considerably from one liquid hydrocarbon or fuel to another. Generally, the higher the boiling point of a hydrocarbon fuel, the higher the flash point. Figure 16.14 shows the relationship between flash point and boiling point for hydrocarbon fuels. Hydrocarbon waxes (such as candle wax) have much higher boiling and flash points than liquid hydrocarbons. The intermolecular forces between these molecules are stronger, so they are less volatile. Consequently, their low vapour pressures and high flash points make them much safer to store and use. Table 16.9 lists the flash points of some common fuels.

Table 16.9 Flash points of some common fuels

Fuel	petrol	octane	kerosene	diesel
Flash point (°C)	−43	+14	+48	+65

In a petrol engine, a spark is used to ignite the vapour–air mixture. Petrol has a much lower flash point than kerosene, so forms combustible mixtures more readily than kerosene. This makes petrol more dangerous to handle than kerosene. Even on very cold days in midwinter, petrol vapours readily form combustible mixtures with air. For this reason, using a gas lighter or smoking near a petrol pump is highly dangerous under all environmental conditions.

Petrol tankers are designed not to rupture in the event of an accident. Static charges are also prevented from building up by grounding the tanker with steel chains. In the family car, the fuel tank is located as far away from the engine as possible. If a combustible vapour–air mixture forms in the tank, it is away from ignition sources in or near the engine.

To avoid the risk of fires and explosions, the following safety precautions should be taken when handling, transporting or storing hydrocarbons.

- Gaseous fuels should be stored in strong, regularly maintained gas cylinders. The gauge, taps and fittings on LPG and propane gas bottles should be tested regularly for leaks to prevent fires and explosions.
- Liquid hydrocarbon fuels, such as kerosene, should be stored in labelled, metal containers with narrow openings and close-fitting caps. The storage cans should be kept in a cool place with good ventilation to avoid the build-up of any leaking vapours. It is not advisable to store large quantities of petrol in containers at home as the fuel is highly volatile and dangerous. Even small quantities should never be stored inside the house.
- Transfer liquid fuel one container to another (e.g. pouring lawnmower fuel into the tank of the mower) outside in a well-ventilated area to prevent the build-up of combustible vapour–air mixtures.
- Ensure that all flammable fuels are stored in fully labelled containers displaying the appropriate HazChem codes.
- Ensure that a fire extinguisher is close to fuel storage areas and that it is checked regularly.

Figure 16.16
HazChem labels for flammable gaseous and liquid substances

16.2 QUESTIONS

1. Name the following hydrocarbons.
   (a) $CH_3CH_2CH_2CH_2CH_2CH_3$
   (b) $CH_3CHCHCH_2CH_2CH_2CH_3$
   (c) $CH_3CH_2CH_2CH_2CH_2CH_2CHCH_2$

2. Name the next member of the homologous series to which each of the following molecules belongs.
   (a) $CH_3CH_2CH_3$
   (b) $CH_3CH_2CH_2CHCH_2$

3. A simple, straight-chain hydrocarbon has a molar weight of 42.1 g/mol. Draw a structural formula for a molecule with this molar weight. Name this molecule systematically.

4. Hydrocarbons P, Q and R have the physical properties shown in table 16.10.

   Classify each hydrocarbon as a solid, liquid or gas at 25 °C.

5. Read each of the following statements and identify the petroleum fraction formed after fractional distillation.
   (a) This fraction is used as a furnace fuel and boils in the range 260–340 °C.
   (b) This fraction is used for polishes and clear waxes.
   (c) This fraction is used as a solvent, petrochemical feedstock and car fuel.

Table 16.10

Hydrocarbon	Melting point (°C)	Boiling point (°C)
P	5.5	80.1
Q	216	340
R	−187.7	−42.1

6. A 10 ML sample of natural gas (at 25 °C and 100 kPa) contains 88% by volume of methane.
   (a) Calculate the volume of methane in the sample at this temperature and pressure.
   (b) Given that 1 mole of any gas occupies 24.79 litres at 25 °C and 100 kPa, calculate the number of moles of methane in the sample.
   (c) Use the information from (b) to calculate the number of methane molecules in the sample.

7. Octane is a component of the gasoline fraction produced by fractional distillation of crude oil.
   (a) Octane is a member of an important homologous series of hydrocarbons. Name that series.
   (b) Write the molecular formula of octane and the formula of the next member of that series.
   (c) (i) Identify the type of bond or force that exists between the atoms of the octane molecule.
      (ii) Identify the type of bond or force that exists between neighbouring octane molecules.
      (iii) State which of the bonds or forces named in (i) and (ii) is stronger.
   (d) A sample of octane is heated and converted into a vapour. Identify the bonds broken during this process.
   (e) Hydrocarbons can be classified as saturated or unsaturated. State the classification for octane. Justify your answer.
   (f) Identify the safety precautions required when handling octane.

8. The following statements concern the steps in fractionating crude oil, but they are out of order. Arrange the steps in a logical sequence.

   Step A: This process is repeated continuously so that the most volatile components rise higher in the column. Refinery gas passes out of the top of the column.

   Step B: Petroleum vapours and steam move up the column, cooling and condensing on bubble caps. The condensed liquid is richer in the least volatile components.

   Step C: Crude oil is heated and vaporised. The vapour then passes into the base of the fractionating column.

   Step D: Condensed liquids at a particular boiling point range are collected in trays. Some of this liquid overflows and falls back to a hotter zone where the more volatile components of the liquid vaporise.

   Step E: Non-volatile, high molecular weight greases collect at the base of the tower as a residue.

   Step F: The trays eventually collect liquids in a fairly narrow boiling range. These form the fractions that are collected.

9. Explain why each of the following safety precautions is taken when handling or storing hydrocarbon fuels.
   (a) LPG gas bottles should be inspected and tested regularly.
   (b) Motormower fuel should be poured into the mower's fuel tank in the open.
   (c) Large quantities of petrol should never be stored at home.

10. (a) The boiling points of the members of the alkane homologous series are shown in table 16.11. Plot a line graph of the boiling point versus molar weight and use the graph to interpolate the boiling point of pentane.
    (b) Explain why boiling point increases with molar weight.

Table 16.11

Alkane	methane	ethane	propane	butane	pentane	hexane	heptane	octane
Molar weight (g/mol)	16.0	30.1	44.1	58.1	72.1	86.2	100.2	114.2
Boiling point (°C)	−162	−89	−42	−0.5	?	69	98	126

eBook *plus*

Weblinks

eBook *plus*

Checkpoint
Revision 6

eBook *plus*

Checkpoint
Revision 6 Answers

SUMMARY

- Carbon can form single, double and triple covalent bonds with other carbon atoms. This allows carbon to produce stable, long-chain molecules.

- Hydrocarbons are binary compounds containing carbon and hydrogen. They can be classified in homologous series, including alkanes and alkenes.

- Alkanes are saturated hydrocarbons while alkenes are unsaturated. Unsaturated hydrocarbons do not have the maximum number of hydrogen atoms per molecule due to the presence of double or triple carbon–carbon bonds.

- IUPAC nomenclature is used to name hydrocarbons. The *-ane* suffix is used to name alkanes and the *-ene* suffix is used to name alkenes.

- The volatility of hydrocarbons and their melting and boiling points can be related to the dispersion forces between the molecules. The stronger the dispersion forces, the lower the volatility of the material.

- Hydrocarbons are non-polar, flammable substances that must be stored and handled with care. Hydrocarbon liquids and gases must be stored in cool places away from ignition sources.

- Hydrocarbons are extracted from petroleum by a physical process called fractional distillation. The hydrocarbons are collected in 'fractions' based on their boiling point ranges.

PRACTICAL ACTIVITIES

16.1 PRACTICAL ACTIVITIES

ALLOTROPY AND BONDING

Aim

To use models to investigate the allotropes of carbon and to use model kits to demonstrate covalent bonding in simple hydrocarbons

Materials

- models of diamond and graphite
- molecular model kits

Method

Part A: Carbon allotropes

1. For each of the models of diamond and graphite, draw a section to show the different geometric arrangement of the carbon atoms.

2. In your drawing of the diamond lattice, highlight a group of atoms to show that they are arranged tetrahedrally.

3. In your drawing of the graphite lattice, highlight a group of atoms to show the hexagonal fused rings in any one plane.

4. Use the Internet to:

   (a) investigate the structure of buckyballs (C_{60}).

   (b) identify the arrangement of single and double covalent bonds in a buckyball molecule. Print a copy of a suitable graphic for your workbook.

   (c) identify uses of the allotropes of carbon and relate these uses to their structures and physical properties.

Part B: Bonding in simple hydrocarbons

1. Use a molecular model kit to make models of the following simple molecules.

   (a) Ethane, C_2H_6
   (b) Ethene, C_2H_4
   (c) Ethyne, C_2H_2 (*Note:* This is an alkyne with a triple bond joining the carbon atoms.)

2. Draw three-dimensional, structural formulae of your models. Use dotted lines for bonds behind the plane of the paper and bold lines for bonds projecting out of the plane of the paper.

3. Identify the model(s):

   (a) in which all atoms are arranged linearly
   (b) that consists of two intersecting tetrahedra
   (c) in which all atoms lie in the same plane.

4. Show, by constructing longer chain hydrocarbon molecules, that the presence of:

   (a) a carbon–carbon double bond leads to a planar region in the molecule and restricted rotation about the carbon atoms
   (b) a carbon–carbon triple bond leads to a linear region in the molecule and restricted rotation about the carbon atoms.

PRACTICAL ACTIVITIES

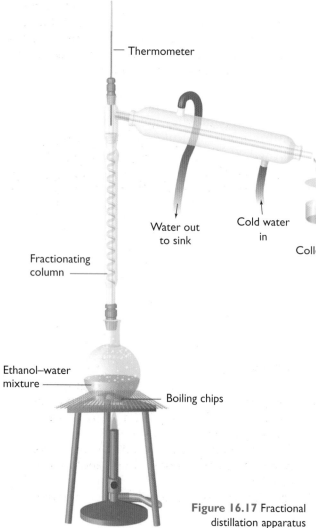

16.2 PRACTICAL ACTIVITIES

FRACTIONAL DISTILLATION

Part A: First-hand investigation

Aim

To separate a mixture of water and ethanol using fractional distillation

Safety issues

- Wear safety glasses throughout this experiment.

Figure 16.17 Fractional distillation apparatus

- Ethanol is flammable and naked flames should be kept away from it and its vapours.
- Identify other safety issues relevant to this experiment by reading the method.

Materials

- Quickfit distillation apparatus with 250 mL round- or flat-bottomed flask
- fractionating column
- 110 °C thermometer with teflon sleeve
- 2 mL graduated pipettes
- electronic balance
- electric heating mantle or gauze mat, tripod and Bunsen burner
- 25 mL ethanol/25 mL water mixture (measured with a 25 mL pipette)
- pipette filler
- boiling chips
- 100 mL beaker
- 11 small beakers
- retort stand, bosshead and clamp
- ethanol

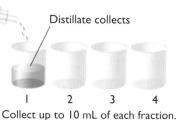

Distillate collects

| 1 | 2 | 3 | 4 |

Collect up to 10 mL of each fraction.

Method

Wear your safety glasses.

1. Use a clean beaker to prepare a mixture of 25.0 mL of water and 25.0 mL of pure ethanol using a 25 mL pipette.

2. Weigh a clean, dry beaker. Use a 2.00 mL graduated pipette to transfer 2.00 mL of the water–ethanol mixture into the beaker. Reweigh and determine the mass of the liquid. Calculate its density ($d = m/V$). Return the 2 mL of water–ethanol mixture to the first beaker.

3. Place boiling chips and the 50 mL ethanol–water mixture in the distillation flask and set up the apparatus ready for distillation as shown in figure 16.17.

PRACTICAL ACTIVITIES

4. Put the flask on a gauze mat supported by a tripod, and heat it slowly with a heating mantle or Bunsen burner. It is vital to adjust the heating to ensure gentle boiling and very slow production of distillate.

5. Use a small, clean beaker (beaker 1) to collect all the distillate produced while the thermometer reads between 78 and 80 °C (that is, in the 78–80 °C boiling range). Allow the temperature to slowly rise and collect a second sample of distillate (beaker 2) in the 81–85 °C boiling range. Collect subsequent samples of distillate in the following boiling ranges:

Beaker 3:	86–90 °C
Beaker 4:	91–95 °C
Beaker 5:	96–98 °C

Do not distill all the liquid. Turn off the heat and allow the vessel to cool.

6. Calculate the density of each fraction by measuring the mass of 2.00 mL of each fraction. Use a clean, small beaker for each mass measurement.

7. Dismantle and store the equipment.

Results
Record your observations in a suitable table.

Questions
Answer the following questions in your report on this experiment.

1. Compare the boiling point range of each fraction collected with the boiling points of pure ethanol (78.3 °C) and water (100 °C).
2. Use your density data to compare the compositions of each fraction collected using table 16.12. Draw a graph of this data and interpolate your density readings.

Table 16.12

Ethanol (%v/v)	0	20	40	60	80	100
Density (g/mL)	1.00	0.97	0.93	0.89	0.84	0.79

3. Comment on the degree of separation of the ethanol–water mixture using fractional distillation.

Part B: Second-hand data

A fractional distillation apparatus similar to that used in part A was used to distill mixtures of ethanol in water.

The composition of fractions is often expressed as mole percentage, which is calculated as:

$$\frac{\text{moles of solute}}{\text{total moles in solution}} \times 100$$

Six mixtures of ethanol in water with different mole percentages were prepared. In turn, each one of the ethanol–water mixtures was distilled in the apparatus. The temperature rose slowly until distillation commenced, and was constant while distillate was collected.

Each distillate was analysed using a refractometer. The mole percentage of ethanol in each distillate was determined by using a calibration graph. The results are shown in table 16.13. Process this data and answer the questions that follow.

Results

Table 16.13 Composition of distillates

Ethanol in original mixture (mole %)	Distillation temperature (°C)	Ethanol in distillate (mole %)
90	78.7	90
80	79.0	86
60	79.5	78
40	81.0	66
20	83.0	53
10	86.0	43

Questions

1. Use millimetre grid paper to plot a graph of the composition of the distillate on the y-axis and composition of the original mixture on the x-axis. Draw a line of best fit.
2. Determine whether the distillate composition is richer, the same or poorer in ethanol for each distillation.
3. Identify the more volatile component of the mixture.

4. Fermentation is a common method used by brewers and winemakers to produce alcohol; sugar solutions are fermented by yeast to produce ethanol. The typical concentration of ethanol in filtered wine is 12%v/v. Convert this volume % to mole %, given that the density (d) of ethanol is 0.785 g/mL and that of water is 1.00 g/mL.

5. The techniques used in fractional distillation do not produce pure (anhydrous) ethanol; there is usually some water in the ethanol. Explain, in terms of bonding, why this is so.

Conclusion

Briefly describe the outcome of your investigation.

16.3 DATA ANALYSIS

ALKANES AND ALKENES

Part A: Model construction

1. Use a molecular model kit to construct models and draw 3-D diagrams of:
   (a) propane
   (b) butane.

2. Name and construct models of all the straight-chain isomers of:
   (a) C_4H_8.
   (b) C_5H_{10}.
   Draw structural formulae for each model constructed.

3. (a) Construct a model of hexane and draw its structural formula.
   (b) Construct branched-chain isomers of hexane. Identify the maximum number of isomers of hexane.

Part B: Safe storage of alkanes

Click on the Methane, Hexane and Gasoline weblinks for this chapter to find material safety data sheets (MSDS) with information on storage of alkanes and petroleum fractions. Use the information you collect to construct a table summarising safety issues in the storage of alkanes.

Chapter 17 COMBUSTION AND REACTION KINETICS

Introduction

Combustion is an important chemical process. The burning of fuels such as coal, oil and natural gas provides heat to keep us warm and to power machines. Combustion of fuels requires oxygen. If oxygen supply is restricted, gases such as carbon monoxide, which pollute the environment, are released. In this chapter, we will investigate combustion and the rate at which combustion reactions and other reactions occur.

In this chapter

Figure 17.1

Combustion reactions require fuel, oxygen and an ignition source.

17.1 *COMBUSTION*

Remember

Before beginning this section, you should be able to:
- identify and use the IUPAC nomenclature for describing straight-chained alkanes and alkenes from C1 to C8
- recall the safety issues associated with the storage of alkanes from C1 to C8 in view of their weak intermolecular forces (dispersion forces).

Key content

By the end of this section, you should be able to:
- describe the indicators of chemical reactions
- identify combustion as an exothermic chemical reaction
- outline the changes in molecules during chemical reactions in terms of bond-breaking and bond-making
- explain that energy is required to break bonds and energy is released when bonds are formed
- describe the energy needed to begin a chemical reaction as activation energy
- describe the energy profiles for endothermic and exothermic reactions
- explain the relationship between ignition temperature and activation energy
- identify the sources of pollution that accompany the combustion of organic compounds, and explain how these can be avoided
- describe chemical reactions by using full balanced chemical equations to summarise examples of complete and incomplete combustion
- solve problems and perform a first-hand investigation to measure the change in mass when a mixture such as wood is burnt in an open container
- identify the changes of state involved in combustion of a burning candle
- perform first-hand investigations to observe and describe examples of endothermic and exothermic chemical reactions.

Chemical change

Let us consider the indicators of chemical change and the chemical bonds that are broken and formed as chemical reactions proceed.

Figure 17.2 Burning wood is an example of a chemical change.

Indicators of chemical change

In this course, you have investigated many different types of chemical reaction and physical change. Physical changes do not involve the production of new materials. For example, when wax melts, the liquid wax is still composed of the same molecules as the solid wax. This physical change is readily reversed by removing heat so that the solid wax reforms. Melting wax requires much less heat than would be required for a chemical reaction involving the wax molecules.

Chemical changes involve the production of new materials. When wax is burnt in air (as in a burning candle), new chemical compounds, such as carbon dioxide and water, are formed. Mixing carbon dioxide and water does not cause wax and oxygen to re-form.

In general, the indicators of chemical change are:
- Reactants are permanently converted into new products with a different appearance or property (e.g. different colour).
- Chemical reactions are difficult to reverse.
- Large energy changes occur.

Chemical reactions involve breaking and making bonds

Chemical changes occur because some or all of the chemical bonds in the reactants are broken; the released atoms, molecules or ions combine to form new products by forming new bonds. Breaking chemical bonds requires energy, which comes from the thermal motion of the particles. Energy is transferred from one particle to another during particle collisions. When new bonds are formed, energy is released to the system and increases the kinetic energy of the particles.

The strength of a chemical bond can be measured by the **bond energy** required to break the bond. An O—H covalent bond is stronger than an H—H bond. The bond energy of O—H is 463 kJ per mole of bonds while the bond energy of H—H is 436 kJ/mol. Triple carbon–carbon bonds are much stronger than single carbon–carbon bonds. Table 17.1 lists the bond energies of some common covalent bonds.

bond energy: the enthalpy change associated with breaking covalent bonds in one mole of a gaseous substance to produce gaseous fragments

Table 17.1 Bond energies of some covalent bonds

Bond	Bond energy (kJ/mol)
C—C	346
C=C	614
C≡C	839
C—H	414
H—H	436
O—H	463
O=O	498
C—O	358
C=O*	745

(*for C=O in carbon dioxide)

Bond energy tables can also be used to determine the amount of energy released when covalent bonds form. Thus, when one mole of H—H bonds form, 436 kJ of energy is released.

SAMPLE PROBLEM 17.1

SOLUTION

Calculate the energy change per mole of oxygen when hydrogen gas burns in oxygen gas to form water vapour.

Step 1: Write the balanced equation for the combustion reaction.
$$2H_2(g) + O_2(g) \rightarrow 2H_2O(g)$$

Step 2: Rewrite the equation to show the covalent bonds of the reactants to be broken and bonds of products to be formed.
$$H—H + H—H + O=O \rightarrow H—O—H + H—O—H$$

Step 3: Identify the bonds to be broken and those to be formed.
Bonds broken: 2 × H—H bonds
                  1 × O=O bond
Bonds formed: 4 × O—H bonds

Step 4: Use table 17.1 to calculate the energy required to break the bonds in the reactants:
2 × bond energy of H—H = 2 × 436 = 872 kJ
1 × bond energy of O=O = 498 kJ
Total energy to break bonds = 872 + 498 = 1370 kJ

Step 5: Use table 17.1 to calculate the energy released when the products form.
4 × bond energy of O—H = 4 × 463 = 1852 kJ

Step 6: Calculate the overall energy change.

The process of breaking the bonds of the reactants is *endothermic.* The process of forming bonds in the products is *exothermic.* By convention, the energy released in an exothermic process is assigned a *negative value.*

Thus, the energy change = (+1370) + (−1852) = −482 kJ

Thus, 482 kJ of energy is released per mole of oxygen reacting in the combustion of hydrogen in oxygen to form water vapour.

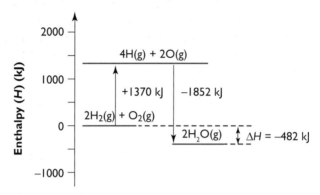

The processes of breaking and making bonds also occur in reactions involving metals and ionic compounds. Because these materials consist of infinite crystalline lattices rather than individual molecules in the gaseous state, other ways are used to describe the energy changes involved. For example, the strength of ionic bonds in metallic oxides, sulfides and chlorides can be compared using data on the amount of energy required to dissociate one mole of an ionic compound into its gaseous ions. This energy is called the *lattice enthalpy.* Table 17.2 compares the lattice enthalpies of various ionic compounds. It suggests that the strength of ionic bonds varies, and that metal oxide bonds are stronger than metal sulfide or metal chloride bonds. We can also conclude that a large amount of energy is released when these metal and non-metal ions react in the gaseous phase to form ionic bonds in a crystal lattice.

Table 17.2 Lattice enthalpies for ionic compounds (kJ/mol)

	O^{2-}	S^{2-}	Cl^-
Na^+	2488	2199	788
K^+	2245	1986	718
Rb^+	2170	1936	693

Activation energy

When a fuel such as hydrogen gas is mixed with oxygen gas at room temperature there is no observable reaction. This mixture of gases is stable at 25 °C. However, if a spark or a flame is supplied, the mixture reacts explosively. Why doesn't the reaction occur at 25 °C? We can explain this difference in behaviour of the reacting particles in terms of energy.

The term '**activation energy**' is used to explain why many reactions do not proceed at low temperatures. Activation energy is the minimum

activation energy: the minimum energy required by reactants in order to react amount of energy needed by the reactants to turn into products. In order for chemicals to react, they must collide with sufficient kinetic energy so that bonds can be broken. At low temperatures, the reactants have low kinetic energy. As the temperature rises, the particles move faster and faster. Eventually, they have sufficient kinetic energy to react.

We can visualise activation energy as an 'energy barrier' that separates the reactants and products. Sometimes we refer to this barrier as the activation energy 'hill'. Figure 17.4 shows an energy profile illustrating this idea for an exothermic reaction. Reactants without sufficient energy to overcome this energy barrier will not react. A spark or flame in a hydrogen–oxygen mixture would provide sufficient energy for some of the molecules to cross the barrier and form products. When this happens, they release heat energy that raises the kinetic energy of other reactant molecules. Very soon, almost all the reactant molecules have sufficient energy to cross the barrier. The reaction becomes self-sustaining (a flame or spark is no longer required) and the reaction occurs rapidly with considerable evolution of heat.

Energy profiles have several other features worth noting.

Endothermic and exothermic reactions

The energy profiles for exothermic and endothermic reactions are different. If the products have more energy than the reactants, the reaction is endothermic and the enthalpy change (ΔH) is positive. If the products have less energy than the reactants, the reaction is exothermic and the enthalpy change is negative. These features are shown in figure 17.5.

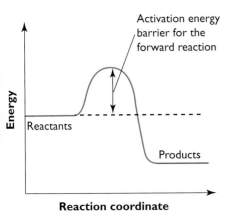

Figure 17.4
Energy profile showing the activation energy barrier for an exothermic reaction

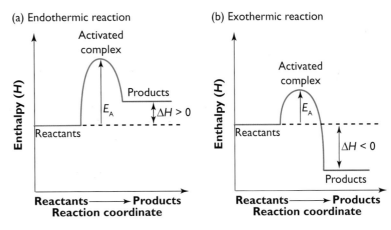

Figure 17.5
Enthalpy change, activation energy and activated complex for (a) endothermic and (b) exothermic reactions

Exothermic reactions are self-sustaining because the liberated heat provides the activation energy required by other reactants in the mixture.

Endothermic reactions are not self-sustaining and energy is needed to keep the reaction going. This may come from the kinetic energy of the molecules in the system; this causes the reaction to slow down and the temperature of the system to decrease.

Activated complex

The **activated complex** is a transition state that exists at the top of the activation energy hill. In this state, the bonds that held the reactants together are partially broken and new bonds holding the products together are partially formed. This complex of atoms exists for a very short time before it starts to break up. At this point, there are two possible ways the reaction could proceed:

activated complex: the (unstable) transition state formed during a reaction (at the top of the activation energy hill) that breaks down to form products

1. No reaction occurs because the activated complex breaks up and the reactants re-form.
2. Reaction occurs because the activated complex separates, forming product molecules.

A reaction has a greater chance of occurring when the system is supplied with energy in excess of the activation energy.

17.1 PRACTICAL ACTIVITIES

Exothermic and endothermic reactions

eBook *plus*

Temperature and reaction rate

Activation energy for the forward and reverse reactions

Not all reactions occur in one direction only. In many reactions, the products recombine and the reactants re-form. To do this, the product molecules must have sufficient energy to overcome the activation barrier for the reverse reaction. The size of this barrier is different from the size of the barrier in the forward reaction, as shown in figure 17.6.

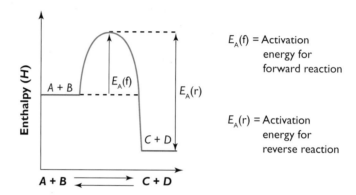

$E_A(f)$ = Activation energy for forward reaction

$E_A(r)$ = Activation energy for reverse reaction

Figure 17.6
Energy profile showing the activation energy for forward and reverse reactions

Combustion and ignition temperature

Heptane is a component of petrol. Mixtures of 1–7%v/v of heptane vapour in air are combustible; if there is too much heptane or too little air, the mixture will not combust. A combustible mixture of heptane vapour and air is stable at room temperature. However, if it is heated, it will eventually reach a temperature at which combustion begins. This minimum temperature is referred to as the **ignition temperature**.

Once combustion of heptane begins, it quickly becomes self-sustaining as the heat liberated raises the temperature of the rest of the mixture above the ignition temperature. The energy equation for such a combustion reaction is:

$$C_7H_{16}(l) + 11O_2(g) \rightarrow 7CO_2(g) + 8H_2O(l) \qquad \Delta H = -4817 \text{ kJ/mol}$$

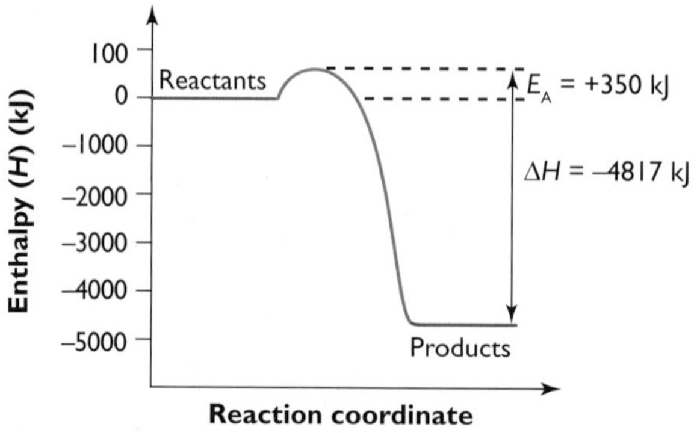

ignition temperature: the minimum temperature at which a combustible fuel–oxidiser mixture ignites spontaneously

Figure 17.7
Energy profile for the combustion of heptane

The activation energy for this reaction is 350 kJ. This means that the reactants must be heated to their ignition temperature or higher to provide at least 350 kJ of energy. For this particular reaction, the ignition temperature is approximately 215 °C. The enthalpy of combustion of heptane is –4817 kJ/mol. Figure 17.7 shows the energy profile for the combustion of heptane.

Ignition temperature is a measure of the activation energy of a reaction. The higher the activation energy, the higher the ignition temperature. Thus, fuels such as butane with a higher ignition temperature (405 °C) than heptane, also have a higher activation energy.

Table 17.3 lists typical ignition temperatures of some fuels. Ignition temperature depends on the methods used to measure it and on the composition of the fuel (e.g. natural gas composition is quite variable).

Table 17.3 Typical values for ignition temperatures of fuels

Fuel	Ignition temperature (°C)
hydrogen	585
natural gas	540–560
petrol	390–420
kerosene	380
diesel	300–350
methane	580
butane	405
pentane	260
hexane	225
heptane	215
octane	206

Petrol has a higher ignition temperature range (390–420 °C) than diesel (300–350 °C). The diesel vapour–air mixture in a diesel engine is compressed until its temperature reaches the ignition temperature. Compression heating is not used in a petrol engine, however, as the ignition temperature is too high. In a petrol engine, the petrol vapour–air mixture is ignited by a spark.

SAMPLE PROBLEM 17.2

A mixture of hexane vapour (5 mL) and air (95 mL) is placed in a 100 mL vessel and the temperature raised to 200 °C. Use the following information to determine whether the fuel vapour–oxidiser mixture will ignite in the absence of a flame at this temperature.

Flash point of hexane = –23 °C
Ignition temperature of hexane = 225 °C
Combustible mixture = 1.2–7.5% hexane in air

SOLUTION

Step 1: Determine the % composition of the mixture.

$$\% \text{ hexane vapour} = 5/100 \times 10 = 5\%$$

Step 2: Determine whether this mixture is a combustible mixture. The composition lies between 1.2% and 7.5% so it is a combustible mixture.

Incomplete combustion and pollution

The release of waste and poisonous substances pollutes the environment, affecting all living things. The products of incomplete combustion of fuels is an important example of pollution. Production of carbon dioxide is also of concern as there is considerable evidence that increasing carbon dioxide levels in the atmosphere contributes to global warming by enhancing the greenhouse effect.

Some pollutants released by the combustion of organic compounds (such as coal, oil and natural gas) include:

- *sulfur dioxide.* Coal and oil often contain sulfur minerals. When these fuels are burnt, the sulfur minerals also burn and release sulfur dioxide, a colourless, choking gas:

$$S(s) + O_2(g) \rightarrow SO_2(g)$$

Sulfur dioxide can be oxidised in the atmosphere to form sulfur trioxide. These oxides of sulfur combine with moisture in the air, forming *acid rain*, which can damage living things as well as the built environment.

- *nitrogen oxides.* When fuels are burnt in air at a high temperature (e.g. in a petrol engine or coal-fired power station), the nitrogen in the air also reacts with oxygen to form oxides of nitrogen, such as NO, NO_2 and N_2O_5:

$$N_2(g) + O_2(g) \rightarrow 2NO(g)$$

$$2NO(g) + O_2(g) \rightarrow 2NO_2(g)$$

Oxides such as NO_2 contribute to the formation of acid rain as well as contributing to the formation of photochemical smog in cities.

- *carbon monoxide and unburnt hydrocarbons.* When organic compounds, such as hexane, are burnt in a limited air supply, the combustion products include carbon monoxide as well as with the exhaust gases:

$$2C_6H_{14}(l) + 13O_2(g) \rightarrow 12CO(g) + 14H_2O(l)$$

Carbon monoxide is a very poisonous gas. It combines more readily with haemoglobin in the blood than oxygen, leading to suffocation.

- *particulates.* Coal-fired power stations and car engines emit ash and other fine particles, such as soot (carbon particles), into the air.

Burning natural gas in a Bunsen burner

You would have used a Bunsen burner many times in your chemistry lessons. The collar at the base of the burner can be rotated to allow different amounts of air to be drawn into the gas before the mixture is ignited. When the hole in the collar is closed, a yellow, safety flame is produced. As the hole is opened gradually and more air mixes with the natural gas, the flame changes from a luminous yellow to a mauve and, finally,

Figure 17.8
Black smoke is a sign of incomplete combustion.

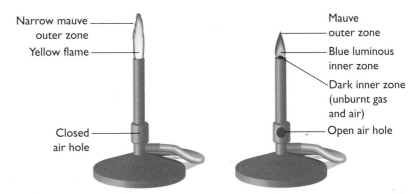

Figure 17.9
Bunsen burner flames

Narrow mauve outer zone

Yellow flame

Closed air hole

Mauve outer zone

Blue luminous inner zone

Dark inner zone (unburnt gas and air)

Open air hole

a blue flame. The different coloured flames show whether combustion of the natural gas is complete or incomplete.

To achieve complete combustion, air must be drawn in through the open hole in the collar as the gas enters the base of the burner through a narrow jet. The gas and air mixture moves through the barrel to the top of the burner where it is ignited. The resulting flame has a mauve outer zone (mantle), a central blue zone with a dark inner zone. The dark inner zone contains unburnt gas and air and is quite cool. The surface of the bright blue zone is the hottest region and is where complete combustion occurs. Complete combustion of methane produces carbon dioxide and water vapour. The mauve outer mantle is a cooler region where a variety of reactions occur; these reactions produce less heat than that produced by the complete combustion of methane in the bright blue zone. For example, in the outer mantle, carbon monoxide formed from the incomplete combustion of methane reacts with oxygen to form carbon dioxide.

Complete combustion of methane:

$$CH_4(g) + 2O_2(g) \rightarrow CO_2(g) + 2H_2O(l) \qquad \Delta_c H = -892 \text{ kJ/mol}$$

where $\Delta_c H$ is the enthalpy of combustion.

If the hole at the base of the barrel is closed, the flame becomes a luminous yellow. The oxygen required for combustion diffuses into the methane from the surrounding air. This process of forming a combustible mixture is not as efficient as that produced with the hole open. The yellow flame indicates poor or incomplete combustion. It is not as hot as the blue or mauve flames because the methane burns to form carbon particles (soot) and water vapour, as well as some carbon monoxide and carbon dioxide. The carbon particles become incandescent and colour the flame yellow, escaping from the combustion zone before they can all burn. The yellow flame has a narrow, blue-mauve outer edge where most of the carbon monoxide burnt.

Incomplete combustion of methane:

$$2CH_4(g) + 3O_2(g) \rightarrow 2CO(g) + 4H_2O(l) \qquad \Delta_c H = -609 \text{ kJ/mol}$$

$$CH_4(g) + O_2(g) \rightarrow C(s) + 2H_2O(l) \qquad \Delta_c H = -498 \text{ kJ/mol}$$

$$2CO(g) + O_2(g) \rightarrow 2CO_2(g) \qquad \Delta_c H = -283 \text{kJ/mol}$$

Combustion of solid and liquid fuels

Common solid fuels used in industry and power generation include coal and coke. Coke is made by heating coal in the absence of air to drive off volatile materials. These solid fuels are not very volatile so they have to be heated to high temperatures to produce ignition. A continuous stream of air or oxygen helps to promote complete combustion and to raise the flame temperature.

Complete combustion of solid fuel:

$$C(s) + O_2(g) \rightarrow CO_2(g) \qquad \Delta_c H = -394 \text{ kJ/mol}$$

If the supply of oxygen is reduced, incomplete combustion results and the flame temperature is much lower.

Incomplete combustion of solid fuel:

$$C(s) + O_2(g) \rightarrow 2CO(g) \qquad \Delta_c H = -111 \text{ kJ/mol}$$

Waxy solids, such as paraffin wax, are used to make candles. Wax does not burn without a fibre wick to help produce a combustible mixture of wax vapour and air. Practical activity 17.2 on page 337 deals with the chemistry of a burning candle.

Volatile, low molecular weight, liquid fuels (such as petrol) readily vaporise to produce combustible mixtures with air. When sparked, the mixture burns completely or incompletely, depending on the ratio of fuel vapour to air. Modern fuel injection systems in cars ensure the optimum fuel–air ratio for maximum power and minimum pollution by carbon monoxide emission. Catalytic converters in the exhaust system also reduce carbon monoxide emission by converting CO to CO_2.

Complete combustion of octane (a petrol component):

$$2C_8H_{18}(l) + 25O_2(g) \rightarrow 16CO_2(g) + 18H_2O(l) \qquad \Delta_c H = -5470 \text{ kJ/mol}$$

Incomplete combustion of octane:

$$2C_8H_{18}(l) + 17O_2(g) \rightarrow 16CO(g) + 18H_2O(l) \qquad \Delta_c H = -3253 \text{ kJ/mol}$$

Heavier liquid fractions, such as kerosene, do not ignite when a lit match is applied to their surface unless a wick is present. Thus, kerosene lamps and home heaters use fibre wicks with high surface areas to produce sufficient vapour to form combustible fuel vapour–air mixtures.

Diesel fuel is also not as volatile as petrol. Therefore, to reduce air pollution from incomplete combustion of diesel, the fuel to air ratio in diesel engines is kept lower than the (stoichiometric) ratio required by the balanced equation. The additional oxygen helps to ensure more complete combustion. Diesel-powered cars that emit black smoke from their exhausts are poorly adjusted and produce less power. The following equation shows a possible combustion reaction in such an engine.

Incomplete combustion of hexadecane (a component of diesel):

$$2C_{16}H_{34}(l) + 25O_2(g) \rightarrow 16C(s) + 16CO(g) + 34H_2O(l)$$

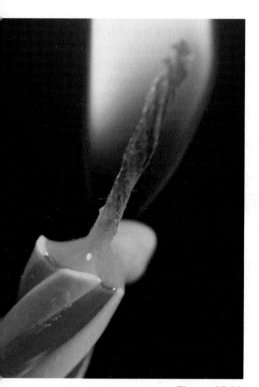

Figure 17.10
The burning wick of a candle

SAMPLE PROBLEM 17.3

Exhaust gases from a poorly tuned car under different driving conditions produce the following relative levels of pollutants. Account for these observations.

Table 17.4

Pollutants	Level of pollutants when cruising at constant speed	Level of pollutants when stationary with engine running
nitrogen oxides	high	low
carbon monoxide	low	high
hydrocarbons	low	high

SOLUTION ▷▷▷▷▷

Complete and
incomplete combustion

17.2 PRACTICAL
ACTIVITIES

Combustion

Insufficient oxygen mixes with unleaded fuel vapours when a car is idling (e.g. at traffic lights). This is less likely in a fuel injection system but was quite common in an old carburettor system. Incomplete combustion results, producing less energy, and leaving unburnt fuel in the exhaust. The following equation illustrates poor combustion of octane.

$$2C_8H_{18}(l) + 17O_2(g) \rightarrow 16CO(g) + 18H_2O(l)$$

When cruising along a highway, the ratio of air to fuel is optimal. With more available oxygen, the fuel vapours burn more completely. Complete combustion increases the temperature in the engine, promoting unwanted side reactions of air components to produce nitrogen oxides. The following equations show reactions in the engine when fuel combustion is complete.

$$2C_8H_{18}(l) + 25O_2(g) \rightarrow 16CO_2(g) + 18H_2O(l)$$

$$N_2(g) + 2O_2(g) \rightarrow 2NO_2(g)$$

SYLLABUS FOCUS

19. USING INSTRUCTION TERMS CORRECTLY

When answering questions, it is important to know what the instruction terms (verbs) require you to do. Here are some examples.

'Evaluate'

This instruction term requires you to make a judgement based on standards or criteria, or to determine the value of a proposal or idea.

Example:

Evaluate the use of hydrogen as an alternative to petrol for powering cars.

Answer:

Hydrogen has a much higher specific energy (143 MJ/kg) than petrol (~47 MJ/kg). Thus, on a weight basis, much more energy is available from hydrogen gas. The gas needs to be compressed, however, to provide sufficient energy density (amount of energy stored in a given volume or mass) to compete with petrol, which is condensed at room temperature. Hydrogen is a clean fuel as it burns to form non-polluting water; petrol burns to form carbon dioxide (a greenhouse gas), carbon monoxide (a toxic pollutant) and some carbon (soot) that contaminates the environment. However, hydrogen currently costs much more to manufacture than petrol and greater safety precautions must be taken due to the explosive nature of hydrogen–oxygen mixtures in the presence of a spark.

'Analyse'

This instruction term requires you to identify components and the relationship between them, or to draw out and relate implications.

Example:

When a fuel burns in oxygen, the temperature of the flame is higher if the reaction has a large heat of combustion and the number of moles of gaseous products that must be heated (per mole of fuel) is low. Analyse the following equations to predict which fuel would have the higher flame temperature. Identify the implications of this prediction.

Acetylene: $C_2H_2(g) + 5O_2(g) \rightarrow$
$\qquad 2CO_2(g) + H_2O(g) \quad \Delta H = -1213 \text{ kJ/mol}$
Propane: $C_3H_8(g) + 5O_2(g) \rightarrow$
$\qquad 3CO_2(g) + 4H_2O(g) \quad \Delta H = -2044 \text{ kJ/mol}$

Answer:

Each equation shows the combustion of 1 mole of fuel. The acetylene reaction releases 1213 kJ of energy per 3 moles of product gases (404 kJ per mole of products). The propane reaction releases 2044 kJ of energy per 7 moles of gaseous products (292 kJ per mole of products). Thus, according to the relationship between flame temperature, heat of combustion and moles of products:

$$\Delta H = -mC\Delta T$$

the acetylene flame should be hotter. In fact, an acetylene flame is very hot and useful in high-temperature welding and cutting of metals.

17.1 QUESTIONS

1. Which of the following is *not* an indicator of chemical change in the specified example?
   A Large amounts of heat are produced when sodium hydroxide and hydrochloric acid are mixed.
   B A colourless gas is evolved when copper (II) carbonate is heated.
   C A white, waxy solid turns into a clear liquid when gently heated.
   D A copper (II) sulfate solution turns a very deep blue when ammonia solution is added.

2. Identify the molecule that requires the greatest input of energy to convert one mole of the gaseous compound into gaseous atoms. (Refer to table 17.1 on page 315.)
   A C_2H_4
   B C_2H_6
   C C_2H_2
   D CH_4

3. Identify which of the following reactions is endothermic.
   A Electrolysis of water
   B Precipitation of lead (II) iodide
   C Neutralisation of zinc oxide by hydrochloric acid
   D Hydration of plaster of Paris

4. The activation energy for the complete combustion of heptane is 350 kJ/mol. The heat released when one mole of heptane burns in excess oxygen to form carbon dioxide and water is 4817 kJ/mol. Calculate the activation energy for the reverse reaction in which carbon dioxide and water combine to form heptane and oxygen.
   A 350 kJ
   B 4817 kJ
   C 4467 kJ
   D 5167 kJ

5. Select the correct statement about ignition temperatures.
   A Octane has a lower ignition temperature than methane.
   B Petrol has a lower ignition temperature than diesel.
   C The ignition temperature of a fuel is lower than its flash point.
   D Compression heating is used in a petrol engine because the ignition temperature of petrol is quite low.

6. Sulfur burns in air with a beautiful mauve flame, forming poisonous sulfur dioxide. The energy profile for the combustion of sulfur in oxygen is shown in figure 17.11. The reaction is:

   $$S(s) + O_2(g) \rightarrow SO_2(g)$$

   (a) Mixing sulfur with air at room temperature does not lead to any reaction. When the sulfur is heated, however, it eventually melts and starts to burn. Explain why sulfur does not burn at room temperature.
   (b) The enthalpy change for the combustion of sulfur is −300 kJ/mol.
       (i) Classify this reaction as endothermic or exothermic.
       (ii) Use figure 17.11 to identify which of the following algebraic quantities equates to ΔH: $H_A - H_C$, $H_C - H_A$, $H_A - H_B$, $H_B - H_A$, $H_C - H_B$.
       (iii) Identify the algebraic quantity in (ii) that equates to the activation energy of the forward reaction.
   (c) Explain why it is difficult to convert sulfur dioxide back into sulfur and oxygen.

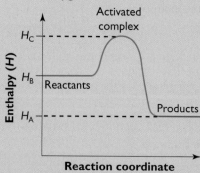

Figure 17.11 Energy profile of the combustion of sulfur

7. A mixture of hydrogen and carbon monoxide was prepared in the mole ratio 3 : 1. (This mixture is sometimes called 'town gas'.)
   (a) Write balanced equations for the combustion of (i) hydrogen and (ii) carbon monoxide in oxygen.
   (b) Use the following data to calculate the energy released in the combustion of 12 moles of the gaseous mixture.

   Heat of combustion for H_2 = 286 kJ/mol
   Heat of combustion for CO = 283 kJ/mol

8. Nitrogen dioxide gas is brown but its dimer, N_2O_4, is colourless. The proportion of each gas in a mixture is dependent on temperature. Figure 17.12 shows the energy profile for the reaction:

$$2NO_2(g) \rightarrow N_2O_4(g)$$

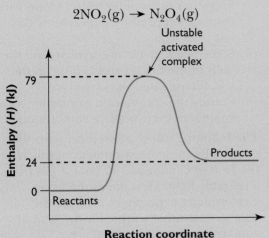

Figure 17.12 Energy profile for the dimerisation of NO_2. Dimerisation is the process where a molecule (or monomer) combines with another similar molecule.

(a) For the reaction above, determine the:
   (i) activation energy (E_A)
   (ii) enthalpy change (ΔH).
(b) As a mixture of NO_2 and N_2O_4 cools, it becomes paler (less brown). Classify this reaction as endothermic or exothermic.
(c) Calculate the activation energy for the decomposition of 1 mole of dinitrogen tetroxide.
(d) Identify whether the activated complex in the decomposition of dinitrogen tetroxide has more or less energy than the reactant or the product.

9. When ammonia decomposes, it forms nitrogen gas and hydrogen gas.

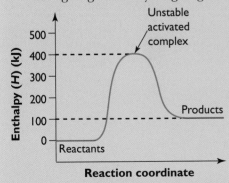

Figure 17.13 Energy profile for decomposition of ammonia

Figure 17.13 shows the energy profile for the decomposition of 2 moles of ammonia gas:

$$2NH_3(g) \rightarrow N_2(g) + 3H_2(g)$$

Use figure 17.13 to calculate the activation energy for the formation of 1 mole of ammonia from its elements.

10. The volatility of a fuel is measured by its equilibrium vapour pressure, which is usually measured at a standard temperature of 25 °C. Table 17.5 provides volatility data for three common fuels.

Table 17.5

Fuel	Vapour pressure (kPa) at 25 °C	Boiling point (°C)
ethanol	10.3	78
octane	1.9	126
dodecane	<0.1	216

(a) A student investigated the combustion of ethanol and dodecane. He placed ethanol and dodecane in two separate spirit lamps and lit each wick. He observed that the ethanol burnt readily with a blue flame and dodecane burnt poorly with a very sooty yellow flame. Account for the student's observations.
(b) The wick of the dodecane lamp was shortened so that less fibre was exposed to the air. This produce a non-sooty flame. Explain this observation.
(c) The student then held a match above the surface of a dish of ethanol. He observed that the fuel started to burn. On repeating the experiment with dodecane, he found that the fuel would not ignite. Explain why repeating the experiment with dodecane failed to produce combustion.
(d) Dodecane is a component of a petroleum fraction. Identify that fraction.
(e) Octane is a component of a petroleum fraction. Identify that fraction.

11. A combustible mixture of diesel vapour and air is placed in a vessel at 250 °C. Use the following information to determine whether this fuel vapour–oxidiser mixture would ignite in the absence of a flame at this temperature.

    Flash point of diesel = 65 °C

    Ignition temperature of diesel = 350 °C

12. Methanol has an ignition temperature of 385 °C and a flash point of 13 °C. Combustible methanol–air mixtures (6–36%v/v) can be quite dangerous as they ignite readily in the presence of an ignition source. The mixture burns with a pale blue flame, which is difficult to see in bright sunlight at a racetrack; racing car drivers have been burnt in such fires.

Table 17.6

Sample	Volume of methanol vapour (mL)	Volume of air (mL)
A	30	70
B	70	30

    Samples A and B with different methanol vapour–air compositions were prepared as in table 17.6.

    Explain which sample would ignite when heated to 450 °C in the absence of flames and sparks.

13. Figure 17.14 shows the apparatus used by a student to collect and analyse some of the gases produced by the combustion of a candle. Use this figure to answer the following questions.

    (a) Explain why the end of the U-tube on the right is connected to a water pump.

    (b) The blue cobalt chloride paper in the U-tube on the left turns pink. Identify the combustion product indicated by this test.

    (c) In the U-tube on the right, the limewater turns milky white. Identify the combustion product indicated by this test.

    (d) Some black specks are observed on the walls of the funnel and U-tube on the left. Identify this black product.

    (e) Classify the combustion of candle wax as complete or incomplete combustion.

14. The following information represents the results of a student experiment in which the heat of combustion of butane gas from a portable lighter was measured using a calorimetry experiment. Analyse the data to determine a value for the heat of combustion per mole of butane.

    Mass of water heated by the butane flame = 50.0 g

    Initial temperature of water in glass calorimeter = 19.7 °C

    Final temperature of water in glass calorimeter = 49.7 °C

    Mass of butane burnt = 0.25 g

    Specific heat capacity of water = 4.2 J/K/g

15. LPG (liquefied petroleum gas) is largely composed of propane. Evaluate a proposal to promote the use of LPG in suitably modified motor vehicles as a replacement for petrol.

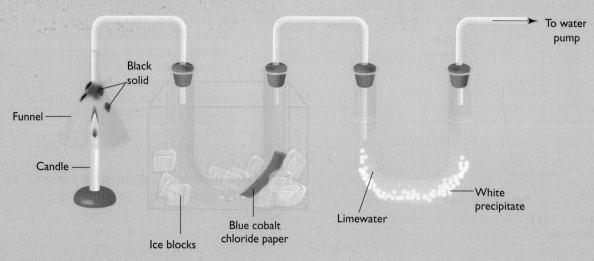

Figure 17.14 Collecting combustion products of a candle

17.2 *REACTION KINETICS*

Particle collisions and reaction rate

When you light a candle or burn natural gas, you are observing a chemical reaction that occurs at a rapid rate or speed. Some reactions are so fast that their rates are affected only by how fast we can mix the reactants. The **reaction rates** of strong acids and bases is an example of this. Other reactions can be very slow and may take hours, days or years to produce appreciable quantities of products. The study of the rates of chemical change is called **chemical kinetics**.

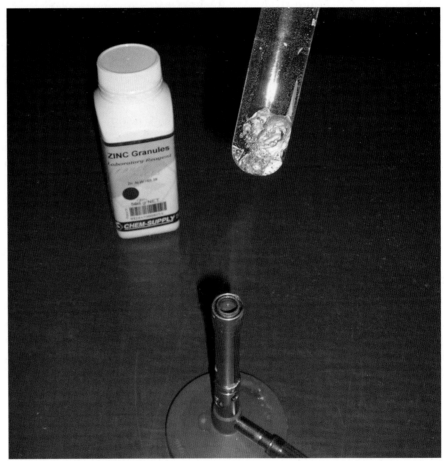

Figure 17.15
Heating zinc metal in acid increases the reaction rate.

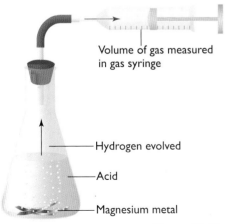

Volume of gas measured in gas syringe

Hydrogen evolved

Acid

Magnesium metal

Figure 17.16
Apparatus for measuring the volume of gas evolved versus time

The effect of temperature on reaction rate

We know from everyday experience that food cooks faster if we supply more heat. The same principles apply to chemical reactions in the laboratory. Generally, as the temperature increases, the reaction rate increases.
Example: Magnesium and hydrochloric acid

The reaction between magnesium strips and dilute hydrochloric acid produces magnesium chloride and hydrogen gas.

$$Mg(s) + 2HCl(aq) \rightarrow MgCl_2(aq) + H_2(g)$$

The rate of the reaction can be monitored by measuring the volume of hydrogen released as a function of time. The effect of increasing temperature on the rate of hydrogen evolution can be determined experimentally. In such an experiment, the mass of magnesium (1.0 g), and the volume (100 mL) and molarity (1.0 mol/L) of the acid are held constant while the temperature is varied.

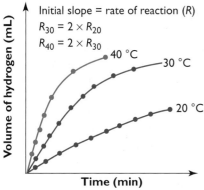

Initial slope = rate of reaction (R)
$R_{30} = 2 \times R_{20}$
$R_{40} = 2 \times R_{30}$

40 °C
30 °C
20 °C

Figure 17.17

Effect of temperature on the rate of the reaction between magnesium and hydrochloric acid

Figure 17.17 shows that the rate of the reaction (as measured by the initial slope of each line) increases as the temperature increases. Closer analysis shows that the rate approximately doubles for each 10 °C rise in temperature.

The effect of concentration on reaction rate

The effect of increasing the concentration of one or more reactants on the rate of the reaction can also be investigated experimentally. In the example of the reaction between magnesium and hydrochloric acid, the effect of varying the concentration of hydrochloric acid could be investigated at constant temperature. Figure 17.18 shows the results

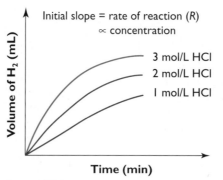

Initial slope = rate of reaction (R)
∝ concentration

3 mol/L HCl
2 mol/L HCl
1 mol/L HCl

Figure 17.18

Effect of the concentration of hydrochloric acid on the rate of its reaction with magnesium

of three experiments in which the acid concentration is increased from 1 to 3 molar. It shows that the initial reaction rate increases as the concentration of acid increases.

Reactions involving gases also show an increase in reaction rate as the pressure or concentration of the reactant gases increases. This can be achieved by reducing the size of the vessel so the reactant molecules have less free space, or by adding more reactant gases to a vessel with a fixed volume.

The effect of surface area

If 1.0 g of magnesium metal is ground into a fine powder and allowed to react at room temperature with 100 mL of 1.0 mol/L hydrochloric acid, the rate of the reaction is very much greater than when using strips of magnesium. The reaction is so rapid that the mixture becomes very hot. The powdered magnesium has a much greater surface area for the acid to attack, which increases the reaction rate.

Using particle models to explain reaction rates

Reactions occur because particles collide with sufficient energy to break bonds and allow new bonds to form. Svante Arrhenius (1859–1927) proposed a model to explain why increasing the temperature increases the reaction rate. He suggested that, at room temperature, only a few molecules in the reaction mixture have enough kinetic energy to react, so few collisions between reactant molecules result in reaction products. Further, in dilute solutions or in low-pressure gas systems, these few energetic molecules would rarely meet, so the reaction would be slow. Arrhenius reasoned that a reaction would occur if the sum of the kinetic energies of the reactants is greater than the minimum required energy (activation energy, E_A). If the reaction mixture is heated, a greater proportion of reactants would have kinetic energy greater than E_A, so more successful collisions would occur.

Later mathematical theories of reaction rates showed that the average kinetic energy, KE, of the colliding particles was directly proportional to the absolute (kelvin) temperature, T, of the system.

$$KE \propto T$$

Thus, if the system is heated from 27 °C (300 K) to 37 °C (310 K), the average kinetic energy of the reactant particles should increase (according to the above relationship) by about 3%. However, this small increase in kinetic energy of the particles does not explain why the reaction rate doubles when the temperature rises by 10 °C. The explanation lies in the non-uniform spread of kinetic energies in the population of molecules. Some molecules have much more kinetic energy than others and these more energetic molecules have energy greater than E_A. Raising the temperature by 10 °C doubles the number of these more energetic molecules, so the reaction rate doubles. Figure 17.19 illustrates this concept.

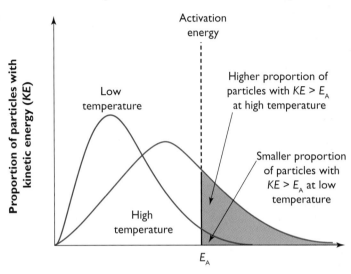

Figure 17.19
Effect of temperature on the proportion of particles with sufficient kinetic energy to react

In summary, the rate of the reaction depends on:

• collision rate, which depends on concentration

• the proportion of collisions with energy greater than E_A, which depends on temperature.

Catalysis

A **catalyst** is a chemical substance that increases the rate of a chemical reaction. Catalysts interact with one or more reactants or intermediates so that chemical bonds can be broken and re-formed more easily. An important characteristic of catalysts is that they are re-formed after the reaction is complete. The reaction pathway (or **mechanism** of the reaction) is altered by the catalytic interaction.

Catalysed reactions have lower activation energy, E_A, than similar uncatalysed reactions. Thus, at any specific temperature, a greater proportion of reactant particles have more energy than the lower activation energy. Figure 17.20 shows the effect of a catalyst on the energy profile of a reaction. Note that the enthalpy change for the reaction is not affected by the presence of a catalyst.

Experimental research is used to identify catalysts. For a substance to be classified as a catalyst, it must:

• increase the reaction rate compared with an uncatalysed control

• be re-formed at some later stage in the reaction.

catalyst: a substance that alters the rate of a reaction without a change in its own concentration

mechanism: the steps involved in a chemical reaction

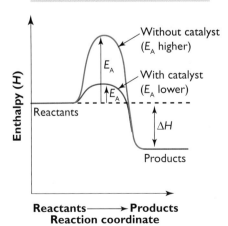

Figure 17.20
Effect of a catalyst on the activation energy of a reaction

An experiment investigated the effect of copper on the rate of the reaction between zinc granules and dilute hydrochloric acid. Figure 17.21 shows the experimental observations and numerical data for the reaction.

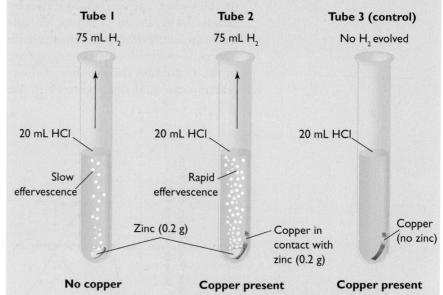

Tube 1	Tube 2	Tube 3 (control)
75 mL H₂	75 mL H₂	No H₂ evolved

20 mL HCl — 20 mL HCl — 20 mL HCl

Slow effervescence — Rapid effervescence

Zinc (0.2 g) — Copper in contact with zinc (0.2 g) — Copper (no zinc)

No copper — **Copper present** — **Copper present**

Mass of copper does not change during reaction.

Figure 17.21 Effect of copper on the rate of the reaction between zinc and hydrochloric acid

Use figure 17.21 to determine whether copper is acting as a catalyst in the reaction.

SOLUTION

Tubes 1 and 2 both contain zinc and produce hydrogen. However, tube 2 also contains copper and produces hydrogen more rapidly than tube 1. This satisfies the criterion that a catalyst increases the reaction rate.

The mass of copper recovered at the end of the experiment is the same as the initial mass of copper. Thus, no copper reacted permanently, satisfying the second criterion for a catalyst.

Thus, copper acted as a catalyst in this reaction.

Adding a catalyst to a reacting system cannot result in any more product than allowed by the stoichiometry of the reaction (as determined by the balanced chemical equation). The product accumulates, however, at a faster rate than without a catalyst. Figure 17.22 shows that, in the reaction between zinc and dilute hydrochloric acid, the volume of hydrogen produced is not affected by the presence of copper. It also shows that the rate of production of hydrogen is much faster in the presence of the copper catalyst.

Catalysts in industry

Let us examine some industrial uses of catalysts.

Manufacture of nitric acid

The manufacture of nitric oxide, NO, by the Ostwald process is an important step in the industrial manufacture of nitric acid. The first step

Initial slope = rate of reaction (R); $R_2 > R_1$

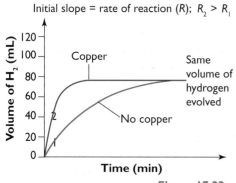

Figure 17.22
Volume of hydrogen evolved on reaction between zinc and hydrochloric acid, with and without the copper catalyst

of this process used a platinum–rhodium catalyst. Because the catalyst and reactants are in different phases, this process is an example of *heterogeneous catalysis*.

The initial reaction is catalytic oxidation of ammonia:

$$4NH_3(g) + 5O_2(g) \rightarrow 4NO(g) + 6H_2O(g)$$

Figure 17.23 shows a simplified view of the reactions that break and re-form bonds on the surface of the metallic catalyst in this initial step.

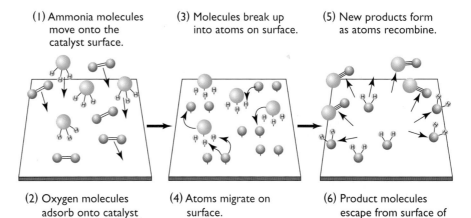

(1) Ammonia molecules move onto the catalyst surface.

(3) Molecules break up into atoms on surface.

(5) New products form as atoms recombine.

(2) Oxygen molecules adsorb onto catalyst surface.

(4) Atoms migrate on surface.

(6) Product molecules escape from surface of catalyst.

Figure 17.23
Reactions at the surface of the platinum–rhodium catalyst

The sum of the remaining reaction steps is:

$$4NO(g) + 3O_2(g) + 2H_2O(l) \rightarrow 4HNO_3(aq)$$

So, the overall reaction is:

$$NH_3(g) + 2O_2(g) \rightarrow HNO_3(aq) + H_2O(l)$$

Manufacture of ethyl acetate

Ethyl acetate, $CH_3CO_2C_2H_5$, is an important industrial solvent. It is manufactured by the reaction of acetic acid and ethanol in the presence of a concentrated sulfuric acid catalyst.

$$CH_3CO_2H(l) + C_2H_5OH(l) \rightarrow CH_3CO_2C_2H_5(l) + H_2O(l)$$

Because the acid catalyst and the reactants are all in the same phase, this reaction is an example of *homogeneous catalysis*. Even though the reaction is quite slow and the yield of product is less than 100%, the catalyst ensures that equilibrium is reached in the shortest possible time.

Rates of combustion reactions

Not all combustion reactions proceed at the same rate. Some are quite slow and others are so rapid that an explosion results. Fuels such as kerosene undergo rapid combustion.

Spontaneous combustion

Some fuels have a high ignition temperature, which prevents spontaneous combustion at room temperature. However, some materials with low activation energy and ignition temperature can combust spontaneously on exposure to air or oxygen. Some examples of where spontaneous combustion can occur are:
- *brown coal deposits.* When mined brown coal is exposed to air, it can oxidise, producing heat. The temperature of the coal deposit increases

17.3 PRACTICAL ACTIVITIES
Reaction rates

17.4 DATA ANALYSIS
Catalysis

eBook *plus*

Catalysis: Hydrogenation of ethylene

and it can combust spontaneously. This may be prevented by spraying water onto it to cool it.

- *haystacks.* The decomposition action of microbes (e.g. bacteria, moulds and protozoans) on moist, mown grass can build up heat in the centre of a stack. If the stack is quite large, the heat builds up faster than the stack can radiate heat. Spontaneous combustion can then occur. Modern farming practices have led to new methods of reducing this danger.
- *oily, cotton rags.* Cotton rags are used to mop up oil spills in some workshops. However, the cotton fibres provide a large surface area for the oil to make contact with the air. If the rags become hot enough, spontaneous combustion can result.
- *white phosphorus.* An allotrope of phosphorus is called 'white' phosphorus, P_4. It must be stored underwater as it will combust spontaneously on contact with air at quite low temperatures.

Slow combustion

Two examples of slow combustion are:

- *rusting.* When iron is exposed to air or oxygen in a moist environment, it oxidises slowly to form a substance called *rust.* Other metals also undergo surface corrosion. These reactions release heat but the rise in temperature is quite small as the reaction occurs only on the surface layers.
- *burning of wood, coal and coke.* When coal or coke or logs of wood are burnt in a fireplace, the combustion is much slower than when paper or twigs burn. These combustion reactions are slow because the fuel has a small surface area. If the surface area of the fuel is increased (e.g. by powdering the coal), the reaction can become very fast and possibly explosive.

Explosive combustion

Figure 17.25 compares the rates of a 'normal' reaction and an explosive reaction as a function of temperature. In explosions, there is a rapid increase in reaction rate with increasing temperature. This may occur if there is a rapid increase in temperature due to a chain reaction that produces an exponential growth in new reactants.

Examples of explosive combustion reactions include:

- *hydrogen and oxygen.* When mixtures of hydrogen gas in air are sparked, the hydrogen burns explosively to form water. This reaction is used in a controlled way in rocket engines; the water vapour formed in the reaction is expelled at high pressure and temperature to provide thrust.
- *hydrogen and chlorine.* Chlorine, like oxygen, can act as an oxidiser. Hydrogen gas and chlorine gas mixtures are stable in the dark but, on exposure to light, chlorine molecules absorb photons and break down to form reactive chlorine *radicals* that rapidly attack hydrogen molecules. A chain reaction begins that leads to an explosion, forming hydrogen chloride gas.
- *dust explosions.* Fine dust particles have very high surface areas. When mixtures of air and particles of a combustible material (e.g. carbon dust, flour dust, carbon toner dust, cellulosic dust) are sparked, they can explode. It is important in grain silos and mines to control the dust

Figure 17.24
The rusting of iron exposed to air is an example of a slow combustion reaction.

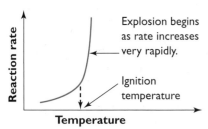

Non-explosive reactions

Rate increases with increasing temperature.

Explosive reactions

Explosion begins as rate increases very rapidly.

Ignition temperature

Figure 17.25
Relationship between reaction rates and temperature for explosive and non-explosive reactions

and monitor conditions to avoid such explosions. Rapid burning of coal dust can be observed by sprinkling a little graphite powder over a Bunsen burner flame.

- *internal combustion engine.* In these engines, fuels such as petrol are injected as fine droplets into the combustion chamber. In the presence of air, the mixture explodes when sparked.

Not all explosive reactions involve combustion. Nitroglycerine, $C_3H_5(NO_3)_3$, is a common explosive used in mining. This substance decomposes explosively to produce carbon dioxide, water vapour, nitrogen and oxygen. The heat released is so great that, when the gaseous products expand, they occupy a volume 10 000 times greater than the explosive itself.

17.5 DATA ANALYSIS
Explosions and safety

17.2 QUESTIONS

1. Identify which of the following changes in reaction conditions would increase the rate of the reaction between zinc and 1 mol/L hydrochloric acid.
   A Use more pieces of zinc of the same size.
   B Lower the temperature.
   C Increase the concentration of hydrochloric acid.
   D Use larger granules of zinc.

2. The rate of combustion of a candle could be increased by
   A increasing the length of the candle.
   B increasing the mass of the candle.
   C using a smaller wick.
   D placing the burning candle in a jar of oxygen rather than air.

3. Select the statement that is true of catalysts.
   A Catalysts lower the activation energy for a reaction.
   B Catalysts are consumed during the reaction.
   C Catalysts are always solids.
   D Catalysts reduce the heat liberated or consumed in a reaction.

4. A student investigated the rate of decomposition of hydrogen peroxide into water and oxygen gas at room temperature. She prepared a detergent–hydrogen peroxide solution and poured 10 mL into each of stoppered measuring cylinders A and B. She then added 100 mg of powdered manganese dioxide to cylinder B. Both cylinders were shaken for 5 seconds and then placed on a bench. A froth formed in both cylinders, but the froth in cylinder B grew and rose up the tube much faster than

in cylinder A. The student hypothesised that the manganese dioxide must be acting as a catalyst. What must she now do to confirm this hypothesis?
   A Show that more manganese dioxide increases the rate of decomposition of peroxide.
   B Increase the temperature to show that more frothing occurs.
   C Repeat the experiment with more hydrogen peroxide.
   D Show that the mass of manganese dioxide at the end is the same as at the start.

5. Caster sugar, used in sponge cakes, dissolves more readily in eggwhite than does granulated sugar because
   A it has a greater surface area than granulated sugar.
   B it has a lower heat of solution than granulated sugar.
   C it can achieve a higher concentration in eggwhite than granulated sugar.
   D its particles are much larger than normal table sugar.

6. In an experiment, cornflour is suspended as a fine smoke in air in a closed container. A flame is introduced and there is an explosion. In a second experiment, the cornflour is placed in a crucible and heated strongly with a Bunsen flame. The material chars but does not explode.
   (a) Account for the differences in these two experiments.
   (b) Explain why mining companies need to control coal dust in coal mines.

7. Figure 17.26 shows the volume of carbon dioxide released when a fixed mass of calcium carbonate reacted with excess hydrochloric acid at constant temperature. In one experiment, calcium carbonate was supplied as marble chips and, in the other, as a powder.

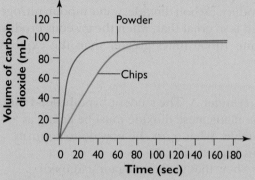

Figure 17.26

(a) Explain why the reaction with the powdered calcium carbonate was much faster than with marble chips.
(b) Explain why the same volume of carbon dioxide was released in each experiment.

8. Jesse winds strips of magnesium around deflagrating spoons. He ignites the ribbons in a Bunsen burner flame and then allows the strips to continue to burn in two separate gas jars. Jar A contains air and jar B contains pure oxygen. Compare the rate of combustion of magnesium in the gas jars.

9. Rust is a serious problem in our built environment. The rusting of iron requires the presence of both water and oxygen. Explain how the rate of this reaction could be increased.

10. Figure 17.27 shows a flask containing chips of calcium carbonate and dilute hydrochloric acid. Explain how this apparatus could be used to measure the rate of the reaction between the acid and calcium carbonate.

11. Explain how haystacks can suddenly burst into flame.

12. Methane–air mixtures are explosive when the methane concentration is between 5 and 15%v/v. An experimentalist investigates the behaviour of burning methane. He takes a tin can with a pressdown lid (e.g. Milo can). He makes a 10 mm hole in the bottom of the can and a 5 mm hole in the lid. The can is filled with methane gas and placed on a tripod. A flame from a candle is applied to the hole in the lid and the methane starts to burn with a blue-yellow flame, which quickly disappears. The experimentalist waits for a while at a safe distance behind a special screen. For a while, nothing seems to happen. Then, there is an explosion that causes the lid to be thrown upwards.

Account for this behaviour of the burning methane.

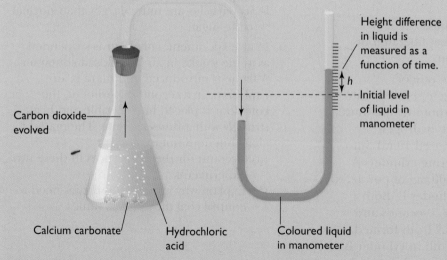

Figure 17.27 Reaction between calcium carbonate and hydrochloric acid

eBook *plus*

Weblinks

eBook *plus*

Module 4
Revision

eBook *plus*

Module 4
Revision Answers

SUMMARY

- Hydrocarbons such as petrol, kerosene and diesel are common fuels. How readily fuels combust depends on several factors including ignition temperature, volatility and flash point.

- Energy is released when hydrocarbons burn. The energy released (per mole) is called the heat of combustion or enthalpy of combustion. Combustion can be described as slow, spontaneous or explosive.

- Chemical reactions involve bond-breaking (endothermic) and bond-forming (exothermic) processes.

- Pollution can result from incomplete combustion of fuels. Carbon monoxide and soot are common pollutants produced by incomplete hydrocarbon combustion.

- Chemical reactions vary in their rate. Catalysts can be used to increase the rate of reactions. Catalysts have an important role in industry.

- Various factors, including temperature, pressure, concentration, surface area and catalysts, affect the rate of a reaction. Changes in reaction rate with temperature can be understood in terms of changes in the kinetic energy of the colliding molecules.

- Catalysts are important in industry as they increase the rate at which products are produced.

- The energy required to begin a chemical reaction is called the activation energy. If molecules do not have sufficient kinetic energy to overcome the activation energy barrier, no reaction occurs.

PRACTICAL ACTIVITIES

17.1 PRACTICAL ACTIVITIES

EXOTHERMIC AND ENDOTHERMIC REACTIONS

Aim

To investigate and classify a range of chemical reactions as endothermic or exothermic

Safety issues

- Wear safety glasses throughout this experiment.

- Take particular care with bases such as sodium hydroxide that they do not come in contact with your eyes or skin.

- Avoid breathing ammonia vapours.

- Identify other safety issues relevant to this experiment by reading the method.

Materials

- clean test tubes
- test-tube rack
- Pasteur pipettes
- 10 mL measuring cylinder
- glass stirring rod
- alcohol thermometer (−10 °C to +100 °C range)
- 2 mol/L HCl
- 2 mol/L NaOH
- universal indicator solution
- copper (II) carbonate solid
- plaster of Paris
- 2 mol/L calcium chloride solution
- 2 mol/L sodium carbonate solution
- magnesium ribbon (5cm)
- hydrated barium hydroxide solid
- ammonium thiocyanate solid

Method

1. Table 17.7 describes seven experiments. These should be done using small quantities of

Table 17.7

Experiment	Reaction	Procedure	Observations	Classification
1	Hydrochloric acid + sodium hydroxide solution	Pour 2 mL of 2 mol/L NaOH into a clean test tube and add 3 drops of universal indicator. Slowly add 30–50 drops of 2 mol/L HCl from a Pasteur pipette.		
2	Copper (II) carbonate + hydrochloric acid	Put about one third of a scoop of copper (II) carbonate into a test tube and add 20–30 drops of hydrochloric acid using a Pasteur pipette.		
3	Dissolution of ammonium nitrate in water	Add half a scoop of ammonium nitrate crystals to 2 mL of water in a test tube.		
4	Hydration of plaster of Paris	Place half a scoop of plaster of Paris in a dry test tube and add drops of water until no further change occurs.		
5	Sodium carbonate solution + calcium chloride solution	Add drops of 2 mol/L calcium chloride solution to 2 mL of 2 mol/L sodium carbonate solution in a test tube.		
6	Magnesium + hydrochloric acid	Put a 5 cm coiled strip of magnesium in 2 mL of 2 mol/L hydrochloric acid.		
7	Hydrated barium hydroxide + ammonium thiocyanate	Mix half a scoop of hydrated barium hydroxide with half a scoop of ammonium thiocyanate. Stir the solid mixture gently with a glass rod. (Do NOT breathe the vapours.)		

PRACTICAL ACTIVITIES

chemicals in clean test tubes, with an alcohol thermometer inserted to measure changes in temperature.

2. Copy and complete table 17.7 as you conduct the experiments. Measure the initial temperature and the highest or lowest temperature reached during the reaction. Record these values, together with other observations in the 'Observations' column. In the 'Classification' column, write 'exothermic' or 'endothermic' to classify the observed reaction.

Questions

Answer the following questions in your report on this experiment.

1. Write balanced equations for each of the reactions performed.

   (*Note:* In experiment 4, plaster of Paris has the formula $2CaSO_4.H_2O$ and the gypsum that forms has the formula $CaSO_4.2H_2O$. In experiment 7, the formula of ammonium thiocyanate is NH_4SCN and barium hydroxide has 8 molecules of water in its crystal. The products of the reaction are ammonia, water and barium thiocyanate.)

2. Explain why the temperature of the system decreases during an endothermic reaction.

Conclusion

Briefly describe the outcome of your investigation.

17.2 PRACTICAL ACTIVITIES

COMBUSTION

Part A: Combustion of wood and magnesium

Aim

To compare the change in weight on the combustion of wood and magnesium

Safety issues

- Wear safety glasses throughout this experiment.
- Identify other safety issues relevant to this experiment by reading the method.

Materials

- wooden sticks (e.g. paddle-pop sticks broken in half)
- 10 cm magnesium ribbon
- tongs
- evaporating basins
- electronic balance
- Bunsen burner

Method

1. Determine the mass of a clean evaporating basin. Determine the mass of a wooden stick.

2. Hold the end of the wooden stick in a pair of tongs and ignite the wood using a Bunsen flame. Allow any wood ash to fall into the basin. Release the end of the wood into the basin and allow the remainder of the wood to finish burning in the basin.

3. When cool, reweigh the basin and ash. Determine the mass of the ash.

4. Weigh a new basin and a 10cm strip of magnesium ribbon.

5. Hold the ribbon over the basin and ignite the free end with a Bunsen flame. Allow the ash to fall into the basin. Allow the remainder of the ribbon to finish burning in the basin.

6. When cool, reweigh the basin and ash. Determine the mass of the ash.

Results
Record your observations in a suitable table.

Questions
Answer the following questions in your report on this experiment:

1. Compare the mass of the wood with the mass of the wood ash. Has there been an increase or decrease in mass?
2. Compare the mass of the magnesium and the ash. Has there been an increase or decrease in mass?
3. Explain the difference in results between the two experiments.

Part B: Combustion of a candle

Aim
To observe the combustion of a candle.

Background
A candle is composed of a fibre wick surrounded by wax. The wax consists of long-chain hydrocarbons; it has a low volatility so combustible mixtures of its vapour with air will form only if the wax is hot. The wick provides a large surface area on which hot, liquid wax molecules can vaporise. The wick and any wax on its surface are ignited initially by the flame of a burning match. The candle produces a flame around the wick due to the presence of a combustible mixture of hydrocarbon vapours and air. The flame is the reaction zone that radiates heat outwards. Some of this radiant heat melts the wax and creates a pool of melted wax that can move upwards through the pores of the wick by capillary action to provide a continuous supply of wax vapour for the flame. The narrow zone of wax vapour around the wick helps to prevent it burning away too rapidly. As the candle burns down, the tip of the wick becomes exposed to the air and chars as it burns. Candle wax burns incompletely due to the slow diffusion of air into the flame zone. The blackening of a beaker placed above the flame shows the presence of unburnt carbon in the flame.

Safety issues
- Wear safety glasses throughout this experiment.
- Identify other safety issues relevant to this experiment by reading the method.

Materials
- candle (e.g. a birthday candle)
- Petri dish
- electronic balance
- matches

Method
1. Stand the candle in the Petri dish and weigh them.
2. Light the candle and make observations as the candle burns at the wick. Note the colours of the wax and the zones of the flame. Is there any black smoke? Note how the wax melts in some areas and re-solidifies in others.
3. Continue the observations until the candle has burnt down 1–2 cm. Draw a labelled diagram of the flame, wick and top of the candle, noting any regions of different colour.
4. Blow out the flame and reweigh the dish and candle.

Results
Record your observations in a suitable way.

Figure 17.28

PRACTICAL ACTIVITIES

Questions

Answer the following questions in your report on this experiment.

1. Explain why the candle loses mass on burning.

2. Identify changes in state during the combustion of a candle.

3. The innermost zone of the flame near the wick is black. In this region, there are unburnt wax vapours. Predict whether this zone will be cool or hot.

4. A yellow, luminous middle zone of the flame indicates a region of incomplete combustion where the flame is moderately hot. The yellow colour indicates the presence of glowing soot particles as a combustion product. Explain why the wax vapours are only partially burnt in this zone.

5. A blue, non-luminous flame indicates regions of complete combustion of the hydrocarbon vapour. Explain why this blue region is at the base and edge of the flame zone and why this part of the flame is very hot.

6. Explain (in terms of ignition temperature and combustible mixtures) why the combustion of the wax vapour is self-sustaining after the lit match is removed.

Conclusion

Briefly describe the outcome of your investigation.

17.3 PRACTICAL ACTIVITIES

REACTION RATES

Part A: Permanganate–oxalic acid reaction

Aim

To investigate the effect of different variables on the rate of the reaction between potassium permanganate and oxalic acid

Background

The reaction between pink-purple permanganate ions and colourless oxalic acid in an acidic medium is shown by the equation:

$$2MnO_4^-(aq) + 5C_2O_4H_2(aq) + 6H^+(aq) \rightarrow$$
$$2Mn^{2+}(aq) + 8H_2O(l) + 10CO_2(g)$$

The average rate of the reaction can be determined by the time taken for the solution to change from pink-purple to colourless.

Safety issues

- Wear safety glasses throughout this experiment.
- Oxalic acid is poisonous. Do not ingest it.
- Potassium permanganate can stain hands and clothing.
- Identify other safety issues relevant to this experiment by reading the method.

Materials

- large test tubes
- burettes
- conical flasks
- thermometers
- hotplate
- stopwatches
- water bath
- 250 mL of 0.10 mol/L oxalic acid, $C_2O_4H_2.2H_2O$
- 250 mL of 4.0 mol/L sulfuric acid
- 250 mL of 0.005 mol/L potassium permanganate, $KMnO_4$
- 50mL of 0.1 mol/L manganese sulfate solution
- deionised water

Method

Part 1: Effect of concentration of oxalic acid

1. All experiments should be done in large test tubes immersed in a constant-temperature water bath at about 30 °C. Note the temperature in your results.

2. In clean test tubes, prepare the mixtures in table 17.8.

Table 17.8

Mixture	Tube 1	Tube 2	Final concentration of oxalic acid in reaction mixture (mol/L)
1	4.0 mL KMnO$_4$	4.0 mL oxalic acid, 2.0 mL sulfuric acid	4.0/10.0 × 0.10 = 0.040
2	4.0 mL KMnO$_4$	3.0 mL oxalic acid, 1.0 mL water, 2.0 mL sulfuric acid	
3	4.0 mL KMnO$_4$	2.0 mL oxalic acid, 2.0 mL water, 2.0 mL sulfuric acid	

3. For each mixture, equilibrate the two test tubes in the water bath. Tip the contents of tube 2 into tube 1 and start timing. Agitate the reaction mixture and record the time (in seconds) when the pink-purple colour first disappears.

4. Calculate the concentration of oxalic acid in each final reaction mixture. The total volume of each reaction mixture is 10.0 mL. The first calculation has been done for you.

5. Combine all class results to improve reliability.

6. Record your observations in a suitable table with the headings 'Mixture', 'Final oxalic acid concentration, and 'Reaction time'.

7. Calculate the mean reaction time and determine the deviation from the mean for each mixture.

Part 2: Effect of temperature

1. Follow the same general procedure as in part 1. However, this time, keep the concentrations constant and vary the temperature.

2. Use the mixture of reactants shown in table 17.9.

Table 17.9

Tube 1	Tube 2
4.0 mL KMnO$_4$	4.0 mL oxalic acid 2.0 mL sulfuric acid

3. Do the experiment as in part 1 at the following water bath temperatures: 30 °C, 40 °C, 50 °C.

4. Record the time for decolourisation as in part 1. Tabulate your results. Combine class results to improve reliability.

5. Calculate the mean reaction time and deviation from the mean for each temperature.

Part 3: Effect of a catalyst

1. Follow the same general procedure as in part 1. However, this time, a small volume of manganese sulfate solution is added to test its catalytic properties. All other variables are constant.

2. Test the reaction mixtures in table 17.10 at 30 °C.

3. Record the time for decolourisation as before. Tabulate your results. Combine class results to improve reliability. Calculate the mean reaction time and the deviation from the mean for each mixture.

Table 17.10

Mixture	Tube 1	Tube 2
1	4.0 mL KMnO$_4$	3.0 mL oxalic acid 2.0 mL sulfuric acid 1.0 mL water
2	4.0 mL KMnO$_4$	3.0 mL oxalic acid 2.0 mL sulfuric acid 0.5 mL water 0.5 mL manganese sulfate

PRACTICAL ACTIVITIES

Questions
Answer the following questions in your report on this experiment.

1. Explain how the reaction time is related to the reaction rate.
2. Discuss the effect on the reaction rate decreasing the concentration of oxalic of acid.
3. Discuss the effect on the reaction rate of increasing the temperature.
4. Discuss the effect on the reaction rate of the presence of manganese sulfate. What other information would be needed to prove that manganese ions were acting catalytically?

Part B: Acid on calcium carbonate

Aim
To investigate the effect of particle size on the rate of the reaction between hydrochloric acid and marble.

Safety issues
- Wear safety glasses throughout this experiment.
- Identify other safety issues relevant to this experiment by reading the method.

Materials
- 2 measuring cylinders
- two 50 mL beakers
- stirring rods
- electronic balance
- stopwatch
- 5.0 g marble chips
- 5.0 g powdered calcium carbonate
- 1 mol/L hydrochloric acid

Method
1. Weigh 5.0 g each of marble chips and powdered calcium carbonate into separate small beakers.
2. Measure 50 mL of 1 mol/L hydrochloric acid into separate measuring cylinders.
3. Add the acid to each beaker and stir the mixtures. Record the time for the mixture in each beaker to stop fizzing.
4. Combined all class results. Compare the reaction times for large and small particles.

Results
Record your observations in a suitable table.

Questions
Answer the following questions in your report on this experiment:

1. Compare the surface area of 5 g of marble chips to 5 g of powdered calcium carbonate.
2. Explain why the reaction rate is much higher for powdered calcium carbonate than for marble chips.
3. Determine which reactant was in excess in this experiment.

Conclusion
Briefly describe the outcome of your investigations.

DATA ANALYSIS

17.4 DATA ANALYSIS

CATALYSIS

Model construction

1. For each step in the following reactions, use a molecular model kit to make models of each reactant and catalyst molecule.
2. Draw a diagram of the models at each step.

Example 1: Decomposition of ozone

1. Make a model of the ozone molecule, O_3. It is an angular (bent) molecule.
2. Make a model of a nitric oxide molecule, NO.
3. NO reacts with O_3 to form NO_2 and O_2. Model this reaction.
4. NO_2 then reacts with reactive oxygen atoms (free radicals) to form nitric oxide and O_2. Model this reaction.
5. Identify the catalyst, which is the atom or molecule used up in one step and re-formed in a later step.
6. Write these reaction steps as a series of balanced equations. Sum these reactions steps to obtain the overall ozone decomposition reaction.

Example 2: Hydrogenation of ethylene

Hydrogenation of ethylene is catalysed by finely divided palladium or platinum. This reaction involves a heterogeneous catalyst. After the gaseous molecules adsorb onto the catalyst's surface, bonds break and new bonds form. The product molecules then desorb from the surface.

1. Let the desktop represent the surface of the catalyst.
2. Make a model of ethylene, C_2H_4, and a model of H_2 gas. Place both molecules on the catalyst surface. They are now adsorbed onto the surface.
3. Break the bond of the hydrogen molecule to form two reactive hydrogen atoms (free radicals). These are bound to the metal atoms but they can move across the surface of the catalyst towards the ethylene.
4. One reactive hydrogen atom attacks a carbon atom of the ethylene molecule, causing the double bond to break and forming a single carbon–carbon bond. Model this reaction.
5. The other hydrogen atom bonds to the second carbon atom to form ethane. Model this reaction.
6. The ethane molecule then desorbs from the catalyst's surface. The surface is now free to catalyse a new reaction.
7. Compare the strength of the metal–hydrogen bond on the catalyst surface with the hydrogen–hydrogen bond in H_2.

DATA ANALYSIS

17.5 DATA ANALYSIS

EXPLOSIONS AND SAFETY

Part A: Hydrogen gas explosion

The reaction that occurs when a mixture of hydrogen and oxygen is sparked is an example of a reaction in which the rate of formation of free radicals determines whether the mixture explodes or not. Changes in parameters such as temperature, pressure and solid surfaces alter the progress of the reaction.

The box below provides some examples of reaction steps that occur in the combustion of hydrogen. Steps A to G are listed in random order. (*Note:* In equations, free radicals are shown by placing a dot next to the molecular formula to represent an unpaired electron.)

$\cdot OH + H_2 \rightarrow H_2O + H\cdot$	(A)
$HO_2\cdot + H_2 \rightarrow H_2O + \cdot OH$	(B)
$H_2 \rightarrow H\cdot + H\cdot$	(C)
$H\cdot + H\cdot \rightarrow H_2$	(D)
$O\cdot + H_2 \rightarrow \cdot OH + H\cdot$	(E)
$H\cdot + O_2 \rightarrow \cdot OH + O\cdot$	(F)
$H\cdot + O_2 \rightarrow HO_2\cdot$	(G)

Answer the following questions using information from the box.

Questions

1. The first step in the combustion of hydrogen is to break the H—H bond to form reactive hydrogen radicals. This is achieved by sparking so that the temperature is high enough to overcome the activation energy barrier. Use the code letter to identify the equation that represents this process.

2. Once the hydrogen free radicals form, they can react with oxygen molecules to generate oxygen and hydroxyl free radicals. Identify the equation that represents this reaction.

3. Once oxygen free radicals form, they can attack hydrogen molecules to form more hydrogen and hydroxyl radicals. Identify the equation that represents this reaction.

4. Above a temperature of 890 K (617 °C), the reaction is always explosive because the production of radicals described in (2) and (3) occur so rapidly that a chain reaction results. Below this temperature, the walls of the vessel can absorb and deactivate radicals. Three of the listed equations describe the propagation of radicals in the gas phase and one describes the termination of radicals to form a stable molecule.

   (a) Identify the three equations involving propagation and formation of new radicals.

   (b) Identify the equation that shows a radical termination step.

5. It is known that some substances, such as KCl, on vessel walls promote the termination of radicals by allowing $HO_2\cdot$ and $H\cdot$ radicals to combine. What molecule forms when these two radicals collide?

6. Explain why hydrogen–oxygen mixtures are safe at room temperature.

7. Identify the safety precautions necessary to store and handle hydrogen safely.

Part B: Dust explosions

Read the following information and answer the questions that follow:

As long ago as 1785, it was recognised that certain types of dust can lead to explosions. Flour dust contains starch and cellulose, which burn under certain conditions. In 1785, flour dust in a baker's storeroom in Italy exploded when it came in contact with an oil lamp.

Dust explosions in industry must be avoided as they can injure or kill workers and damage equipment and buildings.

Various dust clouds in air can form flammable mixtures. If an ignition source is present, an explosion can occur in which the flame propagates rapidly through the dust cloud. A flash fire results if the flame propagates in an open space. In a closed space, the pressure wave leads to an explosion. The maximum pressure in a dust explosion is typically 500–1000 kPa.

DATA ANALYSIS

The severity of the explosion is related to the heat released in the combustion reaction. Some examples are shown in table 17.11.

The conditions that lead to dust particle explosions are:

- suspended dust particles less than 0.1 mm in diameter
- suspended dust concentration between 50 and 3000 g/m^3
- moisture content of dust less than 11%
- oxygen concentration greater than 12%
- presence of an ignition source (e.g. open flame, hot surface or electrical discharge)
- presence of a combustible mixture in a closed space.

The types of dust that form combustible mixtures with air include:

- metals (e.g. Al, Mg, Zn and Fe)
- non-metals (e.g. C and S)
- natural organic materials (e.g. starch, cellulose and coal)
- synthetic organic materials (e.g. pigments and plastics).

Various industrial standards for dust level are set to maintain safety. The Australian government has set the industrial hygiene range at about 1–10 mg/m^3.

Some common procedures used to prevent dust explosions include:

- using pneumatic dust collectors to keep dust levels low at all times
- venting of dust
- adding inert dust to reduce the concentration of combustible dust (e.g. rock dust in coal mines)

- using unreactive gases (N_2, CO_2, inert gases) in reaction vessels to prevent oxygen reaching the dust
- regular monitoring and maintaining electrical equipment to avoid sparking.

Primary dust explosions can also lead to secondary explosions. The primary blast wave can cause dust in other areas to become suspended and burn explosively as the primary flame front propagates outwards.

Questions

1. Explain why flour dust can be dangerous in bakeries.
2. A closed storage room contains suspended dust from sugarcane fibres. The dust particles are 0.01 mm in size and the concentration of dust is 1000 g/m^3. Identify the additional conditions required to cause the explosion of this dust suspension.
3. A dust of finely powdered aluminium is created in a metal grinding factory. The sparks from the grinding caused the dust suspension to explode.
   (a) Write a balanced equation for the reaction that occurred.
   (b) Explain how the factory managers could prevent such explosions in the future.
4. Identify which of the following produces the most severe explosions: carbohydrate dusts, active metal dusts, non-metal dusts.
5. Explain how secondary explosions can result from primary explosions in suspended dust.

Table 17.11

Dust	sulfur	carbon	starch	zinc	aluminium	magnesium
Heat released per mole O$_2$ (kJ)	297	394	470	700	1117	1204

SAMPLE EXAMINATION PAPER

CHEMISTRY PRELIMINARY COURSE

Time limit: 2 hours

Structure of the paper:

Part A: 20 multiple choice questions (1 mark each)

Part B: extended response questions (50 marks)

Total marks: 70

Use the periodic table (inside front cover) and data sheet (inside back cover) as required.

Part A: Multiple choice questions

1. A new factory is established to provide compressed and liquefied gases to industry, universities and hospitals. A university requires a sample of compressed argon. The most suitable separation method would be

   A simple distillation of liquid air.

   B fractional distillation of liquid air.

   C froth flotation.

   D centrifugation of filtered air at 0 °C.

2. The set of elements that contains a metal, a semi-metal and a non-metal is

   A sulfur, potassium, boron.

   B zinc, germanium, plutonium.

   C copper, carbon, bromine.

   D silicon, rubidium, nickel.

3. Identify the ionic compound.

   A Sulfur dioxide

   B Germanium dioxide

   C Nitrogen trichloride

   D Calcium iodide

4. Identify the reactions in which heat and light energy are released.

   A Combustion of aluminium powder in oxygen

   B Neutralisation of calcium hydroxide with nitric acid

   C Electrolysis of water

   D Corrosion of steel

5. Select the statement that is true of solder.

   A Solder is an alloy of zinc and tin.

   B Solder has zero electrical conductivity.

   C Solder is brittle and soft.

   D Electricians use solder because of its low melting point.

6. When zinc is placed in dilute hydrochloric acid, a slow effervescence is observed. Select the correct statement about this process.

   A Each zinc atom loses two electrons as it ionises.

   B Gaseous carbon dioxide is evolved.

   C This reaction is slower than the reaction between tin and dilute acid.

   D The hydrogen ions in the acid lose electrons to the metal.

7. Select the correct statement concerning the trends from left to right across the third period (Na to Ar) of the periodic table.

   A Ionisation energy decreases.

   B Electrical conductivity increases.

   C Electronegativity increases.

   D Boiling point increases.

8. Select the statement that is true about Mendeleev's 1869 periodic table.

   A The table was successful because he left spaces for elements yet to be discovered.

   B His table was based on the sub-atomic structure of the atom.

   C Mendeleev used the atomic number as the basis for his elemental classification system.

   D Mendeleev predicted the existence of the noble gases many years before they were discovered.

9. Select the true statement about aluminium.

   A Aluminium was not discovered until the nineteenth century because its ores were rare and only found deep in the Earth's crust.

   B Aluminium is the second most abundant metal in the Earth's crust.

   C Most aluminium deposits are not economical as the minerals are widely dispersed.

   D Although considerable amounts of electrical energy are required to extract aluminium from its ore, aluminium has become one of the major metals used in the last 100 years.

10. Ten moles of nitrogen dioxide gas is placed in a closed vessel at 0 °C and 100 kPa. Nitrogen gas is placed in an equal size vessel at the same temperature and pressure. Select the correct statement.

A   The mass of nitrogen present in the second vessel is 28.0 g.

B   The mass of nitrogen dioxide gas present is 460 g.

C   There are ten times as many molecules of nitrogen dioxide in the first vessel as nitrogen molecules in the second vessel.

D   There are 6.02×10^{23} molecules of nitrogen dioxide in the first vessel.

11. Nitrogen and hydrogen cyanide have similar molar weights but quite different melting and boiling points. Hydrogen cyanide's much greater melting and boiling point is explained by

A   hydrogen cyanide being a more polar molecule than nitrogen.

B   hydrogen cyanide being an ionic solid.

C   hydrogen bonding existing between neighbouring hydrogen cyanide molecules.

D   hydrogen cyanide having a covalent network structure.

12. Some solutes were tested for their solubility in water. Identify the solute with the greatest solubility at room temperature.

A   Calcium nitrate

B   Carbon dioxide

C   Germanium dioxide

D   Nitrogen gas

13. The number of moles of nitrate ions present in 400 mL of a 0.20 mol/L solution of barium nitrate is

A   0.08

B   0.16

C   0.06

D   0.32

14. A 10-litre sample of water (density = 1.0 kg/L) is contaminated with 10 ppm of lead ions. The mass of lead in this sample is

A   100 mg.

B   10 g.

C   20 mg.

D   1000 mg.

15. A beaker containing 500g of water at 25 °C is heated until its temperature is 90 °C. Calculate the quantity of heat required (specific heat capacity of water = 4.18 J/K/g).

A   135.85 J

B   156.75 J

C   67 925 J

D   135 850 J

16. The products of photosynthesis are

A   carbon dioxide.

B   carbon dioxide, water and oxygen.

C   oxygen and glucose.

D   oxygen and water.

17. Select the correct statement concerning the allotropes of carbon.

A C_{60} is a covalent molecular crystal.

B   Diamond is a covalent molecular crystal.

C   Graphite is harder than diamond.

D   Carbon nanotubes are harder than diamond.

18. Identify which of the following alkanes is a component of the refinery gas fraction when petroleum is fractionally distilled.

A   Octane

B   Ethane

C   Decane

D   Octadecane

19. Select the reaction that is exothermic.

A   Dissolution of ammonium nitrate in water

B   Electrolysis of salt water

C   Dissolution of potassium hydroxide in water

D   Electrical decomposition of molten potassium chloride

20. The rate of the oxidation reaction between red-hot iron wool and air could be increased by

A   injecting carbon dioxide into the vessel.

B   rolling the iron wool into a tight ball.

C   using infra-red radiation to keep the iron wool hot.

D   increasing the oxygen concentration in the air.

Part B: Extended response questions

21. (*3 marks*)

Copper minerals are often blue or green in colour. Ancient people in the Middle East recognised copper in rocks by these blue or green mineral veins. Azurite is a deep blue copper mineral. Malachite is a beautiful green mineral and a basic copper carbonate with the formula $CuCO_3.Cu(OH)_2$.

(a) Bert added a chip of malachite to a beaker containing some dilute hydrochloric acid. Malachite reacts with dilute hydrochloric acid to produce a blue-green solution. Write a balanced equation for this reaction.

(b) Explain whether Bert would observe any differences between the reactions of malachite and azurite with hydrochloric acid.

(c) Explain how metallic copper could be extracted easily from the blue-green solution produced by malachite and hydrochloric acid.

22. (*3 marks*)

Industrial chemists investigate ways of increasing the rates of reactions so that products are formed as fast as possible. Adding a catalyst is one way of increasing the rate of a reaction. Other ways of increasing the reaction rate are:

(a) increasing the temperature

(b) increasing the surface area of any solids.

For each of (a) and (b) above, identify a reaction that illustrates the procedure. In each case, name the chemicals involved and write a balanced equation for the reaction.

23. (*4 marks*)

Bessie was asked to determine experimentally the concentration of lead ions in water. She decided to perform a gravimetric analysis in which the lead ions were precipitated as an insoluble sulfate. A solution containing sulfate ions was added in excess to 100 mL of the lead ion solution. The precipitate was filtered, dried and weighed. The mass of the dried precipitate was 0.950 g.

(a) Name a solution that is a source of sulfate ions.

(b) Write an ionic equation for the precipitation reaction.

(c) Calculate the molar concentration of lead ions in the original solution.

(d) Explain why the collected precipitate must be thoroughly dried before weighing.

24. (*4 marks*)

Claude placed a sample of powdered silver oxide in a modified test tube as shown in the figure below. He then passed methane gas through the heated tube. At the end of the experiment, the tube was cooled and Claude discovered that the silver oxide had been reduced to metallic silver.

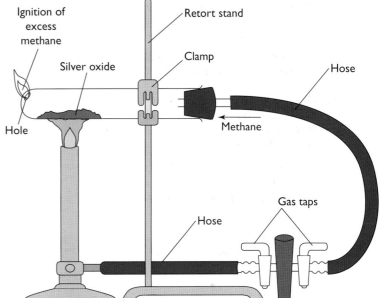

(a) Claude ignited the excess methane as it emerged with the product gases from a small hole at the end of the test tube. Name the possible products of methane combustion.

(b) Write a balanced equation for the reaction of silver oxide with methane.

(c) Explain why Claude heated the reactants.

(d) Calculate the mass of silver that would form from reduction of 30.0 g of silver oxide.

25. (*4 marks*)

Cecilia observed her teacher sprinkle aluminium powder in a blue Bunsen flame. The aluminium sparkled brilliantly as it burned in the air. The reaction of aluminium powder with oxygen is shown in the following reaction:

$$4Al(s) + 3O_2(g) \rightarrow 2Al_2O_3(s) \qquad \Delta H = -3352 \text{ kJ}$$

(a) Calculate the mass of aluminium required to produce 10.2 g of aluminium oxide on combustion.

(b) Assuming that the light energy released accounts for only 1% of the total energy released, calculate the heat energy released during the formation of 10.2 g of aluminium oxide.

(c) Explain why firework manufacturers use powdered aluminium rather than larger pieces.

(d) Identify another metal that could be used to produce brilliant flashes of light in fireworks.

26. (*6 marks*)

The water cycle is an important process and summarises the ways in which water moves from place to place on Earth.

(a) Identify the energy source that powers the water cycle.

(b) Energy is released when water freezes to form ice. The equation for this process is:

$$H_2O(l) \rightarrow H_2O(s) \qquad \Delta H = -6 \text{ kJ/mol}$$

Calculate how much energy is released by 180 g of water at 0 °C to produce ice at 0 °C.

(c) Each year, 4×10^{14} m³ of water evaporates from the oceans. In addition, 3×10^{13} m³ of water runs off the land into the oceans. Determine the required amount of annual precipitation into the oceans to ensure that there is no net loss of water from the oceans.

(d) Identify the locations and structures where most water on Earth exists in solid form.

27. (*3 marks*)

The petrochemical industry is important economically for Australia and petroleum is mined in various locations.

(a) Identify two locations in Australia where petrochemicals are mined.

(b) (i) Describe how petroleum is separated into its useful fractions.

(ii) Identify the fraction with the lowest boiling point range.

(iii) Identify the fraction that contains solid waxes and greases.

(c) Copy and complete the following table by stating uses of the named fractions.

Fraction	Use
gasoline (naphtha fraction)	
kerosene	
diesel oil	

28. (*4 marks*)

X is a white solid that melts at 784 °C to form a colourless liquid. The solid crystal shatters when hammered and does not conduct electricity unless melted.

Y is a yellow substance with a melting point of 113 °C and a boiling point of 445 °C. It does not conduct electricity in either the solid or liquid state.

(a) (i) Classify the type of bonding present in crystals of X.

(ii) Identify the type of crystal lattice structure present in X.

(b) (i) Identify the state in which Y exists at room temperature.

(ii) Identify the state of Y at 250 °C.

(c) Identify the forces holding the particles in place in the lattice of a crystal of Y.

(d) Compare the solubility of X and Y in water and in an organic solvent such as kerosene.

29. (*4 marks*)

Many brands of liquid-fuel lighters use both liquid and gaseous butane in their fuel reservoirs. Butane has a boiling point of –0.5 °C.

(a) Butane boils below room temperature. Explain the existence of liquid butane in the fuel reservoir.

(b) Each time a liquid-fuel lighter is used, about 1000 J of energy is released and 0.03 g of fuel is consumed. The flame produced is yellow in colour.

   (i) Classify the combustion reaction as complete or incomplete.

   (ii) Calculate the heat released from the combustion of butane (in kJ/mol).

   (iii) Explain why the answer in (ii) differs from the published heat of combustion (2877 kJ/mol) for butane.

30. (*4 marks*)

Human history can be divided into various ages such as the Iron Age, Stone Age, Bronze Age and Copper Age.

(a) Classify these ages from oldest to most recent.

(b) Describe an ancient metal extraction process in the period known as the Copper or Bronze Age.

(c) Explain why there are more metals available for use in the last 50 years than there were just 200 years ago.

31. (*6 marks*)

Justify the increased recycling of metals in our society and across the world.

32. (*5 marks*)

You have performed a first-hand investigation to show the decomposition of a carbonate by heat, using appropriate tests to identify carbon dioxide and the oxide as the products of the reaction.

(a) Describe how you selected the carbonate to investigate.

(b) Discuss the safety issues involved in your investigation.

(c) Explain how you identified the products of the decomposition.

PRECISION AND ACCURACY IN MEASUREMENTS

During chemical experiments, it is important to reduce errors in measurements. The measurements we make have a certain degree of *uncertainty*. Our aim is to reduce this uncertainty.

Systematic errors: The instruments you use may not be *calibrated* accurately so the measurements show a regular (or systematic) error. For example, if you boil pure water at 101.3 kPa and use a thermometer to measure the boiling point, you should read a temperature of 100 °C. If your thermometer reads (say) 102 °C, it has a systematic error of +2 °C. Instruments should be calibrated, therefore, against known standards before they are used. Another source of systematic error is experimenter bias. *Parallax error* is an example of experimenter bias. You must ensure that you use the instrument correctly to avoid parallax error. Probes and data loggers can help minimise this problem.

Random (accidental) errors: You should always conduct experiments with the greatest precision using calibrated instruments. You will find, however, that repeated measurements do not yield exactly the same results. These small differences are the result of unknown factors, so cannot be controlled. They are called random or accidental errors. Making many measurements (>5) will help to ensure the *reliability* of your data.

Limits of reading: Each measuring instrument's accuracy is affected by the 'limit of reading' of its scale. For example, a thermometer may have 1 °C graduations. This is its limit of reading. The error is half the limit of reading (that is, ±0.5 °C). To reduce this error, you could use a thermometer with smaller graduations. For example, using a thermometer with graduations 0.2 °C apart reduces the error to ±0.1 °C.

Experimental accuracy: The accuracy of a result is how close a measurement is to the accepted value. The *absolute error* or *percentage error* is a measure of the degree of accuracy of the measurement.

Example:

If a student measures the heat of combustion of ethanol and obtains a value of 1310 kJ/mol instead of the accepted value of 1367 kJ/mol, the:

(a) absolute error = 1367 − 1310 = 57 kJ

(b) percentage error = 57/1367 x 100/1 = 4%.

Precision: It is important that the result of an experiment is reproducible each time you or other chemists repeat the experiment. Precision is a measure of the *reproducibility* of the measurement. The results of all the repeated experiments should be consistent and clustered around the mean. Some results lie close to the mean while others deviate by a larger amount. The size of the *average deviation* from the mean is one measure of the uncertainty or absolute error of the measurement. The *maximum deviation* or *standard deviation* from the mean are other statistical methods of estimating precision. If the uncertainty is small, the measurements are very precise.

Consider the following experimental measurements of the enthalpy of combustion of methane using two different pieces of equipment. The average deviations from the mean in the experimental measurements and the accepted values from the literature are shown.

Apparatus 1: ΔH(methane) = −920 ± 20 kJ/mol

Apparatus 2: ΔH(methane) = −880 ± 80 kJ/mol

Accepted value: ΔH(methane) = −890 kJ/mol

Measurement of the heat of combustion of methane in apparatus 1 was more precise than that in apparatus 2; the average deviation from the mean was lower because successive measurements were more closely grouped. However, the accuracy of measurements in apparatus 2 was greater as the percentage error in apparatus 2 (1%) was lower than in apparatus 1 (3%). This means that apparatus 2 produced more accurate results.

Deviation from the mean: Statistical procedures can be used to measure the uncertainty in a measurement from the range of results obtained by repetitions. Spreadsheet applications (such as Microsoft Excel) can be used to measure the standard deviation of a measurement. Alternatively, the maximum **deviation from the mean** can be used as simpler means of estimating uncertainty.

Sample data: Each group of students in a class measures the mass of 25.0 mL of ethanol (delivered from a burette) using a calibrated electronic balance. Each result is recorded and the mean calculated. The reading with the greatest deviation from this mean is used as a measure of the uncertainty or absolute error. The mass (in grams) measured by each group is: 19.60, 19.55, 19.65, 19.52, 19.64, 19.56, 19.55, 19.62.

Mean = 19.59 g

Maximum deviation from the mean = 0.07 g

Thus, mass of 25.0 mL of ethanol = 19.59 ± 0.07 g

Accepted mass of 25.0 mL ethanol = 19.63 g
(from *SI Chemical Data 5th edition*)

Precision of measurement = ± 0.07 g

Accuracy of measurement = ± 0.04 g = 0.2%

GLOSSARY

A

activated complex: the (unstable) transition state formed during a reaction (at the top of the activation energy hill) that breaks down to form products

activation energy: the minimum energy required by reactants in order to react

adhesion: the force of attraction between unlike molecules or unlike materials

alkane: a simple, saturated binary compound of carbon and hydrogen atoms with single bonds between the carbon atoms. The general formula for all members of this homologous series is C_nH_{2n+2}.

alkene: a simple, unsaturated binary compound of carbon and hydrogen atoms with a double bond between a pair of carbon atoms. The general formula for all members of this homologous series is C_nH_{2n}.

alkyl group: an alkane molecule with a missing hydrogen atom. An alkyl group is always attached to another molecule and cannot exist separately (e.g. —CH_3 is a methyl group).

allotropes: different structural forms of an element based on the different spatial arrangements of the bonds between the atoms

alloy: a mixture of a metal with one or more other elements (These other elements are usually metals.)

atomic mass unit (amu): 1 amu = 1.661 x 10^{-27} kg

Avogadro constant: the number of elementary particles (atoms) in exactly 12 g of carbon-12. This number is equal to 6.022 x 10^{23}.

B

binary compounds: compounds made up of only two elements

boiling point: the temperature at which the pressure exerted by the vapour above a liquid is equal to the external atmospheric pressure. Normal boiling points are measured at a standard pressure of 100 kPa.

bond energy: the enthalpy change associated with breaking covalent bonds in one mole of a gaseous substance to produce gaseous fragments

brittle: describes a substance that shatters into fragments when hammered

C

calorimeter: apparatus used to measure heat changes during a chemical reaction or change of state

carbohydrate: general name for a class of carbon compounds that includes sugars, starch and cellulose. Carbohydrates contain the elements carbon, hydrogen and oxygen.

catalyst: a substance that alters the rate of a reaction without a change in its own concentration

chemical kinetics: the study of the rates of chemical change

chemical properties: the properties relating to the chemical reaction of a substance with other chemicals (such as acids, bases and oxidising agents)

cloud model of the atom: a model of the atom in which quantum theory uses mathematical probability functions to describe electrons as waves

cohesion: the attraction between like molecules or like materials

coke: the black solid formed by destructive distillation of coal. Coke is mainly composed of carbon.

concentrated: describes a solution with a large amount of solute per litre

cryogenic: describes very low temperature processes or applications

D

decomposition: the process of breaking a compound down into its component elements or simpler compounds

delocalised electrons: electrons that are not bound to any one atom but are free to move throughout the lattice

diatomic molecule: a molecule consisting of two atoms chemically bonded together

diluted: describes a solution with a small amount of solute per litre. It can be made by adding more solvent to a concentrated solution.

dipole: an asymmetric charge distribution within a molecule such that there is a distance between the centres of positive and negative charge

dipole–dipole force: a force caused by the positive end of one dipole attracting the negative end of another dipole.

dispersion force: an intermolecular attractive force caused by a temporary dipole inducing a temporary dipole in a nearby molecule.

dissolution: disintegration or breaking apart of the particles of a solid when dissolving in a solvent

double covalent bond: a covalent bond in which two electron pairs are shared between neighbouring atoms

ductile: able to be drawn into wires without breaking

dynamic equilibrium: an equilibrium in which opposing reactions occur simultaneously. Processes occur but they are in state of balance.

E

electrolysis: the decomposition of a chemical substance (in solution or the molten state) by the application of electrical energy

electrolyte: substance that releases ions into solution, which then is capable of conducting an electric current

electronegativity: a measure of the electron-attracting ability of an element. Non-metals are very electronegative while metals are electropositive.

endothermic: describes a chemical reaction in which energy is absorbed from the surroundings

enthalpy: the heat content of a system at constant pressure

equilibrium vapour pressure: the pressure in a closed system when the rate of vaporisation of a substance (normally a pure liquid or a solution) equals the rate of condensation; also called 'vapour pressure'

exothermic: describes a chemical reaction in which energy is released to the surroundings

F

flash point: the minimum temperature at which the vapour pressure of a fuel (e.g. a hydrocarbon such as octane) is just high enough to form a combustible mixture with air

fossil fuel: fuel formed from once-living organisms

fuel: a substance that burns in air or oxygen to release useful energy

fullerenes: a family of carbon allotropes in which the carbon atoms are arranged in cage- or tube-like structures

functional group: a group of atoms attached to or part of a hydrocarbon chain that influence the physical and chemical properties of the molecule

G

galvanised: describes a metal (such as iron) coated with zinc to protect it from corrosion

gangue: the unwanted (non-valuable) material present in an ore body

glucose: a simple sugar with the molecular formula $C_6H_{12}O_6$

H

heterogeneous alloy: an alloy in which the component atoms are not uniformly distributed throughout the lattice. Examples include pearlite steel, containing regions of cementite crystals, Fe_3C, and some solders that contain crystals of lead or tin.

heterogeneous mixture: a mixture in which the particles are not uniformly distributed

homogeneous alloy: an alloy in which the component atoms are uniformly distributed throughout the lattice. Examples include cupronickel and mild steel.

homogeneous mixture: a mixture in which all the particles are uniformly distributed

homologous series: a family of compounds with similar chemical properties and a gradation of physical properties with increasing molar weight or chain length. A general formula describes all members of the series.

hydrogen bond: a strong type of polar attraction caused by the interaction of a highly electropositive hydrogen atom with the lone pairs of electrons of fluorine, oxygen or nitrogen atoms bonded to hydrogen atoms in another molecule. (Hydrogen bonds have some covalent character due to delocalisation of electrons.)

I

ignition temperature: the minimum temperature at which a combustible fuel–oxidiser mixture ignites spontaneously

immiscible: describes two liquids that do not mix, but form separate layers

inert: describes a substance that does not react with other substances

intermolecular forces: weak attractive forces between all types of matter. These forces are weaker than chemical bonds.

ionisation energy: the minimum energy required to remove an electron completely from a gaseous atom

isomers: compounds with the same molecular formula but different structural formulae

isotopes: atoms of an element that have different mass numbers (*A*) due to the presence of different numbers of neutrons

isotopes: atoms with the same atomic number but different mass numbers due to the presence of different numbers of neutrons

J

joule: the SI unit of energy (heat)

K

Kelvin: unit (K) on the absolute temperature scale, where 0 °C = 273 K and 100 °C = 373 K. One degree celsius is equal to 1 kelvin unit.

kinetic energy: the energy of motion possessed by a particle. The higher the temperature of a substance, the greater the kinetic energy of its particles.

L

lattice: the geometric arrangement of particles in a crystal

leach: use a liquid to dissolve a valuable product from a solid mixture such as a matte

lustrous: shiny

M

malleable: able to be shaped without breaking by rolling, hammering or pressing

matte: a smelted mixture in which the percentage of metal is higher than in the unsmelted ore concentrate

mechanism: the steps involved in a chemical reaction

metallic bond: a strong attractive force that holds metal ions in their crystal lattice; the attraction between metal ions and the sea of mobile electrons

metallic character: the tendency of an element to have the properties of metals. The presence of mobile electrons in the lattice is indicative of metals.

metallurgy: the science of metals

mineral: a naturally occurring, crystalline solid that has a fixed chemical composition or a composition that varies between strict limits. Some minerals are pure elements, such as gold and sulfur, but most minerals are chemical compounds.

miscible: describes liquids that mix to form one phase. For example, water and ethanol mix to form alcoholic solutions in all proportions.

molarity: the concentration of a solution expressed in mol/L

N

naphtha: a component of the gasoline fraction that is used as a feedstock to manufacture ethylene for the plastics industry

native metal: a metal found free (uncombined) in nature

O

ore: a material from the lithosphere containing minerals from which a commercial metal can be extracted

oxidation: loss of electrons

P

peroxide: a compound containing the peroxide radical O_2^{2-}

petrochemical feedstock: petroleum fractions used to manufacture other products such as plastics

petroleum: viscous, oily liquid composed of crude oil and natural gas that was formed by geological processes acting on marine organisms over millions of years

photosynthesis: the biochemical process in which chlorophyll molecules absorb solar energy to power an electron transfer reaction in which water and carbon dioxide are converted to oxygen and organic nutrients, such as sugar

physical properties: the properties characteristic of a chemical substance (such as melting point, boiling point, colour, density and conductivity)

physical separation techniques: separation processes that do not chemically alter the components of the mixture. These processes include filtration, evaporation, crystallisation, distillation, froth flotation, magnetic separation and centrifugation.

polar: describes a covalent bond in which there is an asymmetric charge distribution due to one atom having greater electronegativity than the other

polar molecule: a molecule with a permanent dipole. One end of the molecule is partially positive and the other end is partially negative.

precipitation: formation of a solid in a chemical reaction when liquids, solutions or gases are mixed

Q

quantum: a fixed amount of energy. Quantum theory states that objects can possess only certain discrete amounts of energy.

R

reaction rate: the change in concentration of a reactant or product per unit time

reducing agent: a substance (such as charcoal or carbon monoxide) that removes oxygen from a metal oxide during smelting to release the metal

reduction: gain of electrons

relative atomic mass: another name for atomic weight, which is now the IUPAC standard terminology

S

sacrificial anode: an active metal that corrodes more readily than another, thus protecting the less active metal

saturated hydrocarbon: hydrocarbon with only single C—C bonds and the maximum number of hydrogen atoms per carbon

saturated solution: a fixed volume of solution at a particular temperature in which no more solute can dissolve

scrubbers: devices that spray water through gaseous and particle emissions to prevent toxic gases and particles escaping to the environment

single covalent bond: a covalent bond in which one electron pair is shared between neighbouring atoms

slag: waste material from a smelter or furnace

smelting: an industrial process in which high temperatures are used to melt and reduce ore concentrates to produce a metal or a matte

solubility: the concentration of a saturated solution of a given substance at a particular temperature. Solubility is normally measured in grams/100 mL.

solute: a substance (present in the smaller amount) that is dissolved in a solvent to produce a solution

solution: a homogeneous mixture of two or more substances. Solutions may exist as solids, liquids or gases.

solvent: a substance (present in the larger amount) that dissolves a solute to form a solution

specific energy: the amount of heat released from a fuel on combustion (usually measured in MJ/kg)

specific heat capacity: the amount of energy required to raise the temperature of 1 gram of a body by 1 Kelvin unit, expressed as J/K/g. Specific heat capacity is also measured in J/K/kg and J/K/mol.

sublimation: the process of a solid turning directly into a vapour without the formation of the liquid state. For example, iodine crystals sublime to form purple iodine vapour on heating.

surface tension: a measure of the attractive tensional forces in the surface of a liquid. These elastic forces hold the water molecules together, preventing the water from spreading out to increase its surface area.

synthesis: the formation of a compound from its elements or a more complex compound from simpler compounds

T

triple covalent bond: a covalent bond in which three electron pairs are shared between neighbouring atoms

U

unsaturated hydrocarbon: hydrocarbon with double or triple bonds between carbon atoms and fewer than the maximum number of hydrogen atoms per carbon

V

valence electrons: electrons that occupy the outer (valence) shell of an atom

valency: the combining power of an element written in terms of the number of hydrogen atoms (which have a valency of +1) that it will combine with

vapour: the gaseous form of a substance that is normally a solid or liquid at standard temperature and pressure

viscosity: a measure of a fluid's resistance to flow

volatile: describes substances that readily vaporise and exert a high vapour pressure.

Y

yield: the amount of product (e.g. a metal) derived from a chemical extraction process (often expressed as a percentage of the maximum theoretical amount)

ANSWERS

MODULE 1 THE CHEMICAL EARTH

Chapter 1 Mixtures in the Earth

1.1 Classification of matter

1. (a) Mixture (b) Mixture (c) Pure substance
   (d) Mixture (e) Pure substance

2. (a) Compound (b) Element (c) Compound
   (d) Element (e) Compound

3. X: mixture; Y: element; Z: compound

4. (a) A homogeneous mixture has a uniform
   composition throughout.

   (b) A heterogeneous mixture has a non-uniform
   composition.

5. Copper (II) oxide is a chemical compound of copper
   and oxygen with its own unique properties. It is not
   simply a mixture of two elements with properties mid-
   way between the two.

6. P: homogeneous; Q: heterogeneous; R: heterogeneous;
   S: homogeneous

7. (a) Homogeneous

   (b) The density of a mixture varies with its
   composition. Pure substances, however, have fixed
   properties.

1.2 Mixtures and the spheres of the Earth

1. (a) Oxygen (b) Oxygen (c) Nitrogen

2. Oxygen, hydrogen, chlorine, sodium

3. Living cells are mostly composed of water. Oxygen is
   the heaviest component of water.

4. (a) See table 1.6: 86.0 + 10.8 + 1.9 + 1.1 + 0.1 = 99.9%

   (b)

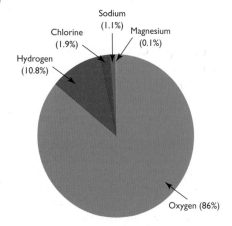

5. (a) Nitrogen, oxygen, argon

   (b) 78.09 + 20.94 + 0.93 = 99.96%v/v

   % of all other gases = 0.04%v/v

(c)

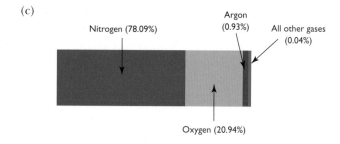

6. Silicon forms many common rock-making minerals
   including quartz (SiO_2), feldspars and micas. These
   are relatively light minerals so tended towards the least
   dense lithospheric layer, the crust, when the Earth
   cooled into its layered structure.

7. Sodium chloride. Sodium ions and chloride ions are
   the most abundant ions in sea water.

8. (a) (i) Silver sulfide (ii) Aluminium oxide
   (iii) Calcium carbonate

   (b) (i) Water
   (ii) Dissolved salts such as potassium chloride

   (c) (i) Carbon dioxide
   (ii) Water

   (d) (i) Proteins, nucleic acids
   (ii) Calcium phosphate in bones

9. (i) Lithosphere (ii) Biosphere (iii) Hydrosphere
   (iv) Lithosphere

1.3 Physical separation techniques

1. (a) Solution (b) Suspension (c) Suspension
   (d) Solution

2. (a) Yes. Lead iodide is relatively insoluble and collects
   in filter paper. Potassium sulfate dissolves in water
   and passes through filter paper.

   (b) No. Both solids are relatively insoluble in water.

3. (a) Distillation (b) Evaporation (c) Evaporation

4. Fluting produces greater surface area, which allows
   the solution/solvent to pass through the paper faster.
   Also, fluting leaves gaps between the paper and funnel
   through which the liquid can flow.

5. Place a watch glass over the evaporating basin so steam
   can escape, but not solids. Concentrate the solution
   and leave it to evaporate slowly and crystallise at room
   temperature.

6. Air condensers rely on conduction and radiation to
   remove heat from the condensing vapours passing
   through the condenser tube. This is less efficient than
   having cool water flowing around the tube. An air
   condenser tube remains much hotter than the tube in
   a water condenser so vapours with lower boiling points,

which require lower temperatures to condense, pass through the tube and escape without condensation. An air condenser can be used if the vapour has a high boiling point so that it readily condenses when in contact with ambient temperature air.

7. (a)

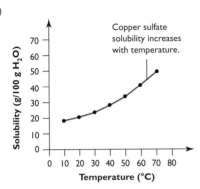

(b) At 25 °C, the solubility of copper sulfate in water is about 22 g/100 g water (from graph). Since half the water has evaporated, there is 11 g of copper sulfate dissolved in 50 g of water. The original amount of copper sulfate was 55 g, so 55 – 11 = 44 g of copper sulfate crystals is formed.

(c) Potassium nitrate is more soluble than copper (II) sulfate at all temperatures (especially high temperatures). Dissolve the 50 g sample in 100 g of hot water (70–80 °C). Cool the solution to 5–10 °C. All the potassium nitrate will remain in solution but most of the copper (II) sulfate will crystallise. Filter off the crystals, wash with icy water and dry gently.

1.4 Gravimetric analysis

1. (a) Qualitative analysis is used to identify and characterise materials, such as which metal ions are in a sample of polluted water.

   Quantitative analysis determines the amount of particular substance, such as the mass of a particular metal in a sample of polluted water.

2. (a) Kerosene is not soluble in water. Since kerosene and water have different densities, they separate into different layers.

   (b) Water, which is more dense

   (c) Weigh the bottle and its contents. Pour the contents quantitatively into a separating funnel and allow two distinct layers to form. Wash and dry the bottle and reweigh it empty. Thus, calculate the mass of the mixture.

   Open the tap of the separating funnel and collect the lower water layer in a pre-weighed beaker.

Close the tap to prevent kerosene entering the beaker. Reweigh the beaker plus water and calculate the mass of water. Thus, calculate the mass of kerosene. Express these masses as a percentage of the total weight of the mixture.

3. % silver = 13.95/15.0 × 100 = 93%w/w

   % copper = (15.0 – 13.95)/15.0 × 100 = 7%w/w

4. Mass of tin = 85/100 × 250 = 212.5 g

   Mass of copper = 8/100 × 250 = 20 g

   Mass of bismuth = 7/100 × 250 = 17.5 g

5. (a) Weigh the beaker and contents. Following filtration, clean and dry the beaker. Reweigh the beaker and subtract its mass from the original mass to obtain the mass of the mixture.

   (b) Filtration

   (c) Salt has too high a boiling point to evaporate, so evaporation will remove the water, leaving the salt behind.

   (d) Mass of mixture = 185.79 – 143.61 = 42.18 g

   Mass of water in mixture = 42.18 – 24.88 – 1.25 = 16.05 g

   % sand = 24.88/42.18 × 100 = 58.99%

   % salt = 1.25/42.18 × 100 = 2.96%

   % water = 16.05/42.18 × 100 = 38.05%

   (e) Loss of material during transfer from the beaker to the filtration apparatus; salt may adhere to the sand if the sand residue is not washed thoroughly; salt spitting may occur if evaporation is too rapid; solids must be dried to constant weight; salt solution may adhere to the beaker unless it is washed with distilled water and poured through the filter paper.

1.5 Industrial separation of mixtures

1. (a) Milling crushes ore to fine grains to release uranium oxide minerals from other unwanted material.

   (b) (i) Leaching dissolves a substance out of a mixture.

       (ii) Unwanted rock minerals (gangue)

   (c) (i) Decanting avoids having to filter the whole mixture. The heavy sediment can remain at the bottom of the settling container as its presence in the filter can slow the filtration.

       (ii) Physical

   (d) The original ore is mildly radioactive but the concentrated product is more radioactive. Storing this material and the mildly radioactive tailings (waste) safely is vital to avoid environmental contamination. Gangue material should not be allowed to wash into local river systems. Leaching solutions and other solvents must not be allowed to enter the watertable before appropriate treatment.

2. (a) Heavier isotopes concentrate at the walls.

   (b) Physical: centrifugation

   Chemical: conversion to uranium hexafluoride

3. (a) A: steam generator; B: distillation retort; C: condenser; D: separator

   (b) (i) A, B (ii) C

4. (a) Sesame

   (b) Oil is insoluble in water. Density of oil is less than water. Fibre consists of large particles that could be sieved.

   (c) (i) Fibre (ii) Water

5. A: 3; B: 5; C: 1; D: 2; E: 4

Practical activity 1.1 Separation of a simple mixture

Analysis

1. Hot water and spitting salt crystals can cause damage to eyes and skin so eye protection should be worn. Do not touch hot containers until they cool.

2. The residue on the filter paper must be washed thoroughly with water.

3. Heat and cool until the weight no longer changes.

4. This prevents the mixture overflowing the filter cone.

Practical activity 1.2 Gravimetric analysis of a mixture 1

Results and analysis

5. To improve accuracy: use an electronic balance that weighs to 2 or 3 decimal places, rather than a mechanical balance; ensure that the salt is dry by heating and weighing until a constant weight is obtained; ensure that all the distilled water collects in the beaker and none is trapped in the condenser.

   To improve reliability: repeat the experiment at least five times, or average the results of five or more groups.

6. Avoid skin contact with hot apparatus and hot vapours; wear safety glasses; ensure that cooling water flows through the condenser at all times.

Practical activity 1.3 Gravimetric analysis of a mixture 2

Results and analysis

6. Reheating and cooling ensures that all the water is evolved and that the final residue is fully dehydrated.

Data analysis 1.4 Separation and analysis of a mixture

Part A: Separation

1. Correct order of jumbled steps: (iii), (ii), (ix), (v), (viii), (i), (vii), (iv), (vi)

2. Sulfuric acid reacts with two of the three components and converts them to new substances that would remain in the mixture. The new substances are not easily reconverted to the original components. Physical separation methods do not chemically change the components.

Part B: Analysis

1. % copper = $0.47/5.0 \times 100 = 9.4\%$ w/w

2. (a) (ii), (v), (vii) (c) (iv), (vi)

3. Use an electronic balance for weighing to 2 or 3 decimal places; ensure quantitative transfer of the black solid; ensure solid copper is weighed and dried until the weight no longer changes; ensure that the residue is washed free of solution; use a larger mass of the original mixture and, therefore, copper (II) oxide to minimise the percentage error.

Data analysis 1.5 Extraction of aluminium from the lithosphere

Part A: Extraction

1. A: iv; B: vii; C: i; D: iii; E: v; F: viii; G: vi; H: ii

2. A, C, E, H

Part B: General questions

1. $Al_2O_3.3H_2O$

2. The ore is economical to mine only if it has a minimum of 40% aluminium. The costs involved in mining need to be recovered by producing sufficient aluminium.

3. The site of the aluminium factory must be near electricity generators but away from areas where pollutants may harm nearby communities. The direction of prevailing winds must be taken into account. A road–rail network and access to shipping are vital to make the operation internationally profitable.

4. Solid

5. Alumina has a very high melting point, so it would not be profitable to melt it. It is easier to dissolve it in cryolite, which has a much lower melting point so is cheaper to melt.

Chapter 2 Elements

2.1 Classifying elements

1. D. Boron has semi-metallic properties.
2. B. Iridium is a typical transition metal.
3. (a) Gas (b) Solid (c) Solid (d) Solid
4. (a) $D = m/V = 155.65/7.50 = 20.75 \text{ g/cm}^3$
   (b) No. The density of the sample is a little low for pure platinum.
   (c) Pt
   (d) Metal
5. (a) Temperature
   (b)

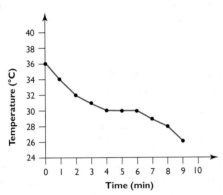

   (c) 30 °C. The graph has a long inflexion at that temperature, which is caused by the phase change at this temperature.
   (d) 30 °C. The freezing point and the melting point are the same. They describe opposite processes.
   (e) Yes. The values are the same.
   (f) Metal
6. (a) Metal (b) Metal (c) Non-metal (d) Semi-metal (e) Non-metal (f) Metal
7. (a) Grey colour, lustrous, good heat conductor
   (b) Its properties are intermediate between metals and non-metals. Even though the grey form is a good heat conductor (typical of metals), it is a poor electrical conductor (typical of non-metals).

2.2 The properties and uses of elements

1. C. Tungsten has a very high melting point and is unreactive.
2. B. Silver is relatively unreactive and magnesium is very reactive.
3. (a) Its high melting point ensures that the filament does not melt or break as it glows white hot.
   (b) It has high tensile strength and forms tungsten carbide in the steel; the carbide is very hard and this reduces wear in drill bits constructed from tungsten steel. Also, it retains this hardness at the high temperatures reached due to the friction of some steel cutting tools (such as drill bits).
4. High melting point (aircraft and spacecraft heat up due to air friction); high tensile strength (considerable stresses build up during flight); thermal conductivity (heat can be lost rapidly); relatively low density (which saves fuel)
5. A: 2 and 3; B: 2 and 4; C: 1; D: 2 and 5; E: 2

Data analysis 2.2 Classifying elements

Part A
2. He: gas; Li: solid; O: gas; F: gas; Ne: gas; S: solid; Cl: gas; Ar: gas; Se: solid; Br: liquid; Kr: gas; I: solid; Xe: gas; Rn: gas

Part B
2. P: non-metal; S: non-metal; Ga: metal; Se: non-metal; I: non-metal; Hg: metal

General questions
1. Upper right side of the periodic table and group VIII (noble gases)
2. Upper right side of the periodic table and group VIII, plus a few solid non-metals
3. In a zigzag pattern between the metals and non-metals

Data analysis 2.3 Properties and uses of elements

Silver: 5, 2; mercury: 4, 6, 9; tin: 2, 3; lead solder: 1, 2, 3, 6, 7; lead sinkers: 2, 3, 6, 8; aluminium: 1, 2, 3, 7; nickel: 2, 3, 5; chromium: 2, 3, 5

Chapter 3 Compounds

3.1 The structure of the atom

1. B. Particles in a gas move rapidly and are normally far apart, so gases are highly compressible.
2. B. The nucleus is very much smaller than the atom; the nucleus is positive.
3. (a) S (b) 16 (c) Iodine (d) 74 (e) Sr (f) 88 (g) Mercury (h) 80 (i) Radon (j) 226
4. (a) 2, 3 (b) 2, 5 (c) 2, 8, 2 (d) 2, 8, 6 (e) 2, 8, 8, 1
5. (a) Silicon (b) 2, 8, 4 (c) 4 (d) $^{29}_{14}\text{Si}$
6. (a) $Z = 2 + 8 + 14 + 2 = 26$
   (b) Iron
   (c) Metal
   (d) (i) $A = 26 + 30 = 56$ (ii) $^{56}_{26}\text{Fe}$

3.2 Ions and ionic bonding

1. (a) *M* is a metal (it has 2 electrons in its valence shell).

   (b) *N* is a non-metal (it has 7 electrons in its valence shell).

   (c) Valency of $M = +2$; valency of $N = -1$. Thus, the formula is MN_2.

2. (a) Ag_2S (b) BaI_2 (c) AlP (d) Mg_3N_2 (e) NH_4NO_3
   (f) $CaSO_3$ (g) $Na_2Cr_2O_7$ (h) $Fe(HCO_3)_3$

3. (a) Strontium chloride (b) Silver iodide (c) Iron (III) sulfide (d) Lead (IV) oxide (e) Calcium dichromate (f) Barium bromide (g) Potassium acetate

4. (a)

   (b)

   (c)

5. (a) Let the unknown valency = x; $2x + (-2) = 0$, so $x = +1$.

   (b) Let the unknown valency = y; $3(+1) + y = 0$, so $y = -3$.

   (c) Let the unknown valency = z; $2z + 3(-2) = 0$, so $z = +3$.

6. (a) $Al = 2, 8, 3$. Losing two electrons forms Al^{2+} with a configuration of 2, 8, 1. This ion is not stable as it does not have an octet in the outer shell.

   (b) $P = 2, 8, 5$. Gaining 3 electrons forms P^{3-} with a configuration of 2, 8, 8. This ion is stable as it has 8 electrons in its outer shell.

7. (a) $Ga \rightarrow Ga^{3+} + 3e^-$ (b) $I + e^- \rightarrow I^-$ (c) $Pb \rightarrow Pb^{2+} + 2e^-$

8. (a) Li: 2, 1; Na: 2, 8, 1; K: 2, 8, 8, 1 (*Note:* Some periodic tables include hydrogen in group I; if so, its configuration is 1.)

   (b) They lose 1 electron to gain noble gas configurations.

3.3 Molecules and covalent bonding

1. (a) HF (b) SCl_2 (c) CBr_4 (d) PI_3 (e) ICl

2. (a) Bromine chloride (b) Phosphorus tribromide (c) Nitrogen triiodide (d) Hydrogen sulfide (e) Hydrogen phosphide

3. (a) 6 ($6 = 3 \times 2$) (b) 5 ($1 + 5 = 3 \times 2$) (c) 5 ($5 = 5 \times 1$)
   (d) 3 [H: +1; O: −2; $0 = +1 + N + 2(-2)$; N= +3]
   (e) 5 [$0 = +1 + N + 3(-2)$; N = +5]

4.

Atoms per molecule	1	2	3	4	5
Examples	Ar Ne	HF CO	O_3 SO_2 N_2O	NH_3 H_3P	CH_4

5. (a)

   (c)

   (b)

   (d)

6. (a) Ionic

   (b) Calcium atoms = $2 + \frac{1}{8}(8) + \frac{1}{2}(2) = 4$; fluoride atoms = 8 The ratio of calcium to fluoride atoms is $4 : 8 = 1 : 2$ so the formula is CaF_2.

Data analysis 3.1 Analysing crystal structures

Metallic crystals

1. All particles are identical.

2. Iron has a body-centred cubic crystal with one iron atom at the centre of the cube and other iron atoms at each corner of the cube.

   Zinc has a hexagonal crystal. The opposite ends of the unit cell are hexagonal, with a zinc atom in the centre of the hexagon and zinc atoms at each corner. The other faces of the crystals are rectangular. Three zinc atoms occupy positions in the centre of the hexagonal crystal.

   Iron and zinc crystals have different geometric shapes, so the locations of atoms differ.

Ionic crystals

1. Ionic bonds

2. 6

3. 6

4. It shows the relative size of each ion

Covalent molecular crystals

1. XeF_2

2. Most noble gases do not form compounds.

3. There is one xenon atom in the bulk of the cell and eight at the corners, so the total number of xenon atoms per cell = $1 + \frac{1}{8}(8) = 2$.

   There are two fluorine atoms in the bulk of the cell and eight at the edges, so the total number of fluorine atoms per cell = $2 + \frac{1}{4}(8) = 4$.

   The ratio of Xe to F = $2 : 4 = 1 : 2$, so the formula is XeF_2.

Chapter 4 Chemical extraction

4.1 Physical and chemical change

1. (a) Physical (b) Physical (c) Chemical (d) Chemical (e) Physical

2. (a) Water is a pure substance, as its physical properties are the same before and after it is boiled and condensed.

   (b) No. Water is composed of elements in fixed atomic proportions. It can be decomposed by chemical means, as shown by electrolysis, so it can not be an element.

3. (a) Physical. No new substances were formed.

   (b) No. No reaction involving electron transfer occurred.

4. (a) $FeO(s) + CO(g) \rightarrow Fe(l) + CO_2(g)$

   (b) $4K(s) + O_2(g) \rightarrow 2K_2O(s)$

   (c) $2Ag_2CO_3(s) \rightarrow 4Ag(s) + 2CO_2(g) + O_2(g)$

   (d) $4Al(s) + 3O_2(g) \rightarrow 2Al_2O_3(s)$

   (e) $2Na(s) + Cl_2(g) \rightarrow 2NaCl(s)$

5. Chemical. A new substance (sulfur dioxide) was formed.

4.2 Energy and chemical change

1. B. UV light causes electrons to be lost from the bromide ions; these are accepted by silver ions to form silver metal.

2. C. If the carbonate has decomposed completely, it should not fizz if acid is added.

3. A. This is a balanced equation involving molecular species present in the atmosphere.

4. (a) Carbon dioxide

   (b) CuO as $CuCO_3(s) \rightarrow CO_2(g) + CuO(s)$

   (c) Mass of carbon dioxide evolved =
   $10.00 - 6.44 = 3.56$ g
   % loss in weight = $3.56/10.00 \times 100 = 35.6\%$

5. (a) Released

   (b) Sodium chloride

   (c) (i) Absorbed
   (ii) Sodium metal forms at the negative electrode and chlorine gas forms at the positive electrode.

6. (a) Mass of zinc = $10\,000/3151 \times 1 = 3.17$ kg
   Mass of magnesium = $10\,000/14\,289 \times 1 = 0.70$ kg

   (b) Magnesium sulfide is more stable as it requires more energy to decompose it.

7. (a) 2

(b) 7.7×10^{-19} J is the bond energy of an O—H bond. The energy required to break the two O—H bonds in one water molecule = 1.54×10^{-18} J. To break 10 000 molecules requires $10\,000 \times 1.54 \times 10^{-18} = 1.54 \times 10^{-14}$ J.

(c) Hydrogen and oxygen atoms in the gaseous state

(d) Hydrogen and oxygen atoms are very reactive. When they combine to form water, they lose energy. Water is a stable compound because it has less energy than hydrogen or oxygen molecules.

Practical activity 4.1 Investigating the electrolysis of water

Results and analysis

3. Positive electrode: oxygen; negative electrode: hydrogen

4. Rate of electrolysis increases as voltage increases.

5. New products (hydrogen, oxygen) are formed as water electrolyses, showing that a chemical change occurs. A fixed volume ratio of hydrogen and oxygen is formed no matter how much acid is added to the water, indicating that water is a compound.

Practical activity 4.2 Thermal decomposition of magnesium carbonate

Results and analysis

2. (a) The limewater turned milky white; this is a positive test for carbon dioxide.

   (b) Phenolphthalein turns a deeper pink in the heated magnesium carbonate than in the unheated, showing that the final product is a stronger base. This indicates that magnesium oxide is produced.

   (c) The heated product fizzes very little, if at all, when acid is added, while the unheated sample fizzes considerably. This lack of fizzing indicates that the magnesium carbonate has decomposed completely.

   (d) $MgCO_3(s) \rightarrow MgO(s) + CO_2(g)$

3. $MgCO_3(s) + 2HCl \rightarrow MgCl_2 + H_2O(l) + CO_2(g)$

Practical activity 4.3 The effect of light on silver halide salts

Results and analysis

2. Sunlight contains less UV radiation than the light from a UV lamp.

3. The control dishes allow us to compare the effects of UV radiation on the salts. Without the dark controls, we cannot make a valid comparison.

4. $NaCl + AgNO_3 \rightarrow AgCl(s) + NaNO_3$
   $NaBr + AgNO_3 \rightarrow AgBr(s) + NaNO_3$

$NaI + AgNO_3 \rightarrow AgI(s) + NaNO_3$

5. (a) $Br^- \rightarrow Br + e^-$

   (b) $Ag^+ + e^- \rightarrow Ag$

Data analysis 4.4 Boiling and electrolysing water

Part A

1. (a) Water molecules (b) Water molecules

2. No new substance is formed as water boils and so the process is physical.

3. The added heat energy breaks the intermolecular forces between the water molecules, rather than contributing to the kinetic energy of the water molecules, which is measured as heat.

Part B

1. Water, hydrogen ions, hydroxide ions

2. Hydrogen (negative tube), oxygen (positive tube)

3. New substances are formed, so electrolysis is a chemical change.

4. It is very unreactive and so does not take part in electrolysis.

5. (a) Half-equation (2). Electrons are removed from water molecules, and oxygen molecules and hydrogen ions are formed.

   (b) Half-equation (1). Electrons are added to water molecules, and hydrogen molecules and hydroxide ions are formed.

Data analysis 4.5 Investigating the purity of limestone by thermal decomposition

1. (a) Mass lost = 27.275 – 25.989 = 1.286 g

   Mass of impure limestone = 27.275 – 24.145 = 3.130 g

   % loss in weight = 1.286/3.130 × 100 = 41.1%

   (b) Mass lost = 27.288 – 25.906 = 1.382 g

   Mass of pure calcium carbonate = 27.288 – 24.145 = 3.143 g

   % loss in weight = 44.0%

2. If 100 g of limestone contains x grams of calcium carbonate, 44.0% of x will be lost on thermal decomposition.

   44.0x/100 = 41.1

   $x = 93.4$

   So, percentage of calcium carbonate in limestone = 93.4%w/w.

3. Assume that the impurities in the limestone do not decompose on heating and that the carbonates in both samples have decomposed completely.

4. Assume that the increase in weight of the tube equals the weight lost on decomposition of limestone.

Weight increase in limestone = 1.286 g

Weight increase in pure calcium carbonate = 1.382 g

5. $CO_2(g) + NaOH(s) \rightarrow NaHCO_3(s)$

Chapter 5 Bonding and structure

5.1 Properties and classification

1. If iron (III) oxide were a mixture, its properties would be intermediate between those of iron and oxygen. However, the properties of iron (III) oxide are very different from those of its component elements.

2. (a) Hydrogen

   (b) $Fe(s) + 2HCl(aq) \rightarrow FeCl_2(aq) + H_2(g)$

   (c) No gas is released when iron (II) oxide dissolves in dilute hydrochloric acid. Water is formed instead of hydrogen.

3. Ionic, covalent molecular, covalent network

4. (a) Covalent molecular (b) Covalent network (c) Ionic

5. Substance A: ionic, because it conducts when dissolved in water

   Substance B: covalent molecular, because it does not conduct in any state and has low melting and boiling points

5.2 Lattices

1. (a) Metallic (b) Covalent network (c) Ionic (d) Ionic (e) Covalent molecular (f) Covalent network

2. If X conducts electricity, it is a metallic crystal with metallic bonding in its lattice. If it conducts weakly, it may be a semi-metal. If the solid does not conduct, melt it or try to dissolve it in water and re-test. If the melt or aqueous solution conducts, X is ionic. If it does not conduct, it is probably covalent molecular. It is likely to be a covalent network crystal if it is very difficult to melt and does not dissolve in any solvent.

3. (a) Manganese has a metallic lattice held together by strong metallic bonds acting in all directions, so it has a high melting point. Oxygen has a covalent molecular lattice held together by weak intermolecular forces, rather than strong covalent bonds, strong metallic bonds or strong electrostatic forces (ionic bonds), so it has a low melting point.

   (b) Zinc's metallic lattice has mobile electrons to carry the current when a potential difference is applied across the crystal. There are no free charge carriers in zinc oxide as the ions are locked into their lattice and the electrons are held strongly by the ions over a wide range of wavelengths. Thus, it does not conduct.

   (c) The delocalised electrons on the surface of nickel can absorb and re-emit light, so nickel is lustrous.

There are no free electrons on the surface of a nickel oxide crystal, so the surface appears dull.

(d) The atomic weight of tungsten is much higher than aluminium, so tungsten has a higher density. Even though they both have about the same number of atoms in a given volume, the mass of tungsten atoms is much greater than that of aluminium atoms, so tungsten has more mass in a given volume.

4. (a) Delocalised electrons and strong lattice forces between silver ions in all directions cause its high melting point.

(b) When a potential difference is applied across a crystal, the mobile, delocalised electrons move and carry the electrical energy.

(c) Delocalised electrons can rapidly absorb and release the energy of light photons. Eventually, the surface becomes coated in an ionic compound (silver sulfide) that has no mobile electrons, so does not reflect light well.

(d) When a silver crystal is stressed, the silver ions slip along the crystal planes to new locations where they are again stabilised by the mobile electron cloud.

(c) Covalent network crystal

5. (a) Covalent molecular crystal

(b) There are weak intermolecular forces between iodine molecules in the lattice. Heating breaks these bonds quickly and allows iodine molecules to escape into the vapour state.

(c) $I_2(g) \rightarrow I_2(s)$

(d) Physical

6. (a) Covalent molecular crystal. It has a low melting point and does not conduct in the solid or melted state.

(b) It is not likely to be soluble in water, but it should be soluble in kerosene. Many waxy solids, such as candle wax, are like this.

7. (a) No. The crystals could be ionic or covalent networks.

(b) Ionic

8. (a) Carbon (*Note:* The carbon atoms in graphite form layers in the covalent network, with delocalised electrons within the layers, so graphite is a 2-dimensional covalent network.)

(b) Good electrical conductor; very high melting point

Practical activity 5.1 Comparing the properties of a compound and its component elements

Results and analysis

2. (a) $Mg(s) + 2HCl \rightarrow MgCl_2 + H_2(g)$

$MgO(s) + 2HCl \rightarrow MgCl_2 + H_2O(l)$

(b) A gas is released when magnesium dissolves in acid but not when magnesium oxide dissolves in acid. The reaction with magnesium involves a transfer of electrons from magnesium to hydrogen ions. The reaction with magnesium oxide is a neutralisation reaction.

Data analysis 5.3 Comparing the properties of crystals

Part A

1. *A*: covalent network (very high melting point; other properties consistent with graphite); *B*: metallic (conducts in solid state and is silvery and lustrous); *C*: covalent molecular (low melting point; does not conduct in any state); *D*: ionic (conducts when dissolved but does not conduct in the solid state)

2. This is one possible key.

1A. The solid does conduct electricity. .... Metallic

1B. The solid does not conduct electricity. .... *Go to 2.*

2A. The crystal has a high melting point. .... *Go to 3.*

2B. The crystal has a low melting point. .... Covalent molecular

3A. The crystal dissolves in water but not kerosene. .... Ionic

3B. The crystal does not dissolve in any solvent. .... Covalent network

Part B

1. Ionic crystal. Its crystals dissolve in water to form a conducting solution.

2. Covalent molecular. The solid and liquid do not conduct and the substance has low melting and boiling points. This information is consistent with *X* being water.

3. The blue solid is a dehydrated form of the red crystals. Heating the red form released water vapour (*X*). Many ionic substances include water in their crystal lattices. The water in the hydrated form of the salt is called 'water of crystallisation'. The water can be driven off by heat to leave the dehydrated or anhydrous form.

MODULE 2 METALS

Chapter 6 Metals and alloys

6.1 History of metals

1. (a) Copper (b) Gold (c) Lead (d) Magnesium (e) Titanium

2. (a) Calcium (b) Iron (c) Copper (d) Lead (e) Titanium (f) Lead (g) Titanium

3. (a) The Copper Age was a time when people mined native copper and copper ores and smelted the ores to make copper for tools and jewellery.

(b) The crushed copper ore was mixed with charcoal and smelted in a high temperature furnace. The coal also provided the heat as it combusted in the air provided by bellows.

4. (a) (i) Copper and tin

(ii) Early bronze contained copper, arsenic and some lead, bismuth and nickel. Later, tin and copper were found to produce the best bronze.

(b) Rulers demanded bronze for their palaces and tombs; the old arsenic bronze was too brittle to be hammered and shaped and so tin bronze replaced it.

(c) Iron requires a high temperature to smelt its ores. Iron is not very malleable and it was harder to remove its impurities. Native iron was also much rarer than native copper. Meteoric iron was also quite rare.

5. (a) Middle East about 1500 BC

(b) The mineral cementite made the iron brittle.

(c) Blacksmiths hammered the iron at red heat to squeeze out the slag and the impurities that made the iron brittle.

(d) The iron is beaten and folded thousands of times. Iron oxides form when iron reacts with air, and these react with the cementite minerals and cause them to decompose into iron. The purer iron is flexible and soft. The edges of the sword are later hardened by increasing the crystal size of the iron layers at these points.

6 (a) Ionic bonds between the lead and oxide ions

(b) Additional oxygen increases the temperature of the flame. Oxygen reacts with carbon to produce considerable amounts of heat energy. The higher flame temperature supplies the required energy to break the bonds in the ore.

(c) Carbon and carbon monoxide reduce lead oxide to lead by removing oxygen. The carbon also burns in oxygen to generate more heat.

(d) Carbon monoxide and carbon dioxide are produced as the carbon combines with the oxygen atoms of the lead oxide leaving behind the lead metal.

(e) Shiny, liquid globules as the lead is above its melting point

(f) lead oxide + carbon → lead + carbon monoxide

(g) Lead vapours and carbon monoxide are both poisonous substances. The experiment should be done in a fume cupboard and the blowpipe should be lengthened with a rubber hose so there is no danger of inhaling fumes. The carbon block is very hot and care must be taken not to touch it. After the experiment, the carbon block should be quenched in water until it is cold.

7. Cobalt and nickel can be extracted from their ores using roasting and smelting technologies. Calcium and magnesium, however, are very reactive metals and they cannot be produced in this way. The discovery of electricity and the techniques of electrolysis enabled Humphrey Davy to extract these metals by electrolysing their molten salts.

8. Metallurgical techniques have improved over the last two hundred years. The roasting and smelting technologies of ancient times have been extended and improved with new chemical knowledge. Chemical engineers have designed smelters and furnaces that can process great quantities of ores continuously. Ores are available from mines all over the world due to improvements in shipping. In addition, electrolytic technologies have allowed active metals such as aluminium to be prepared rapidly and continuously. New alloys are under constant development to meet demands for new materials with particular properties and characteristics.

6.2 Alloys

1. B. Copper is soft but nickel makes it harder.

2. C. Mild steel is very malleable.

3. C. The more copper in the brass, the redder it is.

4. (a) The atoms of the solid solute are uniformly distributed throughout the solid solvent.

(b) Heterogeneous. The atoms of A are not uniformly distributed throughout B's lattice.

5. (a) It is too brittle due to its high carbon content.

(b) Carbon

(c) They make the steel much harder and tougher (particularly at high temperatures).

(d) Chromium and nickel

6. (a) It is harder than copper so was used in ancient times for tools.

(b) 5000 kg of Cu = 100 – 14 = 86% of tin bronze
Weight of tin = 5000/86 × 14 = 814 kg

(c) Copper: 92/100 × 5000 = 4600 kg;
aluminium: 6/100 × 5000 = 300 kg; nickel: 100 kg

7. X: axe head. It is made of high carbon steel for strength.

Y: nails. They are made of mild or low carbon steel, which is ductile.

Z: girder. It is made of medium carbon (structural) steel, which is more malleable than high carbon steel but not as hard.

Data analysis 6.1 Timeline: the history of copper

1.

Date (BP)	Region	Place	Feature
10 000	Middle East	Iraq/Sumeria	Native copper melted, forged, and cast
9 250	Middle East	Turkey	Copper artefacts
5 800	Middle East	Iran	Copper chisels and spanners
5 600	Asia	Thailand	Bronze jewellery and tools
5 300	Middle East	Israel	Copper saws, axes and spearheads
5 000	Middle East	Egypt	Copper casting
5 000	Asia	India	Copper mining
4 900	Middle East	Cyprus	Copper coins
4 500	Middle East	Egypt	Copper tubes used in waterworks
4 400	Europe	Bohemia	Copper mining
3 400	Asia	China	Bronze casting
3 200	Asia	India	Copper used to repair Buddha statue
2 220	Asia	China	Copper coins
1 300	Americas	Peru	Copper and bronze tools
600	Europe	Europe	Copper sheeting on ship hulls
500	Americas	North America	Native Americans — copper jewellery
500	Americas	West Indies	Copper mining and casting
348	Europe	Netherlands	Brass pendulum
266	Europe	Hungary	Copper minerals in spring water
256	Americas	North America	Copper mining
215	Europe	Europe	Copper rolling mills
205	Europe	Italy	Volta's battery using copper discs
192	Europe	Netherlands	Brass telescope
191	Europe	Germany	Electromagnetic telegraph used copper wiring
169	Europe	England	Dynamo using copper wiring
118	Americas	USA	Copper used in Statue of Liberty
7	Americas	USA	Copper microcircuitry on silicon chips

(*Note:* These dates are based on 2006 so will change each year.)

2. The table shows that copper mining and smelting was confined to the Middle East and nearby areas of Asia for about 500 years before spreading east to Asia and west to Europe. It was not until about 1300 years ago that it spread to South America and then into North America. In more modern times, copper is used worldwide.

Data analysis 6.2 Melting points of solders

1.

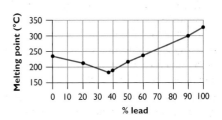

2. $256\,°C$

3. The lead–tin solder has a melting point of $184\,°C$ (from the graph). The lead–tin–silver solder has a melting point of $180\,°C$ (from table 6.13). Thus, the addition of silver lowers the melting point by $4\,°C$.

4. The melting point of 93% Pb : 7% Sn solder is about $310\,°C$ (from the graph). The 93% Pb : 5% Sn : 2% Ag solder has a melting point of $301\,°C$ (from table 6.13. Thus, the melting point of this high lead solder is reduced by the replacement of a small percentage of tin by silver.

   (*Note:* The melting curves of alloys can be quite complex and the addition of other components does not always produce predictable results.)

5. The melting point decreases from $256\,°C$ to $250\,°C$.

Chapter 7 Metals and reactions

7.1 Metals and their reactivity

1. B. Tin is lower in the activity series.

2. D. Sodium is a very reactive metal.

3. A. Tin dissolves slowly in acids but is not attacked by steam at red heat; iron is attacked by both acids and steam.

4. (a) Calcium (b) Cobalt (c) Potassium (d) Mercury (e) Magnesium

5. (a) $Zn(s) + H_2O(g) \rightarrow ZnO(s) + H_2(g)$

   (b) $2Mg(s) + O_2(g) \rightarrow 2MgO(s)$

   (c) $2K(s) + 2HCl(aq) \rightarrow 2KCl(aq) + H_2(g)$

   (d) $Mg(s) + H_2SO_4(aq) \rightarrow MgSO_4(aq) + H_2(g)$

6. (a) $Ca(s) \rightarrow Ca^{2+}(aq) + 2e^-$

   $2H^+(aq) + 2e^- \rightarrow H_2(g)$

   $Ca(s) + 2H^+(aq) \rightarrow Ca^{2+}(aq) + H_2(g)$

   (b) $Zn(s) \rightarrow Zn^{2+}(aq) + 2e^-$

   $2H^+(aq) + 2e^- \rightarrow H_2(g)$

   $Zn(s) + 2H^+(aq) \rightarrow Zn^{2+}(aq) + H_2(g)$

   (c) $K(s) \rightarrow K^+(aq) + e^-$

   $2H^+(aq) + 2e^- \rightarrow H_2(g)$

   $2K(s) + 2H^+(aq) \rightarrow 2K^+(aq) + H_2(g)$

7. (a) Hydrogen

   (b) $X(s) + H_2O(g) \rightarrow XO(s) + H_2(g)$

   (c) Fe (iron). It is divalent and forms a black oxide; it is one of a group of three metals (Al, Zn, Fe) that react with steam only when they are red hot. Silver does not react.

7.2 Reactivity and uses of metals

1. B. Group I and II metals are more reactive than group III metals.

2. A. Titanium is expensive to manufacture but it is strong and lightweight.

3. B. Tin is lower in the activity series than iron so corrodes less readily than iron.

4. C. The first three ionisation energies are much lower than the rest.

5. D. Rubidium's valence electron is further from the nucleus than sodium's.

6. (a) $Ga(g) \rightarrow Ga^+(g) + e^-$

   $Ga^+(g) \rightarrow Ga^{2+}(g) + e^-$

   $Ga^{2+}(g) \rightarrow Ga^{3+}(g) + e^-$

   (b) The third ionisation step. As the third electron has to be removed from a doubly positive ion, there is a strong electrostatic attraction to be overcome.

   (c) $Ga(s) \rightarrow Ga^{3+}(aq) + 3e^-$

   (d) $2Ga(s) + 6H^+(aq) \rightarrow 2Ga(aq) + 3H_2(g)$

7. (a) X has 2 valence electrons. Y has 7 valence electrons.

   (b) X has 2 valence electrons so is a metal.
   Y has 7 valence electrons so is a non-metal.

   (c) Valency of $X = +2$. Valency of $Y = -1$. So the formula is XY_2.

Practical activity 7.1 The activity series of metals

   Results and analysis

3. (a) Carbon dioxide

4. (a) Oxygen

   (c) $2Ag_2CO_3(s) \rightarrow 4Ag(s) + 2CO_2(g) + O_2(g)$

Chapter 8 The periodic table

8.1 The historical development of the periodic table

1. A. These are members of the current group VI.

2. B. Newlands arranged elements according to atomic weight.

3. C. Mendeleev recognised that each column contained elements with similar chemical and physical properties.

4. A. Meyer's graphs showed the repeating patterns.

5. D. A new column or group was added to the right of the table.

6. The numbering of the charge on the centre refers to the atomic number, which is equal to the number of protons in the nucleus. The atomic number, rather than the atomic weight, was used to arrange the elements of the periodic table.

7. Thomson suggested that elements with similar electron arrangements belonged to the same family of the periodic table. Bohr suggested that elements of the same periodic group would have the same number of valance shell electrons.

8. (a) 'eka' means 'like' or 'similar to'.

   (b) Mendeleev believed in the predictive power of the periodic table. By examining the properties of the elements above and below gallium in the same group, and looking at the trends in properties along a period, he was able to make predictions about the properties of a missing element.

   (c) $EaCl_3$

8.2 Periodic trends

1. Mo, Y, V, Au, Os

2. (a) Er, Ce, Dy

   (b) Lr, Pu, Np

3. (a) Active, low-density metals with +2 valency

   (b) Reactive, non-metals with –2 valency, trending to semi-metals (Te) and soft metals (Po)

   (c) Unreactive, monatomic noble gases with 0 valency.

   (d) All radioactive metals. Some are naturally occurring and others have been synthesised in nuclear reactors or in particle accelerators. They also react vigorously with water to release hydrogen gas and produce alkaline solutions. The typical valencies of these metals are +3, +4, +5 and +6.

4. (a) Usually constant in each group and equal to the group number. Maximum valency increases from groups I to VII.

(b) Increases across a period; decreases down a group

(c) Increases across a period; decreases down a group

(d) Generally decreases across a period; generally increases down a group

5. (a) -2 in CaA; 2 in ACl_2; 4 in AO_2; 6 in AO_3

   (b) Sulfur, selenium and tellurium would form the compounds described. Element A could not be oxygen as A cannot form compounds with itself. Element A is not likely to be polonium, which is metallic and would not form molecular compounds with chlorine or oxygen.

6. The halogens are diatomic. The intermolecular forces between the molecules increase as the size of the molecule increases. This produces a higher melting point.

7. C. The valencies of Na, Mg, Al are $+1$, $+2$ and $+3$ respectively; the valencies of P, S and Cl are -3, -2 and -1 respectively. This trend is shown in the graph.

8.

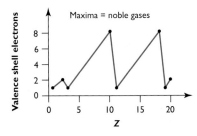

9. P is in group I as its first ionisation energy is much lower than the second.

   Q is in group VI as there is a steady increase for the first six electrons and then a significant increase.

   R is in group IV as the first four values increase gradually but the fifth electron is much harder to remove.

10. B: group VII; C: group VIII; D: group I; E: group II. The ionisation energy of C is higher than B. It then drops to a low value for D and rises again for E. This indicates that D belongs to the next higher period so must be a member of group I. Thus B and C belong to groups VII and VIII and E belongs to group II.

11. (a) Group VII — the halogens. These are diatomic molecules with the first two being gases under normal laboratory conditions. The valency of the second member (-1) is consistent with group VII elements.

    (b) $2Na(s) + Cl_2(g) \rightarrow 2NaCl(s)$

12. Na_3N: valency of $N = -3$; H_3N: valency of $N = 3$; PCl_3: valency of $P = 3$; H_3AsO_4: valency of As $= 5$; SbF_3: valency of Sb $= 3$; $BiBr_3$: valency of Bi $= +3$

13. X is most likely to be the melting point of these elements as it increases to group IV (silicon — a semi-metal) and then decreases for groups V and VI (non-metals).

Data analysis 8.1 Modelling the periodic table

Part A

1. The correct order from left to right is: F, C, E, A, H, D, G, B.

2. Element A — CF: ACl_4; CB: covalent

   Element G — OF: G_2O; OB: covalent; CF: GCl; CB: covalent

Part B

1. The following predicted values were obtained by determining the average of the property down a group (column 1) and the average across a period (column 2). The formula of the oxide is based on the similarity in valency down a group.

E (group prediction)
density = 7.8 g/cm^3
melting point = 544 °C
boiling point = 1087 °C
heat conductivity = 29 J/s/m/K
electrical conductivity = 2.4 MS/m
first ionisation energy = 832 kJ
formula of oxide = E_2O_3

E (period prediction)
density = 6.8 g/cm^3
melting point = 341 °C
boiling point = 1796 °C
heat conductivity = 35 J/s/m/K
electrical conductivity = 4.4 MS/m
first ionisation energy = 796 kJ
formula of oxide = E_2O_3

2. The chemical data book shows that the element is antimony. The correct values for these physical properties are:

Sb
density = 6.7 g/cm^3
melting point = 631 °C
boiling point = 1635 °C
heat conductivity = 24.3 J/s/m/K
electrical conductivity = 2.3 MS/m
first ionisation energy = 840 kJ
formula of oxide = Sb_2O_3

Better predictions of the density and boiling point were obtained by taking trends across a period. Trends down a group were better predictors of heat conductivity, electrical conductivity and ionisation energy. The melting point prediction was not close to the correct value. This exercise shows how Mendeleev used information about the properties of known elements to predict the properties of missing elements. He based this prediction on trends in properties down groups and across periods.

Data analysis 8.2 Computer graphing: periodic trends

Part A

3.
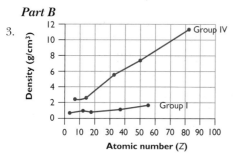

4. Electronegativity increases across period 3.

5. Electronegativity increases across period 3 as the elements become more non-metallic. Non-metals tend to gain electrons to stabilise their valence shells.

6. Element 18 is a noble gas (argon) and does not form compounds. Its valence shell is stable.

Part B

3.

4. (a) Density generally increases down group I.

   (b) Density generally increases down group IV.

5. In group I, $Z = 19$ does not fit the trend. In group IV, the density of $Z = 6$ is higher than expected.

6. Group IV elements are more dense than group I elements.

Chapter 9 Chemical analysis

9.1 Atomic weight and the mole theory

1. (a) $2HgO(s) \rightarrow 2Hg(l) + O_2(g)$

   (b) By the law of mass conservation, mass $(O_2) = 100 - 92.6 = 7.4$ g

2. (a) Calcium oxide and magnesium oxide

   (b) Each metal has a different atomic weight. Thus, the number of moles of reactant metals is different, and so different numbers of moles of each metal oxide are formed. As each has a different molecular weight, the masses of products are different.

3. (a) $M_r(CuSO_4) = 63.55 + 32.07 + 4(16.00) = 159.62$

   (b) $M_r(CaCO_3) = 40.08 + 12.01 + 3(16.00) = 100.09$

   (c) $M_r(NH_3) = 14.01 + 3(1.008) = 17.034$

4. (a) $M_r(CaCO_3) = 100.09$
   $\%O = 3(16.00)/100.09 \times 100 = 47.96\%$

   (b) $M_r(CH_3CO_2H) = 60.052$
   $\%O = 2(16.00)/60.052 \times 100 = 53.29\%$

5. (a) Volume ratio = carbon monoxide : ozone : carbon dioxide = 3 : 1 : 3

   This is a simple, whole-number ratio consistent with Gay-Lussac's law.

   (b) $3CO(g) + O_3(g) \rightarrow 3CO_2(g)$

   The mole ratio from the equation is 3 : 1 : 3, which is consistent with the volume ratio.

6. Volumes of combining gases
   $= CH_4 : O_2 : CO_2 : H_2O$
   $= (40 - 0) : (100 - 20) : 40 : 80$
   $= 40 : 80 : 40 : 80$
   $= 1 : 2 : 1 : 2$

   This is a simple, whole-number ratio as required by Gay-Lussac's law.

7. Let the number of atoms in the sulfur molecule = x, so its formula is S_x.
   Volume ratio $= S_x : O_2 : SO_2$
   $= 5 : 10 : 10$
   $= 1 : 2 : 2$

   This is the same as the molecule ratio according to Avogadro's law. Thus the balanced equation is:
   $$S_x + 2O_2 \rightarrow 2SO_2$$
   For the equation to balance, $x = 2$: that is, S_2 molecules in the vapour state.

8. $M(CO_2) = 12.01 + 2(16.00) = 44.01$ g/mol
   $n(CO_2) = m/M$
   $= 4.4/44.01$
   $= 0.10$ mol (2 significant figures)

9. (a) $M(NaCl) = 22.99 + 35.45 = 58.44$ g/mol

   (b) $n(NaCl) = m/M = 10/58.44 = 0.17$ mol

   (c) Each mole of NaCl contains 1 mole of sodium ions and 1 mole of chloride ions so $n(Cl^-) = 0.17$ mol. One mole contains an Avogadro number of ions so 0.17 mol contains $0.17 \times 6.022 \times 10^{23} = 1.0 \times 10^{23}$ Cl^- ions.

10. $M(Zn(OH)_2) = 65.39 + 2(16.00) + 2(1.008)$
    $= 99.406$ g/mol

$n(Zn(OH)_2) = m/M = 10/99.406 = 0.101$ mol

Each mole of zinc hydroxide contains 2 moles of hydroxide ions so:

$n(OH^-) = 2(0.101) = 0.202$ mol

Each mole contains an Avogadro number of ions so:
number of hydroxide ions $= 0.202 \times 6.022 \times 10^{23}$
$= 1.22 \times 10^{23}$ ions

11. (a) $CaCO_3(s) + 2HCl(aq) \rightarrow$
$$CaCl_2(aq) + H_2O(l) + CO_2(g)$$

   (b) $M(CaCO_3) = 100.09$ g/mol
$$n(CaCO_3) = m/M = 10/100.09 = 0.0999 \text{ mol}$$
$$= 0.10 \text{ mol (2 significant figures)}$$

   From the balanced equation, 1 mole of calcium carbonate forms 1 mole of carbon dioxide.

   $n(CO_2) = 0.10$ mol

   $M(CO_2) = 44.01$ g/mol

   $m(CO_2) = nM = 0.10 \times 44.01 = 4.4$ g

   (c) Each mole of carbon dioxide contains an Avogadro number of molecules.

   Number of molecules $= 0.10 \times 6.022 \times 10^{23}$
   $$= 6.02 \times 10^{22}$$

12. The balanced equation is $2Mg + O_2 \rightarrow 2MgO$. This shows that 2 moles of Mg reacts with 1 mole of oxygen gas.

   $n(O_2) = 3.011 \times 10^{21}/6.0^{22} \times 10^{23} = 5.0 \times 10^{-3}$ mol

   $n(Mg) = 2n(O_2) = 2(5.0 \times 10^{-3}) = 1.0 \times 10^{-2}$ mol

   $m(Mg) = nM = 1.0 \times 10^{-2} \times 24.31 = 0.2431$ g

13. (a) $2NO + O_2 \rightarrow 2NO_2$

   (b) $M(NO) = 14.01 + 16.00 = 30.01$ g/mol

   $M(O_2)$ 32.00 g/mol

   Calculate the number of moles of each gas.

   $n(NO) = m/M = 60/30.01 = 1.999$ mol

   $n(O_2) = m/M = 60/32.00 = 1.875$ mol

   The balanced equation shows that 2 moles of NO combines with 1 mole of O_2, so there is more oxygen than that needed to react with all of the NO. All of the NO will react to form NO_2 (1 : 1 mole ratio).

   $n(NO_2) = 1.999$ mol

   Number of NO_2 molecules formed
   $= 1.999 \times 6.022 \times 10^{23}$
   $= 1.20 \times 10^{24}$ molecules

14. (a) $CuO(s) + H_2(g) \rightarrow Cu(s) + H_2O(g)$

   (b) $M(CuO) = 63.55 + 16.00 = 79.55$ g/mol

   $n(CuO) = m/M = 10/79.55 = 0.126$ mol

   Each mole of CuO needs 1 mole of H_2 for complete reduction so:

   $n(H_2) = 0.126$ mol

Number of H_2 molecules $= 0.126 \times 6.022 \times 10^{23}$
$$= 7.59 \times 10^{22}$$

15. $M(CuSO_4.5H_2O) = 63.55 + 32.07 + 4(16.00) +$
$$10(1.008) + 5(16.00)$$
$$= 249.7 \text{ g/mol}$$

   $n = m/M = 50/249.7 = 0.200$ mol

   Each mole of hydrated copper (II) sulfate releases 5 moles of water vapour. Thus, 0.200 moles of hydrated copper (II) sulfate releases $5 \times 0.200 = 1.000$ mol water.

   (a) $m(H_2O) = n.M(H_2O) = 1.000 \times 18.016$
   $$= 18.02 \text{ g water vapour}$$

   (b) Number of water molecules
   $= n \times 6.022 \times 10^{23}$
   $= 1.000 \times 6.022 \times 10^{23}$
   $= 6.022 \times 10^{23}$ molecules

9.2 Empirical and molecular formulae

1. (a) $M(H_2SO_3) = 82.086$ g/mol
   %H= 2.46; %S = 39.06; %O = 58.48

   (b) $M(P_4O_{10}) = 283.88$ g/mol
   %P = 43.64; %O = 56.36

   (c) $M(Ca(OH)_2) = 74.096$ g/mol
   %Ca = 54.09; %O = 43.19; %H = 2.72

2. A and C. The empirical formulae are $ZnCl_2$ and UF_6 as their ratios of elements are the simplest possible.

3. (a) W: CBrF; X: CF; Y: $C_3H_4Br_2$

   (b) W: $C_2Br_2F_2$; X: C_2F_2; Y: $C_6H_8Br_4$

4. (a) $n(N) = 11.640/14.01 = 0.831$
   $n(Cl) = 88.360/35.45 = 2.493$
   $n(N) : n(Cl) = 0.831 : 2.493 = 1 : 3$
   Empirical formula = NCl_3

   (b) $n(Na) = 36.51/22.99 = 1.588$ mol
   $n(S) = 25.39/32.07 = 0.792$ mol
   $n(O) = 38.10/16.00 = 2.381$ mol
   $n(Na) : n(S) : n(O) = 1.588 : 0.792 : 2.381 = 2 : 1 : 3$
   Empirical formula = Na_2SO_3

   (c) $n(Mg) = 16.4/24.31 = 0.675$ mol
   $n(N) = 18.9/14.01 = 1.349$ mol
   $n(O) = 64.7/16.00 = 4.044$ mol
   $n(Mg) : n(N) : n(O) = 0.675 : 1.349 : 4.044 = 1 : 2 : 6$
   Empirical formula = MgN_2O_6

   (d) $n(Mn) = 72.03/54.94 = 1.311$ mol
   $n(O) = 27.97/16.00 = 1.748$ mol
   $n(Mn) : n(O) = 1.311 : 1.748 = 1 : 1.333 = 3 : 4$
   Empirical formula = Mn_3O_4

5. $m(\text{Hg}) = 3.678$ g

$m(\text{O}) = 3.972 - 3.678 = 0.294$ g

$n(\text{Hg}) = 3.678/200.6 = 0.0183$ mol

$n(\text{O}) = 0.294/16.00 = 0.0184$ mol

$n(\text{Hg}) : n(\text{O}) = 0.0123 : 0.0125 = 1 : 1$

Empirical formula = HgO

6. (a) $n(\text{C}) = 88.81/12.01 = 7.395$ mol

$n(\text{H}) = 11.19/1.008 = 11.002$ mol

$n(\text{C}) : n(\text{H}) = 7.395 : 11.002 = 1 : 1.5 = 2 : 3$

Empirical formula = C_2H_3

(b) Mass of $C_2H_3 = 27.044$, which is half of the molecular weight (54.09). Thus the molecular formula is twice the empirical formula.

Molecular formula = C_4H_6

7. $n(\text{Si}) = 87.45/28.09 = 3.113$ mol

$n(\text{H}) = 12.55/1.008 = 12.450$ mol

$n(\text{Si}) : n(\text{H}) = 3.133 : 12.450 = 1 : 4$

Empirical formula = SiH_4

8. (a) The formula for the sulfate of the trivalent metal is $M_2(SO_4)_3$. Let the atomic weight of $M = x$. Molar weight of the compound
$= 2x + 3(32.07) + 12(16.00) = 2x + 288.21$ g/mol.

The percentage of sulfur is 24.06% by experiment. Therefore,

$24.06 = 3(32.07)/(2x + 288.21) \times 100$

Solve this equation for x.

$x = 55.83$

Atomic weight of M is 55.83.

(b) M is Fe, a trivalent metal with an atomic weight of 55.85.

Practical activity 9.1 The empirical formula of magnesium oxide

Questions

6. Heat the crucible and lid to constant mass before the experiment begins; use a 2- or 3-decimal place electronic balance; use a larger mass of magnesium to reduce the percentage error; ensure that all the magnesium has burnt; do not let the MgO smoke escape from the crucible.

8. Add drops of water to the final product to decompose any magnesium nitride and then heat the crucible and contents to constant weight. The final product will be MgO only.

Data analysis 9.2 Moles and volumes of gases

Part A

1. Reaction 1: $\text{Mg(s)} + \text{H}_2\text{SO}_4 \longrightarrow \text{MgSO}_4 + \text{H}_2\text{(g)}$

Reaction 2: $\text{Mg(s)} + 2\text{H}_2\text{SO}_4 \longrightarrow$
$\text{MgSO}_4 + 2\text{H}_2\text{O(l)} + \text{SO}_2\text{(g)}$

2. (a) 1 : 1 (b) 1 : 1

3. The mole ratios are the same as the ratio of volumes of gases collected.

4. Reaction 1: $n(\text{H}_2) = 2.039/24.79 = 0.0823$ mol

Reaction 2: $n(\text{SO}_2) = 0.0823$ mol

5. $n(\text{Mg}) = m/M = 2.0/24.31 = 0.0823$ mol

6. $n(\text{Mg}) : n(\text{gas}) = 0.0823 : 0.0823 = 1 : 1$

This agrees with the ratio of coefficients in each equation.

Part B

1. Oxygen

2. HgO

3. $2\text{Hg(l)} + \text{O}_2\text{(g)} \longrightarrow 2\text{HgO(s)}$

4. $m(\text{Hg reacted}) = 100.000$ g

$n(\text{Hg}) = m/M = 100.000/200.6 = 0.499$ mol

$m(\text{HgO formed}) = 107.976$ g

$n(\text{HgO}) = m/M = 107.976/216.6 = 0.499$ mol

$V(\text{O}_2 \text{ reacted}) = 20.000 - 13.821 = 6.179$ L

$n(\text{O}_2) = 6.179/24.79 = 0.249$ mol

Thus the mole ratio is:

$\text{Hg} : \text{O}_2 : \text{HgO} = 0.499 : 0.249 : 0.499 = 2 : 1 : 2$

This ratio agrees with the mole ratio in the balanced equation.

Chapter 10 Extraction and recycling of metals

10.1 Ores and resources

1. C. Sulfides of copper, nickel and iron can form in this way.

2. A. The formation of ores occurred in the geological past. Once the reserves are mined, there are none to replace them. The process continues in some zones today but we cannot make use of these sources.

3. D. SnO_2 — cassiterite

4. A. Most of Australia's iron ore is mined in Western Australia (see fig. 10.3 on page 183)

5. %zinc $= 5.5/50 \times 100 = 11.0\%$

6. Theoretical yield of iron $= 63/100 \times 200 = 126$ tonne

7. (a) Field geologists investigate a potential ore body to discover the depth and area it occupies. They take core samples, which are analysed for the percentage content of each metal. If there is little ore or it is low grade, there may be insufficient yield of metal to make the ore body viable to mine. Exploration may take many years to complete.

(b) The prices of metals vary from day to day on the world market. Variations in the value of the dollar and the cost of equipment, transportation costs and wages affect the profit to be made on selling the metal. In some cases, it is more economical to sell the unrefined ore than the metal.

(c) The yield of metal depends on the size of the ore body and the concentration of metal in the ore. It also depends on the physical and chemical techniques used to extract the metal from its ore. If the yield is too low, the ore body may not be economically viable. Lower grade ores may be mined profitably if more efficient extraction techniques are used. This is the job of an industrial chemist.

10.2 Extraction and recycling

1. (a) Molar weight of malachite = 221.126 g/mol

$$\%Cu \text{ in malachite} = 2(63.55)/221.126 \times 100$$
$$= 57.5\%$$

Molar weight of chalcopyrite = 183.54 g/mol

$$\%Cu \text{ in chalcopyrite} = 63.55/183.54 \times 100 = 34.6\%$$

(b) Few deposits of high-grade surface deposits of copper minerals, such as malachite, are left to be mined. Only the deeper, unoxidised sulfide ores remain. A large proportion of the world's high-grade copper ores have been mined, so lower grade ores or ore bodies that are deeper in the crust need to be mined in the future.

2. 34.6% Cu in chalcopyrite (see question 1), so 100 g of ore contains 0.5 g of copper.

Mass of chalcopyrite that contains 0.5 g of copper = 100/34.6 × 0.5 = 1.45g

%chalcopyrite in ore = 1.45/100 × 100 = 1.45%

3. e, b, a, f, g, d, c

4. (a) Roasting converts chalcopyrite to chalcocite, iron oxide and sulfur dioxide.

$$2CuFeS_2(s) + 4O_2(g) \rightarrow$$
$$Cu_2S(l) + 2FeO(s) + 3SO_2(g)$$

(b) Smelting with coal and sand at 1000 °C forms a molten copper matte containing chalcocite and cuprite. A slag forms, which removes iron (II) oxide.

$$2Cu_2S(s) + 3O_2(g) \rightarrow 2Cu_2O(l) + 2SO_2(g)$$
$$FeO(s) + SiO_2(s) \rightarrow FeSiO_3(l)$$

(c) Converting at 1200 °C produces molten copper as chalcocite and cuprite react.

$$2Cu_2S(l) + 3O_2(g) \rightarrow 2Cu_2O(l) + 2SO_2(g)$$
$$2Cu_2O(l) + Cu_2S(l) \rightarrow 6Cu(l) + SO_2(g)$$

5. Sulfur dioxide is an acidic oxide that dissolves in water to form the weak acid, sulfurous acid, which can be oxidised to sulfuric acid. Sulfur dioxide in emissions can produce acid rain that damages the natural and built environments.

6. (a) Arsenic, gold, platinum, nickel, silver, sulfur, iron

(b) Blister copper is made into anodes and electrolytically refined. Acidified copper sulfate is used as an electrolyte. The pure copper is deposited on the cathode.

(c) Anode: $Cu(s) \rightarrow Cu^{2+}(aq) + 2e^-$
Cathode: $Cu^{2+}(aq) + 2e^- \rightarrow Cu(s)$

7. (a) Aluminium products are in greater demand, particularly for beverage cans, lightweight structural metals and alloys. These lightweight alloys help reduce greenhouse emissions and fuel usage.

(b) Recycling; prevention of corrosion; finding substitutes such as more abundant metals or non-metal alternatives

8. (a) Only 5% of the total energy needed to make aluminium from raw materials is used to make aluminium from scrap aluminium. Thus, recycling is more energy efficient.

(b) Less greenhouse gas (20 kg CO_2/kg Al) is produced when aluminium is recycled, mainly because less coal must be burnt to make electricity for the electrolytic smelting of alumina.

Data analysis 10.1 The viability of mining a vanadium ore deposit

1. Uranium ores

2. Shallow, open-cut mining was the best option to extract the vanadium ore and shale oil.

3. The market price of extracted oil from the shale was too low to make a profit. The site was sold to another company but, even after further developmental work, they came to similar conclusion about profitability.

4. The vanadium ore was mixed with clay, hydrated pyrite and silicates in the oil shale. Some vanadium was organically bound. The vanadium in the hydrated oxide minerals was three times higher than in the clay.

5. Beneficiation is removal of waste material to increase the metal content of ore.

6. Acid leaching was rapid but too expensive. Alkaline leaching extracted 75% of the vanadium oxide but the high consumption of sodium carbonate needs to be minimised.

7. Further work should continue to develop metallurgical techniques that will make the deposit economically viable. Sale of vanadium would make the oil shale extraction more attractive to investors.

8. This report shows how important the prediction of final yield is to the commercial viability of mining an ore body. The article shows that decades of geological research has identified the nature of the ore body and the total mass of minerals (oil and vanadium) it contains. By knowing the yield, economists can determine profitability. Economists have determined that the oil shale alone would not be economical to mine as the oil extracted could not compete on the market. Mining and extracting the vanadium would make it more attractive but new technologies are required to produce a profit. Metallurgists and chemists continue research and development to find ways to make deposits economically viable in the future.

Data analysis 10.2 Recycling aluminium and steel

1. Aluminium can be recycled repeatedly, which extends the useful life of the metal. Recycled aluminium is cheaper than aluminium extracted from the ore.

2. Only 5% of the energy used to mine and electrolytically smelt aluminium ore is needed to recycle aluminium. Up to 21 kWh of electricity is saved per kilogram of aluminium produced by recycling. At the same time, less carbon dioxide is emitted into the atmosphere, reducing the effects of global warming due to greenhouse gases.

3. Aluminium cans are collected and stored temporarily at local collection centres. At a centralised sorting centre, the cans are screened magnetically or mechanically to remove steel cans. The cans are crushed, weighed and transported to a furnace. Molten aluminium is poured into moulds. Cooling produces ingots of solid aluminium, which are rolled thinly and turned into new cans.

4. Aluminium alloys reduce the weight of cars so less fuel is needed to move them. This reduces fuel use and greenhouse gases emission.

5. There is an 80% energy saving in recycling steel over making new steel. Less coal is mined for blast furnaces, greenhouse gas emission is reduced and less water is used during production .

6. The costs of recycling may be higher than the money received for sales of the recycled product.

MODULE 3: WATER

Chapter 11 Water in nature

11.1 Distribution and importance of water

1. B. Oil is the smaller component. It is added to petrol to produce the fuel.

2. C. Copper is in the larger amount in brass. Zinc is dissolved in copper.

3. C. Water dissolves many solutes that can be transported in the cells and bodies of living things.

4. B. The density rises by 0.08 g/cm^3 for each rise of $10\,°\text{C}$.

5. C. Although carbon dioxide is the fourth most abundant gas in dry air, it is much more soluble in water than nitrogen, oxygen or argon. It is also important in photosynthesis and in biochemical reactions in animal cells.

6. (a) At high altitude, the air pressure is lower than at sea level. Thus, a lower temperature is required for vapour to escape from the liquid surface. Water boils when the vapour pressure reaches the local air pressure.

   (b) The boiling point of water increases with pressure. Food cooks faster at the higher temperatures ($>100\,°\text{C}$) inside a pressure cooker.

7. (a) Acts as medium for transport of nutrients and wastes; is required for reproduction; evaporates as sweat to cool the body and regulate heat; is required for digestion of dietary fat

   (b) $67/100 \times 50 = 33.5 \text{ kg}$

   (c) Gaseous molecules must be dissolved in water so they can diffuse across the respiratory membranes of the lung.

8. (a) Oceans are the major sinks for water that erodes the land. As rivers and streams weather and erode the land, minerals become dissolved and transported into the oceans. Minerals also dissolve in the oceans through hydrothermal vents in the ocean floor. Less water moves underground than into oceans, but even this water finds its way into the oceans. As evaporation occurs, the salt concentration increases until a steady state is reached.

   (b) Hot water under pressure can dissolve more minerals than cooler surface water.

9. $D = 18.84/15.375 = 1.23 \text{ g/mL}$

10. (a)

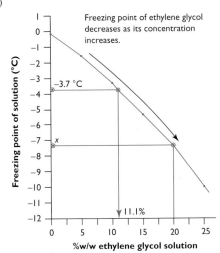

Freezing point of ethylene glycol decreases as its concentration increases.

(b) $x = -7.3\,°C$

(c) To lower the freezing point (especially in cold climates so that the water in the radiator does not freeze and cause damage) or elevate the boiling point (important in hot climates to prevent radiator water boiling)

(d) % by weight of solution = $4/36 × 100 = 11.1\%$

From the graph, the freezing point would be $-3.7\,°C$.

11. (a) $6CO_2(g) + 6H_2O(l) \rightarrow C_6H_{12}O_6(aq) + 6O_2(g)$

(b) $M(CO_2) = 44.01$ g/mol

$n(CO_2) = m/M = 11\,000/44.01 = 249.94$ mol

From the balanced equation, 1 mole of CO_2 requires 1 mole of water for reaction. So,

$n(H_2O) = 249.94$ mol

$M(H_2O) = 18.016$ g/mol

$m(H_2O) = nM = 249.94 × 18.016 = 4502.9$ g
$= 4.5$ kg

(c) From the balanced equation, 1 mole of O_2 is produced for each mole of CO_2 reacted. So,

$n(O_2) = 249.94$ mol

$m(O_2) = nM = 249.94 × 32.00 = 7998$ g $= 7.998$ kg

12. (a) Oxygen has the greatest percentage by weight $= 8 × 16/(278.35) × 100 = 46\%$

(b) $2KAlSi_3O_8(s) + H_2O(l) + 2H^+(aq) \rightarrow$
$Al_2Si_2O_5(OH)_4(s) + 4SiO_2(s) + 2K^+(aq)$

(c) Carbon dioxide dissolves in water to form carbonic acid. Organic acids are produced by bacterial decay of the remains of dead organisms.

Practical activity 11.1 The effect of salt on the boiling point of water

Part A — Questions

1. Thermometers are mass produced and do not necessarily read $100\,°C$ at the boiling point of water. This experiment aims to determine how salt affects the boiling point of water; no conclusions can be made unless the thermometer is calibrated.

2. Boiling point increases as salt concentration increases, until the solution becomes saturated.

3. Repeat the experiment at least five times.

Part B — Questions

2. The boiling point of water increases in the presence of salt.

3. At $100\,°C$, the heat energy converts liquid water to vapour, rather than increasing its temperature.

4. The concentration of salt increases as water evaporates, so the boiling point increases due to the increasing salt concentration.

5. The solution is saturated so the boiling point cannot increase further.

Data analysis 11.2 The density of water and ice

Part A

1.

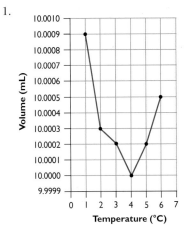

(b) $4\,°C$

(c)

Temperature (°C)	Density (g/mL)
1	0.999 91
2	0.999 97
3	0.999 98
4	1.000 00
5	0.999 98
6	0.999 95

(c) $4\,°C$

Part B

1.
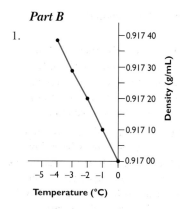

Temperature (°C)

2. As ice cools, it becomes more dense so it contracts.

3. $V = m/D = 10.00/0.91737 = 10.901$ mL

4. Melted ice water has a higher density than ice at $0\,^{\circ}C$ so ice floats.

5. As water in lakes cools during winter, the cold water sinks and stays at $4\,^{\circ}C$. Further cooling to freezing point produces low-density ice that floats and acts as an insulator. The water below the surface does not freeze as readily so aquatic organisms can survive without being frozen in ice. In addition, the presence of salts further lowers the freezing point.

6. There are many open spaces in the ice lattice. On average, water molecules are further apart in ice than in liquid water. Thus, liquid water at $0\,^{\circ}C$ is more dense than ice at the same temperature.

Chapter 12 Structure and bonding in water

12.1 Intermolecular forces and polarity of molecules

1. (a) Polar (b) Polar (c) Polar (d) Non-polar (e) Polar (f) Non-polar

2. C—O, O—F, C—N, H—S, Br—Cl, S—S

3. (a) (i) OF_2 (ii) NH_3

(iii) CCl_4

(b) (i) 2 bonding pairs and 2 non-bonding pairs
   (ii) 3 bonding pairs and 1 non-bonding pair
   (iii) 4 bonding pairs

(c) (i) Polar (ii) Polar (iii) Non-polar

4. (a) A measure of a fluid's resistance to flow

   (b) As the temperature increases, the viscosity decreases. At high temperatures, the greater rotational and vibrational kinetic energy of the water molecules interferes with the formation of hydrogen bonds between the water molecules. Thus, the intermolecular forces weaken and the water flows more readily.

5. The chains in HDPE are closer together and longer than in LDPE so its dispersion forces are stronger and the melting point is higher. The branching of chains in LDPE and its lower molecular weight reduces the dispersion interactions, so its melting point is lower.

6. The boiling point increases as the molecular weight of hydrogen halides increases. The polarity and, therefore, the dipole–dipole forces between molecules decreases from HCl to HI. (I is less electronegative than Cl.) Thus, one would expect the boiling point to decrease. However, the dispersion forces between molecules increases as the number of electrons in the molecules increases. Consequently, the contribution of dispersion forces increased as the dipole–dipole interaction decreases, causing an increase in boiling point down the group.

7. Methanol has the highest boiling point as strong hydrogen bonding exists between H and O atoms in neighbouring molecules. There are dipole–dipole interactions between hydrogen sulfide molecules. However, ethane is non-polar so has dispersion forces only. Therefore, H_2S has a higher boiling point than C_2H_6.

8. Ionic bonding and the covalent disulfide bonds are strong chemical bonds. Hydrogen bonding is about 10% as strong as a covalent bond. Dispersions forces are relatively weak.

9. Hydrogen bonding between the H and O atoms of OH groups on opposite chains

10. Water forms rounded drops because surface tension acts produce the lowest energy surface, which is a sphere. Detergents lower the surface tension so the water spreads out rather than forming spherical droplets.

11. Butane has a higher boiling point as it has stronger dispersion forces between its molecules than methylpropane, even though they have the same molecular weight. This difference is caused by molecular geometry differences. Butane has an effectively greater surface area and its straight chains can interact more closely than the branched chain molecule of methylpropane.

12.2 Interactions with water

1. D. Sodium nitrate is an ionic salt that can form ion–dipole interactions with water.

2. C. Pentane is a non-polar hydrocarbon similar to kerosene.

3. B. Many but not all ionic compounds dissolve in water.

4. A. Hydrogen chloride forms hydrogen ions and chloride ions.

5. B. Cellulose chains have OH groups that form hydrogen bonds with water's hydroxyl groups.

6. (a) $MgSO_4(s) \rightarrow Mg^{2+}(aq) + SO_4^{2-}(aq)$

   (b) $HF(aq) + H_2O(l) \rightarrow H_3O^+(aq) + F^-(aq)$

   (c) $C_{12}H_{22}O_{11}(s) \rightarrow C_{12}H_{22}O_{11}(aq)$

7. (a) Sucrose and glycerine have many OH groups that can form hydrogen bonds with water. Sodium chloride can bond strongly through ion–dipole attractions. This cannot happen in kerosene, which is a non-polar solvent, so sucrose, glycerine and sodium chloride do not dissolve in kerosene.

   (b) Paraffin wax is a non-polar hydrocarbon with long hydrocarbon chains. Water cannot form strong enough bonds with it to dissolve it. The chemical bonds between the atoms in SiO_2 are so strong that the solvent cannot break and establish new stable interactions. Oleic acid is slightly polar but has a very long hydrocarbon chain that prevents water solubility.

   (c) The chemical bonds in silica are very strong so the particles cannot be further stabilised by dissolving in any solvent.

   (d) Ethanol's solvent properties are often intermediate between water and kerosene. It is a polar solvent, but not as polar as water. It can form hydrogen bonds with some solutes, but not as strongly as water. Its small hydrocarbon chain allows a little paraffin and oleic acid to dissolve, but the solubility is low. Glycerine, however, is a small carbon chain that has many OH groups that can form hydrogen bonds with ethanol.

8. (a) Less soluble

   (b) From the graph, mass dissolved/100 g water = 0.09 g. So, mass of CO_2 dissolved = 0.9 g/kg water

   (c) Carbon dioxide dissolves sparingly in water as its electronegative oxygen atoms are attracted to the electropositive hydrogen atoms of water. As the temperature increases and the water molecules move about more rapidly, these intermolecular forces are broken, so less carbon dioxide can remain dissolved.

9. Methanoic acid is the name of this molecule. It will form strong hydrogen bonds with water but only dispersion interactions are possible with non-polar kerosene. Thus, the substance is very soluble in water but insoluble or sparingly soluble in kerosene.

10. The polar —COOH group forms hydrogen bond with water molecules. The long, non-polar hydrocarbon chain cannot be stabilised effectively with water so this part is insoluble. The long chain is insoluble in the water so floats on the surface with the polar —COOH group dissolved in the surface layer of the water.

Practical activity 12.1 Comparison of the melting and boiling points of molecules

Part 1

Data set A

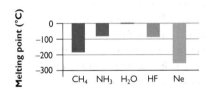

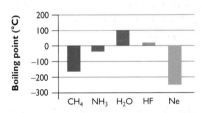

Data set B

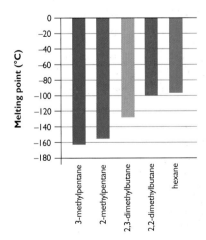

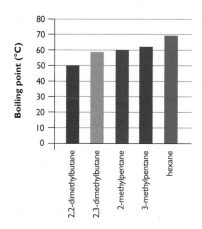

Data set C

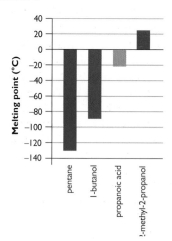

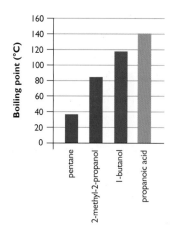

Questions

1. Methane and neon have low melting and boiling points as dispersion forces are the only intermolecular force holding the particles together. In the other three molecules, hydrogen bonding is the dominant intermolecular force. This is much stronger than dispersion forces so the melting and boiling points are significantly higher.

2. In general, branching in hydrocarbons lowers the melting and boiling points. Therefore, the straight-chain molecule, hexane, has the highest melting and boiling points. This means that the dispersion forces are slightly stronger in hexane than in the branched molecules as it has an effectively greater surface area, so each chain can get closer to neighbouring chains.

3. In general, non-polar molecules, such as pentane, have lower melting and boiling points than polar molecules. The presence of strong dipoles or hydrogen bonding increases the boiling point. This is particularly evident in propanoic acid.

4. The open structure of the ice lattice creates a solid that is less dense than water, allowing it to float on water.

Practical activity 12.3 Investigating solubility in water

Part A — Questions

2. Most of the ionic salts tested were water soluble and form strong ion–dipole bonds with the water solvent. Some molecular solutes (sucrose, ethanol, butan 1-ol) are water soluble and form hydrogen bonds with the water solvent. Other covalent molecular substances cannot form sufficiently strong bonds with the solvent to allow dissolution to occur. The strong covalent bonds in the covalent network lattice prevent dissolution in water.

3. Weigh the solutes using a balance and measure volumes using a burette; agitate the tubes for extended times to allow complete dissolution; for those solids that dissolve incompletely, filter, and dry and weigh the residue to determine the amount dissolved.

Chapter 13 Solutions and solubility

13.1 Solutions and precipitation

1. A. Sodium nitrate is a soluble ionic salt. Barium sulfate and calcium carbonate are ionic but insoluble.

2. C. Barium sulfate is insoluble.

3. B. Iron (III) hydroxide is insoluble.

4. D. Calcium sulfate is insoluble.

5. D. There was no reaction with either reagent. If chloride or carbonate ions were present, they would precipitate with silver ions. If sulfate ions were present, they would precipitate with barium ions.

6. (a) Yes. Silver chloride

   (b) Yes. Silver carbonate

(c) No. All ion combinations produce soluble salts.

(d) Yes. Lead (II) hydroxide

7. (a) Sodium carbonate. Only calcium carbonate precipitates.

(b) Silver nitrate. Only silver chloride precipitates.

(c) Barium nitrate. Only barium sulfate precipitates.

(d) Sodium chloride. Only silver chloride precipitates.

8. In each case, choose a nitrate and a sodium (or potassium) salt.

(a) Silver nitrate and sodium bromide solutions

(b Lead (II) nitrate and sodium chromate solutions

(c) Nickel (II) nitrate and sodium carbonate solutions

(d) Copper (II) nitrate and sodium sulfide solutions

(e) Barium nitrate and sodium phosphate solutions

9. (a) $Ag^+(aq) + Cl^-(aq) \rightarrow AgCl(s)$

(b) $Ba^{2+}(aq) + SO_4^{2-}(aq) \rightarrow BaSO_4(s)$

(c) $Cu^{2+}(aq) + S^{2-}(aq) \rightarrow CuS(s)$

10. (a) $Ca^{2+}(aq) + SO_4^{2-}(aq) \rightarrow PbSO_4(s)$

(b) $CaSO_4$

(c) $Ag^+(aq) + I^-(aq) \rightarrow AgI(s)$

(d) Ba^{2+}, NO_3^-

(e) K^+, Cl^-

(f) $CaCrO_4$

11. (a) At about 3.5 minutes, when the slope of the line is 0

(b) At about 3.5 minutes. When saturation is achieved, the system is in equilibrium.

(c) $NaCl(s) \rightleftharpoons Na^+(aq) + Cl^-(aq)$

(d) The graph plateaus at about 3.5 g of salt per 10 g of water. So, solubility = 35 g/100 g H_2O

(e) The concentrations are the same (35 g/100 g water). The addition of extra salt does not change the equilibrium because the solution is already saturated once equilibrium is established. Only a temperature change or the addition of more solvent will change this.

12. The use of radioactive isotopes is the usual method. Radioactive chlorine reacts with sodium to form radioactive sodium chloride, which is chemically identical to normal sodium chloride. However, it emits radiation, which can be detected with a Geiger counter.

A saturated salt solution is prepared. A radioactive crystal is added and some of the aqueous solution is removed periodically and tested for radioactivity. Over time, the level of radioactivity in the solution rises. This shows that some of the radioactive crystal

is dissolving. As the solution was already saturated and remains so, some non-radioactive ions must be crystallising at the same time. Thus, the equilibrium is dynamic.

13 (a) Method 1 — Dissolve green copper (II) chloride in water and add the correct molar quantity of sodium carbonate solution to precipitate all the copper (II) ions as insoluble copper (II) carbonate. Filter and wash the precipitate. Collect the precipitate in a beaker and dissolve it in a minimum of dilute sulfuric acid, until effervescence just stops. The solution formed contains copper (II) sulfate. Evaporate and crystallise the solution to obtain copper (II) sulfate crystals. Filter these crystals and dry them gently.

Method 2 — Use method 1 but replace sodium carbonate with sodium hydroxide. In this case, insoluble copper (II) hydroxide forms.

(b) Dissolve blue copper (II) sulfate crystals in water and add the correct molar quantity of barium chloride solution. A white precipitate of barium sulfate forms, which can be filtered. Collect the green filtrate, which contains copper (II) ions and chloride ions. Evaporate and crystallise the solution to produce green copper (II) chloride crystals. Filter the crystals and dry gently.

13.2 Concentration of solutions

1. C. The molar weight of nitric acid is 63 g/mol, so 4 moles weighs 252 g.

2. D. $n = cV = 0.020 \times 0.025 = 0.00050$ mol

3. A. $M(NaBr) = 102.9$

$n = m/M = 10/102.9 = 0.0972$ mol

$c = n/V = 0.0972/0.200 = 0.49$ mol/L

4. A. $c_2 = c_1 V_1 / V_2 = 0.40 \times 25/100 = 0.10$ mol/L

5. C. $c = 5.0/50.0 \times 100 = 10.0\%$v/v

6. $c_1 V_1 = c_2 V_2$

$0.500 \times 30.0 \times 10^{-3} = 0.100 V_2$

$V_2 = 0.15$ L

Therefore, dilute the solution until the total volume is 150 mL.

7. $c_1 V_1 = c_2 V_2$

$18.0 \times 5.0 \times 10^{-3} = 0.10 V_2$

$V_2 = 0.90$ L = 900 mL

Thus, the volume of water that needs to be added is $900 - 5 = 895$ mL.

8. Let the atomic weight of element $E = x$.

$M(E\text{Br}_2) = x + 2 \times 79.9 = x + 159.8 \text{ g/mol}$

$n(E\text{Br}_2) = m/M = 20.0 \times (x + 159.8) \text{ mol}$

$c = n/V$

$0.20 = n/0.500 = 20.0 \times (x + 159.8) \times 0.500$

$x = 40.2$

The atomic weight of E is 40.2.

9. (a)

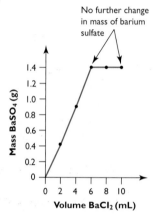

(b) The sulfate has precipitated completely as barium sulfate. Excess barium ions produce no more precipitate.

(c) 6 mL. This is the point on the graph after which the mass of barium sulfate no longer changes.

(d) $n(\text{BaCl}_2) = cV = 1.0 \times 6.0 \times 10^{-3} = 6.0 \times 10^{-3} \text{ mol}$

$n(\text{metal sulfate}) = cV = 1.0 \times 2.0 \times 10^{-3}$
$= 2.0 \times 10^{-3} \text{ mol}$

$6.0 \times 10^{-3}/2.0 \times 10^{-3} = 3.0 \text{ mol}$

Therefore, 3 moles of barium chloride reacts with 1 mole of metal sulfate.

(e) $\text{Ba}^{2+} + \text{SO}_4^{2-} \longrightarrow \text{BaSO}_4(s)$

This is a 1 : 1 mole ratio so 3 moles of barium ions will react with 3 moles of sulfate ions. So, in 1 mole of metal sulfate, there are 3 moles of sulfate ions.

(f) $M_2(\text{SO}_4)_3$. The metal must be trivalent as each mole of the sulfate salt has 3 moles of sulfate.

10. $m(\text{C}) = 2/100 \times 50 = 1 \text{ kg}$

11. 1960 sample: $c(\text{CO}_2) = 3180 \text{ mL}/10 \text{ kL} = 318 \text{ ppm}$

1980 sample: $c(\text{CO}_2) = 169 \text{ μL}/0.500 \text{ L} = 338 \text{ ppm}$

Increase $= 338 - 318 = 20 \text{ ppm}$

12. Sample A: $c(\text{F}^-) = 2.4 \text{ mg}/0.002 \text{ kg} = 1200 \text{ ppm}$. This is 200 ppm over the acceptable level of 1000 ppm.

Sample B: $c(\text{F}^-) = 1.125 \text{ mg}/0.0015 \text{ kg} = 750 \text{ ppm}$. This is below the acceptable level.

13. (a) The weight of water in fresh tissue can be affected by various environmental conditions and by species. It is more reliable to express the concentration on a dry weight basis.

(b) 5 ppm = 5 mg per kg of tissue

Mass of mercury $= 5 \times 0.8 = 4.0 \text{ mg}$

(c) Concentration in water $= 5/30\,000$
$= 1.67 \times 10^{-4} \text{ ppm}$

14. (a) $m(\text{Cd}) = 200 \text{ mg/kg} \times 1500 \text{ kg} = 300\,000 \text{ mg}$
$= 300 \text{ g} = 0.300 \text{ kg}$

(b) $c(\text{Cd in lake}) = 0.300/2.5 = 0.12 \text{ ppm}$. This is well below the acceptable limit.

Practical activity 13.1 Investigating solubility using precipitation reactions

Questions

1. Most chloride salts are soluble except silver chloride and lead chloride.

Most carbonates are insoluble except potassium carbonate.

Most sulfates are soluble except lead sulfate, barium sulfate and calcium sulfate.

Most hydroxides are insoluble except potassium hydroxide and barium hydroxide.

3. Example equations:

$\text{Ag}^+ + \text{Cl}^- \longrightarrow \text{AgCl}(s)$

$\text{Pb}^{2+} + 2\text{Cl}^- \longrightarrow \text{PbCl}_2(s)$

$\text{Ba}^{2+} + \text{SO}_4^{2-} \longrightarrow \text{BaSO}_4(s)$

$\text{Ca}^{2+} + \text{CO}_3^{2-} \longrightarrow \text{CaCO}_3(s)$

$\text{Pb}^{2+} + 2\text{OH}^- \longrightarrow \text{Pb(OH)}_2(s)$

Practical activity 13.2 Preparing and diluting solutions

Questions

2. A measuring cylinder is not manufactured as accurately as burettes, pipettes and volumetric flasks.

Chapter 14 Water and energy

14.1 Energy changes in aqueous systems

1. A. Silver has the lowest specific heat capacity so reaches the highest temperature when absorbing the same amount of heat.

2. B. Use the calorimetry equation:
$12\,000 = 50 \times 4.18(T_f - 25)$; solve for T_f.

3. A. Water is not the only polar molecule but its hydrogen bonding is stronger than that in alcohol.

4. D. 54 g is equal to 2.997 moles of water.

5. A. The reaction is exothermic so the enthalpy change is negative.

6. (a) Mass of solution = 50 + 1 = 51 g

   $\Delta H = -mC\Delta T = -51 \times 4.2 \times 4.7 = -1006.7$ J

   (b) $M(NaOH) = 22.99 + 16.00 + 1.008 = 39.998$ g/mol

   $n(NaOH) = m/M = 1.0/39.998 = 0.0250$ mol

   Molar heat of solution = 1006.7/0.0250
   = 40 268 J/mol
   = 40.3 kJ/mol

7. $M(CaCl_2 6H_2O)$
   $= 40.08 + (2 \times 35.45) + (12 \times 1.008) + (6 \times 16.00)$
   $= 219.076$ g/mol

   $n(CaCl_2.6H_2O) = m/M = 11/219.076 = 0.0502$ mol

   Heat $= n\Delta H = 0.0502 \times 18 = 0.9036$ kJ $= 903.6$ J

   $\Delta H = -mC\Delta T$

   $903.6 = -111 \times 4.1 \times (T_f - 25)$
   $T_f = 23.0\,°C$

8. $\Delta H = -mC\Delta T = -200 \times 2.1 \times (0 - (-20)) = 8400$ J

9. $M(C_2H_5OH) = (2 \times 12.01) + (6 \times 1.008) + 16.00$
   $= 46.068$ mol

   $n = m/M = 100/46.068 = 2.171$ mol

   q = heat to melt solid + heat to warm liquid to boiling point + heat to vaporise liquid

   $= n\Delta H(fusion) + mC\Delta T + n\Delta H(vaporisation)$

   $= (2.171 \times 5000) + (100 \times 2.44)(78 + 114) + (2.171 \times 38\,000)$

   $= 10\,855 + 46\,848 + 82\,498$

   $= 140\,201$ J

   $= 0.14$ MJ

10. (a) Thermal pollution is the heating of natural water systems due to the discharge of heated water from various factories, such as from the cooling towers of coal-fired power stations and nuclear power stations.

    (b) Fish can withstand only a moderate change in the temperature of their environment. Warm water dissolves less oxygen so fish may suffocate from lack of oxygen. Warm water may also alter the balance of the ecosystem and allow competition between fish that tolerate warm water and those that cannot. This has occurred in Australia with the European carp, which is now a pest in many inland waterways.

Practical activity 14.1 Calorimetry: measuring the heat of solution

Part B — Questions

1. To determine the effect of the environment on the calorimeter

2. Repeat the experiments at least five times each and control all variables.

3. Temperature probes are more accurate than thermometers as they can measure temperatures to more decimal places and they do not rely on the ability of the experimenter to read a scale. Probes must also be calibrated if their data is to be reliable.

MODULE 4: ENERGY

Chapter 15 Photosynthesis and fuels

15.1 Chemical energy from fossil fuels

1. A. Australia has vast coal reserves, which are used to generate electricity and in ore smelters.

2. B. The Sun's energy is absorbed by plants and converted to chemical energy. This is a means of storing energy for future use.

3. A. Peat contains the remains of plant twigs, leaves and stems.

4. D. NSW and Queensland have large reserves of black coal.

5. C. Australian crude has high amounts of low molecular weight hydrocarbons but low amounts of heavier hydrocarbons.

6. (a) $6CO_2(g) + 6H_2O(l) \rightarrow C_6H_{12}O_6(s) + 6O_2(g)$

   (b) Endothermic

   (c) Water

   (d) Chlorophyll

   (e) In the chlorophyll–protein reaction centre, light energy is used to excite chlorophyll molecules so that electrons are released. These energised electrons are transferred to water molecules.

7. (a) Peat, lignite (brown coal), black coal (bituminous coal), anthracite

   (b) Anthracite has the highest percentage of carbon as it is the most metamorphosed of all the coal types. The greater the percentage of carbon, the greater the heat released on combustion.

8. (a) Heat $= 50 \times 30 = 1500$ MJ

   (b) Bituminous coal has a higher carbon content and a lower moisture content than brown coal. Therefore, it produces more heat on combustion.

9. (a) Methane, CH_4, is a hydrocarbon because it is composed of carbon and hydrogen atoms.

   (b) 1 kg of methane produces 56 MJ (56 000 kJ) of energy on combustion. x kg of methane produces 100 kJ of energy. By ratio, solve for x.

   $x = 100/56\,000 = 1.79 \times 10^{-3}$ kg methane

(c) 100 g of methane = 100/1000 = 0.10 kg

Energy released = 0.10 × 56 = 5.6 MJ

10. (a) Mass of 1 litre of petrol = DV = 0.7 × 1 = 0.7 kg

Energy released = 0.7 × 47 = 32.9 MJ

Mass of 1 litre of kerosene = DV = 0.8 × 1 = 0.8 kg

Energy released = 0.8 × 50 = 40.0 MJ

Thus, 1 litre of kerosene produces more energy than 1 litre of petrol.

(b) Coal is used mainly as a fuel in coal-fired power stations and to raise the temperature in steel furnaces. Oil is rarely used in this way. It is commonly used as a raw material for the production of liquid fuels for cars, trucks and aeroplanes. It is also used in some oil-fired heaters and engines.

Data analysis 15.1 Australian petroleum

Part A

(a) and (b) Answers will vary with new discoveries.

Basin	Location	Current reserves of natural gas as % of total (1998)
Carnarvon	Western Australia (off shore)	54
Browse	Western Australia (off shore)	22
Gippsland	Southeast Victoria (off shore)	9
Bonaparte/ Amadeus	Northwest Australia (off shore)/south Northern Territory	9
Cooper/ Eromanga	South Australia/south Queensland/ northwest NSW	5
Adavale/ Bowen/Surat	Southeast Queensland	<1
Perth	Perth (off shore)	<1
Bass	Bass Strait	<1
Otway	Western Bass Strait	<1

(d) Answers will vary. North West Shelf produces more gas than oil. Bass Strait produces mainly oil and some gas.

Part B

(a) (i)

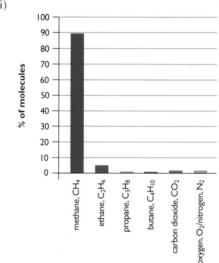

(ii)

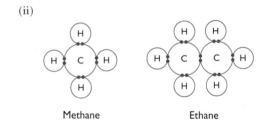

Methane   Ethane

(iii) Methane, ethane, propane, butane

(b) (i) and (ii)

Compound	Classification
benzene	aromatic
cyclohexane	naphthene
3,3-dimethylpentane	paraffin
heptane	paraffin
2,2,4-trimethylpentane	paraffin
methylcyclohexane	naphthene
2,2-dimethylhexane	paraffin
methylbenzene (toluene)	aromatic
cycloheptane	naphthene
2-methylheptane	paraffin

(iii) 6–8

(iv)

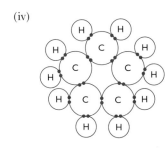

Chapter 16 Carbon and carbon compounds

16.1 Carbon

1. C. Carbon has 6 electrons; 2 in the K shell and 4 in the L shell.

2. A. Allotropic forms of other elements exist (e.g. P, O, S, Se).

3. B. Unlike graphite, all valence shell electrons are involved in bonding.

4. D. Graphite has a more open crystalline structure than diamond.

5. C. Electric arc discharge is one of the three methods of making fullerenes.

6. C. A triple bond contains 6 electrons as three pairs.

7.

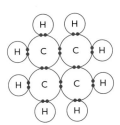

8. Single carbon–carbon bonds: 4; double carbon–carbon bonds: 1; triple carbon–carbon bonds: 1

9. (a) The weak dispersion forces between the crystal layers allow shearing forces to displace the layers. This makes graphite a good lubricant.

   (b) Diamond's crystal lattice is very strong in three dimensions. The atoms are arranged tetrahedrally and there are no weak planes within the crystal. The crystal is very hard and useful in cutting and grinding tools.

   (c) Graphite has a very high melting point and is a very good electrical conductor. Thus, it can withstand the high temperatures of an electrolytic furnace and conducts electricity into the melt.

10. $C(s) + O_2(g) \rightarrow CO_2(g)$

16.2 Hydrocarbons

1. (a) Hexane

   (b) Oct-2-ene (or 2-octene)

   (c) Oct-1-ene (or 1-octene). Number from the right-hand side to give the double bond the lowest locant.

2. (a) Butane

   (b) Hex-1-ene (or 1-hexene)

3.

$$H \diagdown \atop H \diagup C = C - \overset{\displaystyle H}{\underset{\displaystyle H}{\vert}} \! C \! \overset{\vert}{\underset{\vert}{}} - H$$

The molecule must contain 3 carbon atoms and 6 hydrogen atoms to give a molar weight of 42.1. It is propene.

4. P: liquid; Q: solid; R: gas

5. (a) Diesel oil (b) Paraffin waxes (c) Petrol

6. (a) $V(CH_4) = 88/100 \times 10 = 8.8$ ML $= 8.8 \times 10^6$ L

   (b) $n(CH_4) = 8.8 \times 10^6/24.79 = 3.55 \times 10^5$ mol

   (c) $N = nN_A = 3.55 \times 10^5 \times 6.022 \times 10^{23}$
   $= 2.14 \times 10^{29}$ molecules

7. (a) Alkane

   (b) C_8H_{18}; C_9H_{20}

   (c) (i) Covalent bonds
       (ii) Dispersion forces
       (iii) Covalent bonds

   (d) Dispersion forces

   (e) Saturated. It has the maximum number of hydrogen atoms per carbon.

   (f) Octane is volatile and flammable. No sparks or flames should come near an octane vapour–air mixture. Transfer octane in a closed metal container with a narrow neck. Keep the vessel full to avoid combustible vapour–air mixtures under the cap.

8. Steps C, B, D, A, F, E

9. (a) The gauge, taps and fittings may leak or be faulty. Inspections help to minimise the risks of fires and explosions.

   (b) In the open air there is good ventilation and it is unlikely that combustible vapour–air mixtures will form.

   (c) Petrol is much more volatile than kerosene and combustible vapour–air mixtures can form readily. It has a very low flash point (–43 °C) so vapour–air mixtures are susceptible to sparking. Petrol must be kept cool in a metal storage can with a narrow neck and tight-fitting lid. Only very small amounts can be stored safely in outside sheds away from the house.

10. (a)

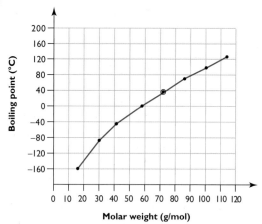

Molar weight (g/mol)

From the graph, the boiling point of pentane = ~30 °C. (36 °C in chemical data book)

(b) As the alkane chains increase in length, the extent of dispersion forces between the chains increases. Thus, more heat is required to separate the chains and convert liquid into vapour.

Practical activity 16.2 Fractional distillation

Part B

1.

Greater % of ethanol in distillate as % of ethanol in original mixture increases

Ethanol in distillate (mole %) vs *Ethanol in original mixture (mole %)*

2. Richer in ethanol until 90%, when it is the same

3. Ethanol

4. 100 mL of 12%v/v ethanol in water contains 12 mL ethanol and 88 mL water. Calculate the mass of each component.

m(ethanol) = DV = 0.785 × 12 = 9.42 g

m(water) = DV = 1.00 × 88 = 88.0 g

Calculate the number of moles of each component.

n(ethanol) = m/M = 9.42/46.1 = 0.204 mol

n(water) = m/M = 88.0/18.016 = 4.885 mol

Total moles = 0.204 + 4.885 = 5.089 mol

Mole %(ethanol) = 0.204/5.089 × 100 = 4.0%

5. Water and ethanol dissolve readily in one another due to strong hydrogen bonding between the molecules. Thus, it is very difficult to separate these molecules by distillation as some water always vaporises with the ethanol.

Data analysis 16.3 Alkanes and alkenes

Part A

2. (a) But-1-ene and but-2-ene (or 1-butene and 2-butene)

   (b) Pent-1-ene, pent-2-ene, pent-3-ene (or 1-pentene, 2-pentene and 3-pentene)

3 (b) Five isomers (hexane, 2-methylpentane, 3-methylpentane, 2,2-dimethylbutane, 2,3-dimethylbutane)

Chapter 17 Combustion and reaction kinetics

17.1 Combustion

1. C. The melting of the wax is a physical change. It can be readily reversed.

2. B. Ethane has six C—H bonds and a C—C bond; the total of the bond energies is greater than that of the other molecules.

3. A. Electrolysis requires energy input to drive the reaction.

4. D. The activation energy for the reverse reaction is the sum of the enthalpy change and the forward activation energy.

5. A. The ignition temperature of alkanes decreases with increasing chain length.

6. (a) The molecules have insufficient kinetic energy to overcome the activation energy barrier at room temperature.

   (b) (i) Exothermic

       (ii) $H_A - H_B$

      (iii) $H_C - H_B$

   (c) The activation energy for the reverse reaction is too high.

7. (a) (i) $2H_2(g) + O_2(g) \rightarrow 2H_2O(l)$

       (ii) $2CO(g) + O_2(g) \rightarrow 2CO_2(g)$

(b) 12 moles of town gas is composed of 9 moles of hydrogen and 3 moles of carbon monoxide.

Heat released by burning 9 moles of H_2 = 9 × 286
$$= 2574 \text{ kJ}$$

Heat released by burning 3 moles of CO = 3 × 283
$$= 849 \text{ kJ}$$

Total heat evolved = 2574 + 849 = 3423 kJ

8. (a) (i) 79 kJ (ii) +24 kJ

   (b) Endothermic. The reaction reverses on cooling.

   (c) 79 – 24 = 55 kJ

   (d) Greater. Energy is supplied to the reactant or product to reach the activation complex.

9. Activation energy (reverse) = (400 – 100)/2
$$= 300/2$$
$$= 150 \text{ kJ}$$

10. (a) The sooty flame in dodecane is indicative of poor or incomplete combustion. The wick assists the less volatile dodecane to vaporise and form a combustible vapour–oxygen mixture. If too much dodecane rises in the wick, excess vapour in the reaction zone can cause poor combustion. The vapour–air mixture that forms around the wick in an ethanol burner is appropriate for nearly complete combustion.

    (b) Trimming the wick alters the vapour to air ratio, allowing more complete combustion. In this case, the ratio was lowered by allowing less dodecane vapour and more air to mix.

    (c) At 25 °C, a combustible (fuel vapour – air) mixture does not form above the liquid dodecane due to its low volatility. A match flame cannot heat sufficient fuel to maintain a high enough vapour concentration. Thus, no sustained combustion can occur (flash point of dodecane ~48 °C). A combustible ethanol vapour – air mixture does form above liquid ethanol as it has higher volatility and lower flash point than dodecane. Thus, sustained combustion occurs without a wick.

    (d) Kerosene

    (e) Petrol

11. The mixture would not ignite. Although it is a combustible mixture, the temperature is lower than the ignition temperature.

12. Sample A (30%v/v) is a combustible mixture so would ignite. Sample B (70%v/v) is not a combustible mixture.

13. (a) The water pump creates a partial vacuum that draws air and vapours through the apparatus.

    (b) Water. Blue cobalt chloride paper turns pink in the presence of water.

(c) Carbon dioxide

(d) Carbon (soot)

(e) Incomplete

14. Heat absorbed by water in calorimeter = $mC\Delta T$
$$= 50.0 × 4.2 × (49.7 – 19.7)$$
$$= 6300 \text{ J} = 6.30 \text{ kJ}$$
$$n(C_4H_{10}) = m/M = 0.25/58.1 = 4.30 × 10^{-3} \text{ mol}$$
Heat of combustion = $6.30/4.30 × 10^{-3}$ = 1465 kJ/mol

15. Both fuels generate carbon dioxide so neither reduces global warming. LPG tends to burn more efficiently than petrol so it extracts more useful energy is extracted but causes less pollution. LPG has a slightly higher heat of combustion per mole (50 MJ/kg) than petrol (~47 MJ/kg). Although propane is less expensive, the weight of its tanks in a car add to the cost of motoring. More gas fields than crude oil fields have been discovered in Australia so LPG is likely to become increasingly available in the short-term future, while crude oil and petrol may become more scarce and costly. LPG tanks must be inspected regularly for leaks so require more maintenance than petrol tanks. The proposal should be supported to allow better use of this abundant natural resource and to reduce demand on petrol supplies.

17.2 Reaction kinetics

1. C. The greater the concentration of hydrogen ions, the greater the number of collisions with the surface of the zinc granules.

2. D. Combustion requires oxygen; the more oxygen, the greater the rate of combustion.

3. A. The reaction is faster as more molecules have sufficient kinetic energy to overcome the activation energy barrier.

4. D. Catalysts accelerate reactions but the same mass is present at the end.

5. A. Caster sugar is finely ground and has a high surface area, which allows it dissolve more readily.

6. (a) The cornflour dust is a fuel with a very high surface area. The flame provides the necessary activation energy for a reaction to occur. Because there is a large surface area with which oxygen molecules can collide, the reaction is so fast that it becomes explosive. There is no explosion in the second experiment as combustion is much slower due to reduced surface contact with air.

    (b) Coal dust is a fuel. It is explosive in the presence of air and a spark or flame. Dust extractors or water sprays can reduce dust levels in the air.

7. (a) The powder has a greater surface area, allowing more successful collisions per unit time.

   (b) The acid was in excess and the same mass of solid was used. The reaction stoichiometry is the same so the same volume of carbon dioxide was produced. However, the reaction took longer with the chips.

8. The magnesium in jar B burns more rapidly and with a much brighter white light. The greater number of collisions between oxygen molecules and the hot magnesium surface increases the reaction rate.

9. Convert the iron into a wool or powder to increase the surface area; increase the temperature and humidity.

10. The carbon dioxide is evolved and passes through a tube to the manometer. The pressure of carbon dioxide causes the liquid level in the manometer to change. The change in level per unit time can be measured and is related to the rate of the reaction.

11. This is an example of spontaneous combustion. Heat is released during microbial decomposition of hay. If the haystack is large, the heat builds up faster than it can escape. Eventually, the ignition temperature is reached and the hay combusts spontaneously.

12. The burning methane causes air to enter the can from the hole in the base. The concentration of methane drops and the concentration of air (and combustion products) rises as the methane burns. Eventually, the concentration of methane reaches 15%, creating an explosive mixture. The methane then explodes rather than burning rapidly.

Practical activity 17.1 Exothermic and endothermic reactions

Questions

1. $HCl + NaOH \rightarrow NaCl + H_2O(l)$

   $CuCO_3(s) + 2HCl \rightarrow CuCl_2 + H_2O(l) + CO_2(g)$

   $NH_4NO_3(s) \rightarrow NH_4^+ + NO_3^-$

   $2CaSO_4.H_2O(s) + 3H_2O(l) \rightarrow 2CaSO_4.2H_2O(s)$

   $Na_2CO_3 + CaCl_2 \rightarrow CaCO_3(s) + 2NaCl$

   $Mg(s) + 2HCl \rightarrow MgCl_2 + H_2(g)$

   $Ba(OH)_2.8H_2O(s) + 2NH_4SCN(s) \rightarrow$
   $\qquad Ba(SCN)_2(s) + 10H_2O(l) + 2NH_3(g)$

2. The energy required for the reactants to form products comes from the kinetic energy of the particles in the surroundings. Thus, the surroundings cool and the temperature drops.

Practical activity 17.2 Combustion

Part A — Questions

1. Decrease in mass

2. Increase in mass

3. The ash is lighter than the wood as some mass is lost to the air in the form of carbon dioxide and water vapour. The white product of combustion of magnesium weighs more than the original magnesium as oxygen atoms from the air have combined with magnesium atoms.

Part B — Questions

1. Hot vapours, gases and solid particles are lost to the air.

2. Solid wax turns to liquid wax; liquid wax turns to wax vapour.

3. Cool

4. There is not enough oxygen diffusion into the centre of the flame for complete combustion.

5. Oxygen diffuses rapidly into these regions so combustion is complete. The maximum amount of heat is liberated so the flame is hotter at these locations.

6. Combustion is an exothermic process. The heat liberated raises the temperature of the vapour–air mixture. The temperature is higher than the flash point so combustible mixtures of wax vapour and oxygen form. The heat liberated raises the temperature above the ignition temperature so the reaction is self-sustaining.

Practical activity 17.3 Reaction rates

Part A — Questions

1. The reaction time is the reciprocal of the reaction rate.

2. As the oxalic acid concentration decreases, the reaction rate decreases as fewer effective collisions lead to reaction.

3. Raising the temperature increases the proportion of particles with kinetic energy higher than the activation energy. This increases the reaction rate.

4. The presence of manganese sulfate increases the reaction rate. To prove that the manganese sulfate acts catalytically, we need to show that none was consumed during the reaction; that is, the mass of manganese sulfate is the same after the reaction as before.

Part B — Questions

1. The powder has a significantly greater surface area.

2. The greater surface area provides many more sites for hydrogen ions from the acid to attack carbonate ions. Thus, more product is formed in the same time.

3. 5.0 g of calcium carbonate: $n = m/M = 5.0/100.09$
$= 0.05$ mol

50 mL of 1.0 mol/L HCl: $n = cV = 1.0 \times 50 \times 10^{-3}$
$= 0.05$ mol

$$CaCO_3(s) + 2HCl \rightarrow CaCl_2 + H_2O(l) + CO_2(g)$$

This equation shows that 1 mole of calcium carbonate requires 2 moles of hydrochloric acid for complete reaction. In the experiment, the mole ratio is 1:1, so calcium carbonate is in excess.

Data analysis 17.4 Catalysis

Example 1

5. NO

6. $NO + O_3 \rightarrow NO_2 + O_2$
$NO_2 + O \rightarrow NO + O_2$
Sum: $O_3 + O \rightarrow 2O_2$

Example 2

7. The metal–hydrogen bond is stronger so the H–H bond breaks to form a more stable intermediate.

Data analysis 17.5 Explosions and safety

Part A

1. C

2. F

3. E

4. (a) A, B, G (b) D

5. H_2O_2

6. The rate of radical formation at room temperature is slow, and the rate at which radicals are terminated is high, so no sustained reaction can occur. The molecules have insufficient energy to overcome the activation energy barrier.

7. Prevent hydrogen from mixing with oxidisers such as oxygen. Keep the gas cool and away from sparks and flames.

Part B

1. Flour dust is composed of combustible material such as starch and cellulose. If the dust is fine and dry enough, a suspension in air can explode if an ignition source is present.

2. The dust needs to be quite dry (moisture content less than 11%) and the dust suspension needs to be in an enclosed space in the presence of an ignition source such as a spark or flame.

3. (a) $4Al(s) + 3O_2(g) \rightarrow 2Al_2O_3(s)$

(b) Extract dust continuously; flood the grinder with an unreactive gas (such as N_2) to prevent oxygen reaching the hot grinding surface; regularly maintain electrical equipment to prevent sparking.

4. Active metal dusts (see table 17.11)

5. The pressure wave from a primary explosion can propagate outwards rapidly causing dust elsewhere to become suspended in the air. The propagating wave front can heat this newly suspended dust to its ignition point so that a secondary explosion can occur.

Sample examination paper

Part A

1. B
2. A
3. D
4. A
5. D
6. A
7. C
8. A
9. D
10. B
11. C
12. A
13. B
14. A
15. D
16. C
17. A
18. B
19. C
20. D

Part B

21. (a) $CuCO_3.Cu(OH)_2(s) + 4HCl(aq) \rightarrow$
$2CuCl_2(aq) + 3H_2O(l) + CO_2(g)$

(b) No differences would be observed. In both cases, the final solution contains copper chloride. Both minerals release bubbles of gas and both solids dissolve in excess acid. Heat is released in both reactions.

(c) Electrolyse the solution using inert graphite electrodes. The copper deposits at the negative electrode.

22. (a) Add a strip of zinc to dilute hydrochloric acid. Increase the temperature of the system by placing the tube in a hot water bath. The rate of gas effervescence increases as the acid gets hotter.

$$Zn(s) + 2HCl(aq) \rightarrow ZnCl_2(aq) + H_2(g)$$

(b) Add powdered calcium carbonate (rather than chips) to dilute hydrochloric acid.

$$CaCO_3(s) + 2HCl(aq) \rightarrow$$
$$CaCl_2(aq) + H_2O(l) + CO_2(g)$$

23. (a) Sodium sulfate solution

(b) $Pb^{2+}(aq) + SO_4^{2-}(aq) \rightarrow PbSO_4(s)$

(c) $M(PbSO_4) = 303.3$ g/mol

$n(Pb^{2+}) = n(PbSO_4)$
   $= m/M = 0.950/303.3 = 3.132 \times 10^{-3}$ mol

$c(Pb^{2+}) = n/V = 3.132 \times 10^{-3}/0.100$
   $= 0.0313$ mol/L

(d) If water is present, the weight of the precipitate would be overestimated, which would cause the calculation of the lead concentration to be too high.

24. (a) Carbon dioxide, carbon monoxide, carbon, water

(b) $4Ag_2O(s) + CH_4(g) \rightarrow$
$$8Ag(s) + CO_2(g) + 2H_2O(g)$$

(c) Heating gives the particles sufficient kinetic energy on collision to overcome the activation energy barrier for the reaction.

(d) $M(Ag_2O) = 231.7$ g/mol

$n(Ag_2O) = m/M = 30.0/231.7 = 0.1295$ mol

Each mole of silver oxide produces 2 moles of silver.

$n(Ag) = 2 \times 0.1295 = 0.259$ mol

$m(Ag) = nM = 0.259 \times 107.9 = 27.9$ g

25. (a) $M(Al_2O_3) = 102.0$ g/mol

From the balanced equation, 4 moles of Al produces 2 moles of aluminium oxide.

$n(Al_2O_3) = m/M = 10.2/102.0 = 0.10$ mol

$n(Al) = 2 \times n(Al_2O_3) = 0.20$ mol

$m(Al) = nM = 0.20 \times 27.0 = 5.4$ g

(b) 4 moles of Al produces 3352 kJ of energy on combustion.

0.20 moles of Al produces $0.20 \times 3352/4 = 167.6$ kJ of energy on combustion.

Heat energy = $99/100 \times 167.6 = 165.9$ kJ

(c) The large surface area of the powder increases the reaction rate so that light and heat are produced faster.

(d) Magnesium

26. (a) Solar energy

(b) $M(H_2O) = 18.016$ g/mol

$n(H2O) = m/M = 180/18.016 = 9.9911$ mol

Energy released = $9.991 \times 6 = 59.95$ kJ

(c) Annual precipitation = $40 - 3 = 37 \times 10^{13}$ m^3

(d) Polar icecaps, glaciers, icebergs

27. (a) North West Shelf of Western Australia, Bass Strait, Bonaparte/Amadeus Basins, Carnarvon Basin, Adavale/Bowen/Surat Basins

(b) (i) A fractionating column separates the components of the crude oil into fractions based on their boiling point ranges. Crude oil is heated to about 370 °C in a pipe still at the bottom of the column. This converts the viscous liquid to vapour and fluid that then pass into the base of the fractionating column. The petroleum vapours and steam move up the column, cooling and condensing on baffles called bubble caps. This condensed liquid is richer in the least volatile components. The liquids that form at particular boiling point ranges are collected in trays. Some liquid overflows these trays and falls back to a hotter zone where it meets hot ascending vapours, which exchange heat and vaporise the more volatile components of the liquid. The trays eventually collect liquids in a fairly narrow boiling range. They are then channelled out and collected.

(ii) Refinery gas

(iii) Residue

(c)

Fraction	Use
gasoline (naphtha fraction)	cracking into smaller molecules to make more petrol and alkenes
kerosene	home heating; aviation fuel; conversion to petrol ('cracking')
diesel oil	furnace fuel; diesel engines; conversion to petrol ('cracking')

28. (a) (i) Ionic (ii) Ionic

(b) (i) Solid (ii) Liquid

(c) Dispersion forces

(d) X is likely to be more soluble in water than Y as ionic compounds can often establish strong ion–dipole interactions that assist the dissolution process. This is not possible in a molecular solid, unless it can hydrolyse and break the covalent bonds, so it remains insoluble. Y (molecular solid) is more likely to dissolve in kerosene, while X (ionic solid) is likely to be insoluble.

29. (a) The pressure is higher than 100 kPa so the gas can liquefy.

   (b) (i) Incomplete (as shown by the yellow flame)

      (ii) M(butane) = 58.1 g/mol

         n(butane) = m/M = 0.03/58.1 = 5.16 × 10^{-4} mol

         Heat = 1000/5.16 × 10^{-4} = 1.938 × 10^6 J/mol
         = 1938 kJ/mol

      (iii) The published value refers to complete combustion. In this case, the combustion is incomplete so less heat is evolved.

30. (a) Stone Age, Copper Age, Bronze Age, Iron Age

   (b) The smelting process involved crushing and grinding the ore to a fine powder, mixing it with charcoal and placing it in a furnace. The charcoal was used as the fuel for the fire and also as the reducing agent. The temperature of the burning charcoal was increased by blasting air into the furnace with bellows. In early, open smelters, the temperature was too low (~800–900 °C) to melt the copper (melting point = 1085 °C) so grains of copper formed in the glassy slag produced by quartz in the ore. The grains were recovered by crushing the solidified slag. In later, closed smelters, the temperature was high enough to melt the copper so it could be drained out of the base and cast into moulds.

   (c) Some metals were not discovered until the nineteenth century because heat energy alone was not sufficient to decompose their compounds. The invention of electrolytic decomposition led to the discovery of active metals, such as sodium and potassium in 1807 and magnesium in 1808. The metals beyond uranium in the periodic table owe their production to nuclear technology developed in the mid-twentieth century. Some of these were produced by neutron bombardment of other elements in nuclear reactors. New elements were formed by firing high-velocity, metallic ions, produced in particle accelerators, into metallic targets. The heavy elements produced by the fusion of two nuclei are highly radioactive and decay rapidly. We use some of these radioactive isotopes in medicine to diagnose and treat disease. Others are used in industry.

   Over the last 200 years, metals have become more readily available due to ongoing improvements in mining, smelting and electrolytic techniques and transportation. Chemists, metallurgists and chemical and mining engineers are responsible for this increase in metal supply. Much of this change has been driven by the need of our technological society to produce new lightweight or strong alloys.

31. Since the 1960s, aluminium has been used extensively in drink cans because it is readily rolled, lightweight, odourless, tasteless and conducts heat away from the drink so that it can be chilled rapidly. The huge use of aluminium has led to a problem of waste disposal. Australia now recycles about 70% of its aluminium drink cans, rather than dumping it in landfills. If more aluminium is recycled, fewer mines are needed, resulting in less pollution from the fluoride compounds released during aluminium manufacture.

   The energy to melt and recycle aluminium is less than 5% of the total energy expended in converting bauxite ore to aluminium. Thus, recycling is energy efficient and also conserves our metal supplies. Over 40% of the global demand for aluminium is met through recycling. Each time one kilogram of aluminium is recycled, 14–21 kWh less electricity is required for electrolysis; 5–8 kg of bauxite does not have to be mined; and 20 kg of greenhouse gases is not emitted into the atmosphere. Recycling also reduces the use of landfill sites in cities and towns.

32. (a) A carbonate is selected that decomposes using the heat from a Bunsen burner flame. Alkali metal carbonates and calcium carbonate are not suitable as they decompose only at very high temperatures. Copper (II) carbonate and magnesium carbonate could be used as they decompose at lower temperatures.

   (b) Safety glasses are always worn to protect the eyes. The selected carbonate is heated in a pyrex tube with a delivery tube passing into limewater. The delivery tube must be removed before heating ceases as a reduction in pressure on cooling can cause water to be drawn back into the reaction tubes, and possibly break the tube. The hot glass must not be handled until it is cold. MSDS forms show that magnesium carbonate or copper carbonate are not overly dangerous to handle. Prevent limewater contacting skin or eyes.

   (c) The carbon dioxide evolved turns limewater milky white. The acid test can be used to identify products; oxides do not fizz when acid is added but carbonates do. Sometimes, a colour change can help identify products. For example, if green copper carbonate is decomposed, the product is black copper oxide. However, if white magnesium carbonate is decomposed, the product is also white; the acid test is needed in this case. A control, with undecomposed carbonate, should be used to show that a chemical change has occurred.

INDEX

accuracy 19
acetic acid 174, 175
acids, reactions with metals 129–30
actinoid series 151
activated complex 317–18
activation energy 316–18
activity series of metals 47, 130–1, 138–9
alkali metals 149
alkaline earth metals 149
alkanes 292, 302–3, 312
   properties 305–6
alkenes 302, 303–4, 312
   isomers 304
   IUPAC nomenclature 303
   properties 305–6
alkyl groups 304
alkynes 309
allotropes of carbon 294–6, 309
alloy steels 118, 119
alloys 46, 112, 113–14
   and their uses 117–22
   crystal lattices 117–18
aluminium 114
   extraction 37–8
   recycling 193, 196–7
ammonium chloride, dissolution 269–70
anions 58, 59, 60, 61
anthracite 285
antifreeze 208
aquifers 205
argon, separation from the air 27–8
aromatics 292
arsenic bronze 112
asthenosphere 7
atmosphere 7
   gases in 9
   separation of argon from the air 27–8
   water content 202
atomic mass units (amu) 54
atomic models
   development 141–2
   to explain changes in mass 165
atomic number (Z) 54, 146
atomic radius, trends in the periodic table 151
atomic theory (Dalton) 141, 142
atomic weight 162–3
atoms 4, 53
   sub-structure 53–4
Australia
   minerals and ores 182–3
   petroleum resources 291
Avogadro constant 168
Avogadro's law 166–8

balanced chemical equations 78
   mole relationships 170–2, 180
binary compounds 63
biosphere 7, 9–10
   elements 10

separation of olive oil from olives 28–9
   water content 202
bituminous coal 284
black coal 284
Bohr, Niels 147
   shell model of the atom 141, 142
boiling points 15, 40
   alkanes and alkenes 305
   hydrides of group VI 221
   noble gases 220
   polar and non-polar molecules 221, 235–6
   trends in the periodic table 152
   water 207–8, 212–13, 224–5, 272
boiling water, particle diagram 88
bond dipoles 216, 217
bond energies 81–2, 315
bond polarity 216
bonding
   and solubility 227–31
   carbon compounds 296–8
   covalent 66–7
   ionic 61–2
bonds
   covalent 81–2, 216, 297
   ionic 81, 96
brass 120
brittleness 43
bromine, separation from salt lakes 27
bromine pentafluoride 68–9
Bronze Age (6000–3000 BP) 112–13
brown coal 284
brown coal deposits, spontaneous combustion 331–2
'buckyballs' 295, 296
Bunsen burner, burning natural gas in 320–1
burning of wood, coal and coke 332
butene 303, 304

caesium chloride 104
calcium 10
calcium carbonate 96
   reaction with acid 341
calorimeters 265–6
calorimetry 265–6, 276–7
calorimetry measurements, limitations 274
candle, combustion 338–9
carbohydrates 281
carbon 294, 296
carbon allotropes 294–6, 309
carbon atoms
   bond angles 297
   covalent bonding 297
carbon compounds
   bonding 296–8
   structural formulae 298
carbon dioxide 9, 98, 104
   reduction of 282
   solubility in water 273
carbon dioxide molecule 67
carbon isotopes 54, 162, 168

Elements - Chemical Data

Element	Symbol	Atomic Number	Atomic Weight*	Element	Symbol	Atomic Number	Atomic Weight*
Actinium	Ac	89	[227]	Meitnerium	Mt	109	[268]
Aluminium	Al	13	26.98	Mendelevium	Md	101	[258]
Americium	Am	95	[243]	Mercury	Hg	80	200.6
Antimony	Sb	51	121.8	Molybdenum	Mo	42	95.94
Argon	Ar	18	39.95	Neodymium	Nd	60	144.2
Arsenic	As	33	74.92	Neon	Ne	10	20.18
Astatine	At	85	[210.0]	Neptunium	Np	93	[237]
Barium	Ba	56	137.3	Nickel	Ni	28	58.69
Berkelium	Bk	97	[247]	Niobium	Nb	41	92.91
Beryllium	Be	4	9.012	Nitrogen	N	7	14.01
Bismuth	Bi	83	209.0	Nobelium	No	102	[259]
Bohrium	Bh	107	[264]	Osmium	Os	76	190.2
Boron	B	5	10.81	Oxygen	O	8	16.00
Bromine	Br	35	79.90	Palladium	Pd	46	106.4
Cadmium	Cd	48	112.4	Phosphorus	P	15	30.97
Caesium	Cs	55	132.9	Platinum	Pt	78	195.1
Calcium	Ca	20	40.08	Plutonium	Pu	94	[244]
Californium	Cf	98	[251]	Polonium	Po	84	[209.0]
Carbon	C	6	12.01	Potassium	K	19	39.10
Cerium	Ce	58	140.1	Praseodymium	Pr	59	140.9
Chlorine	Cl	17	35.45	Promethium	Pm	61	[145]
Chromium	Cr	24	52.00	Protactinium	Pa	91	231.0
Cobalt	Co	27	58.93	Radium	Ra	88	[226]
Copernicium	Cn	112	[277]	Radon	Rn	86	[222.0]
Copper	Cu	29	63.55	Rhenium	Re	75	186.2
Curium	Cm	96	[247]	Rhodium	Rh	45	102.9
Darmstadtium	Ds	110	[271]	Roentgenium	Rg	111	[272]
Dubnium	Db	105	[262]	Rubidium	Rb	37	85.47
Dysprosium	Dy	66	162.5	Ruthenium	Ru	44	101.1
Einsteinium	Es	99	[252]	Rutherfordium	Rf	104	[261]
Erbium	Er	68	167.3	Samarium	Sm	62	150.4
Europium	Eu	63	152.0	Scandium	Sc	21	44.96
Fermium	Fm	100	[257]	Seaborgium	Sg	106	[266]
Flerovium	Fl	114	[289]	Selenium	Se	34	78.96
Fluorine	F	9	19.00	Silicon	Si	14	28.09
Francium	Fr	87	[223]	Silver	Ag	47	107.9
Gadolinium	Gd	64	157.3	Sodium	Na	11	22.99
Gallium	Ga	31	69.72	Strontium	Sr	38	87.62
Germanium	Ge	32	72.64	Sulfur	S	16	32.07
Gold	Au	79	197.0	Tantalum	Ta	73	180.9
Hafnium	Hf	72	178.5	Technetium	Tc	43	[97.91]
Hassium	Hs	108	[277]	Tellurium	Te	52	127.6
Helium	He	2	4.003	Terbium	Tb	65	158.9
Holmium	Ho	67	164.9	Thallium	Tl	81	204.4
Hydrogen	H	1	1.008	Thorium	Th	90	232.0
Indium	In	49	114.8	Thulium	Tm	69	168.9
Iodine	I	53	126.9	Tin	Sn	50	118.7
Iridium	Ir	77	192.2	Titanium	Ti	22	47.87
Iron	Fe	26	55.85	Tungsten	W	74	183.8
Krypton	Kr	36	83.80	Uranium	U	92	238.0
Lanthanum	La	57	138.9	Vanadium	V	23	50.94
Lawrencium	Lr	103	[262]	Xenon	Xe	54	131.3
Lead	Pb	82	207.2	Ytterbium	Yb	70	173.0
Lithium	Li	3	6.941	Yttrium	Y	39	88.91
Livermorium	Lv	116	[293]	Zinc	Zn	30	65.41
Lutetium	Lu	71	175.0	Zirconium	Zr	40	91.22
Magnesium	Mg	12	24.31				
Manganese	Mn	25	54.94				

* The values used in this book are the set of atomic weights to four significant figures prepared by the Committee on Teaching of Chemistry for IUPAC. Where the atomic weight is not known, the relative atomic mass of the most common radioactive isotope is shown in parentheses. The atomic weights of Np and Tc are given for their technologically important artificial isotopes: ^{237}Np and ^{99}Tc.

Common numerical constants

Avogadro constant, N_A .... 6.022×10^{23} mol^{-1}

Volume of 1 mole ideal gas: at 100 kPa and:

         at 0 °C (273.15 K) .... 22.71 L

         at 25 °C (298.15 K) .... 24.79 L

Ionisation constant for water at 25 °C (298.15 K), K_w .... 1.0×10^{-14}

Specific heat capacity of water .... 4.18×10^3 Jkg^{-1}K^{-1}

Some useful formulae

$$pH = -\log_{10}[H^+] \qquad\qquad\qquad \Delta H = -mC\Delta T$$

Some standard potentials

$K^+ + e^-$	$\rightleftharpoons$	$K(s)$	-2.94 V
$Ba^{2+} + 2e^-$	$\rightleftharpoons$	$Ba(s)$	-2.91 V
$Ca^{2+} + 2e^-$	$\rightleftharpoons$	$Ca(s)$	-2.87 V
$Na^+ + e^-$	$\rightleftharpoons$	$Na(s)$	-2.71 V
$Mg^{2+} + 2e^-$	$\rightleftharpoons$	$Mg(s)$	-2.36 V
$Al^{3+} + 3e^-$	$\rightleftharpoons$	$Al(s)$	-1.68 V
$Mn^{2+} + 2e^-$	$\rightleftharpoons$	$Mn(s)$	-1.18 V
$H_2O + e^-$	$\rightleftharpoons$	$\frac{1}{2}H_2(g) + OH^-$	-0.83 V
$Zn^{2+} + 2e^-$	$\rightleftharpoons$	$Zn(s)$	-0.76 V
$Fe^{2+} + 2e^-$	$\rightleftharpoons$	$Fe(s)$	-0.44 V
$Ni^{2+} + 2e^-$	$\rightleftharpoons$	$Ni(s)$	-0.24 V
$Sn^{2+} + 2e^-$	$\rightleftharpoons$	$Sn(s)$	-0.14 V
$Pb^{2+} + 2e^-$	$\rightleftharpoons$	$Pb(s)$	-0.13 V
$H^+ + e^-$	$\rightleftharpoons$	$\frac{1}{2}H_2(g)$	0.00 V
$SO_4^{2-} + 4H^+ + 2e^-$	$\rightleftharpoons$	$SO_2(aq) + 2H_2O$	0.16 V
$Cu^{2+} + 2e^-$	$\rightleftharpoons$	$Cu(s)$	0.34 V
$\frac{1}{2}O_2(g) + H_2O + 2e^-$	$\rightleftharpoons$	$2OH^-$	0.40 V
$Cu^+ + e^-$	$\rightleftharpoons$	$Cu(s)$	0.52 V
$\frac{1}{2}I_2(s) + e^-$	$\rightleftharpoons$	I^-	0.54 V
$\frac{1}{2}I_2(aq) + e^-$	$\rightleftharpoons$	I^-	0.62 V
$Fe^{3+} + e^-$	$\rightleftharpoons$	Fe^{2+}	0.77 V
$Ag^+ + e^-$	$\rightleftharpoons$	$Ag(s)$	0.80 V
$\frac{1}{2}Br_2(l) + e^-$	$\rightleftharpoons$	Br^-	1.08 V
$\frac{1}{2}Br_2(aq) + e^-$	$\rightleftharpoons$	Br^-	1.10 V
$\frac{1}{2}O_2(g) + 2H^+ + 2e^-$	$\rightleftharpoons$	H_2O	1.23 V
$\frac{1}{2}Cl_2(g) + e^-$	$\rightleftharpoons$	Cl^-	1.36 V
$\frac{1}{2}Cr_2O_7^{2-} + 7H^+ + 3e^-$	$\rightleftharpoons$	$Cr^{3+} + \frac{7}{2}H_2O$	1.36 V
$\frac{1}{2}Cl_2(aq) + e^-$	$\rightleftharpoons$	Cl^-	1.40 V
$MnO_4^- + 8H^+ + 5e^-$	$\rightleftharpoons$	$Mn_2^+ + 4H_2O$	1.51 V
$\frac{1}{2}F_2(g) + e^-$	$\rightleftharpoons$	F^-	2.89 V